THE GREAT
WRITERS
L I B R A R Y

The VIRGIN *and the* GIPSY

and other stories

This edition is the copyright © 1988 of Marshall Cavendish Ltd.
Published in 1988 for the Great Writers library by Marshall Cavendish Partworks Ltd,
58 Old Compton Street, London W1V 5PA.

Printed and bound in Spain by Printer Industria Gráfica, Barcelona. D.L.B. 355-1988.

ISBN 0-86307-694-7

This is a facsimile edition from a collection published in 1934
by William Heinemann Ltd, London.

"Warm me!" she moaned, with chattering teeth. "Warm me!
I shall die of shivering."
A terrible convulsion went through her curled-up white body,
enough indeed to rupture her and cause her to die.
The gipsy nodded, and took her in his arms, and held her in a
clasp like a vice, to still his own shuddering.

THE VIRGIN AND THE GIPSY

The
VIRGIN
and the
GIPSY
and other stories

D.H. LAWRENCE

CONTENTS

CONTENTS

I

WHEN the vicar's wife went off with a young and penniless man the scandal knew no bounds. Her two little girls were only seven and nine years old respectively. And the vicar was such a good husband. True, his hair was grey. But his moustache was dark, he was handsome, and still full of furtive passion for his unrestrained and beautiful wife.

Why did she go ? Why did she burst away with such an *éclat* of revulsion, like a touch of madness ?

Nobody gave any answer. Only the pious said she was a bad woman. While some of the good women kept silent. They knew.

The two little girls never knew. Wounded, they decided that it was because their mother found them negligible.

The ill wind that blows nobody any good swept away the vicarage family on its blast. Then lo and behold ! the vicar, who was somewhat distinguished as an essayist and a controversialist, and whose case had aroused sympathy among the bookish men, received the living of Papplewick. The Lord had tempered the wind of misfortune with a rectorate in the north country.

The rectory was a rather ugly stone house down by the river Papple, before you come into the village. Further on, beyond where the road crosses the stream, were the big old stone cotton-mills, once driven by water. The road curved up-hill, into the bleak stone streets of the village.

The vicarage family received decided modification, upon its transference into the rectory. The vicar, now the rector, fetched up his old mother and his sister, and a brother from the city. The two little girls had a very different *milieu* from the old home.

The rector was now forty-seven years old ; he had displayed an intense and not very dignified grief after the flight of his wife. Sympathetic ladies had stayed him from suicide. His hair was almost white, and he had a wild-eyed, tragic look. You had only to look at him, to know how dreadful it all was, and how he had been wronged.

Yet somewhere there was a false note. And some of the ladies, who had sympathized most profoundly with the vicar, secretly rather disliked the rector. There was a certain furtive self-righteousness about him, when all was said and done.

The little girls, of course, in the vague way of children, accepted the family verdict. Granny, who was over seventy and whose sight was failing, became the central figure in the house. Aunt Cissie, who was over forty, pale, pious, and gnawed by an inward worm, kept house. Uncle Fred, a stingy and grey-faced man of forty, who just lived dingily for himself, went into town every day. And the rector, of course, was the most important person, after Granny.

They called her the Mater. She was one of those physically vulgar, clever old bodies who had got her own way all her life by buttering the weaknesses of her menfolk. Very quickly she took her cue. The rector still "loved " his delinquent wife, and would "love her " till he died. Therefore hush ! The rector's feeling was sacred. In his heart was enshrined the pure girl he had wedded and worshipped.

Out in the evil world, at the same time, there wandered a disreputable woman who had betrayed the rector and abandoned his little children. She was now yoked to a young and despicable man, who no doubt would bring her the degradation she deserved. Let this be clearly understood, and then hush ! For in the pure loftiness of the rector's heart still bloomed the pure white snow-flower of his young bride. This white snow-flower did not wither. That other creature, who had gone off with that despicable young man, was none of his affair.

The Mater, who had been somewhat diminished and insignificant as a widow in a small house, now climbed into the chief arm-chair in the rectory, and planted her old bulk firmly again. She was not going to be dethroned. Astutely she gave a sigh of homage to the rector's fidelity to the pure white snow-flower, while she pretended to disapprove. In sly reverence for her son's great love, she spoke no word against that nettle which flourished in the evil world, and which had once been called Mrs. Arthur Saywell. Now, thank heaven, having married again, she was no more Mrs. Arthur Saywell. No woman bore the rector's name. The pure white snow-flower bloomed *in perpetuum*, without nomenclature. The family even thought of her as She-who-was-Cynthia.

All this was water on the Mater's mill. It secured her against Arthur's ever marrying again. She had him by his feeblest weakness, his skulking self-love. He had married an imperishable white snow-flower. Lucky man ! He had been injured. Unhappy man ! He had suffered. Ah, what a heart of love ! And he had—forgiven ! Yes, the white snow-flower was forgiven. He even had made provision in his will for her, when that other scoundrel—but hush ! Don't even *think* too near to that horrid nettle in the rank outer world ! She-who-was-Cynthia. Let the white snow-flower bloom inaccessible on the heights of the past. The present is another story.

The children were brought up in this atmosphere of cunning self-sanctification and of unmentionability. They too, saw the snow-flower on inaccessible heights. They too knew that it was throned in lone splendour aloft their lives, never to be touched.

At the same time, out of the squalid world sometimes would come a rank, evil smell of selfishness and degraded lust, the smell of that awful nettle, She-who-was-Cynthia. This nettle actually contrived at intervals, to get a little note through to the girls, her children. And at this the silver-haired Mater shook inwardly with hate. For if She-who-was-Cynthia ever came back, there wouldn't be much left of the Mater. A secret gust of hate went from the old granny to the girls, children of that foul nettle of lust, that Cynthia who had had such an affectionate contempt for the Mater.

Mingled with all this, was the children's perfectly distinct recollection of their real home, the vicarage in the south, and their glamorous but not very dependable mother, Cynthia. She had made a great glow, a flow of life, like a swift and dangerous sun in the home, forever coming and going. They always associated her presence with brightness, but also with danger ; with glamour, but with fearful selfishness.

Now the glamour was gone, and the white snow-flower, like a porcelain wreath, froze on its grave. The danger of instability, the peculiarly *dangerous* sort of selfishness, like lions and tigers, was also gone. There was now a complete stability, in which one could perish safely.

But they were growing up. And as they grew, they became more definitely confused, more actively puzzled. The Mater, as she grew older, grew blinder. Somebody had to lead her about. She did not get up till towards midday. Yet blind or bed-ridden, she held the house.

Besides, she wasn't bed-ridden. Whenever the *men* were present, the Mater was in her throne. She was too cunning to court neglect. Especially as she had rivals.

Her great rival was the younger girl, Yvette. Yvette had some of the vague, careless blitheness of She-who-was-Cynthia. But this one was more docile. Granny perhaps had caught her in time. Perhaps !

The rector adored Yvette, and spoiled her with a doting fondness ; as much as to say : am I not a soft-hearted, indulgent old boy ! He liked to have this opinion of himself, and the Mater knew his weaknesses to a hair's-breadth. She knew them, and she traded on them by turning them into decorations for him, for his character. He wanted, in his own eyes, to have a fascinating character, as women want to have fascinating dresses. And the Mater cunningly put beauty-spots over his defects and deficiencies. Her mother-love gave her the clue to his weaknesses, and she hid them for him with decorations. Whereas She-who-was-Cynthia— ! But don't mention *her*, in this connection. In her eyes, the rector was almost hump-backed and an idiot.

The funny thing was, Granny secretly hated Lucille, the elder girl, more than the pampered Yvette. Lucille, the uneasy and irritable, was more conscious of being under Granny's power, than was the spoilt and vague Yvette.

On the other hand, Aunt Cissie hated Yvette. She hated her very name. Aunt Cissie's life had been sacrificed to the Mater, and Aunt Cissie knew it, and the Mater knew she knew it. Yet as the years went on, it became a convention. The convention of Aunt Cissie's sacrifice was accepted by everybody, including the self-same Cissie. She prayed a good deal about it. Which also showed that she had her own private feelings somewhere, poor thing. She had ceased to be Cissie, she had lost her life and her sex. And now, she was creeping towards fifty, strange green flares of rage would come up in her, and at such times, she was insane.

But Granny held her in her power. And Aunt Cissie's one object in life was to look after the Mater.

Aunt Cissie's green flares of hellish hate would go up against all young things, sometimes. Poor thing, she prayed and tried to obtain forgiveness from heaven. But what had been done to her, *she* could not forgive, and the vitriol would spurt in her veins sometimes.

It was not as if the Mater were a warm, kindly soul. She wasn't. She only seemed it, cunningly. And the fact dawned gradually on the girls. Under her old-fashioned lace cap, under her silver hair, under the black silk of her stout, short, forward-bulging body, this old woman had a cunning heart, seeking forever her own female power. And through the weakness of the unfresh, stagnant men she had bred, she kept her power, as her years rolled on, from seventy to eighty, and from eighty on the new lap, towards ninety.

For in the family there was a whole tradition of "loyalty"; loyalty to one another, and especially to the Mater. The Mater, of course, was the pivot of the family. The family was her own extended ego. Naturally she covered it with her power. And her sons and daughters, being weak and disintegrated, naturally were loyal. Outside the family, what was there for them but danger and insult and ignominy? Had not the rector experienced it, in his marriage? So now, caution! Caution and loyalty, fronting the world! Let there be as much hate and friction *inside* the family, as you like. To the outer world, a stubborn fence of unison.

II

But it was not until the girls finally came home from school that they felt the full weight of Granny's dead old hand on their lives. Lucille was now nearly twenty-one, and Yvette nineteen. They had been to a good girls' school, and had had a finishing year in Lausanne, and were quite the usual thing, tall young creatures with fresh, sensitive faces and bobbed hair and young-manly, deuce-take-it manners.

"What's so awfully *boring* about Papplewick," said Yvette, as they stood on the Channel boat watching the grey, grey cliffs of Dover draw near, " is that there are no *men* about. Why doesn't Daddy have some good old sports for friends? As for Uncle Fred, he's the limit!"

"Oh, you never know what will turn up," said Lucille, more philosophic.

"You jolly well know what to expect," said Yvette. " Choir on Sundays, and I hate mixed choirs. Boys' voices are *lovely*, when there are no women. And Sunday School and Girls' Friendly, and socials, all the dear old souls that inquire after Granny! Not a decent young fellow for miles."

"Oh, I don't know!" said Lucille. " There's always the Framleys. And you know Gerry Somercotes *adores* you."

"Oh, but I *hate* fellows who adore me!" cried Yvette, turning up her sensitive nose. " They *bore* me. They hang on like lead."

"Well, what *do* you want, if you can't stand being adored? *I* think it's perfectly all right to be adored. You know you'll never marry them, so why not let them go on adoring, if it amuses them."

"Oh, but I *want* to get married," cried Yvette.

"Well, in that case, let them go on adoring you till you find one that you can *possibly* marry."

" I never should, that way. Nothing puts me off like an adoring fellow. They *bore* me so ! They make me feel beastly."

" Oh, so they do me, if they get pressing. But at a distance, I think they're rather nice."

" I should like to fall *violently* in love."

" Oh, very likely ! I shouldn't ! I should hate it. Probably so would you, if it actually happened. After all, we've got to settle down a bit, before we know what we want."

" But don't you *hate* going back to Papplewick ? " cried Yvette, turning up her young, sensitive nose.

" No, not particularly. I suppose we shall be rather bored. I wish Daddy would get a car. I suppose we shall have to drag the old bikes out. Wouldn't you like to get up to Tansy Moor ? "

" Oh, *love* it ! Though it's an awful *strain*, shoving an old push-bike up those hills."

The ship was nearing the grey cliffs. It was summer, but a grey day. The two girls wore their coats with fur collars turned up, and little *chic* hats pulled down over their ears. Tall, slender, fresh-faced, naive, yet confident, too confident, in their school-girlish arrogance, they were so terribly English. They seemed so free, and were as a matter of fact so tangled and tied up, inside themselves. They seemed so dashing and unconventional, and were really so conventional, so, as it were, shut up indoors inside themselves. They looked like bold, tall young sloops, just slipping from the harbour into the wide seas of life. And they were, as a matter of fact, two poor young rudderless lives, moving from one chain anchorage to another.

The rectory struck a chill into their hearts as they entered. It seemed ugly, and almost sordid, with the dank air of that middle-class, degenerated comfort which has ceased to be comfortable and has turned stuffy, unclean. The hard, stone house struck the girls as being unclean, they could not have said why. The shabby furniture seemed somehow sordid, nothing was fresh. Even the food at meals had that awful dreary sordidness which is so repulsive to a young thing coming from abroad. Roast beef and wet cabbage, cold mutton and mashed potatoes, sour pickles, inexcusable puddings.

Granny, who " loved a bit of pork," also had special dishes, beef-tea and rusks, or a small savoury custard. The grey-faced Aunt Cissie ate nothing at all. She would sit at table, and take a single lonely and naked boiled potato on to her plate. She never ate meat. So she sat in sordid durance, while the meal went on, and Granny quickly slobbered her portion—lucky if she spilled nothing on her protuberant stomach. The food was not appetizing in itself : how could it be, when Aunt Cissie hated food herself, hated the fact of eating, and never could keep a maid-servant for three months? The girls ate with repulsion, Lucille bravely bearing up, Yvette's tender nose showing her disgust. Only the rector, white-haired, wiped his long grey moustache with his serviette, and cracked jokes. He too was getting heavy and inert, sitting in his study all day, never taking exercise. But he cracked sarcastic little jokes all the time, sitting there under the shelter of the Mater.

The country, with its steep hills and its deep, narrow valleys, was dark and gloomy, yet had a certain powerful strength of its own. Twenty miles away was the black industrialism of the north. Yet the village of Papplewick was comparatively lonely, almost lost, the life in it stony and dour. Everything was stone, with a hardness that was almost poetic, it was so unrelenting.

It was as the girls had known : they went back into the choir, they helped in the parish. But Yvette struck absolutely against Sunday School, the Band of Hope, the Girls' Friendlies—indeed against all those functions that were conducted by determined old maids and obstinate, stupid, elderly men. She avoided church duties as much as possible, and got away from the rectory whenever she could. The Framleys, a big, untidy, jolly family up at the Grange, were an enormous stand-by. And if anybody asked her out to a meal, even if a woman in one of the workmen's houses asked her to stay to tea, she accepted at once. In fact, she was rather thrilled. She liked talking to the working men, they had often such fine, hard heads. But of course they were in another world.

So the months went by. Gerry Somercotes was still an adorer. There were others, too, sons of farmers or mill-owners. Yvette really ought to have had a good time. She was always out to parties and dances, friends came for her in their motor-cars, and off she went to the city, to the afternoon dance in the chief hotel, or in the gorgeous new Palais de Danse, called the Pally.

Yet she always seemed like a creature mesmerized. She was never free to be quite jolly. Deep inside her worked an intolerable irritation, which she thought she *ought* not to feel, and which she hated feeling, thereby making it worse. She never understood at all whence it arose.

At home, she truly was irritable, and outrageously rude to Aunt Cissie. In fact, Yvette's awful temper became one of the family by-words.

Lucille, always more practical, got a job in the city as private secretary to a man who needed somebody with fluent French and shorthand. She went back and forth every day, by the same train as Uncle Fred. But she never travelled with him, and wet or fine, bicycled to the station, while he went on foot.

The two girls were both determined that what they wanted was a really jolly social life. And they resented with fury that the rectory was, for their friends, impossible. There were only four rooms downstairs : the kitchen, where lived the two discontented maid-servants : the dark dining-room : the rector's study : and the big, " homely," dreary living-room or drawing-room. In the dining-room there was a gas fire. Only in the living-room was a good hot fire kept going. Because, of course, here Granny reigned.

In this room the family was assembled. At evening, after dinner, Uncle Fred and the rector invariably played cross-word puzzles with Granny.

" Now, Mater, are you ready ? N blank blank blank blank W : a Siamese functionary."

" Eh ? Eh ? M blank blank blank blank W ? "

Granny was hard of hearing.

" No, Mater. Not M ! N blank blank blank blank W : a Siamese functionary."

" N blank blank blank blank W : a Chinese functionary."

" SIAMESE."

" Eh ? "

" SIAMESE ! SIAM ! "

" A Siamese functionary ! Now what can that be ? " said the old lady profoundly, folding her hands on her round stomach. Her two sons proceeded to make suggestions, at which she said Ah ! Ah ! The rector was amazingly clever at cross-word puzzles. But Fred had a certain technical vocabulary.

" This certainly is a hard nut to crack," said the old lady, when they were all stuck.

Meanwhile Lucille sat in a corner with her hands over her ears, pretending to read, and Yvette irritably made drawings, or hummed loud and exasperating tunes, to add to the family concert. Aunt Cissie continually reached for a chocolate, and her jaws worked ceaselessly. She literally lived on chocolates. Sitting in the distance, she put another into her mouth, then looked again at the parish magazine. Then she lifted her head, and saw it was time to fetch Granny's cup of Horlick's.

While she was gone, in nervous exasperation Yvette would open the window. The room was never fresh, she imagined it smelt :

smelt of Granny. And Granny, who was hard of hearing, heard like a weasel when she wasn't wanted to.

"Did you open the window, Yvette? I think you might remember there are older people than yourself in the room," she said.

"It's stifling! It's unbearable! No wonder we've all of us always got colds."

"I'm sure the room is large enough, and a good fire burning." The old lady gave a little shudder. "A draught to give us all our death."

"Not a draught at all," roared Yvette. "A breath of fresh air."

The old lady shuddered again, and said:

"Indeed!"

The rector, in silence, marched to the window and firmly closed it. He did not look at his daughter meanwhile. He hated thwarting her. But she must know what's what!

The cross-word puzzles, invented by Satan himself, continued till Granny had had her Horlick's, and was to go to bed. Then came the ceremony of Good night! Everybody stood up. The girls went to be kissed by the blind old woman, the rector gave his arm, and Aunt Cissie followed with a candle.

But this was already nine o'clock, although Granny was really getting old, and should have been in bed sooner. But when she was in bed, she could not sleep, till Aunt Cissie came.

"You see," said Granny, "I have *never* slept alone. For fifty-four years I never slept a night without the Pater's arm round me. And when he was gone I tried to sleep alone. But as sure as my eyes closed to sleep, my heart nearly jumped out of my body, and I lay in a palpitation. Oh, you may think what you will, but it was a fearful experience, after fifty-four years of perfect married life! I would have prayed to be taken first, but the Pater, well, no I don't think he would have been able to bear up."

So Aunt Cissie slept with Granny. And she hated it. She said *she* could never sleep. And she grew greyer and greyer, and the food in the house got worse, and Aunt Cissie had to have an operation.

But the Mater rose as ever, towards noon, and at the midday meal, she presided from her arm-chair, with her stomach protruding; her reddish, pendulous face, that had a sort of horrible majesty, dropping soft under the wall of her high brow, and her blue eyes peering unseeing. Her white hair was getting scanty, it was altogether a little indecent. But the rector jovially cracked his jokes to her, and she pretended to disapprove. But she was perfectly complacent, sitting in her ancient obesity, and after meals, getting the wind from her stomach, pressing her bosom with her hand as she " rifted " in gross physical complacency.

What the girls minded most was that, when they brought their young friends to the house, Granny always was there, like some awful idol of old flesh, consuming all the attention. There was only the one room for everybody. And there sat the old lady, with Aunt Cissie keeping an acrid guard over her. Everybody must be presented first to Granny : she was ready to be genial, she liked company. She had to know who everybody was, where they came from, every circumstance of their lives. And then, when she was *au fait*, she could get hold of the conversation.

Nothing could be more exasperating to the girls. " Isn't old Mrs. Saywell wonderful ! She takes *such* an interest in life, at nearly ninety ! "

" She does take an interest in people's affairs, if that's life," said Yvette.

Then she would immediately feel guilty. After all, it *was* wonderful to be nearly ninety, and have such a clear mind ! And Granny never *actually* did anybody any harm. It was more that she was in the way. And perhaps it was rather awful to hate somebody because they were old and in the way.

Yvette immediately repented, and was nice. Granny blossomed forth into reminiscences of when she was a girl, in the little town in Buckinghamshire. She talked and talked away, and was *so* entertaining. She really *was* rather wonderful.

Then in the afternoon Lottie and Ella and Bob Framley came, with Leo Wetherell.

" Oh, come in ! "—and in they all trooped to the sitting-room, where Granny, in her white cap, sat by the fire.

" Granny, this is Mr. Wetherell."

" Mr. What-did-you-say ? You must excuse me, I'm a little deaf ! "

Granny gave her hand to the uncomfortable young man, and gazed silently at him, sightlessly.

" You are not from our parish ? " she asked him.

" Dinnington ! " he shouted.

" We want to go a picnic to-morrow, to Bonsall Head, in Leo's car. We can all squeeze in," said Ella, in a low voice.

" Did you say Bonsall Head ? " asked Granny.

" Yes ! "

There was a blank silence.

" Did you say you were going in a car ? "

" Yes ! In Mr. Wetherell's."

" I hope he's a good driver. It's a very dangerous road."

" He's a *very* good driver."

" Not a very good driver ? "

" Yes ! He *is* a very good driver."

" If you go to Bonsall Head, I think I must send a message to Lady Louth."

Granny always dragged in this miserable Lady Louth, when there was company.

" Oh, we shan't go that way," cried Yvette.

" Which way ? " said Granny. " You must go by Heanor."

The whole party sat, as Bob expressed it, like stuffed ducks, fidgeting on their chairs.

Aunt Cissie came in—and then the maid with the tea. There was the eternal and everlasting piece of bought cake. Then appeared a plate of little fresh cakes. Aunt Cissie had actually sent to the baker's.

" Tea, Mater ! "

The old lady gripped the arms of her chair. Everybody rose and stood, while she waded slowly across, on Aunt Cissie's arm, to her place at table.

During tea Lucille came in from town, from her job. She was simply worn out, with black marks under her eyes. She gave a cry, seeing all the company.

As soon as the noise had subsided, and the awkwardness was resumed, Granny said :

" You have never mentioned Mr. Wetherell to me, have you, Lucille ? "

" I don't remember," said Lucille.

" You can't have done. The name is strange to me."

Yvette absently grabbed another cake, from the now almost empty plate. Aunt Cissie, who was driven almost crazy by Yvette's vague and inconsiderate ways, felt the green rage fuse in her heart. She picked up her own plate, on which was the one cake she allowed herself, and said with vitriolic politeness, offering it to Yvette :

" Won't you have mine ? "

" Oh, thanks ! " said Yvette, starting in her angry vagueness. And with an appearance of the same insouciance, she helped herself to Aunt Cissie's cake also, adding as an afterthought : " If you're sure you don't want it."

She now had two cakes on her plate. Lucille had gone white as

a ghost, bending to her tea.   Aunt Cissie sat with ·a green
look of poisonous resignation.   The awkwardness was an
agony.

But Granny. bulkily enthroned and unaware, only said, in the
centre of the cyclone :

" If you are motoring to Bonsall Head to-morrow, Lucille, I wish
you would take a message from me to Lady Louth."

" Oh ! " said Lucille, giving a queer look across the table at the
sightless old woman.   Lady Louth was the King Charles' Head of
the family, invariably produced by Granny for the benefit of
visitors.   " Very well ! "

" She was so very kind last week.   She sent her chauffeur over
with a Cross-word Puzzle book for me."

" But you thanked her then," cried Yvette.

" I should like to send her a note."

" We can post it," cried Lucille.

" Oh no ! I should like you to take it.   When Lady Louth called
last time. . . . "

The young ones sat like a shoal of young fishes dumbly mouthing
at the surface of the water, while Granny went on about Lady
Louth.   Aunt Cissie, the two girls knew, was still helpless, almost
unconscious in a paroxysm of rage about the cake.   Perhaps, poor
thing, she was praying.

It was a mercy when the friends departed.   But by that time
the two girls were both haggard-eyed.   And it was then that Yvette,
looking round, suddenly saw the stony, implacable will-to-power in
the old and motherly-seeming Granny.   She sat there bulging
backwards in her chair, impassive, her reddish, pendulous old face
rather mottled, almost unconscious, but implacable, her face like a
mask that hid something stony, relentless.   It was the static inertia
of her unsavoury power.   Yet in a minute she would open her
ancient mouth to find out every detail about Leo Wetherell.   For
the moment she was hibernating in her oldness, her agedness.   But
in a minute her mouth would open, her mind would flicker awake
and with her insatiable greed for life, other people's life, she would
start on her quest for every detail.   She was like the old toad which
Yvette had watched, fascinated, as it sat on the ledge of the beehive,
immediately in front of the little entrance by which the bees emerged,
and which, with a demonish lightning-like snap of its pursed jaws,
caught every bee as it came out to launch into the air, swallowed
them one after the other, as if it could consume the whole hive-
full, into its aged, bulging, purse-like wrinkledness.   It had been

swallowing bees as they launched into the air of spring, year after year, year after year, for generations.

But the gardener, called by Yvette, was in a rage, and killed the creature with a stone.

" 'Appen tha *art* good for th' snails," he said, as he came down with the stone. " But tha 'rt none goin' ter emp'y th' bee-'ive into thy guts."

III

THE next day was dull and low, and the roads were awful, for it had been raining for weeks, yet the young ones set off on their trip, without taking Granny's message either. They just slipped out while she was making her slow trip upstairs after lunch. Not for anything would they have called at Lady Louth's house. That widow of a knighted doctor, a harmless person indeed, had become an obnoxity in their lives.

Six young rebels, they sat very perkily in the car as they swished through the mud. Yet they had a peaked look too. After all, they had nothing really to rebel against, any of them. They were left so very free in their movements. Their parents let them do almost entirely as they liked. There wasn't really a fetter to break, nor a prison-bar to file through, nor a bolt to shatter. The keys of their lives were in their own hands. And there they dangled inert.

It is very much easier to shatter prison bars than to open undiscovered doors to life. As the younger generation finds out somewhat to its chagrin. True, there was Granny. But poor old Granny, you couldn't actually say to her : " Lie down and die, you old woman ! " She might be an old nuisance, but she never really *did* anything. It wasn't fair to hate her.

So the young people set off on their jaunt, trying to be very full of beans. They could really do as they liked. And so, of course, there was nothing to do but sit in the car and talk a lot of criticism of other people, and silly flirty gallantry that was really rather a bore. If there had only been a few " strict orders " to be disobeyed ! But nothing : beyond the refusal to carry the message to Lady Louth, of which the rector would approve because he didn't encourage King Charles' Head either.

They sang, rather scrappily, the latest would-be comic songs, as they went through the grim villages. In the great park the deer were in groups near the road, roe deer and fallow, nestling in the gloom of the afternoon under the oaks by the road, as if for the stimulus of human company.

Yvette insisted on stopping and getting out to talk to them. The girls, in their Russian boots, tramped through the damp grass, while the deer watched them with big, unfrightened eyes. The hart trotted away mildly, holding back his head, because of the weight of the horns. But the doe, balancing her big ears, did not rise from under the tree, with her half-grown young ones, till the girls were almost in touch. Then she walked light-foot away, lifting her tail from her spotted flanks, while the young ones nimbly trotted.

" Aren't they awfully dainty and nice ! " cried Yvette. " You'd wonder they could lie so cosily in this horrid wet grass."

" Well, I suppose they've got to lie down *sometime*," said Lucille. " And it's *fairly* dry under the tree." She looked at the crushed grass, where the deer had lain.

Yvette went and put her hand down, to feel how it felt.

" Yes ! " she said doubtfully, " I believe it's a bit warm."

The deer had bunched again a few yards away, and were standing motionless in the gloom of the afternoon. Away below the slopes of grass and trees, beyond the swift river with its balustraded bridge, sat the huge ducal house, one or two chimneys smoking bluely. Behind it rose purplish woods.

The girls, pushing their fur collars up to their ears, dangling one long arm, stood watching in silence, their wide Russian boots protecting them from the wet grass. The great house squatted square and creamy-grey below. The deer, in little groups, were scattered under the old trees close by. It all seemed so still, so unpretentious, and so sad.

" I wonder where the Duke is now," said Ella.

" Not here, wherever he is," said Lucille. " I expect he's abroad where the sun shines."

The motor horn called from the road, and they heard Leo's voice :

" Come on, boys ! If we're going to get to the Head and down to Amberdale for tea, we'd better move."

They crowded into the car again, with chilled feet, and set off through the park, past the silent spire of the church, out through the great gates and over the bridge, on into the wide, damp, stony village of Woodlinkin, where the river ran. And thence, for a long time, they stayed in the mud and dark and dampness of the valley, often with sheer rock above them ; the water brawling on one hand, the steep rock or dark trees on the other.

Till, through the darkness of overhanging trees, they began to climb, and Leo changed the gear. Slowly the car toiled up through the whitey-grey mud, into the stony village of Bolehill, that hung on the slope, round the old cross, with its steps, that stood where the road branched, on past the cottages whence came a wonderful smell of hot tea-cakes, and beyond, still upwards, under dripping trees and past broken slopes of bracken, always climbing. Until the cleft became shallower, and the trees finished, and the slopes on either side were bare, gloomy grass, with low dry-stone walls. They were emerging on to the Head.

The party had been silent for some time. On either side the road was grass, then a low stone fence, and the swelling curve of the hill-summit, traced with the low, dry stone walls. Above this, the low sky.

The car ran out, under the low, grey sky, on the naked tops.

" Shall we stay a moment ? " called Leo.

" Oh yes ! " cried the girls.

And they scrambled out once more, to look around. They knew the place quite well. But still, if one came to the Head, one got out to look.

The hills were like the knuckles of a hand, the dales were below, between the fingers, narrow, steep, and dark. In the deeps a train was steaming, slowly pulling north : a small thing of the under-world. The noise of the engine re-echoed curiously upwards. Then came the dull, familiar sound of blasting in a quarry.

Leo, always on the go, moved quickly.

" Shall we be going ? " he said. " Do we *want* to get down to Amberdale for tea ? Or shall we try somewhere nearer ? "

They all voted for Amberdale, for the Marquis of Grantham.

" Well, which way shall we go back ? Shall we go by Codnor and over Crosshill, or shall we go by Ashbourne ? "

There was the usual dilemma. Then they finally decided on the Codnor top road. Off went the car, gallantly.

They were on the top of the world, now, on the back of the fist. It was naked, too, as the back of your fist, high under heaven, and dull, heavy green. Only it was veined with a network of old stone walls, dividing the fields, and broken here and there with ruins of old lead-mines and works. A sparse stone farm bristled with six naked sharp trees. In the distance was a patch of smoky grey stone, a hamlet. In some fields grey, dark sheep fed silently, sombrely. But there was not a sound nor a movement. It was the roof of England, stony and arid as any roof. Beyond, below, were the shires.

" ' And see the coloured counties,' " said Yvette to herself. Here anyhow they were not coloured. A stream of rooks trailed out from nowhere. They had been walking, pecking, on a naked field that had been manured. The car ran on between the grass and the stone walls of the upland lane, and the young people were silent, looking out over the far network of stone fences, under the sky, looking for the curves downward that indicated a drop to one of the underneath, hidden dales.

Ahead was a light cart, driven by a man, and trudging along at the side was a woman, sturdy and elderly, with a pack on her back. The man in the cart had caught her up, and now was keeping pace.

The road was narrow. Leo sounded the horn sharply. The man on the cart looked round, but the woman on foot only trudged steadily, rapidly forward, without turning her head.

Yvette's heart gave a jump. The man on the cart was a gipsy, one of the black, loose-bodied, handsome sort. He remained seated on his cart, turning round and gazing at the occupants of the motor-car, from under the brim of his cap. And his pose was loose, his gaze insolent in its indifference. He had a thin black moustache under his thin, straight nose, and a big silk handkerchief of red and yellow tied round his neck. He spoke a word to the woman. She stood a second, solid, to turn round and look at the occupants of the car, which had now drawn quite close. Leo honked the horn again, imperiously. The woman, who had a grey-and-white kerchief tied round her head, turned sharply, to keep pace with the cart, whose driver also had settled back, and was lifting the reins, moving his loose, light shoulders. But still he did not pull aside.

Leo made the horn scream, as he put the brakes on and the car slowed up near the back of the cart. The gipsy turned round at the din, laughing in his dark face under his dark-green cap, and said something which they did not hear, showing white teeth under the line of black moustache, and making a gesture with his dark, loose hand.

" Get out o' the way then ! " yelled Leo.

For answer, the man delicately pulled the horse to a standstill, as it curved to the side of the road. It was a good roan horse and a good, natty, dark-green cart.

Leo, in a rage, had to jam on the brake and pull up too.

" Don't the pretty young ladies want to hear their fortunes ? " said the gipsy on the cart, laughing except for his dark, watchful eyes, which went from face to face, and lingered on Yvette's young, tender face.

She met his dark eyes for a second, their level search, their insolence, their complete indifference to people like Bob and Leo,

THE VIRGIN AND THE GIPSY

and something took fire in her breast. She thought : " He is stronger than I am ! He doesn't care ! "

" Oh yes, let's ! " cried Lucille at once.

" Oh yes ! " chorused the girls.

" I say ! What about the time ? " cried Leo.

" Oh, bother the old time ! Somebody's always dragging in time by the forelock," cried Lucille.

" Well, if you don't mind *when* we get back, *I* don't," said Leo heroically.

The gipsy man had been sitting loosely on the side of his cart, watching the faces. He now jumped softly down from the shaft, his knees a bit stiff. He was apparently a man something over thirty, and a beau in his way. He wore a sort of shooting-jacket, double-breasted, coming only to the hips, of dark green-and-black frieze ; rather tight black trousers, black boots, and a dark-green cap ; with the big yellow-and-red bandanna handkerchief round his neck. His appearance was curiously elegant, and quite expensive in its gipsy style. He was handsome, too, pressing in his chin with the old, gipsy conceit, and now apparently not heeding the strangers any more, as he led his good roan horse off the road, preparing to back his cart.

The girls saw for the first time a deep recess in the side of the road, and two caravans smoking. Yvette got quickly down. They had suddenly come upon a disused quarry, cut into the slope of the roadside, and in this sudden lair, almost like a cave, were three caravans, dismantled for the winter. There was also deep at the back, a shelter built of boughs, as a stable for the horse. The grey, crude rock rose high above the caravans, and curved round towards the road. The floor was heaped chips of stone, with grasses growing among. It was a hidden, snug winter camp.

The elderly woman with the pack had gone into one of the caravans, leaving the door open. Two children were peeping out, shewing black heads. The gipsy man gave a little call, as he backed his cart into the quarry, and an elderly man came out to help him untackle.

The gipsy himself went up the steps into the newest caravan, that had its door closed. Underneath, a tied-up dog ranged forth. It was a white hound, spotted liver-coloured. It gave a low growl as Leo and Bob approached.

At the same moment, a dark-faced gipsy-woman with a pink shawl or kerchief round her head and big gold ear-rings in her ears, came down the steps of the newest caravan, swinging her flounced, voluminous green skirt. She was handsome in a bold, dark, long-faced way, just a bit wolfish. She looked like one of the bold, loping Spanish gipsies.

"Good morning, my ladies and gentlemen," she said, eyeing the girls from her bold, predative eyes. She spoke with a certain foreign stiffness.

"Good afternoon!" said the girls.

"Which beautiful little lady like to hear her fortune? Give me her little hand?"

She was a tall woman, with a frightening way of reaching forward her neck like a menace. Her eyes went from face to face, very active, heartlessly searching out what she wanted. Meanwhile the man, apparently her husband, appeared at the top of the caravan steps smoking a pipe, and with a small, black-haired child in his arms. He stood on his limber legs, casually looking down on the group, as if from a distance, his long black lashes lifted from his full, conceited, impudent black eyes. There was something peculiarly transfusing in his stare. Yvette felt it, felt it in her knees. She pretended to be interested in the white-and-liver-coloured hound.

"How much do you want, if we all have our fortunes told?" asked Lottie Framley, as the six fresh-faced young Christians hung back rather reluctantly from this pagan pariah woman.

"All of you? Ladies and gentlemen, all?" said the woman shrewdly.

"I don't want mine told! You go ahead!" cried Leo.

"Neither do I," said Bob. "You four girls."

"The four ladies?" said the gipsy woman, eyeing them shrewdly, after having looked at the boys. And she fixed her price. "Each one give me a sheeling, and a little bit more for luck? A little bit!" She smiled in a way that was more wolfish than cajoling, and the force of her will was felt, heavy as iron beneath the velvet of her words.

"All right," said Leo. "Make it a shilling a head. Don't spin it out too long."

"Oh, *you!*" cried Lucille at him. "We want to hear it *all.*"

The woman took two wooden stools, from under a caravan, and placed them near the wheel. Then she took the tall, dark Lottie Framley by the hand, and bade her sit down.

"You don't care if everybody hear?" she said, looking up curiously into Lottie's face.

Lottie blushed dark with nervousness, as the gipsy woman held her hand, and stroked her palm with hard, cruel-seeming fingers.

"Oh, I don't mind," she said.

The gipsy woman peered into the palm tracing the lines of the hand with a hard, dark forefinger. But she seemed clean.

And slowly she told the fortune, while the others, standing listening, kept on crying out : " Oh, that's Jim Baggaley ! Oh, I, I don't believe it ! Oh, that's not true ! A fair woman who lives beneath a tree ! Why, whoever's that ? " until Leo stopped them with a manly warning :

" Oh, hold on, girls ! You give everything away."

Lottie retired blushing and confused, and it was Ella's turn. She was much more calm and shrewd, trying to read the oracular words. Lucille kept breaking out with : " Oh, I say ! " The gipsy man at the top of the steps stood imperturbable, without any expression at all. But his bold eyes kept staring at Yvette, she could feel them on her cheek, on her neck, and she dared not look up. But Framley would sometimes look up at him, and got a level stare back from the handsome face of the male gipsy, from the dark conceited proud eyes. It was a peculiar look, in the eyes that belonged to the tribe of the humble : the pride of the pariah, the half-sneering challenge of the outcast, who sneered at law-abiding men, and went his own way. All the time, the gipsy man stood there, holding his child in his arms, looking on without being concerned.

Lucille was having her hand read—" You have been across the sea, and there you met a man—a brown-haired man—but he was too old——"

" Oh, I *say* ! " cried Lucille, looking round at Yvette.

But Yvette was abstracted, agitated, hardly heeding : in one of her mesmerized states.

" You will marry in a few years—not now, but a few years—perhaps four—and you will not be rich, but you will have plenty —enough—and you will go away, a long journey."

" With my husband, or without ? " cried Lucille.

" With him——"

When it came to Yvette's turn, and the woman looked up boldly, cruelly, searching for a long time in her face, Yvette said nervously :

" I don't think I want mine told. No, I won't have mine told ! No, I won't, really ! "

" You are afraid of something ? " said the gipsy woman cruelly.

" No, it's not that——" Yvette fidgeted.

" You have some secret ? You are afraid I shall say it ? Come, would you like to go in the caravan, where nobody hears ? "

The woman was curiously insinuating ; while Yvette was always wayward, perverse. The look of perversity was on her soft, frail young face now, giving her a queer hardness.

" Yes ! " she said suddenly. " Yes ! I might do that ! "

" Oh, I say ! " cried the others. " Be a sport ! "

" I don't think you'd *better !* " cried Lucille.

" Yes ! " said Yvette, with that hard little way of hers. " I'll do that. I'll go in the caravan."

The gipsy woman called something to the man on the steps. He went into the caravan for a moment or two, then reappeared, and came down the steps, setting the small child on its uncertain feet, and holding it by the hand. A dandy, in his polished black boots, tight black trousers and tight dark-green jersey, he walked slowly across with the toddling child to where the elderly gipsy was giving the roan horse a feed of oats, in the bough shelter between pits of grey rock, with dry bracken upon the stone chip floor. He looked at Yvette as he passed, staring her full in the eyes, with his pariah's bold yet dishonest stare. Something hard inside her met his stare. But the surface of her body seemed to turn to water. Nevertheless, something hard in her registered the peculiar pure lines of his face, of his straight, pure nose, of his cheeks and temples. The curious dark, suave purity of all his body, outlined in the green jersey : a purity like a living sneer.

And as he loped slowly past her, on his flexible hips, it seemed to her still that he was stronger than she was. Of all the men she had ever seen, this one was the only one who was stronger than she was, in her own kind of strength, her own kind of understanding.

So, with curiosity, she followed the woman up the steps of the caravan, the skirts of her well-cut tan coat swinging and almost showing her knees, under the pale-green cloth dress. She had long, long-striding, fine legs, too slim rather than too thick, and she wore curiously-patterned pale-and-fawn stockings of fine wool, suggesting the legs of some delicate animal.

At the top of the steps she paused and turned, debonair, to the others, saying in her naive, lordly way, so off-hand :

" I won't let her be long."

Her grey fur collar was open, showing her soft throat and pale green dress, her little plaited tan-coloured hat came down to her ears, round her soft, fresh face. There was something soft and yet overbearing, unscrupulous, about her. She knew the gipsy man had turned to look at her. She was aware of the pure dark nape of his neck, the black hair groomed away. He watched as she entered his house.

What the gipsy told her, no one ever knew. It was a long time to wait, the others felt. Twilight was deepening on the gloom, and it was turning raw and cold. From the chimney on the second caravan came smoke and a smell of rich food. The horse was fed, a yellow blanket strapped round him, and two gipsy men talked together in the distance, in low tones. There was a peculiar feeling of silence and secrecy in that lonely, hidden quarry.

At last the caravan door opened, and Yvette emerged, bending forward and stepping with long, witch-like slim legs down the steps. There was a stooping, witch-like silence about her as she emerged on the twilight.

" Did it seem long ? " she said vaguely, not looking at anybody and keeping her own counsel hard within her soft, vague waywardness. " I hope you weren't bored ! Wouldn't tea be nice ! Shall we go ? "

" You get in ! " said Bob. " I'll pay."

The gipsy-woman's full, metallic skirts of jade-green alpaca came swinging down the steps. She rose to her height, a big, triumphant-looking woman with a dark wolf face. The pink cashmere kerchief stamped with red roses, was slipping to one side over her black and crimped hair. She gazed at the young people in the twilight with bold arrogance.

Bob put two half-crowns in her hand.

" A little bit more, for luck, for your young lady's luck," she wheedled, like a wheedling wolf. " Another bit of silver, to bring you luck."

" You've got a shilling for luck, that's enough," said Bob calmly and quietly, as they moved away to the car.

" A little bit of silver ! Just a little bit, for your luck in love ! "

Yvette, with the sudden long, startling gestures of her long limbs, swung round as she was entering the car, and with long arm out-stretched, strode and put something into the gipsy's hand, then stepped, bending her height, into the car.

" Prosperity to the beautiful young lady, and the gipsy's blessing on her," came the suggestive, half-sneering voice of the woman.

The engine *birred !* then *birred !* again more fiercely, and started. Leo switched on the lights, and immediately the quarry with the gipsies fell back into the blackness of night.

" Good night ! " called Yvette's voice, as the car started. But hers was the only voice that piped up, chirpy and impudent in its nonchalance. The headlights glared down the stone lane.

" Yvette, you've got to tell us what she said to you," cried Lucille, in the teeth of Yvette's silent will *not* to be asked.

" Oh, nothing at *all* thrilling," said Yvette, with false warmth. " Just the usual old thing : a dark man who means good luck, and a fair one who means bad : and a death in the family, which if it means Granny, won't be so *very* awful : and I shall marry when I'm twenty-three, and have heaps of money and heaps of love, and two children. All sounds very nice, but it's a bit too much of a good thing, you know."

" Oh, but why did you give her more money ? "

" Oh well, I wanted to ! You *have* to be a bit lordly with people like that——"

IV

THERE was a terrific rumpus down at the rectory, on account of Yvette and the Window Fund. After the war, Aunt Cissie had set her heart on a stained glass window in the church, as a memorial for the men of the parish who had fallen. But the bulk of the fallen had been nonconformists, so the memorial took the form of an ugly little monument in front of the Wesleyan chapel.

This did not vanquish Aunt Cissie. She canvassed, she had bazaars, she made the girls get up amateur theatrical shows, for her precious window. Yvette, who quite liked the acting and showing-off part of it, took charge of the farce called *Mary in the Mirror*, and gathered in the proceeds, which were to be paid to the Window Fund when accounts were settled. Each of the girls was supposed to have a money-box for the Fund.

Aunt Cissie, feeling that the united sums must now almost suffice, suddenly called in Yvette's box. It contained fifteen shillings. There was a moment of green horror.

" Where is all the rest ? "

" Oh ! " said Yvette casually. " I just borrowed it. It wasn't so awfully much."

" What about the three pounds thirteen for *Mary in the Mirror* ? " asked Aunt Cissie, as if the jaws of Hell were yawning.

" Oh quite ! I just borrowed it. I can pay it back."

Poor Aunt Cissie ! The green tumour of hate burst inside her, and there was a ghastly, abnormal scene, which left Yvette shivering with fear and nervous loathing.

Even the rector was rather severe.

" If you needed money, why didn't you tell me ? " he said coldly. " Have you ever been refused anything in reason ? "

" I—I thought it didn't matter," stammered Yvette.

" And what have you done with the money ? "

" I suppose I've spent it," said Yvette, with wide distraught eyes and a peaked face.

" Spent it, on what ? "

" I can't remember everything : stockings and things, and I gave some of it away."

Poor Yvette ! Her lordly airs and ways were already hitting back at her, on the reflex. The rector was angry : his face had a snarling, doggish look, a sort of sneer. He was afraid his daughter was developing some of the rank, tainted qualities of She-who-was-Cynthia.

" You *would* do the large with somebody else's money, wouldn't you ? " he said, with a cold, mongrel sort of sneer, which showed what an utter unbeliever he was, at the heart. The inferiority of a heart which has no core of warm belief in it, no pride in life. He had utterly no belief in her.

Yvette went pale, and very distant. Her pride, that frail, precious flame which everybody tried to quench, recoiled like a flame blown far away, on a cold wind, as if blown out, and her face, white now and still like a snowdrop, the white snow-flower of his conceit, seemed to have no life in it, only this pure, strange abstraction.

" He has no belief in me ! " she thought in her soul. " I am really nothing to him. I am nothing, only a shameful thing. Everything is shameful, everything is shameful ! "

A flame of passion or rage, while it might have overwhelmed or infuriated her, would not have degraded her as did her father's unbelief, his final attitude of a sneer against her.

He became a little afraid, in the silence of sterile thought. After all, he needed the *appearance* of love and belief and bright life, he would never dare to face the fat worm of his own unbelief that stirred in his heart.

" What have you to say for yourself ? " he asked.

She only looked at him from that senseless snowdrop face which haunted him with fear, and gave him a helpless sense of guilt. That other one, She-who-was-Cynthia, she had looked back at him with the same numb, white fear, the fear of his degrading unbelief, the worm which was his heart's core. He *knew* his heart's core was a fat, awful worm. His dread was lest any one else should know. His anguish of hate was against any one who knew, and recoiled.

He saw Yvette recoiling, and immediately his manner changed to the worldly old good-humoured cynic which he affected.

" Ah well ! " he said. " You have to pay it back, my girl, that's all. I will advance you the money out of your allowance. But I

shall charge you four per cent a month's interest. Even the devil
himself must pay a percentage on his debts. Another time, if you
can't trust yourself, don't handle money which isn't your own.
Dishonesty isn't pretty."

Yvette remained crushed, and deflowered and humiliated. She
crept about, trailing the rays of her pride. She had a revulsion
even from herself. Oh, why had she ever touched the leprous
money! Her whole flesh shrank as if it were defiled. Why was
that? Why, why was that?

She admitted herself wrong in having spent the money. " Of
course I shouldn't have done it. They are quite right to be angry,"
she said to herself.

But where did the horrible wincing of her flesh come from?
Why did she feel she had caught some physical contagion?

" Where you're so *silly*, Yvette," Lucille lectured her : poor
Lucille was in great distress—" is that you give yourself away to them
all. You might *know* they'd find out. I could have raised the money
for you, and saved all this bother. It's perfectly awful! But you
never will think beforehand where your actions are going to land
you! Fancy Aunt Cissie saying all those things to you! How
awful! Whatever would Mamma have said, if she'd heard
it?"

When things went very wrong, they thought of their mother, and
despised their father and all the low brood of the Saywells. Their
mother, of course, had belonged to a higher, if more dangerous and
" immoral " world. More selfish, decidedly. But with a showier
gesture. More unscrupulous and more easily moved to contempt :
but not so humiliating.

Yvette always considered that she got her fine, delicate flesh from
her mother. The Saywells were all a bit leathery, and grubby somewhere inside. But then the Saywells never let you down. Whereas
the fine She-who-was-Cynthia had let the rector down with a bang,
and his little children along with him. Her little children! They
could not quite forgive her.

Only dimly, after the row, Yvette began to realize the other
sanctity of herself, the sanctity of her sensitive, clean flesh and blood,
which the Saywells with their so-called morality succeeded in
defiling. They always wanted to defile it. They were the life
unbelievers. Whereas, perhaps She-who-was-Cynthia had only
been a moral unbeliever.

Yvette went about dazed and peaked and confused. The rector
paid in the money to Aunt Cissie, much to that lady's rage. The

helpless tumour of her rage was still running. She would have liked to announce her niece's delinquency in the parish magazine. It was anguish to the destroyed woman that she could not publish the news to all the world. The selfishness ! The selfishness ! The selfishness !

Then the rector handed his daughter a little account with himself : her debt to him, interest thereon, the amount deducted from her small allowance. But to her credit he had placed a guinea, which was the fee he had to pay for complicity.

" As father of the culprit," he said humorously, " I am fined one guinea. And with that I wash the ashes out of my hair."

He was always generous about money. But somehow, he seemed to think that by being free about money he could absolutely call himself a generous man. Whereas he used money, even generosity, as a hold over her.

But he let the affair drop entirely. He was by this time more amused than anything, to judge from appearances. He thought still he was safe.

Aunt Cissie, however, could not get over her convulsion. One night when Yvette had gone rather early, miserably, to bed, when Lucille was away at a party, and she was lying with soft, peaked limbs aching with a sort of numbness and defilement, the door softly opened, and there stood Aunt Cissie, pushing her grey-green face through the opening of the door. Yvette started up in terror.

" Liar ! Thief ! Selfish little beast ! " hissed the maniacal face of Aunt Cissie. " You little hypocrite ! You liar ! You selfish beast ! You greedy little beast ! "

There was such extraordinary impersonal hatred in that grey-green mask, and those frantic words, that Yvette opened her mouth to scream with hysterics. But Aunt Cissie shut the door as suddenly . as she had opened it, and disappeared. Yvette leaped from her bed and turned the key. Then she crept back, half demented with fear of the squalid abnormal, half numbed with paralysis of damaged pride. And amid it all, up came a bubble of distracted laughter. It *was* so filthily ridiculous !

Aunt Cissie's behaviour did not hurt the girl so very much. It was after all somewhat fantastic. Yet hurt she was : in her limbs, in her body, in her sex, hurt. Hurt, numbed, and half destroyed, with only her nerves vibrating and jangled. And still so young, she could not conceive what was happening.

Only she lay and wished she were a gipsy. To live in a camp, in a caravan, and never set foot in a house, not know the existence of a parish, never look at a church. Her heart was hard with repugnance against the rectory. She loathed these houses with their indoor sanitation and their bathrooms, and their extraordinary repulsiveness. She hated the rectory, and everything it implied. The whole stagnant, sewerage sort of life, where sewerage is never mentioned, but where it seems to smell from the centre to every two-legged inmate, from Granny to the servants, was foul. If gipsies had no bathrooms, at least they had no sewerage. There was fresh air. In the rectory there was *never* fresh air. And in the souls of the people, the air was stale till it stank.

Hate kindled her heart, as she lay with numbed limbs. And she thought of the words of the gipsy woman : " There is a dark man who never lived in a house. He loves you. The other people are treading on your heart. They will tread on your heart till you think it is dead. But the dark man will blow the one spark up into fire again, good fire. You will see what good fire."

Even as the woman was saying it, Yvette felt there was some duplicity somewhere. But she didn't mind. She hated with the cold, acrid hatred of a child the rectory interior, the sort of putridity in the life. She liked that big, swarthy, wolf-like gipsy-woman, with the big gold rings in her ears, the pink scarf over her wavy black hair, the tight bodice of brown velvet, the green, fan-like skirt. She liked her dusky, strong, relentless hands, that had pressed so firm, like wolf's paws, in Yvette's own soft palm. She liked her. She liked the danger and the covert fearlessness of her. She liked her covert, unyielding sex, that was immoral, but with a hard, defiant pride of its own. Nothing would ever get that woman under. She would despise the rectory and the rectory morality, utterly ! She would strangle Granny with one hand. And she would have the same contempt for Daddy and for Uncle Fred, as men, as she would have for fat old slobbery Rover, the Newfoundland dog. A great, sardonic female contempt, for such domesticated dogs, calling themselves men.

And the gipsy man himself ! Yvette quivered suddenly, as if she had seen his big, bold eyes upon her, with the naked insinuation of desire in them. The absolutely naked insinuation of desire made her lie prone and powerless in the bed, as if a drug had cast her in a new, molten mould.

She never confessed to anybody that two of the ill-starred Window Fund pounds had gone to the gipsy woman. What if Daddy and Aunt Cissie knew *that* ! Yvette stirred luxuriously in the bed. The thought of the gipsy had released the life of her limbs, and crystallized in her heart the hate of the rectory : so that now she felt potent, instead of impotent.

When, later, Yvette told Lucille about Aunt Cissie's dramatic interlude in the bedroom doorway, Lucille was indignant. " Oh, hang it all ! " cried she. " She might let it drop now. I should think we've heard enough about it by now ! Good heavens, you'd think Aunt Cissie was a perfect bird of paradise ! Daddy's dropped it, and after all, it's his business if it's anybody's. Let Aunt Cissie shut up ! "

It was the very fact that the rector had dropped it, and that he again treated the vague and inconsiderate Yvette as if she were some specially-licensed being, that kept Aunt Cissie's bile flowing. The fact that Yvette really was most of the time unaware of other people's feelings, and being unaware, couldn't care about them, nearly sent Aunt Cissie mad. Why should that young creature, with a delinquent mother, go through life as a privileged being, even unaware of other people's existence, though they were under her nose ?

Lucille at this time was very irritable. She seemed as if she simply went a little unbalanced, when she entered the rectory. Poor Lucille, she was so thoughtful and responsible. She did all the extra troubling, thought about doctors, medicines, servants, and all that sort of thing. She slaved conscientiously at her job all day in town, working in a room with artificial light from ten till five. And she came home to have her nerves rubbed almost to frenzy by Granny's horrible and persistent inquisitiveness and parasitic agedness.

The affair of the Window Fund had apparently blown over, but there remained a stuffy tension in the atmosphere. The weather continued bad. Lucille stayed at home on the afternoon of her half holiday, and did herself no good by it. The rector was in his study, she and Yvette were making a dress for the latter young woman, Granny was resting on the couch.

The dress was of blue silk velours, French material, and was going to be very becoming. Lucille made Yvette try it on again : she was nervously uneasy about the hang, under the arms.

" Oh, bother ! " cried Yvette, stretching her long, tender, childish arms, that tended to go bluish with the cold. " Don't be so frightfully *fussy*, Lucille ! It's quite all right."

" If that's all the thanks I get, slaving my half-day away making dresses for you, I might as well do something for myself ! "

" Well, Lucille ! You know I never *asked* you ! You know you can't bear it unless you *do* supervise," said Yvette, with that irritating blandness of hers, as she raised her naked elbows and peered over her shoulder into the long mirror.

" Oh yes ! you never *asked* me ! " cried Lucille. " As if I didn't know what you meant, when you started sighing and flouncing about."

" I ! " said Yvette, with vague surprise. " Why, when did I start sighing and flouncing about ? "

" Of course you know you did."

" Did I ? No, I didn't know ! When was it ? " Yvette could put a peculiar annoyance into her mild, straying questions.

" I shan't do another thing to this frock, if you don't stand still and *stop* it," said Lucille, in her rather sonorous, burning voice.

" You know you are most awfully nagging and irritable, Lucille," said Yvette, standing as if on hot bricks.

" Now, Yvette ! " cried Lucille, her eyes suddenly flashing in her sister's face, with wild flashes. " Stop it at once ! Why should everybody put up with your abominable and overbearing temper ? "

" Well, I don't know about *my* temper," said Yvette, writhing slowly out of the half-made frock, and slipping into her dress again.

Then, with an obstinate little look on her face, she sat down again at the table, in the gloomy afternoon, and began to sew at the blue stuff. The room was littered with blue clippings, the scissors were lying on the floor, the workbasket was spilled in chaos all over the table, and a second mirror was perched perilously on the piano.

Granny, who had been in a semi-coma, called a doze, roused herself on the big, soft couch and put her cap straight.

" I don't get much peace for my nap," she said, slowly feeling her thin white hair, to see that it was in order. She had heard vague noises.

Aunt Cissie came in, fumbling in a bag for a chocolate.

" I never saw such a mess ! " she said. " You'd better clear some of that litter away, Yvette."

" All right," said Yvette. " I will in a minute."

" Which means never ! " sneered Aunt Cissie, suddenly darting and picking up the scissors.

There was silence for a few moments, and Lucille slowly pushed her hands in her hair, as she read a book.

" You'd better clear away, Yvette," persisted Aunt Cissie.

" I will, before tea," replied Yvette, rising once more and pulling the blue dress over her head, flourishing her long, naked arms through the sleeveless armholes. Then she went between the mirrors, to look at herself once more.

As she did so, she sent the second mirror, that she had perched carelessly on the piano, sliding with a rattle to the floor. Luckily it did not break. But everybody started badly.

" She's smashed the mirror ! " cried Aunt Cissie.

" Smashed a mirror ! Which mirror ! Who's smashed it ? " came Granny's sharp voice.

" I haven't smashed anything," came the calm voice of Yvette. " It's quite all right."

" You'd better not perch it up there again," said Lucille.

Yvette, with a little impatient shrug at all the fuss, tried making the mirror stand in another place. She was not successful.

" If one had a fire in one's own room," she said crossly, " one needn't have a lot of people fussing when one wants to sew."

" Which mirror are you moving about ? " asked Granny.

" One of our own that came from the vicarage," said Yvette rudely.

" Don't break it in *this* house, wherever it came from," said Granny.

There was a sort of family dislike for the furniture that had belonged to She-who-was-Cynthia. It was most of it shoved into the kitchen, and the servants' bedrooms.

" Oh, *I'm* not superstitious," said Yvette, " about mirrors or any of that sort of thing."

" Perhaps you're not," said Granny. " People who never take the responsibility for their own actions usually don't care what happens."

" After all," said Yvette, " I may say it's my own looking-glass, even if I did break it."

" And I say," said Granny, " that there shall be no mirrors broken in *this* house, if we can help it ; no matter who they belong to, or did belong to. Cissie, have I got my cap straight ? "

Aunt Cissie went over and straightened the old lady. Yvette loudly and irritatingly trilled a tuneless tune.

" And now, Yvette, will you please clear away ? " said Aunt Cissie.

" Oh, bother ! " cried Yvette angrily. " It's simply *awful* to live with a lot of people who are always nagging and fussing over trifles."

" What people, may I ask ? " said Aunt Cissie ominously.

Another row was imminent. Lucille looked up with a queer cast in her eyes. In the two girls, the blood of She-who-was-Cynthia was roused.

" Of course you may ask ! You know quite well I mean the people in this beastly house," said the outrageous Yvette.

" At least," said Granny, " we don't come of half-depraved stock."

There was a second's electric pause. Then Lucille sprang from her low seat, with sparks flying from her.

" You shut up ! " she shouted, in a blast full upon the mottled majesty of the old lady.

The old woman's breast began to heave with heaven knows what emotions. The pause this time, as after the thunderbolt, was icy.

Then Aunt Cissie, livid, sprang upon Lucille, pushing her like a fury.

" Go to your room ! " she cried hoarsely. " Go to your room ! "

And she proceeded to push the white but fiery-eyed Lucille from the room. Lucille let herself be pushed, while Aunt Cissie vociferated :

" Stay in your room till you've apologized for this—till you've apologized to the Mater for this ! "

" I shan't apologize ! " came the clear voice of Lucille, from the passage, while Aunt Cissie shoved her.

Aunt Cissie drove her more wildly upstairs.

Yvette stood tall and bemused in the sitting-room, with the air of offended dignity, at the same time bemused, which was so odd on her. She still was bare-armed, in the half-made blue dress. And even *she* was half-aghast at Lucille's attack on the majesty of age. But also, she was coldly indignant against Granny's aspersion of the maternal blood in their veins.

" Of course I meant no offence," said Granny.

" Didn't you ? " said Yvette coolly.

" Of course not. I only said we're not depraved, just because we happen to be superstitious about breaking mirrors."

Yvette could hardly believe her ears. Had she heard right ? Was it possible ! Or was Granny, at her age, just telling a barefaced lie ?

Yvette knew that the old woman was telling a cool, barefaced lie. But already, so quickly, Granny believed her own statement.

The rector appeared, having left time for a lull.

" What's wrong ? " he asked cautiously, genially.

" Oh, nothing ! " drawled Yvette. " Lucille told Granny to shut up, when she was saying something. And Aunt Cissie drove her up to her room. *Tant de bruit pour une omelette !* Though Lucille *was* a bit over the mark, that time."

The old lady couldn't quite catch what Yvette said.

" Lucille really will have to learn to control her nerves," said the old woman. " The mirror fell down, and it worried me. I said so to Yvette, and she said something about superstitions and the people in the beastly house. I told her the people in the house were not depraved, if they happened to mind when a mirror was broken. And at that Lucille flew at me and told me to shut up. It really is disgraceful how these children give way to their nerves. I know it's nothing but nerves."

Aunt Cissie had come in during this speech. At first even she was dumb. Then it seemed to her, it was as Granny had said.

" I have forbidden her to come down until she comes to apologize to the Mater," she said.

" I doubt if she'll apologize," said the calm, queenly Yvette, holding her bare arms.

" And I don't want any apology," said the old lady. " It is merely nerves. I don't know what they'll come to, if they have nerves like that, at their age ! She must take Vibrofat. I am sure Arthur would like his tea, Cissie."

Yvette swept her sewing together, to go upstairs. And again she trilled her tune, rather shrill and tuneless. She was trembling inwardly.

" More glad rags ! " said her father to her, genially.

" More glad rags ! " she reiterated sagely, as she sauntered upstairs, with her day dress over one arm. She wanted to console Lucille, and ask her how the blue stuff hung now.

At the first landing she stood as she nearly always did, to gaze through the window that looked to the road and the bridge. Like the Lady of Shalott, she seemed always to imagine that someone would come along singing *Tirra-lirra !* or something equally intelligent, by the river.

V

IT was nearly tea-time. The snowdrops were out by the short drive going to the gate from the side of the house, and the gardener was pottering at the round, damp flower-beds, on the wet grass that sloped to the stream. Past the gate went the whitish muddy road, crossing the stone bridge almost immediately, and winding in a curve up to the steep, clustering, stony, smoking northern village, that perched over the grim stone mills which Yvette could see ahead down the narrow valley, their tall chimneys long and erect.

The rectory was on one side the Papple, in the rather steep valley, the village was beyond and above, further down, on the other side the swift stream. At the back of the rectory the hill went up steep, with a grove of dark, bare larches, through which the road disappeared. And immediately across stream from the rectory, facing the house, the river-bank rose steep and bushy, up to the sloping, dreary meadows, that sloped up again to dark hillsides of trees, with grey rock cropping out.

But from the end of the house, Yvette could only see the road curving round past the wall with its laurel hedge, down to the bridge, then up again round the shoulder to that first hard cluster of houses in Papplewick village, beyond the dry-stone walls of the steep fields.

She always expected *something* to come down the slant of the road from Papplewick, and she always lingered at the landing window. Often a cart came, or a motor-car, or a lorry with stone, or a labourer, or one of the servants. But never anybody who sang *Tirra-lirra !* by the river. The tirra-lirra-ing days seem to have gone by.

This day, however, round the corner on the white-grey road, between the grass and the low stone walls, a roan horse came stepping bravely and briskly downhill, driven by a man in a cap, perched on the front of his light cart. The man swayed loosely to the swing of the cart, as the horse stepped downhill, in the silent sombreness of the afternoon. At the back of the cart, long duster-brooms of reed and feather stuck out, nodding on their stalks of cane.

Yvette stood close to the window, and put the casement-cloth curtains behind her, clutching her bare upper arms with her hands.

At the foot of the slope the horse started into a brisk trot to the bridge. The cart rattled on the stone bridge, the brooms bobbed and flustered, the driver sat as if in a kind of dream, swinging along. It was like something seen in a sleep.

But as he crossed the end of the bridge, and was passing along the rectory wall, he looked up at the grim stone house that seemed to have backed away from the gate, under the hill. Yvette moved her hands quickly on her arms. And as quickly, from under the peak of his cap, he had seen her, his swarthy predative face was alert.

He pulled up suddenly at the white gate, still gazing upwards at the landing window ; while Yvette, always clasping her cold and mottled arms, still gazed abstractedly down at him, from the window.

His head gave a little, quick jerk of signal, and he led his horse well aside, on to the grass. Then, limber and alert, he turned back the tarpaulin of the cart, fetched out various articles, pulled forth two or three of the long brooms of reed or turkey-feathers, covered the cart, and turned towards the house, looking up at Yvette as he opened the white gate.

She nodded to him, and flew to the bathroom to put on her dress, hoping she had disguised her nod so that he wouldn't be sure she had nodded. Meanwhile she heard the hoarse deep roaring of that old fool, Rover, punctuated by the yapping of that young idiot, Trixie.

She and the housemaid arrived at the same moment at the sitting-room door.

" Was it the man selling brooms ? " said Yvette to the maid. " All right ! " and she opened the door. " Aunt Cissie, there's a man selling brooms. Shall I go ? "

" What sort of a man ? " said Aunt Cissie, who was sitting at tea with the rector and the Mater : the girls having been excluded for once from the meal.

" A man with a cart," said Yvette.

" A gipsy," said the maid.

Of course Aunt Cissie rose at once. She had to look at him.

The gipsy stood at the back door, under the steep dark bank where the larches grew. The long brooms flourished from one hand, and from the other hung various objects of shining copper and brass : a saucepan, a candlestick, plates of beaten copper. The man himself was neat and dapper, almost rakish, in his dark green cap and double-breasted green check coat. But his manner was subdued, very quiet : and at the same time proud, with a touch of condescension and aloofness.

" Anything to-day, lady ? " he said, looking at Aunt Cissie with dark, shrewd, searching eyes, but putting a very quiet tenderness into his voice.

Aunt Cissie saw how handsome he was, saw the flexible curve of his lips under the line of black moustache, and she was fluttered. The merest hint of roughness or aggression on the man's part would have made her shut the door contemptuously in his face. But he managed to insinuate such a subtle suggestion of submission into his male bearing, that she began to hesitate.

" The candlestick is lovely ! " said Yvette. " Did you make it ? "

And she looked up at the man with her naive, childlike eyes, that were as capable of double meanings as his own.

" Yes, lady ! " He looked back into her eyes for a second, with

2 L

that naked suggestion of desire which acted on her like a spell, and
robbed her of her will. Her tender face seemed to go into a sleep.
" It's awfully nice ! " she murmured vaguely.

Aunt Cissie began to bargain for the candlestick : which was a
low, thick stem of copper, rising from a double bowl. With patient
aloofness the man attended to her, without ever looking at Yvette,
who leaned against the doorway and watched in a muse.

" How is your wife ? " she asked him suddenly, when Aunt Cissie
had gone indoors to show the candlestick to the rector, and ask him
if he thought it was worth it.

The man looked fully at Yvette, and a scarcely discernible smile
curled his lips. His eyes did not smile : the insinuation in them
only hardened to a glare.

" She's all right. When are you coming that way again ? " he
murmured, in a low, caressive, intimate voice.

" Oh, I don't know," said Yvette vaguely.

" You come Fridays, when I'm there," he said.

Yvette gazed over his shoulder as if she had not heard him.
Aunt Cissie returned, with the candlestick and the money to pay
for it. Yvette turned nonchalant away, trilling one of her broken
tunes, abandoning the whole affair with a certain rudeness.

Nevertheless, hiding this time at the landing window, she stood
to watch the man go. What she wanted to know, was whether he really
had any power over her. She did not intend him to see her this time.

She saw him go down to the gate, with his brooms and pans, and
out to the cart. He carefully stowed away his pans and his brooms,
and fixed down the tarpaulin over the cart. Then with a slow,
effortless spring of his flexible loins, he was on the cart again, and
touching the horse with the reins. The roan horse was away at
once, the cart-wheels grinding uphill, and soon the man was gone,
without looking round. Gone like a dream which was only a
dream, yet which she could not shake off.

" No, he hasn't any power over me ! " she said to herself : rather
disappointed really, because she wanted somebody, or something,
to have power over her.

She went up to reason with the pale and overwrought Lucille,
scolding her for getting into a state over nothing.

" What does it *matter*," she expostulated, " if you told Granny to
shut up ! Why, everybody ought to be told to shut up, when they're
being beastly. But she didn't mean it, you know. No, she didn't
mean it. And she's quite sorry she said it. There's absolutely no
reason to make a fuss. Come on, let's dress ourselves up and sail

down to dinner like duchesses.   Let's have our own back that way.
Come on, Lucille ! "

There was something strange and mazy, like having cobwebs over
one's face, about Yvette's vague blitheness ;   her queer, misty side-
stepping from an unpleasantness.   It was cheering too.   But it was
like walking in one of those autumn mists, when gossamer strands
blow over your face.   You don't quite know where you are.

She succeeded, however, in persuading Lucille, and the girls got
out their best party frocks´:   Lucille in green and silver, Yvette in a
pale lilac colour with turquoise chenille threading.   A little rouge
and powder, and their best slippers, and the gardens of paradise
began to blossom.   Yvette hummed and looked at herself, and put
on her most *dégagé* airs of one of the young marchionesses.   She had
an odd way of slanting her eyebrows and pursing her lips, and to
all appearances detaching herself from every earthly consideration,
and floating through the cloud of her own pearl-coloured reserves.
It was amusing, and not quite convincing.

" Of course I am beautiful, Lucille," she said blandly.   " And
you're perfectly lovely, now you look a bit reproachful.   Of course
you're the most aristocratic of the two of us, with your nose !   And
now your eyes look reproachful, that adds an appealing look, and
you're perfect, perfectly lovely.   But I'm more *winning*, in a way.
Don't you agree ? "   She turned with arch, complicated simplicity
to Lucille.

She was truly simple in what she said.   It was just what she
thought.   But it gave no hint of the very different *feeling* that also
preoccupied her :   the feeling that she had been looked upon, not
from the outside, but from the inside, from her secret female self.
She was dressing herself up and looking her most dazzling, just to
counteract the effect that the gipsy had had on her, when he had
looked at her, and seen none of her pretty face and her pretty ways,
but just the dark, tremulous potent secret of her virginity.

The two girls started downstairs in state when the dinner-gong
rang :   but they waited till they heard the voices of the men.   Then
they sailed down and into the sitting-room, Yvette preening herself
in her vague, debonair way, always a little bit absent ;   and Lucille
shy, ready to burst into tears.

" My goodness gracious ! " exclaimed Aunt Cissie, who was still
wearing her dark-brown knitted sports coat.   " What an apparition !·
Wherever do you think you're going ? "

" We're dining with the family," said Yvette naively, " and
we've put on our best gewgaws in honour of the occasion."

The rector laughed aloud, and Uncle Fred said :
" The family feels itself highly honoured."
Both the elderly men were quite gallant, which was what Yvette
wanted.
" Come and let me feel your dresses, do ! " said Granny.   " Are
they your best ?   It *is* a shame I can't see them."
" To-night, Mater," said Uncle Fred, " we shall have to take the
young ladies in to dinner, and live up to the honour.   Will you go
with Cissie ? "
" I certainly will," said Granny.   " Youth and beauty must come
first."
" Well, to-night, Mater ! " said the rector, pleased.
And he offered his arm to Lucille, while Uncle Fred escorted
Yvette.
But it was a draggled, dull meal, all the same.   Lucille tried to be
bright and sociable, and Yvette really was most amiable, in her
vague, cobwebby way.   Dimly, at the back of her mind, she was
thinking :   Why are we all only like mortal pieces of furniture ?
Why is nothing *important ?*
That was her constant refrain to herself :   Why is nothing important ?   Whether she was in church, or at a party of young
people, or dancing in the hotel in the city, the same little bubble
of a question rose repeatedly on her consciousness :   Why is nothing
important ?
There were plenty of young men to make love to her :   even
devotedly.   But with impatience she had to shake them off.   Why
were they so unimportant ?—so irritating !
She never even thought of the gipsy.   He was a perfectly negligible
incident.   Yet the approach of Friday loomed strangely significant.
" What are we doing on Friday ? " she said to Lucille.   To which
Lucille replied that they were doing nothing.   And Yvette was
vexed.
Friday came, and in spite of herself she thought all day of the
quarry off the road up high Bonsall Head.   She wanted to be there.
That was all she was conscious of.   She wanted to be there.   She
had not even a dawning idea of going there.   Besides, it was raining
again.   But as she sewed the blue dress, finishing it for the party up
at Lambley Close to-morrow, she just felt that her soul was up there,
at the quarry, among the caravans, with the gipsies.   Like one lost,
or whose soul was stolen, she was not present in her body, the shell
of her body.   Her intrinsic body was away at the quarry, among
the caravans.

The next day, at the party, she had no idea that she was being sweet to Leo. She had no idea that she was snatching him away from the tortured Ella Framley. Not until, when she was eating her pistachio ice, he said to her :

" Why don't you and me get engaged, Yvette ? I'm absolutely sure it's the right thing for us both."

Leo was a bit common, but good-natured and well-off. Yvette quite liked him. But engaged ! How perfectly silly ! She felt like offering him a set of her silk underwear, to get engaged to.

" But I thought it was Ella ! " she said, in wonder.

" Well ! It might ha' been, but for you. It's your doings, you know ! Ever since those gipsies told your fortune, I felt it was me or nobody, for you, and you or nobody, for me."

" Really ! " said Yvette, simply lost in amazement. " Really ! "

" Didn't you feel a bit the same ? " he asked.

" Really ! " Yvette kept on gasping softly, like a fish.

" You felt a bit the same, didn't you ? " he said.

" What ? About what ? " she asked, coming to.

" About me, as I feel about you."

" Why ? What ? Getting engaged, you mean ? I ? No ! Why how *could* I ? I could never have dreamed of such an impossible thing."

She spoke with her usual heedless candour, utterly unoccupied with his feelings.

" What was to prevent you ? " he said, a bit nettled. " I thought you did."

" Did you *really now* ? " she breathed in amazement, with that soft, virgin, heedless candour which made her her admirers and her enemies.

She was so completely amazed, there was nothing for him to do but twiddle his thumbs in annoyance.

The music began, and he looked at her.

" No ! I won't dance any more," she said, drawing herself up and gazing away rather loftily over the assembly, as if he did not exist. There was a touch of puzzled wonder on her brow, and her soft, dim virgin face did indeed suggest the snowdrop of her father's pathetic imagery.

" But of course *you* will dance," she said, turning to him with young condescension. " Do ask somebody to have this with you."

He rose, angry, and went down the room.

She remained soft and remote in her amazement. Expect Leo to propose to her ! She might as well have expected old Rover the

Newfoundland dog to propose to her. Get engaged, to any man on earth? No, good heavens, nothing more ridiculous could be imagined!

It was then, in a fleeting side-thought, that she realized that the gipsy existed. Instantly, she was indignant. Him, of all things! Him! Never!

"Now why?" she asked herself, again in hushed amazement. "Why? It's *absolutely* impossible : absolutely! So why is it?"

This was a nut to crack. She looked at the young men dancing, elbows out, hips prominent, waists elegantly in. They gave her no clue to her problem. Yet she did particularly dislike the forced elegance of the waists and the prominent hips, over which the well-tailored coats hung with such effeminate discretion.

"There is something about me which they don't see and never would see," she said angrily to herself. And at the same time, she was relieved that they didn't and couldn't. It made life so very much simpler.

And again, since she was one of the people who are conscious in visual images, she saw the dark-green jersey rolled on the black trousers of the gipsy, his fine, quick hips, alert as eyes. They were elegant. The elegance of these dancers seemed so stuffed, hips merely wadded with flesh. Leo the same, thinking himself such a fine dancer, and a fine figure of a fellow!

Then she saw the gipsy's face ; the straight nose, the slender mobile lips, and the level, significant stare of the black eyes, which seemed to shoot her in some vital, undiscovered place, unerring.

She drew herself up angrily. How dared he look at her like that? So she gazed glaringly at the insipid beaux on the dancing floor. And she despised them. Just as the raggle-taggle gipsy women despise men who are not gipsies, despise their dog-like walk down the streets, she found herself despising this crowd. Where among them was the subtle, lonely, insinuating challenge that could reach her?

She did not want to mate with a housedog.

Her sensitive nose turned up, her soft brown hair fell like a soft sheath round her tender, flower-like face, as she sat musing. She seemed so virginal. At the same time, there was a touch of the tall young virgin *witch* about her, that made the housedog men shy off. She might metamorphose into something uncanny before you knew where you were.

This made her lonely, in spite of all the courting. Perhaps the courting only made her lonelier.

Leo, who was a sort of mastiff among the housedogs, returned after his dance, with fresh cheery-o ! courage.

" You've had a little think about it, haven't you ? " he said, sitting down beside her : a comfortable, well-nourished, determined sort of fellow. She did not know why it irritated her so unreasonably, when he hitched up his trousers at the knee, over his good-sized but not very distinguished legs, and lowered himself assuredly on to a chair.

" Have I ? " she said vaguely. " About what ? "

" You know what about," he said. " Did you make up your mind ? "

" Make up my mind about what ? " she asked, innocently.

In her upper consciousness, she truly had forgotten.

" Oh ! " said Leo, settling his trousers again. " About me and you getting engaged, you know." He was almost as off-hand as she.

" Oh, that's *absolutely* impossible," she said, with mild amiability, as if it were some stray question among the rest. " Why, I never even thought of it again. Oh, don't talk about that sort of non-sense ! That sort of thing is *absolutely* impossible," she reiterated like a child.

" That sort of thing is, is it ? " he said, with an odd smile at her calm, distant assertion. " Well, what sort of thing *is* possible, then ? You don't want to die an old maid, do you ? "

" Oh, I don't mind," she said absently.

" I do," he said.

She turned round and looked at him in wonder.

" Why ? " she said. " Why should you mind if I was an old maid ? "

" Every reason in the world," he said, looking up at her with a bold, meaningful smile, that wanted to make its meaning blatant, if not patent.

But instead of penetrating into some deep, secret place, and shooting her there, Leo's bold and patent smile only hit her on the outside of the body, like a tennis ball, and caused the same kind of sudden irritated reaction.

" I think this sort of thing is awfully silly," she said, with minx-like spite. " Why, you're practically engaged to—to——" she pulled herself up in time—" probably half a dozen other girls. I'm not flattered by what you've said. I should hate it if anybody knew ! Hate it ! I shan't breathe a word of it, and I hope you'll have the sense not to. There's Ella ! "

And keeping her face averted from him, she sailed away like a tall, soft flower, to join poor Ella Framley.

Leo flapped his white gloves.

"Catty little bitch!" he said to himself. But he was of the mastiff type, he rather liked the kitten to fly in his face. He began definitely to single her out.

VI

THE next week it poured again with rain. And this irritated Yvette with strange anger. She had intended it should be fine. Especially she insisted it should be fine towards the week-end. Why, she did not ask herself.

Thursday, the half-holiday, came with a hard frost, and sun. Leo arrived with his car, the usual bunch. Yvette disagreeably and unaccountably refused to go.

"No thanks, I don't feel like it," she said.

She rather enjoyed being Mary-Mary-quite-contrary.

Then she went for a walk by herself, up the frozen hills, to the Black Rocks.

The next day also came sunny and frosty. It was February, but in the north country the ground did not thaw in the sun. Yvette announced that she was going for a ride on her bicycle, and taking her lunch as she might not be back till afternoon.

She set off, not hurrying. In spite of the frost, the sun had a touch of spring. In the park, the deer were standing in the distance, in the sunlight, to be warm. One doe, white-spotted, walked slowly across the motionless landscape.

Cycling, Yvette found it difficult to keep her hands warm, even when bodily she was quite hot. Only when she had to walk up the long hill, to the top, and there was no wind.

The upland was very bare and clear, like another world. She had climbed on to another level. She cycled slowly, a little afraid of taking the wrong lane, in the vast maze of stone fences. As she passed along the lane she thought was the right one, she heard a faint tapping noise, with a slight metallic resonance.

The gipsy man was seated on the ground with his back to the cart-shaft, hammering a copper bowl. He was in the sun, bare headed, but wearing his green jersey. Three small children were moving quietly round, playing in the horse's shelter: the horse and cart were gone. An old woman, bent, with a kerchief round her head, was cooking over a fire of sticks. The only sound was the rapid, ringing tap-tap-tap! of the small hammer on the dull copper.

The man looked up at once, as Yvette stepped from her bicycle but he did not move, though he ceased hammering. A delicate, barely discernible smile of triumph was on his face. The old woman looked round, keenly, from under her dirty grey hair. The man spoke a half-audible word to her, and she turned again to her fire. He looked up at Yvette.

"How are you all getting on?" she asked politely.

"All right, eh! You sit down a minute?" He turned as he sat, and pulled a stool from under the caravan for Yvette. Then, as she wheeled her bicycle to the side of the quarry, he started hammering again, with that bird-like, rapid light stroke.

Yvette went to the fire to warm her hands.

"Is this the dinner cooking?" she asked childishly, of the old gipsy, as she spread her long tender hands, mottled red with the cold, to the embers.

"Dinner, yes!" said the old woman. "For him! And for the children."

She pointed with the long fork at the three black-eyed, staring children, who were staring at her from under their black fringes. But they were clean. Only the old woman was not clean. The quarry itself they had kept perfectly clean.

Yvette crouched in silence, warming her hands. The man rapidly hammered away with intervals of silence. The old hag slowly climbed the steps to the third, oldest caravan. The children began to play again, like little wild animals, quiet and busy.

"Are they your children?" asked Yvette, rising from the fire and turning to the man.

He looked her in the eyes, and nodded.

"But where's your wife?"

"She's gone out with the basket. They've all gone out, cart and all, selling things. I don't go selling things. I make them, but I don't go selling them. Not often. I don't often."

"You make all the copper and brass things?" she said.

He nodded, and again offered her the stool. She sat down.

"You said you'd be here on Fridays," she said. "So I came this way, as it was so fine."

"Very fine day!" said the gipsy, looking at her cheek, that was still a bit blanched by the cold, and the soft hair over her reddened ear, and the long, still mottled hands on her knee.

"You get cold, riding a bicycle?" he asked.

"My hands!" she said, clasping them nervously.

"You didn't wear gloves?"

"I did, but they weren't much good."

2 L*

" Cold comes through," he said.

" Yes ! " she replied.

The old woman came slowly, grotesquely down the steps of the caravan, with some enamel plates.

" The dinner cooked, eh ? " he called softly.

The old woman muttered something, as she spread the plates near the fire. Two pots hung from a long iron horizontal bar, over the embers of the fire. A little pan seethed on a small iron tripod. In the sunshine, heat and vapour wavered together.

He put down his tools and the pot, and rose from the ground.

" You eat something along of us ? " he asked Yvette, not looking at her.

" Oh, I brought my lunch," said Yvette.

" You eat some stew ? " he said. And again he called quietly, secretly to the old woman, who muttered in answer, as she slid the iron pot towards the end of the bar.

" Some beans, and some mutton in it," he said.

" Oh thanks awfully ! " said Yvette. Then, suddenly taking courage, added : " Well yes, just a very little, if I may."

She went across to untie her lunch from her bicycle, and he went up the steps to his own caravan. After a minute, he emerged, wiping his hands on a towel.

" You want to come up and wash your hands ? " he said.

" No, I think not," she said. " They are clean."

He threw away his wash-water, and set off down the road with a high brass jug, to fetch clean water from the spring that trickled into a small pool, taking a cup to dip it with.

When he returned, he set the jug and the cup by the fire, and fetched himself a short log, to sit on. The children sat on the floor by the fire, in a cluster, eating beans and bits of meat with spoon or fingers. The man on the log ate in silence, absorbedly. The woman made coffee in the black pot on the tripod, hobbling upstairs for the cups. There was silence in the camp. Yvette sat on her stool, having taken off her hat and shaken her hair in the sun.

" How many children have you ? " Yvette asked suddenly.

" Say five," he replied slowly, as he looked up into her eyes.

And again the bird of her heart sank down and seemed to die. Vaguely, as in a dream, she received from him the cup of coffee. She was aware only of his silent figure, sitting like a shadow there on the log, with an enamel cup in his hand, drinking his coffee in silence. Her will had departed from her limbs, he had power over her : his shadow was on her.

And he, as he blew his hot coffee, was aware of one thing only, the mysterious fruit of her virginity, her perfect tenderness in the body.

At length he put down his coffee-cup by the fire, then looked round at her. Her hair fell across her face, as she tried to sip from the hot cup. On her face was that tender look of sleep, which a nodding flower has when it is full out. Like a mysterious early flower, she was full out, like a snowdrop which spreads its three white wings in a flight into the waking sleep of its brief blossoming. The waking sleep of her full-opened virginity, entranced like a snowdrop in the sunshine, was upon her.

The gipsy, supremely aware of her, waited for her like the substance of shadow, as shadow waits and is there.

At length his voice said, without breaking the spell:

"You want to go in my caravan now, and wash your hands?"

The childlike, sleep-waking eyes of her moment of perfect virginity looked into his, unseeing. She was only aware of the dark strange effluence of him bathing her limbs, washing her at last purely willless. She was aware of *him*, as a dark, complete power.

"I think I might," she said.

He rose silently, then turned to speak, in a low command, to the old woman. And then again he looked at Yvette, and putting his power over her, so that she had no burden of herself, or of action.

"Come!" he said.

She followed simply, followed the silent, secret, overpowering motion of his body in front of her. It cost her nothing. She was gone in his will.

He was at the top of the steps, and she at the foot, when she become aware of an intruding sound. She stood still, at the foot of the steps. A motor-car was coming. He stood at the top of the steps, looking round strangely. The old woman harshly called something, as with rapidly increasing sound, a car rushed near. It was passing.

Then they heard the cry of a woman's voice, and the brakes on the car. It had pulled up, just beyond the quarry.

The gipsy came down the steps, having closed the door of the caravan.

"You want to put your hat on," he said to her.

Obediently she went to the stool by the fire, and took up her hat. He sat down by the cart-wheel, darkly, and took up his tools. The rapid tap-tap-tap of his hammer, rapid and angry now like the sound of a tiny machine-gun, broke out just as the voice of the woman was heard crying:

" May we warm our hands at the camp fire ? "

She advanced, dressed in a sleek but bulky coat of sable fur. A man followed, in a blue great-coat ; pulling off his fur gloves and pulling out a pipe.

" It looked so tempting," said the woman in the coat of many dead little animals, smiling a broad, half-condescending, half-hesitant simper, around the company.

No one said a word.

She advanced to the fire, shuddering a little inside her coat, with the cold. They had been driving in an open car.

She was a very small woman, with a rather large nose : probably a Jewess. Tiny almost as a child, in that sable coat she looked much more bulky than she should, and her wide, rather resentful brown eyes of a spoilt Jewess gazed oddly out of her expensive get-up.

She crouched over the low fire, spreading her little hands, on which diamonds and emeralds glittered.

" Ugh ! " she shuddered. " Of course we ought not to have come in an open car ! But my husband won't even let me say I'm cold ! " She looked round at him with her large, childish, reproachful eyes, that had still the canny shrewdness of a bourgeois Jewess : a rich one, probably.

Apparently she was in love, in a Jewess's curious way, with the big, blond man. He looked back at her with his abstracted blue eyes, that seemed to have no lashes, and a small smile creased his smooth, curiously naked cheeks. The smile didn't mean anything at all.

He was a man one connects instantly with winter sports, ski-ing and skating. Athletic, unconnected with life, he slowly filled his pipe, pressing in the tobacco with long, powerful, reddened finger.

The Jewess looked at him to see if she got any response from him. Nothing at all, but that odd, blank smile. She turned again to the fire, tilting her eyebrows and looking at her small, white, spread hands.

He slipped off his heavily-lined coat, and appeared in one of the handsome, sharp-patterned knitted jerseys, in yellow and grey and black, over well-cut trousers, rather wide. Yes, they were both expensive ! And he had a magnificent figure, an athletic, prominent chest. Like an experienced camper, he began building the fire together, quietly : like a soldier on campaign.

" D'you think they'd mind if we put some fir-cones on, to make a blaze ? " he asked of Yvette, with a silent glance at the hammering gipsy.

" Love it, I should think," said Yvette, in a daze, as the spell of the gipsy slowly left her, feeling stranded and blank.

The man went to the car, and returned with a little sack of cones, from which he drew a handful.

" Mind if we make a blaze ? " he called to the gipsy.

" Eh ? "

" Mind if we make a blaze with a few cones ! "

" You go ahead ! " said the gipsy.

The man began placing the cones lightly, carefully on the red embers. And soon, one by one, they caught fire, and burned like roses of flame, with a sweet scent.

" Ah, lovely, lovely ! " cried the little Jewess, looking up at her man again. He looked down at her quite kindly, like the sun on ice. " Don't you love fire ? Oh, I love it ! " the little Jewess cried to Yvette, across the hammering.

The hammering annoyed her. She looked round with a slight frown on her fine little brows, as if she would bid the man stop. Yvette looked round too. The gipsy was bent over his copper bowl, legs apart, head down, lithe arm lifted. Already he seemed so far from her.

The man who accompanied the little Jewess strolled over to the gipsy, and stood in silence looking down on him, holding his pipe to his mouth. Now they were two men, like two strange male dogs, having to sniff one another.

" We're on our honeymoon," said the little Jewess, with an arch, resentful look at Yvette. She spoke in a rather high, defiant voice, like some bird, a jay, or a rook, calling.

" Are you really ? " said Yvette.

" Yes ! Before we're married ! Have you heard of Simon Fawcett ? "—she named a wealthy and well-known engineer of the north country. " Well, I'm Mrs. Fawcett, and he's just divorcing me ! " She looked at Yvette with curious defiance and wistfulness.

" Are you really ! " said Yvette.

She understood now the look of resentment and defiance in the little Jewess's big, childlike brown eyes. She was an honest little thing, but perhaps her honesty was *too* rational. Perhaps it partly explained the notorious unscrupulousness of the well-known Simon Fawcett.

" Yes ! As soon as we get the divorce, I'm going to marry Major Eastwood."

Her cards were now all on the table. She was not going to deceive anybody.

Behind her, the two men were talking briefly. She glanced round, and fixed the gipsy with her big brown eyes.

He was looking up, as if shyly, at the big fellow in the sparkling jersey, who was standing pipe in mouth, man to man, looking down.

" With the horses back of Arras," said the gipsy, in a low voice.

They were talking war. The gipsy had served with the artillery teams, in the Major's own regiment.

" *Ein schöner Mensch!* " said the Jewess. " A handsome man, eh ? "

For her, too, the gipsy was one of the common men, the Tommies.

" Quite handsome ! " said Yvette.

" You are cycling ? " asked the Jewess in a tone of surprise.

" Yes ! Down to Papplewick. My father is rector of Papplewick : Mr. Saywell ! "

" Oh ! " said the Jewess. " I know ! A clever writer ! Very clever ! I have read him."

The fir-cones were all consumed already, the fire was a tall pile now of crumbling, shattering fire-roses. The sky was clouding over for afternoon. Perhaps towards evening it would snow.

The Major came back, and slung himself into his coat.

" I thought I remembered his face ! " he said. " One of our grooms, A1 man with horses."

" Look ! " cried the Jewess to Yvette. " Why don't you let us motor you down to Normanton. We live in Scoresby. We can tie the bicycle on behind."

" I think I will," said Yvette.

" Come ! " called the Jewess to the peeping children, as the blond man wheeled away the bicycle. " Come ! Come here ! " and taking out her little purse, she held out a shilling.

" Come ! " she cried. " Come and take it ! "

The gipsy had laid down his work, and gone into his caravan. The old woman called hoarsely to the children, from her enclosure. The two elder children came stealing forward. The Jewess gave them the two bits of silver, a shilling and a florin, which she had in her purse, and again the hoarse voice of the unseen old woman was heard.

The gipsy descended from his caravan and strolled to the fire. The Jewess searched his face with the peculiar bourgeois boldness of her race.

" You were in the war, in Major Eastwood's regiment ? " she said.

" Yes, lady ! "

" Imagine you both being here now ! It's going to snow." She looked up at the sky.

THE VIRGIN AND THE GIPSY

"Later on," said the man, looking at the sky.

He too had gone inaccessible. His race was very old, in its peculiar battle with established society, and had no conception of winning. Only now and then it could score.

But since the war, even the old sporting chance of scoring now and then, was pretty well quenched. There was no question of yielding. The gipsy's eyes still had their bold look : but it was hardened and directed far away, the touch of insolent intimacy was gone. He had been through the war.

He looked at Yvette.

"You're going back in the motor-car ? " he said.

"Yes ! " she replied, with a rather mincing mannerism. " The weather is so treacherous ! "

"Treacherous weather ! " he repeated, looking at the sky.

She could not tell in the least what his feelings were. In truth, she wasn't very much interested. She was rather fascinated, now, by the little Jewess, mother of two children, who was taking her wealth away from the well-known engineer and transferring it to the penniless, sporting young Major Eastwood, who must be five or six years younger than she. Rather intriguing !

The blond man returned.

"A cigarette, Charles ! " cried the little Jewess, plaintively.

He took out his case, slowly, with his slow, athletic movement. Something sensitive in him made him slow, cautious, as if he had hurt himself against people. He gave a cigarette to his wife, then one to Yvette, then offered the case, quite simply, to the gipsy. The gipsy took one.

"Thank you, sir ! "

And he went quietly to the fire, and stooping, lit it at the red embers. Both women watched him.

"Well, good-bye ! " said the Jewess, with her old bourgeois free-masonry. " Thank you for the warm fire."

"Fire is everybody's," said the gipsy.

The young child came toddling to him.

"Good-bye ! " said Yvette. " I hope it won't snow for you."

"We don't mind a bit of snow," said the gipsy.

"Don't you ? " said Yvette. " I should have thought you would ! "

"No ! " said the gipsy.

She flung her scarf royally over her shoulder, and followed the fur coat of the Jewess, which seemed to walk on little legs of its own.

YVETTE was rather thrilled by the Eastwoods, as she called them. The little Jewess had only to wait three months now, for the final decree. She had boldly rented a small summer cottage, by the moors up at Scoresby, not far from the hills. Now it was dead winter, and she and the Major lived in comparative isolation, without any maid-servant. He had already resigned his commission in the regular army, and called himself Mr. Eastwood. In fact, they were already Mr. and Mrs. Eastwood, to the common world.

The little Jewess was thirty-six, and her two children were both over twelve years of age. The husband had agreed that she should have the custody, as soon as she was married to Eastwood.

So there they were, this queer couple, the tiny, finely-formed little Jewess with her big, resentful, reproachful eyes, and her mop of carefully-barbered black, curly hair, an elegant little thing in her way ; and the big, pale-eyed young man, powerful and wintry, the remnant, surely, of some old uncanny Danish stock : living together in a small modern house near the moors and the hills, and doing their own housework.

It was a funny household. The cottage was hired furnished, but the little Jewess had brought along her dearest pieces of furniture. She had an odd little taste for the rococo, strange curving cupboards inlaid with mother-of-pearl, tortoiseshell, ebony, heaven knows what ; strange tall flamboyant chairs from Italy, with sea-green brocade : astonishing saints with wind-blown, richly-coloured carven garments and pink faces : shelves of weird old Saxe and Capo di Monte figurines : and finally, a strange assortment of astonishing pictures painted on the back of glass, done probably in the early years of the nineteenth century, or in the late eighteenth.

In this crowded and extraordinary interior she received Yvette, when the latter made a stolen visit. A whole system of stoves had been installed into the cottage, every corner was warm, almost hot. And there was the tiny rococo figurine of the Jewess herself, in a perfect little frock, and an apron, putting slices of ham on the dish, while the great snow-bird of a major, in a white sweater and grey trousers, cut bread, mixed mustard, prepared coffee, and did all the rest. He had even made the dish of jugged hare which followed the cold meats and caviare.

The silver and the china were really valuable, part of the bride's trousseau. The Major drank beer from a silver mug, the little Jewess and Yvette had champagne in lovely glasses, the Major

THE VIRGIN AND THE GIPSY

brought in coffee. They talked away. The little Jewess had a burning indignation against her first husband. She was intensely moral, so moral, that she was a divorcée. The Major too, strange wintry bird, so powerful, handsome, too, in his way, but pale round the eyes as if he had no eyelashes, like a bird, he too had a curious indignation against life, because of the false morality. That powerful, athletic chest hid a strange, snowy sort of anger. And his tenderness for the little Jewess was based on his sense of outraged justice, the abstract morality of the north blowing him, like a strange wind, into isolation.

As the afternoon drew on, they went to the kitchen, the Major pushed back his sleeves, showing his powerful athletic white arms, and carefully, deftly washed the dishes, while the women wiped. It was not for nothing his muscles were trained. Then he went round attending to the stoves of the small house, which only needed a moment or two of care each day. And after this, he brought out a small, closed car and drove Yvette home, in the rain, depositing her at the back gate, a little wicket among the larches, through which the earthen steps sloped downwards to the house.

She was really amazed by this couple.

" Really, Lucille ! " she said. " I do meet the most extra-ordinary people ! " And she gave a detailed description.

" I think they sound rather nice ! " said Lucille. " I like the Major doing the housework, and looking so frightfully Bond-streety with it all. I should think *when they're married*, it would be rather fun knowing them."

" Yes ! " said Yvette vaguely. " Yes ! Yes, it would ! "

The very strangeness of the connection between the tiny Jewess and that pale-eyed, athletic young officer made her think again of her gipsy, who had been utterly absent from her consciousness, but who now returned with sudden painful force.

" What is it, Lucille," she asked, " that brings people together ? People like the Eastwoods, for instance ? And Daddy and Mamma, so frightfully unsuitable ? And that gipsy woman who told my fortune, like a great horse, and the gipsy man, so fine and delicately cut ? What is it ? "

" I suppose it's sex, whatever that is," said Lucille.

" Yes, what is it ? It's not really anything *common*, like common sensuality, you know, Lucille. It really isn't."

" No, I suppose not," said Lucille. " Anyhow, I suppose it needn't be."

" Because, you see, the *common* fellows, you know, who make a girl feel *low* : nobody cares much about them. Nobody feels any connection with them. Yet they're supposed to be the sexual sort."

" I suppose," said Lucille, " there's the low sort of sex, and there's the other sort, that isn't low. It's frightfully complicated, really ! I *loathe* common fellows. And I never feel anything *sexual* "—she laid a rather disgusted stress on the word—" for fellows who aren't common. Perhaps I haven't got any sex."

" That's just it ! " said Yvette. " Perhaps neither of us has. Perhaps we haven't really *got* any sex, to connect us with men."

" How horrible it sounds : *connect us with men !* " cried Lucille, with revulsion. " Wouldn't you hate to be connected with men that way ? Oh I think it's an awful pity there has to *be* sex ! It would be so much better if we could still be men and women, without that sort of thing."

Yvette pondered. Far in the background was the image of the gipsy as he had looked round at her, when she had said : " The weather is so treacherous." She felt rather like Peter when the cock crew, as she denied him. Or rather, she did not deny the gipsy ; she didn't care about his part in the show, anyhow. It was some hidden part of herself which she denied : that part which mysteriously and unconfessedly responded to him. And it was a strange, lustrous black cock which crew in mockery of her.

" Yes ! " she said vaguely. " Yes ! Sex is an awful bore, you know, Lucille. When you haven't got it, you feel you *ought* to have it, somehow. And when you've got it—or *if* you have it—" she lifted her head and wrinkled her nose disdainfully—" you hate it."

" Oh, I don't know ! " cried Lucille. " I think I should *like* to be awfully in love with a man."

" You think so ! " said Yvette, again wrinkling her nose. " But if you were you wouldn't."

" How do you know ? " asked Lucille.

" Well, I don't really," said Yvette. " But I think so ! Yes, I think so ! "

" Oh, it's very likely ! " said Lucille disgustedly. " And anyhow one would be sure to get out of love again, and it would be merely disgusting."

" Yes," said Yvette. " It's a problem." She hummed a little tune.

" Oh, hang it all, it's not a problem for us two yet. We're neither of us really in love, and we probably never shall be, so the problem is settled that way."

"I'm not so sure!" said Yvette sagely. "I'm not so sure. I believe, one day, I shall fall *awfully* in love."

"Probably you never will," said Lucille brutally. "That's what most old maids are thinking all the time."

Yvette looked at her sister from pensive but apparently insouciant eyes.

"Is it?" she said. "Do you really think so, Lucille? How perfectly awful for them, poor things! Why ever do they *care*?"

"Why do they?" said Lucille. "Perhaps they don't, really— Probably it's all because people say: *Poor old girl, she couldn't catch a man.*"

"I suppose it is!" said Yvette. "They get to mind the beastly things people always do say about old maids. What a shame!"

"Anyhow we have a good time, and we do have lots of boys who make a fuss of us," said Lucille.

"Yes!" said Yvette. "Yes! But I couldn't possibly marry any of them."

"Neither could I," said Lucille. "But why should we? Why should we bother about marrying, when we have a perfectly good time with the boys, who are awfully good sorts, and you must say, Yvette, awfully sporting and *decent* to us."

"Oh, they are!" said Yvette absently.

"I think it's time to think of marrying somebody," said Lucille, "when you feel you're *not* having a good time any more. Then marry, and just settle down."

"Quite!" said Yvette.

But now, under all her bland, soft amiability, she was annoyed with Lucille. Suddenly she wanted to turn her back on Lucille.

Besides, look at the shadows under poor Lucille's eyes, and the wistfulness in the beautiful eyes themselves. Oh, if some awfully nice, kind, protective sort of man would but marry her! And if the sporting Lucille would let him!

Yvette did not tell the rector, nor Granny, about the Eastwoods. It would only have started a lot of talk which she detested. The rector wouldn't have minded, for himself, privately. But he too knew the necessity of keeping as clear as possible from that poisonous, many-headed serpent, the tongue of the people.

"But I don't *want* you to come if your father doesn't know," cried the little Jewess.

"I suppose I'll have to tell him," said Yvette. "I'm sure he doesn't mind, really. But if he knew, he'd have to, I suppose.'"

The young officer looked at her with an odd amusement, bird-like and unemotional, in his keen eyes.   He too was by way of falling in love with Yvette.   It was her peculiar virgin tenderness, and her straying, absent-minded detachment from things, which attracted him.

She was aware of what was happening, and she rather preened herself.   Eastwood piqued her fancy.   Such a smart young officer, awfully good class, so calm and amazing with a motor-car, and quite a champion swimmer, it was intriguing to see him quietly, calmly washing dishes, smoking his pipe, doing his job so alert and skilful. Or, with the same interested care with which he made his investigation into the mysterious inside of an automobile, concocting jugged hare in the cottage kitchen.   Then going out in the icy weather and cleaning his car till it looked like a live thing, like a cat when she has licked herself.   Then coming in to talk so unassumingly and responsively, if briefly, with the little Jewess.   And apparently, never bored.   Sitting at the window with his pipe in bad weather, silent for hours, abstracted, musing, yet with his athletic body alert in its stillness.

Yvette did not flirt with him.   But she *did* like him.

" But what about your future ? " she asked him.

" What about it ? " he said, taking his pipe from his mouth, the unemotional point of a smile in his bird's eyes.

" A career !   Doesn't every man have to carve out a career ? —like some huge goose with gravy ? "   She gazed with odd naiveté into his eyes.

" I'm perfectly all right to-day, and I shall be all right to-morrow," he said, with a cold, decided look.   " Why shouldn't my future be continuous to-days and to-morrows ? "

He looked at her with unmoved searching.

" Quite ! " she said.   " I hate jobs, and all that side of life." But she was thinking of the Jewess's money.

To which he did not answer.   His anger was of the soft, snowy sort, which comfortably muffles the soul.

They had come to the point of talking philosophically together. The little Jewess looked a bit wan.   She was curiously naive, and not possessive in her attitude to the man.   Nor was she at all catty with Yvette.   Only rather wan, and dumb.

Yvette, on a sudden impulse, thought she had better clear herself.

" I think life's *awfully* difficult," she said.

" Life is ! " cried the Jewess.

" What's so beastly, is that one is supposed to *fall in love*, and get married ! " said Yvette, curling up her nose.

"Don't you *want* to fall in love and get married ? " cried the Jewess, with great glaring eyes of astounded reproach.

"No, not particularly ! " said Yvette. "Especially as one feels there's nothing else to do. It's an awful chicken-coop one has to run into."

"But you don't know what love is ! " cried the Jewess.

"No ! " said Yvette. "Do you ? "

"I ! " bawled the tiny Jewess. "I ! My goodness, don't I ! " She looked with reflective gloom at Eastwood, who was smoking his pipe, the dimples of his disconnected amusement showing on his smooth, scrupulous face. He had a very fine, smooth skin, which yet did not suffer from the weather, so that his face looked naked as a baby's. But it was not a round face : it was characteristic enough, and took queer ironical dimples, like a mask which is comic but frozen.

"Do you mean to say you don't know what love is ? " insisted the Jewess.

"No ! " said Yvette, with insouciant candour. "I don't believe I do ! Is it awful of me, at my age ? "

"Is there never any man that makes you feel quite, quite different ? " said the Jewess, with another big-eyed look at Eastwood. He smoked, utterly unimplicated.

"I don't think there is," said Yvette. "Unless—yes !—unless it is that gipsy "—she had put her head pensively sideways.

"Which gipsy ? " bawled the little Jewess.

"The one who was a Tommy and looked after horses in Major Eastwood's regiment in the war," said Yvette coolly.

The little Jewess gazed at Yvette with great eyes of stupor.

"You're not in love with that *gipsy* ! " she said.

"Well ! " said Yvette. "I don't know. He's the only one that makes me feel—different ! He really is ! "

"But how ? How ? Has he ever *said* anything to you ? "

"No ! No ! "

"Then how ? What has he done ? "

"Oh, just looked at me ! "

"How ? "

"Well, you see, I don't know. But different ! Yes, different ! Different, quite different from the way any man ever looked at me."

"But *how* did he look at you ? " insisted the Jewess.

"Why—as if he really, but *really*, desired me," said Yvette, her meditative face looking like the bud of a flower.

" What a vile fellow ! What *right* had he to look at you like that ? " cried the indignant Jewess.

" A cat may look at a king," calmly interposed the Major, and now his face had the smiles of a cat's face.

" You think he oughtn't to ? " asked Yvette, turning to him.

" Certainly not ! A gipsy fellow, with half a dozen dirty women trailing after him ! Certainly not ! " cried the tiny Jewess.

" I wondered ! " said Yvette. " Because it *was* rather wonderful, really ! And it *was* something quite different in my life."

" I think," said the Major, taking his pipe from his mouth, " that desire is the most wonderful thing in life. Anybody who can really feel it, is a king, and I envy nobody else ! " He put back his pipe.

The Jewess looked at him stupefied.

" But, Charles ! " she cried. " Every common low man in Halifax feels nothing else ! "

He again took his pipe from his mouth.

" That's merely appetite," he said.

And he put back his pipe.

" You think the gipsy is the real thing ? " Yvette asked him.

He lifted his shoulders.

" It's not for me to say," he replied. " If I were you, I should know, I shouldn't be asking other people."

" Yes—but——" Yvette trailed out.

" Charles ! You're wrong ! How *could* it be the real thing ! As if she could possibly marry him and go round in a caravan ! "

" I didn't say marry him," said Charles.

" Or a love affair ! Why, it's monstrous ! What would she think of herself ! That's not love ! That's—that's prostitution ! "

Charles smoked for some moments.

" That gipsy was the best man we had, with horses. Nearly died of pneumonia. I thought he *was* dead. He's a resurrected man to me. I'm a resurrected man myself, as far as that goes." He looked at Yvette. " I was buried for twenty hours under snow," he said. " And not much the worse for it, when they dug me out."

There was a frozen pause in the conversation.

" Life's awful ! " said Yvette.

" They dug me out by accident," he said.

" Oh !——" Yvette trailed slowly. " It might be destiny, you know."

To which he did not answer.

VIII

THE rector heard about Yvette's intimacy with the Eastwoods, and she was somewhat startled by the result. She had thought he. wouldn't care. Verbally, in his would-be humorous fashion, he was so entirely unconventional, such a frightfully good sport. As he said himself, he was a conservative anarchist ; which meant, he was like a great many more people, a mere unbeliever. The anarchy extended to his humorous talk, and his secret thinking. The conservatism, based on a mongrel fear of the anarchy, controlled every action. His thoughts, secretly, were something to be scared of. Therefore, in his life, he was fanatically afraid of the unconventional.

When his conservatism and his abject sort of fear were uppermost, he always lifted his lip and bared his teeth a little, in a dog-like sneer.

"I hear your latest friends are the half-divorced Mrs. Fawcett and the *maquereau* Eastwood," he said to Yvette.

She didn't know what a *maquereau* was, but she felt the poison in the rector's fangs.

"I just know them," she said. "They're awfully nice, really. And they'll be married in about a month's time."

The rector looked at her insouciant face with hatred. Somewhere inside him, he was cowed, he had been born cowed. And those who are born cowed are natural slaves, and deep instinct makes them fear with poisonous fear those who might suddenly snap the slave's collar round their necks.

It was for this reason the rector had so abjectly curled up, still so abjectly curled up before She-who-was-Cynthia : because of his slave's fear of her contempt, the contempt of a born-free nature for a base-born nature.

Yvette too had a free-born quality. She too, one day, would know him, and clap the slave's collar of her contempt round his neck.

But should she ? He would fight to the death, this time, first. The slave in him was cornered this time, like a cornered rat, and with the courage of a cornered rat.

" suppose they're your sort ! " he sneered.

"Well, they are, really," she said, with that blithe vagueness. "I do like them awfully. They seem so solid, you know, so honest."

"You've got a peculiar notion of honesty ! " he sneered. "A young sponge going off with a woman older than himself, so that he can live on her money ! The woman leaving her home and her children ! I don't know where you get your idea of honesty. Not from me, I hope. And you seem to be very well acquainted with them, considering you say you just know them. Where did you meet them?"

"When I was out bicycling. They came along in their car, and we happened to talk. She told me at once who she was, so that I shouldn't make a mistake. She *is* honest."

Poor Yvette was struggling to bear up.

"And how often have you seen them since?"

"Oh, I've just been over twice."

"Over where?"

"To their cottage in Scoresby."

He looked at her in hate, as if he could kill her. And he backed away from her, against the window-curtains of his study, like a rat at bay. Somewhere in his mind he was thinking unspeakable depravities about his daughter, as he had thought them of She-who-was-Cynthia. He was powerless against the lowest insinuations of his own mind. And these depravities which he attributed to the still-uncowed but frightened girl in front of him, made him recoil, showing all his fangs in his handsome face.

"So you just know them, do you?" he said. "Lying is in your blood, I see. I don't believe you get it from me."

Yvette half averted her mute face, and thought of Granny's bare-faced prevarication. She did not answer.

"What takes you creeping round such couples?" he sneered. "Aren't there enough decent people in the world for you to know? Any one would think you were a stray dog, having to run round indecent couples, because the decent ones wouldn't have you. Have you got something worse than lying in your blood?"

"What have I got worse than lying in my blood?" she asked. A cold deadness was coming over her. Was she abnormal, one of the semi-criminal abnormals? It made her feel cold and dead.

In his eyes, she was just brazening out the depravity that underlay her virgin, tender, bird-like face. She-who-was-Cynthia had been like this: a snow-flower. And he had convulsions of sadistic horror, thinking what might be the *actual* depravity of She-who-was-Cynthia. Even his *own* love for her, which had been the lust-love of the born cowed, had been a depravity, in secret, to him. So what must an illegal love be?

"You know best yourself, what you have got," he sneered. "But it is something you had best curb, and quickly, if you don't intend to finish in a criminal-lunacy asylum."

"Why?" she said, pale and muted, numbed with frozen fear. "Why criminal lunacy? What have I done?"

"That is between you and your Maker," he jeered. "I shall never ask. But certain tendencies end in criminal lunacy, unless they are curbed in time."

"Do you mean like knowing the Eastwoods?" asked Yvette, after a pause of numb fear.

"Do I mean like nosing round such people as Mrs. Fawcett, a Jewess, and ex-Major Eastwood, a man who goes off with an older woman for the sake of her money? Why yes, I do!"

"But you *can't* say that," cried Yvette. "He's an awfully simple, straightforward man."

"He is apparently one of your sort."

"Well in a way I thought he was. I thought you'd like him too," she said simply, hardly knowing what she said.

The rector backed into the curtains, as if the girl menaced him with something fearful.

"Don't say any more," he snarled, abject. "Don't say any more. You've said too much, to implicate you. I don't want to learn any more horrors."

"But what horrors?" she persisted.

The very naïveté of her unscrupulous innocence repelled him, cowed him still more.

"Say no more!" he said, in a low, hissing voice. "But I will kill you before you shall go the way of your mother."

She looked at him, as he stood there backed against the velvet curtains of his study, his face yellow, his eyes distraught like a rat's with fear and rage and hate, and a numb, frozen loneliness came over her. For her too, the meaning had gone out of everything.

It was hard to break the frozen, sterile silence that ensued. At last, however, she looked at him. And in spite of herself, beyond her own knowledge, the contempt for him was in her young, clear, baffled eyes. It fell like the slave's collar over his neck, finally.

"Do you mean I mustn't know the Eastwoods?" she said.

"You can know them if you wish," he sneered. "But you must not expect to associate with your Granny and your Aunt Cissie, and Lucille, if you do. I cannot have *them* contaminated. Your Granny was a faithful wife and a faithful mother, if ever one existed. She has already had one shock of shame and abomination to endure. She shall never be exposed to another."

Yvette heard it all dimly, half hearing.

"I can send a note and say you disapprove," she said dimly.

"You follow your own course of action. But remember, you have to choose between clean people, and reverence for your

Granny's blameless old age, and people who are unclean in their
minds and their bodies."

Again there was a silence. Then she looked at him, and her face
was more puzzled than anything. But somewhere at the back of her
perplexity was that peculiar calm, virgin contempt of the free-born
for the base-born. He, and all the Saywells, were base-born.

"All right," she said. "I'll write and say you disapprove."

He did not answer. He was partly flattered, secretly triumphant,
but abjectly.

"I have tried to keep this from your Granny and Aunt Cissie,"
he said. "It need not be public property, since you choose to make
your friendship clandestine."

There was a dreary silence.

"All right," she said. "I'll go and write."

And she crept out of the room.

She addressed her little note to Mrs. Eastwood. "Dear Mrs.
Eastwood, Daddy doesn't approve of my coming to see you. So
you will understand if we have to break it off. I'm awfully sorry
——" That was all.

Yet she felt a dreary blank when she had posted her letter. She
was now even afraid of her own thoughts. She wanted, now, to
be held against the slender, fine-shaped breast of the gipsy. She
wanted him to hold her in his arms, if only for once, for once, and
comfort and confirm her. She wanted to be confirmed by him,
against her father, who had only a repulsive fear of her.

And at the same time she cringed and winced, so that she could
hardly walk, for fear the thought was obscene, a criminal lunacy.
It seemed to wound her heels as she walked, the fear. The fear, the
great cold fear of the base-born, her father, everything human and
swarming. Like a great bog humanity swamped her, and she sank
in, weak at the knees, filled with repulsion and fear of every person
she met.

She adjusted herself, however, quite rapidly to her new conception of people. She had to live. It is useless to quarrel with one's
bread and butter. And to expect a great deal out of life is puerile.
So, with the rapid adaptability of the post-war generation, she
adjusted herself to the new facts. Her father was what he was. He
would always play up to appearances. She would do the same.
She too would play up to appearances.

So, underneath the blithe, gossamer-straying insouciance, a
certain hardness formed, like rock crystallizing in her heart. She
lost her illusions in the collapse of her sympathies. Outwardly,

she seemed the same. Inwardly she was hard and detached, and, unknown to herself, revengeful.

Outwardly she remained the same. It was part of her game. While circumstances remained as they were, she must remain, at least in appearance, true to what was expected of her.

But the revengefulness came out in her new vision of peopie. Under the rector's apparently gallant handsomeness, she saw the weak, feeble nullity. And she despised him. Yet still, in a way, she liked him too. Feelings are so complicated.

It was Granny whom she came to detest with all her soul. That obese old woman, sitting there in her blindness like some great red-blotched fungus, her neck swallowed between her heaped-up shoulders and her rolling, ancient chins, so that she was neckless as a double potato, her Yvette really hated, with that pure, sheer hatred which is almost a joy. Her hate was so clear, that while she was feeling strong, she enjoyed it.

The old woman sat with her big, reddened face pressed a little back, her lace cap perched on her thin white hair, her stub nose still assertive, and her old mouth shut like a trap. This motherly old soul, her mouth gave her away. It always had been one of the compressed sort. But in her great age, it had gone like a toad's, lipless, the jaw pressing up like the lower jaw of a trap. The look Yvette most hated was the look of that lower jaw pressing relentlessly up, with an ancient prognathous thrust, so that the snub nose in turn was forced to press upwards, and the whole face was pressed a little back, beneath the big, wall-like forehead. The will, the ancient, toad-like, obscene *will* in the old woman, was fearful, once you saw it : a toad-like self-will that was godless, and less than human ! It belonged to the old, enduring race of toads, or tortoises. And it made one feel that Granny would never die. She would live on like these higher reptiles, in a state of semi-coma, for ever.

Yvette dared not even suggest to her father that Granny was not perfect. He would have threatened his daughter with the lunatic asylum. That was the threat he always seemed to have up his sleeve : the lunatic asylum. Exactly as if a distaste for Granny and for that horrible house of relatives was in itself a proof of lunacy, dangerous lunacy.

Yet in one of her moods of irritable depression, she did once fling out :

" How perfectly beastly this house is ! Aunt Lucy comes, and Aunt Nell, and Aunt Alice, and they make a ring like a ring of crows, with Granny and Aunt Cissie, all lifting their skirts up and warming their legs at the fire, and shutting Lucille and me out. We're nothing but outsiders in this beastly house ! "

Her father glanced at her curiously. But she managed to put a petulance into her speech, and a mere cross rudeness into her look, so that he could laugh, as at a childish tantrum. Somewhere, though, he knew that she coldly, venomously meant what she said, and he was wary of her.

Her life seemed now nothing but an irritable friction against the unsavoury household of the Saywells, in which she was immersed. She loathed the rectory with a loathing that consumed her life, a loathing so strong that she could not really go away from the place. While it endured, she was spellbound to it, in revulsion.

She forgot the Eastwoods again. After all, what was the revolt of the little Jewess, compared to Granny and the Saywell bunch ! A husband was never more than a semi-casual thing ! But a family !—an awful, smelly family that would never disperse, stuck half dead round the base of a fungoid old woman ! How was one to cope with that ?

She did not forget the gipsy entirely. But she had no time for him. She, who was bored almost to agony, and who had nothing at all to do, she had not time to think even, seriously, of anything. Time being, after all, only the current of the soul in its flow.

She saw the gipsy twice. Once he came to the house, with things to sell. And she, watching him from the landing window, refused to go down. He saw her too, as he was putting his things back into his cart. But he too gave no sign. Being a race that exists only to be harrying the outskirts of our society, forever hostile and living only by spoil, he was too much master of himself, and too wary, to expose himself openly to the vast and gruesome clutch of our law. He had been through the war. He had been enslaved against his will, that time.

So now, he showed himself at the rectory, and slowly, quietly busied himself at his cart outside the white gate, with that air of silent and forever-unyielding outsideness which gave him his lonely, predative grace. He knew she saw him. And she should see him unyielding, quietly hawking his copper vessels, on an old, old war-path against such as herself.

Such as herself ? Perhaps he was mistaken. Her heart, in its stroke, now rang hard as his hammer upon his copper, beating against circumstances. But he struck stealthily on the outside, and she still more secretly on the inside of the establishment. She liked him. She liked the quiet, noiseless clean-cut presence of him. She liked that mysterious endurance in him, which endures in opposition, without any idea of victory. And she liked that peculiar added relentlessness, the disillusion in hostility, which belongs to after the war. Yes, if she belonged to any side, and to any clan, it was to his. Almost she could have found it in her heart to go with him, and be a pariah gipsy-woman.

But she was born inside the pale. And she liked comfort, and a certain prestige. Even as a mere rector's daughter, one did have a certain prestige. And she liked that. Also she liked to chip against the pillars of the temple, from the inside. She wanted to be safe under the temple roof. Yet she enjoyed chipping fragments off the supporting pillars. Doubtless many fragments had been whittled away from the pillars of the Philistine, before Samson pulled the temple down.

" I'm not sure one shouldn't have one's fling till one is twenty-six, and then give in, and marry ! "

This was Lucille's philosophy, learned from older women. Yvette was twenty-one. It meant she had five more years in which to have this precious fling. And the fling meant, at the moment, the gipsy. The marriage, at the age of twenty-six, meant Leo or Gerry.

So, a woman could eat her cake and have her bread and butter.

Yvette, pitched in gruesome, deadlocked hostility to the Saywell household, was very old and very wise : with the agedness and the wisdom of the young, which always overleaps the agedness and the wisdom of the old, or the elderly.

The second time she met the gipsy by accident. It was March, and sunny weather, after unheard-of rains. Celandines were yellow in the hedges, and primroses among the rocks. But still there came a smell of sulphur from far-away steel-works, out of the steel-blue sky.

And yet it was spring !

Yvette was cycling slowly along by Codnor Gate, past the lime quarries, when she saw the gipsy coming away from the door of a stone cottage. His cart stood there in the road. He was returning with his brooms and copper things, to the cart.

She got down from her bicycle. As she saw him, she loved with curious tenderness the slim lines of his body in the green jersey, the turn of his silent face. She felt she knew him better than she knew anybody on earth, even Lucille, and belonged to him, in some way, for ever.

" Have you made anything new and nice ? " she asked innocently, looking at his copper things.

" I don't think," he said, glancing back at her.

The desire was still there, still curious and naked, in his eyes. But it was more remote, the boldness was diminished. There was a tiny glint, as if he might dislike her. But this dissolved again, as he saw her looking among his bits of copper and brass-work. She searched them diligently.

There was a little oval brass plate, with a queer figure like a palm-tree beaten upon it.

" I like that," she said. " How much is it ? "

" What you like," he said.

This made her nervous : he seemed off-hand, almost mocking.

" I'd rather you said," she told him, looking up at him.

" You give me what you like," he said.

" No ! " she said, suddenly. " If you won't tell me I won't have it."

" All right," he said. " Two shilling."

She found half-a-crown, and he drew from his pocket a handful of silver, from which he gave her her sixpence.

" The old gipsy dreamed something about you," he said, looking at her with curious, searching eyes.

" Did she ! " cried Yvette, at once interested. " What was it ? "

" She said : ' Be braver in your heart, or you lose your game.' She said it this way : ' Be braver in your body, or your luck will leave you.' And she said as well : ' Listen for the voice of water.' "

Yvette was very much impressed.

" And what does it mean ? " she asked.

" I asked her," he said. " She says she don't know."

" Tell me again what it was," said Yvette.

" 'Be braver in your body, or your luck will go.' And : ' Listen for the voice of water.' "

He looked in silence at her soft, pondering face. Something almost like a perfume seemed to flow from her young bosom direct to him, in a grateful connection.

" I'm to be braver in my body, and I'm to listen for the voice of water ! All right ! " she said. " I don't understand, but perhaps I shall."

She looked at him with clear eyes. Man or woman is made up of many selves. With one self, she loved this gipsy man. With many selves, she ignored him or had a distaste for him.

" You're not coming up to the Head no more ? " he asked.

Again she looked at him absently.

" Perhaps I will," she said, " some time. Some time."

" Spring weather ! " he said, smiling faintly and glancing round at the sun. " We're going to break camp soon, and go away."

" When ? " she said.

" Perhaps next week."

" Where to ? "

Again he made a move with his head.

" Perhaps up north," he said.

She looked at him.

" All right ! " she said. " Perhaps I *will* come up before you go, and say good-bye to your wife and to the old woman who sent me the message."

IX

YVETTE did not keep her promise. The few March days were lovely, and she let them slip. She had a curious reluctance, always, towards taking action, or making any real move of her own. She always wanted someone else to make a move for her, as if she did not want to play her own game of life.

She lived as usual, went out to her friends, to parties, and danced with the undiminished Leo. She wanted to go up and say good-bye to the gipsies. She wanted to. And nothing prevented her.

On the Friday afternoon especially she wanted to go. It was sunny, and the last yellow crocuses down the drive were in full blaze, wide open, the first bees rolling in them. The Papple rushed under the stone bridge, uncannily full, nearly filling the arches. There was the scent of a mezereon tree.

And she felt too lazy, too lazy, too lazy. She strayed in the garden by the river, half dreamy, expecting something. While the gleam of spring sun lasted, she would be out of doors. Indoors Granny, sitting back like some awful old prelate, in her bulk of black silk and her white lace cap, was warming her feet by the fire, and hearing everything that Aunt Nell had to say. Friday was Aunt Nell's day. She usually came for lunch, and left after an early tea. So the mother and the large, rather common daughter, who was a widow at the age of forty, sat gossiping by the fire, while Aunt Cissie prowled in and out. Friday was the rector's day for going to town : it was also the housemaid's half day.

Yvette sat on a wooden seat in the garden, only a few feet above the bank of the swollen river, which rolled a strange, uncanny mass of water. The crocuses were passing in the ornamental beds, the grass was dark green where it was mown, the laurels looked a little brighter. Aunt Cissie appeared at the top of the porch steps, and called to ask if Yvette wanted that early cup of tea. Because of the river just below, Yvette could not hear what Aunt Cissie said, but she guessed, and shook her head. An early cup of tea, indoors, when the sun actually shone? No thanks!

She was conscious of her gipsy, as she sat there musing in the sun. Her soul had the half painful, half easing knack of leaving her, and straying away to some place, to somebody. that had caught her imagination. Some days she would be at the Framleys', even though she did not go near them. Some days, she was all the time in spirit with the Eastwoods. And to-day it was the gipsies. She was up at their encampment in the quarry. She saw the man hammering his copper, lifting his head to look at the road; and the children playing in the horse-shelter: and the women, the gipsy's wife and the strong, elderly woman, coming home with their packs, along with the elderly man. For this afternoon, she felt intensely that *that* was home for her: the gipsy camp, the fire, the stool, the man with the hammer, the old crone.

It was part of her nature, to get these fits of yearning for some place she knew; to be in a certain place; with somebody who meant home to her. This afternoon it was the gipsy camp. And the man in the green jersey made it home to her. Just to be where he was, that was to be at home. The caravans, the brats, the other women: everything was natural to her, her home, as if she had been born there. She wondered if the gipsy was aware of her: if he could see her sitting on the stool by the fire; if he would lift his head and see her as she rose, looking at him slowly and significantly, turning towards the steps of his caravan. Did he know? Did he know?

Vaguely she looked up the steep of dark larch trees north of the house, where unseen the road climbed, going towards the Head. There was nothing, and her glance strayed down again. At the foot of the slope the river turned, thrown back harshly, ominously, against the low rocks across stream, then pouring past the garden to the bridge. It was unnaturally full, and whitey-muddy, and ponderous. "Listen for the voice of water," she said to herself. "No need to listen for it, if the voice means the noise!"

And again she looked at the swollen river breaking angrily as it came round the bend. Above it the black-looking kitchen garden hung, and the hard-natured fruit trees. Everything was on the tilt, facing south and south-west, for the sun. Behind, above the house and the kitchen garden hung the steep little wood of withered-seeming larches. The gardener was working in the kitchen garden, high up there, by the edge of the larch-wood.

She heard a call. It was Aunt Cissie and Aunt Nell. They

were on the drive, waving Good-bye ! Yvette waved back. Then
Aunt Cissie, pitching her voice against the waters, called :
"I shan't be long. Don't forget Granny is alone ! "
"All right ! " screamed Yvette rather ineffectually.

And she sat on her bench and watched the two undignified, long-
coated women walk slowly over the bridge and begin the curving
climb on the opposite slope, Aunt Nell carrying a sort of suit-case
in which she brought a few goods for Granny and took back vegetables or whatever the rectory garden or cupboard was yielding.
Slowly the two figures diminished, on the whitish, up-curving road,
labouring slowly up towards Papplewick village. Aunt Cissie was
going as far as the village for something.

The sun was yellowing to decline. What a pity ! Oh, what a
pity the sunny day was going, and she would have to turn indoors,
to those hateful rooms, and Granny ! Aunt Cissie would be back
directly : it was past five. And all the others would be arriving
from town, rather irritable and tired, soon after six.

As she looked uneasily round, she heard, across the running of
water, the sharp noise of a horse and cart rattling on the road hidden
in the larch trees. The gardener was looking up too. Yvette turned
away again, lingering, strolling by the full river a few paces, unwilling to go in ; glancing up the road to see if Aunt Cissie were
coming. If she saw her, she would go indoors.

She heard somebody shouting, and looked round. Down the
path through the larch trees the gipsy was bounding. The gardener,
away beyond, was also running. Simultaneously she became aware
of a great roar, which, before she could move, accumulated to a
vast deafening snarl. The gipsy was gesticulating. She looked round,
behind her.

And to her horror and amazement, round the bend of the river
she saw a shaggy, tawny wave-front of water advancing like a wall
of lions. The roaring sound wiped out everything. She was powerless, too amazed and wonder-struck, she wanted to see it.

Before she could think twice, it was near, a roaring cliff of water.
She almost fainted with horror. She heard the scream of the gipsy,
and looked up to see him bounding upon her, his black eyes starting
out of his head.

"Run ! " he screamed, seizing her arm.

And in the instant the first wave was washing her feet from under
her, swirling, in the insane noise, which suddenly for some reason
seemed like stillness, with a devouring flood over the garden. The
horrible mowing of water !

2 M

The gipsy dragged her heavily, lurching, plunging, but still keeping foot-hold both of them, towards the house. She was barely conscious : as if the flood was in her soul.

There was one grass-banked terrace of the garden, near the path round the house. The gipsy clawed his way up this terrace to the dry level of the path, dragging her after him, and sprang with her past the windows to the porch steps. Before they got there, a new great surge of water came mowing, mowing trees down even, and mowed them down too.

Yvette felt herself gone in an agonizing mill-race of icy water, whirled, with only the fearful grip of the gipsy's hand on her wrist. They were both down and gone. She felt a dull but stunning bruise somewhere.

Then he pulled her up. He was up, streaming forth water, clinging to the stem of the great wistaria that grew against the wall, crushed against the wall by the water. Her head was above water, he held her arm till it seemed dislocated : but she could not get her footing. With a ghastly sickness like a dream, she struggled and struggled, and could not get her feet. Only his hand was locked on her wrist.

He dragged her nearer till her one hand caught his leg. He nearly went down again. But the wistaria held him, and he pulled her up to him. She clawed at him, horribly ; and got to her feet, he hanging on like a man torn in two, to the wistaria trunk.

The water was above her knees. The man and she looked into each other's ghastly streaming faces.

" Get to the steps ! " he screamed.

It was only just round the corner : four strides ! She looked at him : she could not go. His eyes glared on her like a tiger's, and he pushed her from him. She clung to the wall, and the water seemed to abate a little. Round the corner she staggered, but staggering, reeled and was pitched up against the cornice of the balustrade of the porch steps, the man after her.

They got on to the steps, when another roar was heard amid the roar, and the wall of the house shook. Up heaved the water round their legs again, but the gipsy had opened the hall door. In they poured with the water, reeling to the stairs. And as they did so, they saw the short but strange bulk of Granny emerge in the hall, away down from the dining-room door. She had her hands lifted and clawing, as the first water swirled round her legs, and her coffin-like mouth was opened in a hoarse scream.

Yvette was blind to everything but the stairs. Blind, unconscious of everything save the steps rising beyond the water, she clambered up like a wet, shuddering cat, in a state of unconsciousness. It was not till she was on the landing, dripping and shuddering till she could not stand erect, clinging to the banisters, while the house shook and the water raved below, that she was aware of the sodden gipsy, in paroxysms of coughing at the head of the stairs, his cap gone, his black hair over his eyes, peering between his washed-down hair at the sickening heave of water below, in the hall. Yvette, fainting, looked too and saw Granny bob up, like a strange float, her face purple, her blind blue eyes bolting, spume hissing from her mouth. One old purple hand clawed at a banister rail, and held for a moment, showing the glint of a wedding ring.

The gipsy, who had coughed himself free and pushed back his hair, said to that awful float-like face below :

" Not good enough ! Not good enough ! "

With a low thud like thunder, the house was struck again, and shuddered, and a strange cracking, rattling, spitting noise began. Up heaved the water like a sea. The hand was gone, all sign of anything was gone, but upheaving water.

Yvette turned in blind unconscious frenzy, staggering like a wet cat to the upper staircase, and climbing swiftly. It was not till she was at the door of her room that she stopped, paralysed by the sound of a sickening, tearing crash, while the house swayed.

" The house is coming down ! " yelled the green-white face of the gipsy, in her face.

He glared into her crazed face.

" Where is the chimney ?   The back chimney—which room ? The chimney will stand——"

He glared with strange ferocity into her face, forcing her to understand. And she nodded with a strange, crazed poise, nodded quite serenely, saying :

" In here ! In here ! It's all right."

They entered her room, which had a narrow fire-place. It was a back room with two windows, one on each side the great chimney-flue. The gipsy, coughing bitterly and trembling in every limb, went to the window to look out.

Below, between the house and the steep rise of the hill, was a wild mill-race of water rushing with refuse, including Rover's green dog-kennel. The gipsy coughed and coughed, and gazed down blankly. Tree after tree went down, mown by the water, which must have been ten feet deep.

Shuddering and pressing his sodden arms on his sodden breast, a

look of resignation on his livid face, he turned to Yvette. A fearful
tearing noise tore the house, then there was a deep, watery explosion.
Something had gone down, some part of the house, the floor heaved
and wavered beneath them. For some moments both were suspended, stupefied. Then he roused.

"Not good enough! Not good enough! This will stand. This
here still stand. See, that chimney! Like a tower. Yes! All
right! All right! You take your clothes off and go to bed. You'll
die of the cold."

"It's all right! It's quite all right!" she said to him, sitting on
a chair and looking up into his face with her white, insane little
face, round which the hair was plastered.

"No!" he cried. "No! Take your things off and I'll rub you
with this towel. I rub myself. If the house falls then die warm.
If it don't fall, then live, not die of pneumonia."

Coughing, shuddering violently, he pulled up his jersey hem and
wrestled with all his shuddering, cold-racked might, to get off his
wet, tight jersey.

"Help me!" he cried, his face muffled.

She seized the edge of the jersey, obediently, and pulled with all her
might. The garment came over his head, and he stood in his braces.

"Take your things off! Rub with this towel!" he commanded
ferociously, the savageness of the war on him. And like a thing
obsessed, he pushed himself out of his trousers, and got out of his
wet, clinging shirt, emerging slim and livid, shuddering in every
fibre with cold and shock.

He seized a towel, and began quickly to rub his body, his teeth
chattering like plates rattling together. Yvette dimly saw it was
wise. She tried to get out of her dress. He pulled the horrible wet
death-gripping thing off her, then, resuming his rubbing, went to
the door, tip-toeing on the wet floor.

There he stood, naked, towel in hand, petrified. He looked west,
towards where the upper landing window had been, and was looking into the sunset, over an insane sea of waters, bristling with uptorn
trees and refuse. The end corner of the house where the porch had
been, and the stairs, had gone. The wall had fallen, leaving the
floors sticking out. The stairs had gone.

Motionless, he watched the water. A cold wind blew in upon
him. He clenched his rattling teeth with a great effort of will, and
turned into the room again, closing the door.

Yvette, naked, shuddering so much that she was sick, was trying
to wipe herself dry.

"All right!" he cried. "All right! The water don't rise no more! All right!"

With his towel he began to rub her, himself shaking all over, but holding her gripped by the shoulder, and slowly, numbedly rubbing her tender body, even trying to rub up into some dryness the pitiful hair of her small head.

Suddenly he left off.

"Better lie in the bed," he commanded, "I want to rub myself."

His teeth went snap-snap-snap-snap, in great snaps, cutting off his words. Yvette crept shaking and semi-conscious into her bed. He, making strained efforts to hold himself still and rub himself warm, went again to the north window, to look out.

The water had risen a little. The sun had gone down, and there was a reddish glow. He rubbed his hair into a black, wet tangle, then paused for breath, in a sudden access of shuddering, then looked out again, then rubbed again on his breast, and began to cough afresh, because of the water he had swallowed. His towel was red : he had hurt himself somewhere : but he felt nothing.

There was still the strange huge noise of water, and the horrible bump of things bumping against the walls. The wind was rising with sundown, cold and hard. The house shook with explosive thuds, and weird, weird frightening noises came up.

A terror creeping over his soul, he went again to the door. The wind, roaring with the waters, blew in as he opened it. Through the awesome gap in the house he saw the world, the waters, the chaos of horrible waters, the twilight, the perfect new moon high above the sunset, a faint thing, and clouds pushing dark into the sky, on the cold, blustery wind.

Clenching his teeth again, fear mingling with resignation, or fatalism, in his soul, he went into the room and closed the door, picking up her towel to see if it were drier than his own, and less blood-stained, again rubbing his head, and going to the window.

He turned away, unable to control his spasms of shivering. Yvette had disappeared right under the bedcolthes, and nothing of her was visible but a shivering mound under the white quilt. He laid his hand on this shivering mound, as if for company. It did not stop shivering.

"All right!" he said. "All right! Water's going down!"

She suddenly uncovered her head and peered out at him from a white face. She peered into his greenish, curiously calm face, semi-conscious. His teeth were chattering unheeded, as he gazed down at her, his black eyes still full of the fire of life and a certain vagabond calm of fatalistic resignation.

" Warm me ! " she moaned, with chattering teeth. " Warm me !
I shall die of shivering."

A terrible convulsion went through her curled-up white body,
enough indeed to rupture her and cause her to die.

The gipsy nodded, and took her in his arms, and held her in a
clasp like a vice, to still his own shuddering. He himself was
shuddering fearfully, and only semi-conscious. It was the shock.

The vice-like grip of his arms round her seemed to her the only
stable point in her consciousness. It was a fearful relief to her heart,
which was strained to bursting. And though his body, wrapped
round her strange and lithe and powerful, like tentacles, rippled
with shuddering as an electric current, still the rigid tension of the
muscles that held her clenched steadied them both, and gradually
the sickening violence of the shuddering, caused by shock, abated,
in his body first, then in hers, and the warmth revived between
them. And as it roused, their tortured, semi-conscious minds
became unconscious, they passed away into sleep.

X

THE sun was shining in heaven before men were able to get across
the Papple with ladders. The bridge was gone. But the flood had
abated, and the house, that leaned forwards as if it were making a
stiff bow to the stream, stood now in mud and wreckage, with a
great heap of fallen masonry and debris at the south-west corner.
Awful were the gaping mouths of rooms !

Inside, there was no sign of life. But across-stream the gardener
had come to reconnoitre, and the cook appeared, thrilled with
curiosity. She had escaped from the back door and up through the
larches to the high-road, when she saw the gipsy bound past the
house : thinking he was coming to murder somebody. At the little
top gate she had found his cart standing. The gardener had led the
horse away to the Red Lion up at Darley, when night had fallen.

This the men from Papplewick learned when at last they got across
the stream with ladders, and to the back of the house. They were
nervous, fearing a collapse of the building, whose front was all
undermined and whose back was choked up. They gazed with
horror at the silent shelves of the rector's rows of books, in his torn-
open study ; at the big brass bedstead of Granny's room, the bed
so deep and comfortably made, but one brass leg of the bedstead
perching tentatively over the torn void ; at the wreckage of the
maid's room upstairs. The housemaid and the cook wept. Then
a man climbed in cautiously through a smashed kitchen window,

into the jungle and morass of the ground floor. He found the body of the old woman : or at least he saw her foot, in its flat black slipper, muddily protruding from a mud-heap of debris. And he fled.

The gardener said he was sure that Miss Yvette was not in the house. He had seen her and the gipsy swept away. But the policeman insisted on a search, and the Framley boys rushing up at last, the ladders were roped together. Then the whole party set up a loud yell. But without result. No answer from within.

A ladder was up, Bob Framley climbed, smashed a window, and clambered into Aunt Cissie's room. The perfect homely familiarity of everything terrified him like ghosts. The house might go down any minute.

They had just got the ladder up to the top floor, when men came running from Darley, saying the old gipsy had been to the Red Lion for the horse and cart, leaving word that his son had seen Yvette at the top of the house. But by that time the policeman was smashing the window of Yvette's room.

Yvette, fast asleep, started from under the bedclothes with a scream, as the glass flew. She clutched the sheets round her nakedness. The policeman uttered a startled yell, which he converted into a cry of : " Miss Yvette ! Miss Yvette ! "

He turned round on the ladder and shouted to the faces below : " Miss Yvette's in bed !—in bed ! "

And he perched there on the ladder, an unmarried man, clutching the window in peril, not knowing what to do.

Yvette sat up in bed, her hair in a matted tangle, and stared with wild eyes, clutching up the sheets at her naked breast. She had been so very fast asleep, that she was still not there.

The policeman, terrified at the flabby ladder, climbed into the room, saying :

" Don't be frightened, Miss ! Don't you worry any more about it. You're safe now."

And Yvette, so dazed, thought he meant the gipsy. Where was the gipsy ? This was the first thing in her mind. Where was her gipsy of this world's-end night ?

He was gone ! He was gone ! And a policeman was in the room ! A policeman !

She rubbed her hand over her dazed brow.

" If you'll get dressed, Miss, we can get you down to safe ground. The house is likely to fall. I suppose there's nobody in the other rooms ? "

He stepped gingerly into the passage and gazed in terror through

the torn-out end of the house, and far off saw the rector coming
down in a motor-car, on the sunlit hill.

Yvette, her face gone numb and disappointed, got up quickly,
closing the bedclothes, and looked at herself a moment, then opened
her drawers for clothing. She dressed herself, then looked in a
mirror, and saw her matted hair with horror. Yet she did not care.
The gipsy was gone, anyhow.

Her own clothes lay in a sodden heap. There was a great sodden
place on the carpet where his had been, and two blood-stained filthy
towels. Otherwise there was no sign of him.

She was tugging at her hair when the policeman tapped at her
door. She called him to come in. He saw with relief that she was
dressed and in her right senses.

" We'd better get out of the house as soon as possible, Miss,"
he reiterated. " It might fall any minute."

" Really ! " said Yvette calmly. " Is it as bad as that ? "

There were great shouts. She had to go to the window. There,
below, was the rector, his arms wide open, tears streaming down his face.

" I'm perfectly all right, Daddy ! " she said, with the calmness
of her contradictory feelings. She would keep the gipsy a secret
from him. At the same time, tears ran down her face.

" Don't you cry, Miss, don't you cry ! The rector's lost his
mother, but he's thanking his stars to have his daughter. We all
thought you were gone as well, we did that ! "

" Is Granny drowned ? " said Yvette.

" I'm afraid she is, poor lady ! " said the policeman, with a grave face.

Yvette wept away into her hanky, which she had had to fetch
from a drawer.

" Dare you go down that ladder, Miss ? " said the policeman.

Yvette looked at the sagging depth of it, and said promptly to
herself : " No ! Not for anything ! " But then she remembered
the gipsy's saying : " Be braver in the body."

" Have you been in all the other rooms ? " she said, in her
weeping, turning to the policeman.

" Yes, Miss ! But you was the only person in the house, you
know, save the old lady. Cook got away in time, and Lizzie was
up at her mother's. It was only you and the poor old lady we was
fretting about. Do you think you dare go down that ladder ? "

" Oh, yes ! " said Yvette, with indifference. The gipsy was gone
anyway.

And now the rector in torment watched his tall, slender daughter
slowly stepping backwards down the sagging ladder, the policeman,

peering heroically from the smashed window, holding the ladder's top end.

At the foot of the ladder Yvette appropriately fainted in her father's arms, and was borne away with him, in the car, by Bob, to the Framley home. There the poor Lucille, a ghost of ghosts, wept with relief till she had hysterics, and even Aunt Cissie cried out among her tears : " Let the old be taken and the young spared ! Oh I *can't* cry for the Mater, now Yvette is spared ! "

And she wept gallons.

The flood was caused by the sudden bursting of the great reservoir, up in Papple Highdale, five miles from the rectory. It was found out later that an ancient, perhaps even a Roman mine tunnel, unsuspected, undreamed of, beneath the reservoir dam, had collapsed, undermining the whole dam. That was why the Papple had been, for that last day, so uncannily full. And then the dam had burst.

The rector and the two girls stayed on at the Framleys', till a new home could be found. Yvette did not attend Granny's funeral. She stayed in bed.

Telling her tale, she only told how the gipsy had got her inside the porch, and she had crawled to the stairs out of the water. It was known that he had escaped : the old gipsy had said so, when he fetched the horse and cart from the Red Lion.

Yvette could tell little. She was vague, confused, she seemed hardly to remember anything. But that was just like her.

It was Bob Framley who said :

" You know, I think that gipsy deserves a medal."

The whole family suddenly was struck.

" Oh, we *ought* to thank him ! " cried Lucille.

The rector himself went with Bob in the car. But the quarry was deserted. The gipsies had lifted camp and gone, no one knew whither.

And Yvette, lying in bed, moaned in her heart : " Oh, I love him ! I love him ! I love him ! " The grief over him kept her prostrate. Yet practically, she too was acquiescent in the fact of his disappearance. Her young soul knew the wisdom of it.

But after Granny's funeral, she received a little letter, dated from some unknown place.

" Dear Miss, I see in the paper you are all right after your ducking, as is the same with me. I hope I see you again one day, maybe at Tideswell cattle-fair, or maybe we come that way again. I come that day to say good-bye ! and I never said it, well, the water give no time, but I live in hopes. Your obdt. servant Joe Boswell."

And only then she realized that he had a name.

2 M *

I

THE small locomotive engine, Number 4, came clanking, stumbling down from Selston with seven full waggons. It appeared round the corner with loud threats of speed, but the colt that it startled from among the gorse, which still flickered indistinctly in the raw afternoon, outdistanced it at a canter. A woman, walking up the railway line to Underwood, drew back into the hedge, held her basket aside, and watched the footplate of the engine advancing. The trucks thumped heavily past, one by one, with slow inevitable movement, as she stood insignificantly trapped between the jolting black waggons and the hedge ; then they curved away towards the coppice where the withered oak leaves dropped noiselessly, while the birds, pulling at the scarlet hips beside the track, made off into the dusk that had already crept into the spinney. In the open, the smoke from the engine sank and cleaved to the rough grass. The fields were dreary and forsaken, and in the marshy strip that led to the whimsey, a reedy pit-pond, the fowls had already abandoned their run among the alders, to roost in the tarred fowl-house. The pit-bank loomed up beyond the pond, flames like red sores licking its ashy sides, in the afternoon's stagnant light. Just beyond rose the tapering chimneys and the clumsy black headstocks of Brinsley Colliery. The two wheels were spinning fast up against the sky, and the winding-engine rapped out its little spasms. The miners were being turned up.

The engine whistled as it came into the wide bay of railway lines beside the colliery, where rows of trucks stood in harbour.

Miners, single, trailing and in groups, passed like shadows diverging home. At the edge of the ribbed level of sidings squat a low cottage, three steps down from the cinder track. A large bony vine clutched at the house, as if to claw down the tiled roof. Round the bricked yard grew a few wintry primroses. Beyond, the long garden sloped down to a bush-covered brook course. There were some twiggy apple trees, winter-crack trees, and ragged cabbages. Beside the path hung dishevelled pink chrysanthemums, like pink cloths hung on bushes. A woman came stooping out of the felt-covered fowl-house, half-way down the garden. She closed and padlocked the door, then drew herself erect, having brushed some bits from her white apron.

She was a tall woman of imperious mien, handsome, with definite black eyebrows. Her smooth black hair was parted exactly. For a few moments she stood steadily watching the miners as they passed along the railway : then she turned towards the brook course. Her face was calm and set, her mouth was closed with disillusionment. After a moment she called :

" John ! " There was no answer. She waited, and then said distinctly :

" Where are you ? "

" Here ! " replied a child's sulky voice from among the bushes. The woman looked piercingly through the dusk.

" Are you at that brook ? " she asked sternly.

For answer the child showed himself before the raspberry-canes that rose like whips. He was a small, sturdy boy of five. He stood quite still, defiantly.

" Oh ! " said the mother, conciliated. " I thought you were down at that wet brook—and you remember what I told you——"

The boy did not move or answer.

" Come, come on in," she said more gently, " it's getting dark. There's your grandfather's engine coming down the line ! "

The lad advanced slowly, with resentful, taciturn movement. He was dressed in trousers and waistcoat of cloth that was too thick and hard for the size of the garments. They were evidently cut down from a man's clothes.

As they went slowly towards the house he tore at the ragged wisps of chrysanthemums and dropped the petals in handfuls along the path.

" Don't do that—it does look nasty," said his mother. He refrained, and she, suddenly pitiful, broke off a twig with three or four wan flowers and held them against her face. When mother and son reached the yard her hand hesitated, and instead of laying the flower aside, she pushed it in her apron-band. The mother and son stood at the foot of the three steps looking across the bay of lines at the passing home of the miners. The trundle of the small train was imminent. Suddenly the engine loomed past the house and came to a stop opposite the gate.

The engine-driver, a short man with round grey beard, leaned out of the cab high above the woman.

" Have you got a cup of tea ? " he said in a cheery, hearty fashion. It was her father. She went in, saying she would mash. Directly, she returned.

" I didn't come to see you on Sunday," began the little grey-bearded man.

" I didn't expect you," said his daughter.

The engine-driver winced ; then, reassuming his cheery, airy manner, he said :

" Oh, have you heard then ? Well, and what do you think—— ? "

" I think it is soon enough," she replied.

At her brief censure the little man made an impatient gesture, and said coaxingly, yet with dangerous coldness :

" Well, what's a man to do ? It's no sort of life for a man of my years, to sit at my own hearth like a stranger. And if I'm going to marry again it may as well be soon as late—what does it matter to anybody ? "

The woman did not reply, but turned and went into the house. The man in the engine-cab stood assertive, till she returned with a cup of tea and a piece of bread and butter on a plate. She went up the steps and stood near the footplate of the hissing engine.

" You needn't 'a' brought me bread an' butter," said her father. " But a cup of tea "—he sipped appreciatively—" it's very nice." He sipped for a moment or two, then : " I hear as Walter's got another bout on," he said.

" When hasn't he ? " said the woman bitterly.

" I heered tell of him in the ' Lord Nelson ' braggin' as he was going to spend that b—— afore he went : half a sovereign that was."

" When ? " asked the woman.

" A' Sat'day night—I know that's true."

" Very likely," she laughed bitterly. " He gives me twenty-three shillings."

" Aye, it's a nice thing, when a man can do nothing with his money but make a beast of himself ! " said the grey-whiskered man. The woman turned her head away. Her father swallowed the last of his tea and handed her the cup.

" Aye," he sighed, wiping his mouth. " It's a settler, it is—— "

He put his hand on the lever. The little engine strained and groaned, and the train rumbled towards the crossing. The woman again looked across the metals. Darkness was settling over the spaces of the railway and trucks : the miners, in grey sombre groups, were still passing home. The winding-engine pulsed hurriedly, with brief pauses. Elizabeth Bates looked at the dreary flow of men, then she went indoors. Her husband did not come.

The kitchen was small and full of firelight ; red coals piled glowing up the chimney mouth. All the life of the room seemed in the white, warm hearth and the steel fender reflecting the red fire. The cloth was laid for tea ; cups glinted in the shadows. At the back, where the lowest stairs protruded into the room, the boy sat struggling with a knife and a piece of whitewood. He was almost hidden in the shadow. It was half-past four. They had but to await the father's coming to begin tea. As the mother watched her son's sullen little struggle with the wood, she saw herself in his silence and pertinacity ; she saw the father in her child's indifference to all but himself. She seemed to be occupied by her husband. He had probably gone past his home, slung past his own door, to drink before he came in, while his dinner spoiled and wasted in waiting. She glanced at the clock, then took the potatoes to strain them in the yard. The garden and fields beyond the brook were closed in uncertain darkness. When she rose with the saucepan, leaving the drain steaming into the night behind her, she saw the yellow lamps were lit along the high road that went up the hill away beyond the space of the railway lines and the field.

Then again she watched the men trooping home, fewer now and fewer.

Indoors the fire was sinking and the room was dark red. The woman put her saucepan on the hob, and set a batter pudding near the mouth of the oven. Then she stood unmoving. Directly, gratefully, came quick young steps to the door. Someone hung on the latch a moment, then a little girl entered and began pulling off her outdoor things, dragging a mass of curls, just ripening from gold to brown, over her eyes with her hat.

Her mother chid her for coming late from school, and said she would have to keep her at home the dark winter days.

" Why, mother, it's hardly a bit dark yet. The lamp's not lighted, and my father's not home."

" No, he isn't. But it's a quarter to five ! Did you see anything of him ? "

The child became serious. She looked at her mother with large, wistful blue eyes.

" No, mother, I've never seen him. Why ? Has he come up an' gone past, to Old Brinsley ? He hasn't, mother, 'cos I never saw him."

" He'd watch that," said the mother bitterly, " he'd take care as you didn't see him. But you may depend upon it, he's seated in the ' Prince o' Wales.' He wouldn't be this late."

The girl looked at her mother piteously.

" Let's have our teas, mother, should we ? " said she.

The mother called John to table. She opened the door once more and looked out across the darkness of the lines. All was deserted : she could not hear the winding-engines.

"Perhaps," she said to herself, " he's stopped to get some ripping done."

They sat down to tea. John, at the end of the table near the door, was almost lost in the darkness. Their faces were hidden from each other. The girl crouched against the fender slowly moving a thick piece of bread before the fire. The lad, his face a dusky mark on the shadow, sat watching her who was transfigured in the red glow.

" I do think it's beautiful to look in the fire," said the child.

" Do you ? " said her mother. " Why ? "

" It's so red, and full of little caves—and it feels so nice, and you can fair smell it."

" It'll want mending directly," replied her mother, " and then if your father comes he'll carry on and say there never is a fire when a man comes home sweating from the pit. A public-house is always warm enough."

There was silence till the boy said complainingly : " Make haste, our Annie."

" Well, I am doing ! I can't make the fire do it no faster, can I ? "

" She keeps wafflin' it about so's to make 'er slow," grumbled the boy.

" Don't have such an evil imagination, child," replied the mother.

Soon the room was busy in the darkness with the crisp sound of crunching. The mother ate very little. She drank her tea determinedly, and sat thinking. When she rose her anger was evident in the stern unbending of her head. She looked at the pudding in the fender, and broke out :

" It is a scandalous thing as a man can't even come home to his dinner ! If it's crozzled up to a cinder I don't see why I should care. Past his very door he goes to get to a public-house, and here I sit with his dinner waiting for him——"

She went out. As she dropped piece after piece of coal on the red fire, the shadows fell on the walls, till the room was almost in total darkness.

"I canna see," grumbled the invisible John. In spite of herself, the mother laughed.

"You know the way to your mouth," she said. She set the dustpan outside the door. When she came again like a shadow on the hearth, the lad repeated, complaining sulkily :

"I canna see."

"Good gracious!" cried the mother irritably, "you're as bad as your father if it's a bit dusk!"

Nevertheless she took a paper spill from a sheaf on the mantelpiece and proceeded to light the lamp that hung from the ceiling in the middle of the room. As she reached up, her figure displayed itself just rounding with maternity.

"Oh, mother—— !" exclaimed the girl.

"What?" said the woman, suspended in the act of putting the lamp glass over the flame. The copper reflector shone handsomely on her, as she stood with uplifted arm, turning to face her daughter.

"You've got a flower in your apron!" said the child, in a little rapture at this unusual event.

"Goodness me!" exclaimed the woman, relieved. "One would think the house was afire." She replaced the glass and waited a moment before turning up the wick. A pale shadow was seen floating vaguely on the floor.

"Let me smell!" said the child, still rapturously, coming forward and putting her face to her mother's waist.

"Go along, silly!" said the mother, turning up the lamp. The light revealed their suspense so that the woman felt it almost unbearable. Annie was still bending at her waist. Irritably, the mother took the flowers out from her apron-band.

"Oh, mother—don't take them out!" Annie cried, catching her hand and trying to replace the sprig.

"Such nonsense!" said the mother, turning away. The child put the pale chrysanthemums to her lips, murmuring :

"Don't they smell beautiful!"

Her mother gave a short laugh.

"No," she said, "not to me. It was chrysanthemums when I married him, and chrysanthemums when you were born, and the first time they ever brought him home drunk, he'd got brown chrysanthemums in his button-hole."

She looked at the children. Their eyes and their parted lips were wondering. The mother sat rocking in silence for some time. Then she looked at the clock.

"Twenty minutes to six!" In a tone of fine bitter carelessness she continued : " Eh, he'll not come now till they bring him. There he'll stick ! But he needn't come rolling in here in his pit-dirt, for *I* won't wash him. He can lie on the floor——Eh, what a fool I've been, what a fool ! And this is what I came here for, to this dirty hole, rats and all, for him to slink past his very door. Twice last week—he's begun now——"

She silenced herself, and rose to clear the table.

While for an hour or more the children played, subduedly intent, fertile of imagination, united in fear of the mother's wrath, and in dread of their father's home-coming, Mrs. Bates sat in her rocking-chair making a " singlet " of thick cream-coloured flannel, which gave a dull wounded sound as she tore off the grey edge. She worked at her sewing with energy, listening to the children, and her anger wearied itself, lay down to rest, opening its eyes from time to time and steadily watching, its ears raised to listen. Sometimes even her anger quailed and shrank, and the mother suspended her sewing, tracing the footsteps that thudded along the sleepers outside ; she would lift her head sharply to bid the children " hush," but she recovered herself in time, and the footsteps went past the gate, and the children were not flung out of their play-world.

But at last Annie sighed, and gave in. She glanced at her waggon of slippers, and loathed the game. She turned plaintively to her mother.

" Mother ! "—but she was inarticulate.

John crept out like a frog from under the sofa. His mother glanced up.

" Yes," she said, " just look at those shirt-sleeves ! "

The boy held them out to survey them, saying nothing. Then somebody called in a hoarse voice away down the line, and suspense bristled in the room, till two people had gone by outside, talking.

" It is time for bed," said the mother.

" My father hasn't come," wailed Annie plaintively. But her mother was primed with courage.

" Never mind. They'll bring him when he does come—like a log." She meant there would be no scene. " And he may sleep on the floor till he wakes himself. I know he'll not go to work to-morrow after this ! "

The children had their hands and faces wiped with a flannel. They were very quiet. When they had put on their nightdresses, they said their prayers, the boy mumbling. The mother looked down at them, at the brown silken bush of intertwining curls in the nape of the girl's neck, at the little black head of the lad, and her heart burst with anger at their father who caused all three such distress. The children hid their faces in her skirts for comfort.

When Mrs. Bates came down, the room was strangely empty, with a tension of expectancy. She took up her sewing and stitched for some time without raising her head. Meantime her anger was tinged with fear.

II

The clock struck eight and she rose suddenly, dropping her sewing on her chair. She went to the stairfoot door, opened it, listening. Then she went out, locking the door behind her.

Something scuffled in the yard, and she started, though she knew it was only the rats with which the place was overrun. The night was very dark. In the great bay of railway lines, bulked with trucks, there was no trace of light, only away back she could see a few yellow lamps at the pit-top, and the red smear of the burning pit-bank on the night. She hurried along the edge of the track, then, crossing the converging lines, came to the stile by the white gates, whence she emerged on the road. Then the fear which had led her shrank. People were walking up to New Brinsley ; she saw the lights in the houses ; twenty yards further on were the broad windows of the " Prince of Wales," very warm and bright, and the loud voices of men could be heard distinctly. What a fool she had been to imagine that anything had happened to him ! He was merely drinking over there at the " Prince of Wales." She faltered. She had never yet been to fetch him, and she never would go. So she continued her walk towards the long straggling line of houses, standing blank on the highway. She entered a passage between the dwellings.

" Mr. Rigley ?—Yes ! Did you want him ? No, he's not in at this minute."

The raw-boned woman leaned forward from her dark scullery and peered at the other, upon whom fell a dim light through the blind of the kitchen window.

" Is it Mrs. Bates ? " she asked in a tone tinged with respect.

" Yes. I wondered if your Master was at home. Mine hasn't come yet."

" 'Asn't 'e ! Oh, Jack's been 'ome an' 'ad 'is dinner an' gone out. 'E's just gone for 'alf an hour afore bedtime. Did you call at the ' Prince of Wales ' ? "

" No——"

" No, you didn't like—— ! It's not very nice." The other woman
was indulgent. There was an awkward pause. " Jack never said
nothink about—about your Mester," she said.

" No !—I expect he's stuck in there ! "

Elizabeth Bates said this bitterly, and with recklessness. She
knew that the woman across the yard was standing at her door
listening, but she did not care. As she turned :

" Stop a minute ! I'll just go an' ask Jack if 'e knows anythink,"
said Mrs. Rigley.

" Oh, no—I wouldn't like to put—— ! "

" Yes, I will, if you'll just step inside an' see as th' childer doesn't
come downstairs and set theirselves afire."

Elizabeth Bates, murmuring a remonstrance, stepped inside. The
other woman apologized for the state of the room.

The kitchen needed apology. There were little frocks and trousers
and childish undergarments on the squab and on the floor, and a
litter of playthings everywhere. On the black American cloth of
the table were pieces of bread and cake, crusts, slops, and a teapot
with cold tea.

" Eh, ours is just as bad," said Elizabeth Bates, looking at the
woman, not at the house. Mrs. Rigley put a shawl over her head
and hurried out, saying :

" I shanna be a minute."

The other sat, noting with faint disapproval the general untidiness
of the room. Then she fell to counting the shoes of various sizes
scattered over the floor. There were twelve. She sighed and said
to herself, " No wonder ! "—glancing at the litter. There came the
scratching of two pairs of feet on the yard, and the Rigleys entered.
Elizabeth Bates rose. Rigley was a big man, with very large bones.
His head looked particularly bony. Across his temple was a blue
scar, caused by a wound got in the pit, a wound in which the coal-
dust remained blue like tattooing.

" 'Asna 'e come whoam yit ? " asked the man, without any form
of greeting, but with deference and sympathy. " I couldna say
wheer he is—'e's non ower theer ! "—he jerked his head to signify
the " Prince of Wales."

" 'E's 'appen gone up to th' ' Yew,' " said Mrs. Rigley.

There was another pause. Rigley had evidently something to get
off his mind :

" Ah left 'im finishin' a stint," he began. " Loose-all 'ad bin gone
about ten minutes when we com'n away, an' I shouted, ' Are ter
comin', Walt ? ' an' 'e said, ' Go on, Ah shanna be but a'ef a minnit,'

so we com'n ter th' bottom, me an' Bowers, thinkin' as 'e wor just behint, an' 'ud come up i' th' next bantle——"

He stood perplexed, as if answering a charge of deserting his mate. Elizabeth Bates, now again certain of disaster, hastened to reassure him :

" I expect 'e's gone up to th' ' Yew Tree,' as you say. It's not the first time. I've fretted myself into a fever before now. He'll come home when they carry him."

" Ay, isn't it too bad ! " deplored the other woman.

" I'll just step up to Dick's an' see if 'e *is* theer," offered the man, afraid of appearing alarmed, afraid of taking liberties.

" Oh, I wouldn't think of bothering you that far," said Elizabeth Bates, with emphasis, but he knew she was glad of his offer.

As they stumbled up the entry, Elizabeth Bates heard Rigley's wife run across the yard and open her neighbour's door. At this, suddenly all the blood in her body seemed to switch away from her heart.

" Mind ! " warned Rigley. " Ah've said many a time as Ah'd fill up them ruts in this entry, sumb'dy 'll be breakin' their legs yit."

She recovered herself and walked quickly along with the miner.

" I don't like leaving the children in bed, and nobody in the house," she said.

" No, you dunna ! " he replied courteously. They were soon at the gate of the cottage.

" Well, I shanna be many minnits. Dunna you be frettin' now, 'e'll be all right," said the butty.

" Thank you very much, Mr. Rigley," she replied.

" You're welcome ! " he stammered, moving away. " I shanna be many minnits."

The house was quiet. Elizabeth Bates took off her hat and shawl, and rolled back the rug. When she had finished, she sat down. It was a few minutes past nine. She was startled by the rapid chuff of the winding-engine at the pit, and the sharp whirr of the brakes on the rope as it descended. Again she felt the painful sweep of her blood, and she put her hand to her side, saying aloud, " Good gracious !—it's only the nine o'clock deputy going down," rebuking herself.

She sat still, listening. Half an hour of this, and she was wearied out.

" What am I working myself up like this for ? " she said pitiably to herself, " I s'll only be doing myself some damage."

She took out her sewing again.

G

At a quarter to ten there were footsteps. One person ! She watched for the door to open. It was an elderly woman, in a black bonnet and a black woollen shawl—his mother. She was about sixty years old, pale, with blue eyes, and her face all wrinkled and lamentable. She shut the door and turned to her daughter-in-law peevishly.

" Eh, Lizzie, whatever shall we do, whatever shall we do ! " she cried.

Elizabeth drew back a little, sharply.

" What is it, mother ? " she said.

The elder woman seated herself on the sofa.

" I don't know, child, I can't tell you ! "—she shook her head slowly. Elizabeth sat watching her, anxious and vexed.

" I don't know," replied the grandmother, sighing very deeply. " There's no end to my troubles, there isn't. The things I've gone through, I'm sure it's enough——! " She wept without wiping her eyes, the tears running.

" But, mother," interrupted Elizabeth, " what do you mean ? What is it ? "

The grandmother slowly wiped her eyes. The fountains of her tears were stopped by Elizabeth's directness. She wiped her eyes slowly.

" Poor child ! Eh, you poor thing ! " she moaned. " I don't know what we're going to do, I don't—and you as you are—it's a thing, it is indeed ! "

Elizabeth waited.

" Is he dead ? " she asked, and at the words her heart swung violently, though she felt a slight flush of shame at the ultimate extravagance of the question. Her words sufficiently frightened the old lady, almost brought her to herself.

" Don't say so, Elizabeth ! We'll hope it's not as bad as that ; no, may the Lord spare us that, Elizabeth. Jack Rigley came just as I was sittin' down to a glass afore going to bed, an' 'e said, ' 'Appen you'll go down th' line, Mrs. Bates. Walt's had an accident. 'Appen you'll go an' sit wi' 'er till we can get him home.' I hadn't time to ask him a word afore he was gone. An' I put my bonnet on an' come straight down, Lizzie. I thought to myself, ' Eh, that poor blessed child, if anybody should come an' tell her of a sudden, there's no knowin' what'll 'appen to 'er.' You mustn't let it upset you, Lizzie—or you know what to expect. How long is it, six months— or is it five, Lizzie ? Ay ! "—the old woman shook her head—" time slips on, it slips on ! Ay ! "

Elizabeth's thoughts were busy elsewhere. If he was killed—

would she be able to manage on the little pension and what she could earn ?—she counted up rapidly. If he was hurt—they wouldn't take him to the hospital—how tiresome he would be to nurse !—but perhaps she'd be able to get him away from the drink and his hateful ways. She would—while he was ill. The tears offered to come to her eyes at the picture. But what sentimental luxury was this she was beginning ? She turned to consider the children. At any rate she was absolutely necessary for them. They were her business.

"Ay !" repeated the old woman, "it seems but a week or two since he brought me his first wages. Ay—he was a good lad, Elizabeth, he was, in his way. I don't know why he got to be such a trouble, I don't. He was a happy lad at home, only full of spirits. But there's no mistake he's been a handful of trouble, he has ! I hope the Lord'll spare him to mend his ways. I hope so, I hope so. You've had a sight o' trouble with him, Elizabeth, you have indeed. But he was a jolly enough lad wi' me, he was, I can assure you. I don't know how it is. . . ."

The old woman continued to muse aloud, a monotonous irritating sound, while Elizabeth thought concentratedly, startled once, when she heard the winding-engine chuff quickly, and the brakes skirr with a shriek. Then she heard the engine more slowly, and the brakes made no sound. The old woman did not notice. Elizabeth waited in suspense. The mother-in-law talked, with lapses into silence.

"But he wasn't your son, Lizzie, an' it makes a difference. Whatever he was, I remember him when he was little, an' I learned to understand him and to make allowances. You've got to make allowances for them——"

It was half-past ten, and the old woman was saying : "But it's trouble from beginning to end ; you're never too old for trouble, never too old for that——" when the gate banged back, and there were heavy feet on the steps.

"I'll go, Lizzie, let me go," cried the old woman, rising. But Elizabeth was at the door. It was a man in pit-clothes.

"They're bringin' 'im, Missis," he said. Elizabeth's heart halted a moment. Then it surged on again, almost suffocating her.

"Is he—is it bad ? " she asked.

The man turned away, looking at the darkness :

"The doctor says 'e'd been dead hours. 'E saw im i' th' lamp-cabin."

The old woman, who stood just behind Elizabeth, dropped into a chair, and folded her hands, crying : "Oh, my boy, my boy ! "

" Hush ! " said Elizabeth, with a sharp twitch of a frown. " Be still, mother, don't waken th' children : I wouldn't have them down for anything ! "

The old woman moaned softly, rocking herself. The man was drawing away. Elizabeth took a step forward.

" How was it ? " she asked.

" Well, I couldn't say for sure," the man replied, very ill at ease. " 'E wor finishin' a stint an' th' butties 'ad gone, an' a lot o' stuff come down atop 'n 'im."

" And crushed him ? " cried the widow, with a shudder.

" No," said the man, " it fell at th' back of 'im. 'E wor under th' face, an' it niver touched 'im. It shut 'im in. It seems 'e wor smothered."

Elizabeth shrank back. She heard the old woman behind her cry :

" What ?—what did e' say it was ? "

The man replied, more loudly : " 'E wor smothered ! "

Then the old woman wailed aloud, and this relieved Elizabeth.

" Oh, mother," she said, putting her hand on the old woman, " don't waken th' children, don't waken th' children."

She wept a little, unknowing, while the old mother rocked herself and moaned. Elizabeth remembered that they were bringing him home, and she must be ready. " They'll lay him in the parlour," she said to herself, standing a moment pale and perplexed.

Then she lighted a candle and went into the tiny room. The air was cold and damp, but she could not make a fire, there was no fireplace. She set down the candle and looked round. The candle-light glittered on the lustre-glasses, on the two vases that held some of the pink chrysanthemums, and on the dark mahogany. There was a cold, deathly smell of chrysanthemums in the room. Elizabeth stood looking at the flowers. She turned away, and calculated whether there would be room to lay him on the floor, between the couch and the chiffonier. She pushed the chairs aside. There would be room to lay him down and to step round him. Then she fetched the old red tablecloth, and another old cloth, spreading them down to save her bit of carpet. She shivered on leaving the parlour ; so, from the dresser-drawer she took a clean shirt and put it at the fire to air. All the time her mother-in-law was rocking herself in the chair and moaning.

" You'll have to move from there, mother," said Elizabeth. " They'll be bringing him in. Come in the rocker."

The old mother rose mechanically, and seated herself by the fire, continuing to lament. Elizabeth went into the pantry for another candle, and there, in the little penthouse under the naked tiles, she heard them coming. She stood still in the pantry doorway, listening. She heard them pass the end of the house, and come awkwardly down the three steps, a jumble of shuffling footsteps and muttering voices. The old woman was silent. The men were in the yard.

Then Elizabeth heard Matthews, the manager of the pit, say : "You go in first, Jim. Mind ! "

The door came open, and the two women saw a collier backing into the room, holding one end of a stretcher, on which they could see the nailed pit-boots of the dead man. The two carriers halted, the man at the head stooping to the lintel of the door.

"Wheer will you have him ? " asked the manager, a short, white-bearded man.

Elizabeth roused herself and came from the pantry carrying the unlighted candle.

"In the parlour," she said.

"In there, Jim ! " pointed the manager, and the carriers backed round into the tiny room. The coat with which they had covered the body fell off as they awkwardly turned through the two doorways, and the women saw their man, naked to the waist, lying stripped for work. The old woman began to moan in a low voice of horror.

"Lay th' stretcher at th' side," snapped the manager, "an' put 'im on th' cloths. Mind now, mind ! Look you now——! "

One of the men had knocked off a vase of chrysanthemums. He stared awkwardly, then they set down the stretcher. Elizabeth did not look at her husband. As soon as she could get in the room, she went and picked up the broken vase and the flowers.

"Wait a minute ! " she said.

The three men waited in silence while she mopped up the water with a duster.

"Eh, what a job, what a job, to be sure ! " the manager was saying, rubbing his brow with trouble and perplexity. "Never knew such a thing in my life, never ! He'd no business to ha' been left. I never knew such a thing in my life ! Fell over him clean as a whistle, an' shut him in. Not four foot of space, there wasn't—yet it scarce bruised him."

He looked down at the dead man, lying prone, half naked, all grimed with coal-dust.

"''Sphyxiated,' the doctor said. It *is* the most terrible job I've ever known. Seems as if it was done o' purpose. Clean over him, an' shut 'im in, like a mouse-trap "—he made a sharp, descending gesture with his hand.

The colliers standing by jerked aside their heads in hopeless comment.

The horror of the thing bristled upon them all.

Then they heard the girl's voice upstairs calling shrilly : " Mother, mother—who is it ? Mother, who is it ? "

Elizabeth hurried to the foot of the stairs and opened the door : " Go to sleep ! " she commanded sharply. " What are you shouting about ? Go to sleep at once—there's nothing——"

Then she began to mount the stairs. They could hear her on the boards, and on the plaster floor of the little bedroom. They could hear her distinctly :

" What's the matter now ?—what's the matter with you, silly thing ? "—her voice was much agitated, with an unreal gentleness.

" I thought it was some men come," said the plaintive voice of the child. " Has he come ? "

" Yes, they've brought him. There's nothing to make a fuss about. Go to sleep now, like a good child."

They could hear her voice in the bedroom, they waited whilst she covered the children under the bedclothes.

" Is he drunk ? " asked the girl, timidly, faintly.

" No ! No—he's not ! He—he's asleep."

" Is he asleep downstairs ? "

" Yes—and don't make a noise."

There was silence for a moment, then the men heard the frightened child again :

" What's that noise ? "

" It's nothing, I tell you, what are you bothering for ? "

The noise was the grandmother moaning. She was oblivious of everything, sitting on her chair rocking and moaning. The manager put his hand on her arm and bade her " Sh—sh ! ! "

The old woman opened her eyes and looked at him. She was shocked by this interruption, and seemed to wonder.

" What time is it ? "—the plaintive thin voice of the child, sinking back unhappily into sleep, asked this last question.

" Ten o'clock," answered the mother more softly. Then she must have bent down and kissed the children.

Matthews beckoned to the men to come away. They put on their caps and took up the stretcher. Stepping over the body, they tiptoed out of the house. None of them spoke till they were far from the wakeful children.

When Elizabeth came down she found her mother alone on the parlour floor, leaning over the dead man, the tears dropping on him.

"We must lay him out," the wife said. She put on the kettle, then returning knelt at the feet, and began to unfasten the knotted leather laces. The room was clammy and dim with only one candle, so that she had to bend her face almost to the floor. At last she got off the heavy boots and put them away.

"You must help me now," she whispered to the old woman. Together they stripped the man.

When they arose, saw him lying in the naïve dignity of death, the women stood arrested in fear and respect. For a few moments they remained still, looking down, the old mother whimpering. Elizabeth felt countermanded. She saw him, how utterly inviolable he lay in himself. She had nothing to do with him. She could not accept it. Stooping, she laid her hand on him, in claim. He was still warm, for the mine was hot where he had died. His mother had his face between her hands, and was murmuring incoherently. The old tears fell in succession as drops from wet leaves ; the mother was not weeping, merely her tears flowed. Elizabeth embraced the body of her husband, with cheek and lips. She seemed to be listening, inquiring, trying to get some connection. But she could not. She was driven away. He was impregnable.

She rose, went into the kitchen, where she poured warm water into a bowl, brought soap and flannel and a soft towel.

"I must wash him," she said.

Then the old mother rose stiffly, and watched Elizabeth as she carefully washed his face, carefully brushing the big blond moustache from his mouth with the flannel. She was afraid with a bottomless fear, so she ministered to him. The old woman, jealous, said :

"Let me wipe him ! "—and she kneeled on the other side drying slowly as Elizabeth washed, her big black bonnet sometimes brushing the dark head of her daughter-in-law. They worked thus in silence for a long time. They never forgot it was death, and the touch of the man's dead body gave them strange emotions, different in each of the women ; a great dread possessed them both, the mother felt the lie was given to her womb, she was denied ; the wife felt the utter isolation of the human soul, the child within her was a weight apart from her.

At last it was finished. He was a man of handsome body, and his face showed no traces of drink. He was blond, full-fleshed, with fine limbs. But he was dead.

"Bless him," whispered his mother, looking always at his face, and speaking out of sheer terror. "Dear lad—bless him!" She spoke in a faint, sibilant ecstasy of fear and mother love.

Elizabeth sank down again to the floor, and put her face against his neck, and trembled and shuddered. But she had to draw away again. He was dead, and her living flesh had no place against his. A great dread and weariness held her : she was so unavailing. Her life was gone like this.

"White as milk he is, clear as a twelve-month baby, bless him, the darling!" the old mother murmured to herself. "Not a mark on him, clear and clean and white, beautiful as ever a child was made," she murmured with pride. Elizabeth kept her face hidden.

"He went peaceful, Lizzie—peaceful as sleep. Isn't he beautiful, the lamb? Ay—he must ha' made his peace, Lizzie. 'Appen he made it all right, Lizzie, shut in there. He'd have time. He wouldn't look like this if he hadn't made his peace. The lamb, the dear lamb. Eh, but he had a hearty laugh. I loved to hear it. He had the heartiest laugh, Lizzie, as a lad——"

Elizabeth looked up. The man's mouth was fallen back, slightly open under the cover of the moustache. The eyes, half shut, did not show glazed in the obscurity. Life with its smoky burning gone from him, had left him apart and utterly alien to her. And she knew what a stranger he was to her. In her womb was ice of fear, because of this separate stranger with whom she had been living as one flesh. Was this what it all meant—utter, intact separateness, obscured by heat of living? In dread she turned her face away. The fact was too deadly. There had been nothing between them, and yet they had come together, exchanging their nakedness repeatedly. Each time he had taken her, they had been two isolated beings, far apart as now. He was no more responsible than she. The child was like ice in her womb. For as she looked at the dead man, her mind, cold and detached, said clearly : "Who am I? What have I been doing? I have been fighting a husband who did not exist. *He* existed all the time. What wrong have I done? What was that I have been living with? There lies the reality, this man." And her soul died in her for fear : she knew she had never seen him, he had never seen her, they had met in the dark and had fought in the dark, not knowing whom they met nor whom they fought. And now she saw, and turned silent in seeing. For she had been wrong. She had said he was something he was not ; she had felt familiar with him. Whereas he was apart all the while, living as she never lived, feeling as she never felt.

In fear and shame she looked at his naked body, that she had

known falsely. And he was the father of her children. Her soul was
torn from her body and stood apart. She looked at his naked body
and was ashamed, as if she had denied it. After all, it was itself.
It seemed awful to her. She looked at his face, and she turned her
own face to the wall. For his look was other than hers, his way was
not her way. She had denied him what he was—she saw it now.
She had refused him as himself. And this had been her life, and his
life. She was grateful to death, which restored the truth. And
she knew she was not dead.

And all the while her heart was bursting with grief and pity for
him. What had he suffered? What stretch of horror for this helpless man! She was rigid with agony. She had not been able to
help him. He had been cruelly injured, this naked man, this other
being, and she could make no reparation. There were the children
—but the children belonged to life. This dead man had nothing to
do with them. He and she were only channels through which life
had flowed to issue in the children. She was a mother—but how
awful she knew it now to have been a wife. And he, dead now,
how awful he must have felt it to be a husband. She felt that in the
next world he would be a stranger to her. If they met there, in the
beyond, they would only be ashamed of what had been before.
The children had come, for some mysterious reason, out of both of
them. But the children did not unite them. Now he was dead, she
knew how eternally he was apart from her, how eternally he had
nothing more to do with her. She saw this episode of her life closed.
They had denied each other in life. Now he had withdrawn. An
anguish came over her. It was finished then : it had become
hopeless between them long before he died. Yet he had been her
husband. But how little!

"Have you got his shirt, 'Lizabeth?"

Elizabeth turned without answering, though she strove to weep
and behave as her mother-in-law expected. But she could not, she
was silenced. She went into the kitchen and returned with the
garment.

"It is aired," she said, grasping the cotton shirt here and there to
try. She was almost ashamed to handle him ; what right had she
or any one to lay hands on him ; but her touch was humble on his
body. It was hard work to clothe him. He was so heavy and inert.
A terrible dread gripped her all the while : that he could be so heavy
and utterly inert, unresponsive, apart. The horror of the distance
between them was almost too much for her—it was so infinite a gap
she must look across.

G *

At last it was finished. They covered him with a sheet and left him lying, with his face bound. And she fastened the door of the little parlour, lest the children should see what was lying there. Then, with peace sunk heavy on her heart, she went about making tidy the kitchen. She knew she submitted to life, which was her immediate master. But from death, her ultimate master, she winced with fear and shame.

THERE was a woman who was beautiful, who started with all the advantages, yet she had no luck. She married for love, and the love turned to dust. She had bonny children, yet she felt they had been thrust upon her, and she could not love them. They looked at her coldly, as if they were finding fault with her. And hurriedly she felt she must cover up some fault in herself. Yet what it was that she must cover up she never knew. Nevertheless, when her children were present, she always felt the centre of her heart go hard. This troubled her, and in her manner she was all the more gentle and anxious for her children, as if she loved them very much. Only she herself knew that at the centre of her heart was a hard little place that could not feel love, no, not for anybody. Everybody else said of her : " She is such a good mother. She adores her children." Only she herself, and her children themselves, knew it was not so. They read it in each other's eyes.

There were a boy and two little girls. They lived in a pleasant house, with a garden, and they had discreet servants, and felt themselves superior to anyone in the neighbourhood.

Although they lived in style, they felt always an anxiety in the house. There was never enough money. The mother had a small income, and the father had a small income, but not nearly enough for the social position which they had to keep up. The father went in to town to some office. But though he had good prospects, these prospects never materialized. There was always the grinding sense of the shortage of money, though the style was always kept up.

At last the mother said, " I will see if *I* can't make something." But she did not know where to begin. She racked her brains, and tried this thing and the other, but could not find anything successful. The failure made deep lines come into her face. Her children were growing up, they would have to go to school. There must be more money, there must be more money. The father, who was always very handsome and expensive in his tastes, seemed as if he never *would* be able to do anything worth doing. And the mother, who had a great belief in herself, did not succeed any better, and her tastes were just as expensive.

And so the house came to be haunted by the unspoken phrase : *There must be more money ! There must be more money !* The children could hear it all the time, though nobody said it aloud. They heard it at Christmas, when the expensive and splendid toys filled the nursery. Behind the shining modern rocking-horse, behind the smart doll's-house, a voice would start whispering : "There *must* be more money ! There *must* be more money !" And the children would stop playing, to listen for a moment. They would look into each other's eyes, to see if they had all heard. And each one saw in the eyes of the other two that they too had heard. "There *must* be more money ! There *must* be more money !"

It came whispering from the springs of the still-swaying rocking-horse, and even the horse, bending his wooden, champing head, heard it. The big doll, sitting so pink and smirking in her new pram, could hear it quite plainly, and seemed to be smirking all the more self-consciously because of it. The foolish puppy, too, that took the place of the teddy-bear, he was looking so extraordinarily foolish for no other reason but that he heard the secret whisper all over the house : "There *must* be more money !"

Yet nobody ever said it aloud. The whisper was everywhere, and therefore no one spoke it. Just as no one ever says : "We are breathing !" in spite of the fact that breath is coming and going all the time.

"Mother," said the boy Paul one day, "why don't we keep a car of our own ? Why do we always use uncle's, or else a taxi ?"

"Because we're the poor members of the family," said the mother.

"But why *are* we, mother ?"

"Well—I suppose," she said slowly and bitterly, "it's because your father has no luck."

The boy was silent for some time.

"Is luck money, mother ?" he asked, rather timidly.

"No, Paul. Not quite. It's what causes you to have money."

"Oh !" said Paul vaguely. "I thought when Uncle Oscar said *filthy lucker*, it meant money."

"*Filthy lucre* does mean money," said the mother. "But it's lucre, not luck."

"Oh !" said the boy. "Then what *is* luck, mother ?"

"It's what causes you to have money. If you're lucky you have money. That's why it's better to be born lucky than rich. If you're rich, you may lose your money. But if you're lucky, you will always get more money."

" Oh ! Will you ? And is father not lucky ? "

" Very unlucky, I should say," she said bitterly.

The boy watched her with unsure eyes.

" Why ? " he asked.

" I don't know. Nobody ever knows why one person is lucky and another unlucky."

" Don't they ? Nobody at all ? Does *nobody* know ? "

" Perhaps God. But He never tells."

" He ought to, then. And aren't you lucky either, mother ? "

" I can't be, if I married an unlucky husband."

" But by yourself, aren't you ? "

" I used to think I was, before I married. Now I think I am very unlucky indeed."

" Why ? "

" Well—never mind ! Perhaps I'm not really," she said.

The child looked at her, to see if she meant it. But he saw, by the lines of her mouth, that she was only trying to hide something from him.

" Well, anyhow," he said stoutly, " I'm a lucky person."

" Why ? " said his mother, with a sudden laugh.

He stared at her. He didn't even know why he had said it.

" God told me," he asserted, brazening it out.

" I hope He did, dear ! " she said, again with a laugh, but rather bitter.

" He did, mother ! "

" Excellent ! " said the mother, using one of her husband's exclamations.

The boy saw she did not believe him ; or rather, that she paid no attention to his assertion. This angered him somewhere, and made him want to compel her attention.

He went off by himself, vaguely, in a childish way, seeking for the clue to " luck." Absorbed, taking no heed of other people, he went about with a sort of stealth, seeking inwardly for luck. He wanted luck, he wanted it, he wanted it. When the two girls were playing dolls in the nursery, he would sit on his big rocking-horse, charging madly into space, with a frenzy that made the little girls peer at him uneasily. Wildly the horse careered, the waving dark hair of the boy tossed, his eyes had a strange glare in them. The little girls dared not speak to him.

When he had ridden to the end of his mad little journey, he

2 H *

climbed down and stood in front of his rocking-horse, staring fixedly
into its lowered face. Its red mouth was slightly open, its big eye
was wide and glassy-bright.

"Now!" he would silently command the snorting steed. "Now,
take me to where there is luck! Now take me!"

And he would slash the horse on the neck with the little whip he
asked Uncle Oscar for. He *knew* the horse could take him to
where there was luck, if only he forced it. So he would mount
again, and start on his furious ride, hoping at last to get there. He
knew he could get there.

"You'll break your horse, Paul!" said the nurse.

"He's always riding like that! I wish he'd leave off!" said his
elder sister Joan.

But he only glared down on them in silence. Nurse gave him up.
She could make nothing of him. Anyhow he was growing beyond
her.

One day his mother and his Uncle Oscar came in when he was on
one of his furious rides. He did not speak to them.

"Hallo, you young jockey! Riding a winner?" said his uncle.

"Aren't you growing too big for a rocking-horse? You're not a
very little boy any longer, you know," said his mother.

But Paul only gave a blue glare from his big, rather close-set eyes.
He would speak to nobody when he was in full tilt. His mother
watched him with an anxious expression on her face.

At last he suddenly stopped forcing his horse into the mechanical
gallop, and slid down.

"Well, I got there!" he announced fiercely, his blue eyes still
flaring, and his sturdy long legs straddling apart.

"Where did you get to?" asked his mother.

"Where I wanted to go," he flared back at her.

"That's right, son!" said Uncle Oscar. "Don't you stop till
you get there. What's the horse's name?"

"He doesn't have a name," said the boy.

"Gets on without all right?" asked the uncle.

"Well, he has different names. He was called Sansovino last
week."

"Sansovino, eh? Won the Ascot. How did you know his
name?"

"He always talks about horse-races with Bassett," said Joan.

The uncle was delighted to find that his small nephew was posted
with all the racing news. Bassett, the young gardener, who had been
wounded in the left foot in the war and had got his present job

through Oscar Cresswell, whose batman he had been, was a perfect blade of the " turf." He lived in the racing events, and the small boy lived with him.

Oscar Cresswell got it all from Bassett.

" Master Paul comes and asks me, so I can't do more than tell him, sir," said Bassett, his face terribly serious, as if he were speaking of religious matters.

" And does he ever put anything on a horse he fancies ? "

" Well—I don't want to give him away—he's a young sport, a fine sport, sir. Would you mind asking him himself ? He sort of takes a pleasure in it, and perhaps he'd feel I was giving him away, sir, if you don't mind."

Bassett was serious as a church.

The uncle went back to his nephew, and took him off for a ride in the car.

" Say, Paul, old man, do you ever put anything on a horse ? " the uncle asked.

The boy watched the handsome man closely.

" Why, do you think I oughtn't to ? " he parried.

" Not a bit of it ! I thought perhaps you might give me a tip for the Lincoln."

The car sped on into the country, going down to Uncle Oscar's place in Hampshire.

" Honour bright ? " said the nephew.

" Honour bright, son ! " said the uncle.

" Well, then, Daffodil."

" Daffodil ! I doubt it, sonny. What about Mirza ? "

" I only know the winner," said the boy. " That's Daffodil."

" Daffodil, eh ? "

There was a pause. Daffodil was an obscure horse comparatively.

" Uncle ! "

" Yes, son ? "

" You won't let it go any further, will you ? I promised Bassett."

" Bassett be damned, old man ! What's he got to do with it ? "

" We're partners. We've been partners from the first. Uncle, he lent me my first five shillings, which I lost. I promised him, honour bright, it was only between me and him ; only you gave me that ten-shilling note I started winning with, so I thought you were lucky. You won't let it go any further, will you ? "

The boy gazed at his uncle from those big, hot, blue eyes, set rather close together. The uncle stirred and laughed uneasily.

"Right you are, son ! I'll keep your tip private. Daffodil, eh ? How much are you putting on him ? "

"All except twenty pounds," said the boy. "I keep that in reserve."

The uncle thought it a good joke.

"You keep twenty pounds in reserve, do you, you young romancer ? What are you betting, then ? "

"I'm betting three hundred," said the boy gravely. "But it's between you and me, Uncle Oscar ! Honour bright ? "

The uncle burst into a roar of laughter.

"It's between you and me all right, you young Nat Gould," he said, laughing. "But where's your three hundred ? "

"Bassett keeps it for me. We're partners."

"You are, are you ! And what is Bassett putting on Daffodil ? "

"He won't go quite as high as I do, I expect. Perhaps he'll go a hundred and fifty."

"What, pennies ? " laughed the uncle.

"Pounds," said the child, with a surprised look at his uncle. "Bassett keeps a bigger reserve than I do."

Between wonder and amusement Uncle Oscar was silent. He pursued the matter no further, but he determined to take his nephew with him to the Lincoln races.

"Now, son," he said, "I'm putting twenty on Mirza, and I'll put five for you on any horse you fancy. What's your pick ? "

"Daffodil, uncle."

"No, not the fiver on Daffodil ! "

"I should if it was my own fiver," said the child.

"Good ! Good ! Right you are ! A fiver for me and a fiver for you on Daffodil."

The child had never been to a race-meeting before, and his eyes were blue fire. He pursed his mouth tight, and watched. A Frenchman just in front had put his money on Lancelot. Wild with excitement, he flayed his arms up and down, yelling "*Lancelot ! Lancelot !* " in his French accent.

Daffodil came in first, Lancelot second, Mirza third. The child, flushed and with eyes blazing, was curiously serene. His uncle brought him four five-pound notes, four to one.

"What am I to do with these ? " he cried, waving them before the boy's eyes.

"I suppose we'll talk to Bassett," said the boy. "I expect I have fifteen hundred now ; and twenty in reserve ; and this twenty."

His uncle studied him for some moments.

" Look here, son ! " he said. " You're not serious about Bassett and that fifteen hundred, are you ? "

" Yes, I am. But it's between you and me, uncle. Honour bright ! "

" Honour bright all right, son ! But I must talk to Bassett."

" If you'd like to be a partner, uncle, with Bassett and me, we could all be partners. Only, you'd have to promise, honour bright, uncle, not to let it go beyond us three. Bassett and I are lucky, and you must be lucky, because it was your ten shillings I started winning with. . . ."

Uncle Oscar took both Bassett and Paul into Richmond Park for an afternoon, and there they talked.

" It's like this, you see, sir," Bassett said. " Master Paul would get me talking about racing events, spinning yarns, you know, sir. And he was always keen on knowing if I'd made or if I'd lost. It's about a year since, now, that I put five shillings on Blush of Dawn for him : and we lost. Then the luck turned, with that ten shillings he had from you : that we put on Singhalese. And since that time, it's been pretty steady, all things considering. What do you say, Master Paul ? "

" We're all right when we're sure," said Paul. " It's when we're not quite sure that we go down."

" Oh, but we're careful then," said Bassett.

" But when are you *sure* ? " smiled Uncle Oscar.

" It's Master Paul, sir," said Basset, in a secret, religious voice. " It's as if he had it from heaven. Like Daffodil, now, for the Lincoln. That was as sure as eggs."

" Did you put anything on Daffodil ? " asked Oscar Cresswell.

" Yes, sir. I made my bit."

" And my nephew ? "

Bassett was obstinately silent, looking at Paul.

" I made twelve hundred, didn't I, Bassett ? I told uncle I was putting three hundred on Daffodil."

" That's right," said Bassett, nodding.

" But where's the money ? " asked the uncle.

" I keep it safe locked up, sir. Master Paul he can have it any minute he likes to ask for it."

" What, fifteen hundred pounds ? "

" And twenty ! And *forty*, that is, with the twenty he made on the course.

" It's amazing ! " said the uncle.

"If Master Paul offers you to be partners, sir, I would, if I were you : if you'll excuse me," said Bassett.

Oscar Cresswell thought about it.

"I'll see the money," he said.

They drove home again, and, sure enough, Bassett came round to the garden-house with fifteen hundred pounds in notes. The twenty pounds reserve was left with Joe Glee, in the Turf Commission deposit.

"You see, it's all right, uncle, when I'm *sure !* Then we go strong, for all we're worth. Don't we, Bassett ? "

"We do that, Master Paul."

"And when are you sure ? " said the uncle, laughing.

"Oh, well, sometimes I'm *absolutely* sure, like about Daffodil," said the boy ; "and sometimes I have an idea ; and sometimes I haven't even an idea, have I, Bassett ? Then we're careful, because we mostly go down."

"You do, do you ! And when you're sure, like about Daffodil, what makes you sure, sonny ? "

"Oh, well, I don't know," said the boy uneasily. "I'm sure, you know, uncle ; that's all."

"It's as if he had it from heaven, sir," Bassett reiterated.

"I should say so ! " said the uncle.

But he became a partner. And when the Leger was coming on Paul was "sure" about Lively Spark, which was a quite inconsiderable horse. The boy insisted on putting a thousand on the horse, Bassett went for five hundred, and Oscar Cresswell two hundred. Lively Spark came in first, and the betting had been ten to one against him. Paul had made ten thousand.

"You see," he said, "I was absolutely sure of him."

Even Oscar Cresswell had cleared two thousand.

"Look here, son," he said, "this sort of thing makes me nervous."

"It needn't, uncle ! Perhaps I shan't be sure again for a long time."

"But what are you going to do with your money ? " asked the uncle.

"Of course," said the boy, "I started it for mother. She said she had no luck, because father is unlucky, so I thought if *I* was lucky, it might stop whispering."

"What might stop whispering ? "

"Our house. I *hate* our house for whispering."

"What does it whisper ? "

"Why—why "—the boy fidgeted—"why, I don't know. But it's always short of money, you know, uncle. "

" I know it, son, I know it."

" You know people send mother writs, don't you, uncle ? "

" I'm afraid I do," said the uncle.

" And then the house whispers, like people laughing at you behind your back. It's awful, that is ! I thought if I was lucky——"

" You might stop it," added the uncle.

The boy watched him with big blue eyes, that had an uncanny cold fire in them, and he said never a word.

" Well, then ! " said the uncle. " What are we doing ? "

" I shouldn't like mother to know I was lucky," said the boy.

" Why not, son ? "

" She'd stop me."

" I don't think she would."

" Oh ! "—and the boy writhed in an odd way—" I *don't* want her to know, uncle."

" All right, son ! We'll manage it without her knowing."

They managed it very easily. Paul, at the other's suggestion, handed over five thousand pounds to his uncle, who deposited it with the family lawyer, who was then to inform Paul's mother that a relative had put five thousand pounds into his hands, which sum was to be paid out a thousand pounds at a time, on the mother's birthday, for the next five years.

" So she'll have a birthday present of a thousand pounds for five successive years," said Uncle Oscar. " I hope it won't make it all the harder for her later."

Paul's mother had her birthday in November. The house had been " whispering " worse than ever lately, and, even in spite of his luck, Paul could not bear up against it. He was very anxious to see the effect of the birthday letter, telling his mother about the thousand pounds.

When there were no visitors, Paul now took his meals with his parents, as he was beyond the nursery control. His mother went into town nearly every day. She had discovered that she had an odd knack of sketching furs and dress materials, so she worked secretly in the studio of a friend who was the chief " artist " for the leading drapers. She drew the figures of ladies in furs and ladies in silk and sequins for the newspaper advertisements. This young woman artist earned several thousand pounds a year, but Paul's mother only made several hundreds, and she was again dissatisfied. She so wanted to be first in something, and she did not succeed, even in making sketches for drapery advertisements.

She was down to breakfast on the morning of her birthday. Paul watched her face as she read her letters. He knew the lawyer's letter. As his mother read it, her face hardened and became more expressionless. Then a cold, determined look came on her mouth. She hid the letter under the pile of others, and said not a word about it.

"Didn't you have anything nice in the post for your birthday, mother?" said Paul.

"Quite moderately nice," she said, her voice cold and absent.

She went away to town without saying more.

But in the afternoon Uncle Oscar appeared. He said Paul's mother had had a long interview with the lawyer, asking if the whole five thousand could not be advanced at once, as she was in debt.

"What do you think, uncle?" said the boy.

"I leave it to you, son."

"Oh, let her have it, then! We can get some more with the other," said the boy.

"A bird in the hand is worth two in the bush, laddie!" said Uncle Oscar.

"But I'm sure to *know* for the Grand National; or the Lincoln-shire; or else the Derby. I'm sure to know for *one* of them," said Paul.

So Uncle Oscar signed the agreement, and Paul's mother touched the whole five thousand. Then something very curious happened. The voices in the house suddenly went mad, like a chorus of frogs on a spring evening. There were certain new furnishings, and Paul had a tutor. He was *really* going to Eton, his father's school, in the following autumn. There were flowers in the winter, and a blossoming of the luxury Paul's mother had been used to. And yet the voices in the house, behind the sprays of mimosa and almond-blossom, and from under the piles of iridescent cushions, simply trilled and screamed in a sort of ecstasy: "There *must* be more money! Oh-h-h; there *must* be more money. Oh, now, now-w! Now-w-w —there *must* be more money!—more than ever! More than ever!"

It frightened Paul terribly. He studied away at his Latin and Greek with his tutors. But his intense hours were spent with Bassett. The Grand National had gone by: he had not "known," and had lost a hundred pounds. Summer was at hand. He was in agony for the Lincoln. But even for the Lincoln he didn't "know," and he lost fifty pounds. He became wild-eyed and strange, as if something were going to explode in him.

"Let it alone, son! Don't you bother about it!" urged Uncle Oscar. But it was as if the boy couldn't really hear what his uncle was saying.

"I've got to know for the Derby! I've got to know for the Derby!" the child reiterated, his big blue eyes blazing with a sort of madness.

His mother noticed how overwrought he was.

"You'd better go to the seaside. . Wouldn't you like to go now to the seaside, instead of waiting? I think you'd better," she said, looking down at him anxiously, her heart curiously heavy because of him.

But the child lifted his uncanny blue eyes.

"I couldn't possibly go before the Derby, mother!" he said. "I couldn't possibly!"

"Why not?" she said, her voice becoming heavy when she was opposed. "Why not? You can still go from the seaside to see the Derby with your Uncle Oscar, if that's what you wish. No need for you to wait here. Besides, I think you care too much about these races. It's a bad sign. My family has been a gambling family, and you won't know till you grow up how much damage it has done. But it has done damage. I shall have to send Bassett away, and ask Uncle Oscar not to talk racing to you, unless you promise to be reasonable about it ; go away to the seaside and forget it. You're all nerves!"

"I'll do what you like, mother, so long as you don't send me away till after the Derby," the boy said.

"Send you away from where? Just from this house?"

"Yes," he said, gazing at her.

"Why, you curious child, what makes you care about this house so much, suddenly? I never knew you loved it."

He gazed at her without speaking. He had a secret within a secret, something he had not divulged, even to Bassett or to his Uncle Oscar.

But his mother, after standing undecided and a little bit sullen for some moments, said :

"Very well, then! Don't go to the seaside till after the Derby, if you don't wish it. But promise me you won't let your nerves go to pieces. Promise you won't think so much about horse-racing and *events*, as you call them!"

"Oh, no," said the boy casually. "I won't think much about them, mother. You needn't worry. I wouldn't worry, mother, if I were you."

"If you were me and I were you," said his mother, "I wonder what we *should* do ! "

"But you know you needn't worry, mother, don't you ? " the boy repeated.

"I should be awfully glad to know it," she said wearily.

"Oh, well, you *can*, you know. I mean, you *ought* to know you needn't worry," he insisted.

"Ought I ? Then I'll see about it," she said.

Paul's secret of secrets was his wooden horse, that which had no name. Since he was emancipated from a nurse and a nursery-governess, he had had his rocking-horse removed to his own bed-room at the top of the house.

"Surely, you're too big for a rocking-horse ! " his mother had remonstrated.

"Well, you see, mother, till I can have a *real* horse, I like to have *some* sort of animal about," had been his quaint answer.

"Do you feel he keeps you company ? " she laughed.

"Oh, yes ! He's very good, he always keeps company, when I'm there," said Paul.

So the horse, rather shabby, stood in an arrested prance in the boy's bedroom.

The Derby was drawing near, and the boy grew more and more tense. He hardly heard what was spoken to him, he was very frail, and his eyes were really uncanny. His mother had sudden strange seizures of uneasiness about him. Sometimes, for half an hour, she would feel a sudden anxiety about him that was almost anguish. She wanted to rush to him at once, and know he was safe.

Two nights before the Derby, she was at a big party in town, when one of her rushes of anxiety about her boy, her first-born, gripped her heart till she could hardly speak. She fought with the feeling, might and main, for she believed in common sense. But it was too strong. She had to leave the dance and go downstairs to telephone to the country. The children's nursery-governess was terribly surprised and startled at being rung up in the night.

"Are the children all right, Miss Wilmot ? "

"Oh, yes, they are quite all right."

"Master Paul ? Is he all right ? "

"He went to bed as right as a trivet. Shall I run up and look at him ? "

"No," said Paul's mother reluctantly. "No ! Don't trouble. It's all right. Don't sit up. We shall be home fairly soon." She did not want her son's privacy intruded upon.

"Very good," said the governess.

It was about one o'clock when Paul's mother and father drove up to their house. All was still. Paul's mother went to her room and slipped off her white fur cloak. She had told her maid not to wait up for her. She heard her husband downstairs, mixing a whisky and soda.

And then, because of the strange anxiety at her heart, she stole upstairs to her son's room. Noiselessly she went along the upper corridor. Was there a faint noise? What was it?

She stood, with arrested muscles, outside his door, listening. There was a strange, heavy, and yet not loud noise. Her heart stood still. It was a soundless noise, yet rushing and powerful. Something huge, in violent, hushed motion. What was it? What in God's name was it? She ought to know. She felt that she knew the noise. She knew what it was.

Yet she could not place it. She couldn't say what it was. And on and on it went, like a madness.

Softly, frozen with anxiety and fear, she turned the door-handle.

The room was dark. Yet in the space near the window, she heard and saw something plunging to and fro. She gazed in fear and amazement.

Then suddenly she switched on the light, and saw her son, in his green pyjamas, madly surging on the rocking-horse. The blaze of light suddenly lit him up, as he urged the wooden horse, and lit her up, as she stood, blonde, in her dress of pale green and crystal, in the doorway.

"Paul!" she cried. "Whatever are you doing?"

"It's Malabar!" he screamed, in a powerful, strange voice. "It's Malabar!"

His eyes blazed at her for one strange and senseless second, as he ceased urging his wooden horse. Then he fell with a crash to the ground, and she, all her tormented motherhood flooding upon her, rushed to gather him up.

But he was unconscious, and unconscious he remained, with some brain-fever. He talked and tossed, and his mother sat stonily by his side.

"Malabar! It's Malabar! Bassett, Bassett, I *know*! It's Malabar!"

So the child cried, trying to get up and urge the rocking-horse that gave him his inspiration.

"What does he mean by Malabar?" asked the heart-frozen mother.

" I don't know," said the father stonily.

" What does he mean by Malabar ? " she asked her brother Oscar.

" It's one of the horses running for the Derby," was the answer.

And, in spite of himself, Oscar Cresswell spoke to Bassett, and himself put a thousand on Malabar : at fourteen to one.

The third day of the illness was critical : they were waiting for a change. The boy, with his rather long, curly hair, was tossing ceaselessly on the pillow. He neither slept nor regained consciousness, and his eyes were like blue stones. His mother sat, feeling her heart had gone, turned actually into a stone.

In the evening, Oscar Cresswell did not come, but Bassett sent a message, saying could he come up for one moment, just one moment ? Paul's mother was very angry at the intrusion, but on second thoughts she agreed. The boy was the same. Perhaps Bassett might bring him to consciousness.

The gardener, a shortish fellow with a little brown moustache, and sharp little brown eyes, tiptoed into the room, touched his imaginary cap to Paul's mother, and stole to the bedside, staring with glittering, smallish eyes at the tossing, dying child.

" Master Paul ! " he whispered. " Master Paul ! Malabar came in first all right, a clean win. I did as you told me. You've made over seventy thousand pounds, you have ; you've got over eighty thousand. Malabar came in all right, Master Paul."

" Malabar ! Malabar ! Did I say Malabar, mother ? Did I say Malabar ? Do you think I'm lucky, mother ? I knew Malabar, didn't I ? Over eighty thousand pounds ! I call that lucky, don't you, mother ? Over eighty thousand pounds ! I knew, didn't I know I knew ? Malabar came in all right. If I ride my horse till I'm sure, then I tell you, Bassett, you can go as high as you like. Did you go for all you were worth, Bassett ? "

" I went a thousand on it, Master Paul."

" I never told you, mother, that if I can ride my horse, and *get there*, then I'm absolutely sure—oh, absolutely ! Mother, did I ever tell you ? I *am* lucky ! "

" No, you never did," said the mother.

But the boy died in the night.

And even as he lay dead, his mother heard her brother's voice saying to her : " My God, Hester, you're eighty-odd thousand to the good, and a poor devil of a son to the bad. But, poor devil, poor devil, he's best gone out of a life where he rides his rocking-horse to find a winner."

THE fashion in women changes nowadays even faster than women's fashions. At twenty, Lina M'Leod was almost painfully modern. At sixty, almost obsolete !

She started off in life to be really independent. In that remote day, forty years ago, when a woman said she was going to be independent, it meant she was having no nonsense with men. She was kicking over the masculine traces, and living her own life, manless.

To-day, when a girl says she is going to be independent, it means she is going to devote her attentions almost exclusively to men ; though not necessarily to " a man."

Miss M'Leod had an income from her mother. Therefore, at the age of twenty, she had turned her back on that image of tyranny, her father, and went to Paris to study art. Art having been studied, she turned her attention to the globe of earth. Being terribly independent, she soon made Africa look small : she dallied energetically with vast hinterlands of China : and she knew the Rocky Mountains and the deserts of Arizona, as if she had been married to them. All this, to escape mere man.

It was in New Mexico she purchased the blue moccasins, blue bead moccasins, from an Indian who was her guide and her subordinate. In her independence she made use of men, of course, but merely as servants, subordinates.

When the war broke out she came home. She was then forty-five, and already going grey. Her brother, two years older than herself, but a bachelor, went off to the war ; she stayed at home in the small family mansion in the country, and did what she could. She was small and erect and brief in her speech, her face was like pale ivory, her skin like a very delicate parchment, and her eyes were very blue. There was no nonsense about her, though she did paint pictures. She never even touched her delicately parchment face with pigment. She was good enough as she was, honest-to-God, and the country town had a tremendous respect for her.

In her various activities she came pretty often into contact with

Percy Barlow, the clerk at the bank. He was only twenty-two when she first set eyes on him, in 1914, and she immediately liked him. He was a stranger in the town, his father being a poor country vicar in Yorkshire. But he was of the confiding sort. He soon confided in Miss M'Leod, for whom he had a towering respect, how he disliked his stepmother, how he feared his father was but as wax in the hands of that downright woman, and how, in consequence, he was homeless. Wrath shone in his pleasant features, but somehow it was an amusing wrath ; at least to Miss M'Leod.

He was distinctly a good-looking boy, with stiff dark hair and odd, twinkling grey eyes under thick dark brows, and a rather full mouth and a queer, deep voice that had a caressing touch of hoarseness. It was his voice that somehow got behind Miss M'Leod's reserve. Not that he had the faintest intention of so doing. He looked up to her immensely : " she's miles above me."

When she watched him playing tennis, letting himself go a bit too much, hitting too hard, running too fast, being too nice to his partner, her heart yearned over him. The orphan in him ! Why should he go and be shot ? She kept him at home as long as possible, working with her at all kinds of war-work. He was so absolutely willing to do everything she wanted : devoted to her.

But at last the time came when he must go. He was now twenty-four, and she forty-seven. He came to say good-bye, in his awkward fashion. She suddenly turned away, leaned her forehead against the wall, and burst into bitter tears. He was frightened out of his wits. Before he knew what was happening he had his arm in front of his face and was sobbing too.

She came to comfort him. " Don't cry, dear, don't ! It will all be all right."

At last he wiped his face on his sleeve and looked at her sheepishly. " It was you crying as did me in," he said. Her blue eyes were brilliant with tears. She suddenly kissed him.

" You are such a dear ! " she said wistfully. Then she added, flushing suddenly vivid pink under her transparent parchment skin : " It wouldn't be right for you to marry an old thing like me, would it ? "

He looked at her dumbfounded.

" No, I'm too old," she added hastily.

" Don't talk about old ! You're not old ! " he said hotly.

" At least I'm too old for *that*," she said sadly.

" Not as far as I'm concerned," he said. " You're younger than me, in most ways, I'm hanged if you're not ! "

"Are you hanged if I'm not?" she teased wistfully.

"I am," he said. "And if I thought you wanted me, I'd be jolly proud if you married me. I would, I assure you."

"Would you?" she said, still teasing him.

Nevertheless, the next time he was home on leave she married him, very quietly, but very definitely. He was a young lieutenant. They stayed in her family home, Twybit Hall, for the honeymoon. It was her house now, her brother being dead. And they had a strangely happy month. She had made a strange discovery: a man.

He went off to Gallipoli, and became a captain. He came home in 1919, still green with malaria, but otherwise sound. She was in her fiftieth year. And she was almost white-haired; long, thick, white hair, done perfectly, and perfectly creamy, colourless face, with very blue eyes.

He had been true to her, not being very forward with women. But he was a bit startled by her white hair. However, he shut his eyes to it, and loved her. And she, though frightened and somewhat bewildered, was happy. But she was bewildered. It always seemed awkward to her, that he should come wandering into her room in his pyjamas when she was half dressed, and brushing her hair. And he would sit there silent, watching her brush the long swinging river of silver, of her white hair, the bare, ivory-white slender arm working with a strange mechanical motion, sharp and forcible, brushing down the long silvery stream of hair. He would sit as if mesmerized, just gazing. And she would at last glance round sharply, and he would rise, saying some little casual thing to her and smiling to her oddly with his eyes. Then he would go out, his thin cotton pyjamas hitching up over his hips, for he was a rather big-built fellow. And she would feel dazed, as if she did not quite know her own self any more. And the queer, ducking motion of his silently going out of her door impressed her ominously, his curious cat head, his big hips and limbs.

They were alone in the house, save for the servants. He had no work. They lived modestly, for a good deal of her money had been lost during the war. But she still painted pictures. Marriage had only stimulated her to this. She painted canvases of flowers, beautiful flowers that thrilled her soul. And he would sit, pipe in fist, silent, and watch her. He had nothing to do. He just sat and watched her small, neat figure and her concentrated movements, as she painted. Then he knocked out his pipe, and filled it again.

She said that at last she was perfectly happy. And he said that he was perfectly happy. They were always together. He hardly went out, save riding in the lanes. And practically nobody came to the house.

But still, they were very silent with one another. The old chatter had died out. And he did not read much. He just sat still, and smoked, and was silent. It got on her nerves sometimes, and she would think as she had thought in the past, that the highest bliss a human being can experience is perhaps the bliss of being quite alone, quite, quite alone.

His bank firm offered to make him manager of the local branch, and, at her advice, he accepted. Now he went out of the house every morning and came home every evening, which was much more agreeable. The rector begged him to sing again in the church choir : and again she advised him to accept. These were the old grooves in which his bachelor life had run. He felt more like himself.

He was popular : a nice, harmless fellow, everyone said of him. Some of the men secretly pitied him. They made rather much of him, took him home to luncheon, and let him loose with their daughters. He was popular among the daughters too : naturally, for if a girl expressed a wish, he would instinctively say : " What ! Would you like it ? I'll get it for you." And if he were not in a position to satisfy the desire, he would say : " I only wish I could do it for you. I'd do it like a shot." All of which he meant.

At the same time, though he got on so well with the maidens of the town, there was no coming forward about him. He was, in some way, not wakened up. Good-looking, and big, and service-able, he was inwardly remote, without self-confidence, almost without a self at all.

The rector's daughter took upon herself to wake him up. She was exactly as old as he was, a smallish, rather sharp-faced young woman who had lost her husband in the war, and it had been a grief to her. But she took the stoic attitude of the young : " You've got to live, so you may as well do it ! " She was a kindly soul, in spite of her sharpness. And she had a very perky little red-brown pomeranian dog that she had bought in Florence in the street, but which had turned out a handsome little fellow. Miss M'Leod looked down a bit on Alice Howells and her pom, so Mrs. Howells felt no special love for Miss M'Leod—" Mrs. Barlow, that is ! " she would add sharply. " For it's quite impossible to think of her as anything but Miss M'Leod ! "

Percy was really more at ease at the rectory, where the pom

yapped and Mrs. Howells changed her dress three or four times a day and looked it, than in the semi-cloisteral atmosphere of Twybit Hall, where Miss M'Leod wore tweeds and a natural knitted jumper, her skirts rather long, her hair done up pure silver, and painted her wonderful flower pictures in the deepening silence of the daytime. At evening she would go up to change, after he came home. And though it thrilled her to have a man coming into her room as he dressed, snapping his collar-stud, to tell her something trivial as she stood bare-armed in her silk slip, rapidly coiling up the rope of silver hair behind her head, still, it worried her. When he was there, he couldn't keep away from her. And he would watch her, watch her, watch her as if she was the ultimate revelation. Sometimes it made her irritable. She was so absolutely used to her own privacy. What was he looking at ? She never watched *him*. Rather she looked the other way. His watching tried her nerves. She was turned fifty. And his great silent body loomed almost dreadful.

He was quite happy playing tennis or croquet with Alice Howells and the rest. Alice was choir-mistress, a bossy little person outwardly, inwardly rather forlorn and affectionate, and not very sure that life hadn't let her down for good. She was now over thirty —and had no one but the pom and her father and the parish— nothing in her really intimate life. But she was very cheerful, busy, even gay, with her choir and school work, her dancing, and flirting, and dressmaking.

She was intrigued by Percy Barlow. " How *can* a man be so nice to *everybody ?* " she asked him, a little exasperated. " Well, why not ? " he replied, with the odd smile of his eyes. " It's not why he shouldn't, but how he manages to do it ! How can you have so much good-nature ? I *have* to be catty to some people, but you're nice to *everybody*."

" Oh, am I ! " he said ominously.

He was like a man in a dream, or in a cloud. He was quite a good bank-manager, in fact very intelligent. Even in appearance, his great charm was his beautifully-shaped head. He had plenty of brains, really. But in his will, in his body, he was asleep. And sometimes this lethargy, or coma, made him look haggard. And sometimes it made his body seem inert and despicable, meaningless.

Alice Howells longed to ask him about his wife. " *Do* you love her ? *Can* you really care for her ? " But she daren't. She daren't ask him one word about his wife. Another thing she couldn't do, she couldn't persuade him to dance. Never, not once. But in everything else he was pliable as wax.

Mrs. Barlow—Miss M'Leod—stayed out at Twybit all the time. She did not even come in to church on Sunday. She had shaken off church, among other things. And she watched Percy depart, and felt just a little humiliated. He was going to sing in the choir ! Yes, marriage was also a humiliation to her. She had distinctly married beneath her.

The years had gone by : she was now fifty-seven, Percy was thirty-four. He was still, in many ways, a boy. But in his curious silence, he was ageless. She managed him with perfect ease. If she expressed a wish, he acquiesced at once. So now it was agreed he should not come to her room any more. And he never did. But sometimes she went to him in his room, and was winsome in a pathetic, heart-breaking way.

She twisted him round her little finger, as the saying goes. And yet secretly she was afraid of him. In the early years he had displayed a clumsy but violent sort of passion, from which she had shrunk away. She felt it had nothing to do with her. It was just his indiscriminating desire for Woman, and for his own satisfaction. Whereas she was not just unidentified Woman, to give him his general satisfaction. So she had recoiled, and withdrawn herself. She had put him off. She had regained the absolute privacy of her room.

He was perfectly sweet about it. Yet she was uneasy with him now. She was afraid of him ; or rather, not of him, but of a mysterious something in him. She was not a bit afraid of *him*, oh no ! And when she went to him now, to be nice to him, in her pathetic winsomeness of an unused woman of fifty-seven, she found him sweet-natured as ever, but really indifferent. He saw her pathos and her winsomeness. In some way, the mystery of her, her thick white hair, her vivid blue eyes, her ladylike refinement still fascinated him. But his bodily desire for her had gone, utterly gone. And secretly, she was rather glad. But as he looked at her, looked at her, as he lay there so silent, she was afraid, as if some finger were pointed at her. Yet she knew, the moment she spoke to him, he would twist his eyes to that good-natured and " kindly " smile of his.

It was in the late, dark months of this year that she missed the blue moccasins. She had hung them on a nail in his room. Not that he ever wore them : they were too small. Nor did she : they were too big. Moccasins are male footwear, among the Indians, not female. But they were of a lovely turquoise-blue colour, made all of little turquoise beads, with little forked flames of dead-white and dark-green. When, at the beginning of their marriage, he had exclaimed over them, she had said : " Yes ! Aren't they a lovely colour ! So blue ! " And he had replied : " Not as blue as your eyes, even then."

So naturally, she had hung them up on the wall in his room, and there they had stayed. Till, one November day, when there were no flowers, and she was pining to paint a still-life with something blue in it—oh, so blue, like delphiniums !—she had gone to his room for the moccasins. And they were not there. And though she hunted, she could not find them. Nor did the maids know anything of them.

So she asked him : " Percy, do you know where those blue moccasins are, which hung in your room ? " There was a moment's dead silence. Then he looked at her with his good-naturedly twinkling eyes, and said : " No, *I* know nothing of them." There was another dead pause. She did not believe him. But being a perfect lady, she only said, as she turned away : " Well then, how curious it is ! " And there was another dead pause. Out of which he asked her what she wanted them for, and she told him. Whereon the matter lapsed.

It was November, and Percy was out in the evening fairly often now. He was rehearsing for a " play " which was to be given in the church schoolroom at Christmas. He had asked her about it. " Do you think it's a bit *infra dig.* if I play one of the characters ? " She had looked at him mildly, disguising her real feeling. " If you don't feel *personally* humiliated," she said, " then there's nothing else to consider." And he had answered : " Oh, it doesn't upset *me* at all." So she mildly said : " Then do it, by all means." Adding at the back of her mind : If it amuses you, child !—but she thought, a change had indeed come over the world, when the master of Twybit Hall, or even, for that matter, the manager of the dignified Stubbs' Bank, should perform in public on a schoolroom stage in amateur theatricals. And she kept calmly aloof, preferring not to know any details. She had a world of her own.

When he had said to Alice Howells : " You don't think other folk'll mind—clients of the bank and so forth—think it beneath my dignity ? " she had cried, looking up into his twinkling eyes : " Oh, you don't have to keep *your* dignity on ice, Percy—any more than I do mine."

The play was to be performed for the first time on Christmas Eve : and after the play, there was the midnight service in church. Percy therefore told his wife not to expect him home till the small hours, at least. So he drove himself off in the car.

As night fell, and rain, Miss M'Leod felt a little forlorn. She was left out of everything. Life was slipping past her. It was Christmas Eve, and she was more alone than she had ever been. Percy only seemed to intensify her aloneness, leaving her in this fashion.

She decided not to be left out. She would go to the play too. It was past six o'clock, and she had worked herself into a highly nervous state. Outside was darkness and rain : inside was silence, forlornness. She went to the telephone and rang up the garage in Shewbury. It was with great difficulty she got them to promise to send a car for her : Mr. Slater would have to fetch her himself in the two-seater runabout : everything else was out.

She dressed nervously, in a dark-green dress with a few modest jewels. Looking at herself in the mirror, she still thought herself slim, young looking and distinguished. She did not see how old-fashioned she was, with her uncompromising erectness, her glistening knob of silver hair sticking out behind, and her long dress.

It was a three-miles drive in the rain, to the small country town. She sat next to old Slater, who was used to driving horses and was nervous and clumsy with a car, without saying a word. He thankfully deposited her at the gate of St. Barnabas' School.

It was almost half-past seven. The schoolroom was packed and buzzing with excitement. " I'm afraid we haven't a seat left, Mrs. Barlow ! " said Jackson, one of the church sidesmen, who was standing guard in the school porch, where people were still fighting to get in. He faced her in consternation. She faced him in consternation. " Well, I shall have to stay somewhere, till Mr. Barlow can drive me home," she said. " Couldn't you put me a chair somewhere ? "

Worried and flustered, he went worrying and flustering the other people in charge. The schoolroom was simply packed solid. But Mr. Simmons, the leading grocer, gave up his chair in the front row to Mrs. Barlow, whilst he sat in a chair right under the stage, where he couldn't see a thing. But he could see Mrs. Barlow seated between his wife and daughter, speaking a word or two to them occasionally, and that was enough.

The lights went down : *The Shoes of Shagput* was about to begin. The amateur curtains were drawn back, disclosing the little amateur stage with a white amateur back-cloth daubed to represent a Moorish courtyard. In stalked Percy, dressed as a Moor, his face darkened. He looked quite handsome, his pale grey eyes queer and startling in his dark face. But he was afraid of the audience—he spoke away from them, stalking around clumsily. After a certain amount of would-be funny dialogue, in tripped the heroine, Alice

Howells, of course. She was an Eastern houri, in white gauze Turkish trousers, silver veil, and—the blue moccasins. The whole stage was white, save for her blue moccasins, Percy's dark-green sash, and a negro boy's red fez.

When Mrs. Barlow saw the blue moccasins, a little bomb of rage exploded in her. This, of all places ! The blue moccasins that she had bought in the western deserts ! The blue moccasins that were not so blue as her own eyes ! *Her* blue moccasins ! On the feet of that creature, Mrs. Howells.

Alice Howells was not afraid of the audience. She looked full at them, lifting her silver veil. And of course she saw Mrs. Barlow, sitting there like the Ancient of Days in judgment, in the front row. And a bomb of rage exploded in *her* breast too.

In the play, Alice was the wife of the grey-bearded old Caliph, but she captured the love of the young Ali, otherwise Percy, and the whole business was the attempt of these two to evade Caliph and negro-eunuchs and ancient crones, and get into each other's arms. The blue shoes were very important : for while the sweet Leila wore them, the gallant Ali was to know there was danger. But when she took them off, he might approach her.

It was all quite childish, and everybody loved it, and Miss M'Leod might have been quite complacent about it all, had not Alice Howells got her monkey up, so to speak. Alice, with a lot of make-up, looked boldly handsome. And suddenly bold she was, bold as the devil. All these years the poor young widow had been " good," slaving in the parish, and only even flirting just to cheer things up, never going very far and knowing she could never get anything out of it, but determined never to mope.

Now the sight of Miss M'Leod sitting there so erect, so coolly " higher plane," and calmly superior, suddenly let loose a devil in Alice Howells. All her limbs went suave and molten, as her young sex, long pent up, flooded even to her finger-tips. Her voice was strange, even to herself, with its long, plaintive notes. She felt all her movements soft and fluid, she felt herself like living liquid. And it was lovely. Underneath it all was the sting of malice against Miss M'Leod, sitting there so erect, with her great knob of white hair.

Alice's business, as the lovely Leila, was to be seductive to the rather heavy Percy. And seductive she was. In two minutes, she had him spell-bound. He saw nothing of the audience. A faint, fascinated grin came on to his face, as he acted up to the young woman in the Turkish trousers. His rather full, hoarse voice changed and became clear, with a new, naked clang in it. When the two sang together, in the simple banal duets of the play, it was with a most fascinating intimacy. And when, at the end of Act One, the lovely Leila kicked off the blue moccasins, saying : " Away, shoes of bondage, shoes of sorrow ! " and danced a little dance all alone, barefoot, in her Turkish trousers, in front of her fascinated hero, his smile was so spell-bound that everybody else was spell-bound too.

Miss M'Leod's indignation knew no bounds. When the blue moccasins were kicked across the stage by the brazen Alice, with the words : " Away, shoes of bondage, shoes of sorrow ! " the elder woman grew pink with fury, and it was all she could do not to rise and snatch the moccasins from the stage, and bear them away. She sat in speechless indignation during the brief curtain between Act One and Act Two. Her moccasins ! Her blue moccasins ! Of the sacred blue colour, the turquoise of heaven.

But there they were, in Act Two, on the feet of the bold Alice. It was becoming too much. And the love-scenes between Percy and the young woman were becoming nakedly shameful. Alice grew worse and worse. She was worked up now, caught in her own spell, and unconscious of everything save of him, and the sting of that other woman, who presumed to own him. Own him ? Ha-ha ! For he was fascinated. The queer smile on his face, the con-centrated gleam of his eyes, the queer way he leaned forward from his loins towards her, the new, reckless, throaty twang in his voice —the audience had before their eyes a man spell-bound and lost in passion.

Miss M'Leod sat in shame and torment, as if her chair was red-hot. She too was fast losing her normal consciousness, in the spell of rage. She was outraged. The second Act was working to its climax. The climax came. The lovely Leila kicked off the blue shoes : " Away, shoes of bondage, away ! " and flew barefoot to the enraptured Ali, flinging herself into his arms. And if ever a man was gone in sheer desire, it was Percy, as he pressed the woman's lithe form against his body, and seemed unconsciously to envelop her, unaware of everything else. While she, blissful in his spell, but still aware of the audience and of the superior Miss M'Leod, let herself be wrapped closer and closer.

Miss M'Leod rose to her feet and looked towards the door. But the way out was packed with people standing holding their breath as the two on the stage remained wrapped in each other's arms, and the three fiddles and the flute softly woke up. Miss M'Leod could not bear it. She was on her feet, and beside herself. She could not get out. She could not sit down again.

"Percy!" she said, in a low clear voice. "Will you hand me my moccasins?"

He lifted his face like a man startled in a dream, lifted his face from the shoulder of his Leila. His gold-grey eyes were like softly-startled flames. He looked in sheer horrified wonder at the little white-haired woman standing below.

"Eh!" he said, purely dazed.

"Will you please hand me my moccasins!"—and she pointed to where they lay on the stage.

Alice had stepped away from him, and was gazing at the risen viper of the little elderly woman on the tip of the audience. Then she watched him move across the stage, bending forward from the loins in his queer mesmerized way, pick up the blue moccasins, and stoop down to hand them over the edge of the stage to his wife, who reached up for them.

"Thank you!" said Miss M'Leod, seating herself, with the blue moccasins in her lap.

Alice recovered her composure, gave a sign to the little orchestra, and began to sing at once, strong and assured, to sing her part in the duet that closed the Act. She knew she could command public opinion in her favour.

He too recovered at once, the little smile came back on his face, he calmly forgot his wife again as he sang his share in the duet. It was finished. The curtains were pulled to. There was immense cheering. The curtains opened, and Alice and Percy bowed to the audience, smiling both of them their peculiar secret smile, while Miss M'Leod sat with the blue moccasins on her lap.

The curtains were closed, it was the long interval. After a few moments of hesitation, Mrs. Barlow rose with dignity, gathered her wrap over her arm, and with the blue moccasins in her hand, moved towards the door. Way was respectfully made for her.

"I should like to speak to Mr. Barlow," she said to Jackson, who had anxiously ushered her in, and now would anxiously usher her out.

"Yes, Mrs. Barlow."

He led her round to the smaller class-room at the back, that acted as dressing-room. The amateur actors were drinking lemonade, and chattering freely. Mrs. Howells came forward, and Jackson whispered the news to her. She turned to Percy.

"Percy, Mrs. Barlow wants to speak to you. Shall I come with you?"

"Speak to me? Aye, come on with me."

The two followed the anxious Jackson into the other half-lighted class-room, where Mrs. Barlow stood in her wrap, holding the moccasins. She was very pale, and she watched the two butter-muslin Turkish figures enter, as if they could not possibly be real. She ignored Mrs. Howells entirely.

" Percy," she said, " I want you to drive me home."

" Drive you home ! " he echoed.

" Yes, please ! "

" Why—when ? " he said, with vague bluntness.

" Now,—if you don't mind——"

" What—in this get-up ? "   He looked at himself.

" I could wait while you changed."

There was a pause. He turned and looked at Alice Howells, and Alice Howells looked at him. The two women saw each other out of the corners of their eyes : but it was beneath notice. He turned to his wife, his black face ludicrously blank, his eyebrows cocked.

" Well, you see," he said, " it's rather awkward. I can hardly hold up the third Act while I've taken you home and got back here again, can I ? "

" So you intend to play in the third Act ? " she asked with cold ferocity.

" Why, I must, mustn't I ? " he said blankly.

" Do you *wish* to ? " she said, in all her intensity.

" I do, naturally. I want to finish the thing up properly," he replied, in the utter innocence of his head ; about his heart he knew nothing.

She turned sharply away.

" Very well ! " she said. And she called to Jackson, who was standing dejectedly by the door : " Mr. Jackson, will you please find some car or conveyance to take me home ? "

" Aye ! I say, Mr. Jackson," called Percy in his strong, demo-cratic voice, going forward to the man. " Ask Tom Lomas if he'll do me a good turn and get my car out of the rectory garage, to drive Mrs. Barlow home. Aye, ask Tom Lomas ! And if not him, ask Mr. Pilkington—Leonard. The key's there. You don't mind, do you ? I'm ever so much obliged——"

The three were left awkwardly alone again.

" I expect you've had enough with two acts," said Percy soothingly to his wife. " These things aren't up to your mark. I know it. They're only child's play. But, you see, they please the people. We've got a packed house, haven't we ? "

His wife had nothing to answer. He looked so ludicrous, with his dark-brown face and butter-muslin bloomers. And his mind

was so ludicrously innocent. His body, however, was not so ridiculously innocent as his mind, as she knew when he turned to the
other woman.

"You and I, we're more on the nonsense level, aren't we?" he
said, with the new, throaty clang of naked intimacy in his voice.
His wife shivered.

"Absolutely on the nonsense level," said Alice, with easy assurance.

She looked into his eyes, then she looked at the blue moccasins
in the hand of the other woman. He gave a little start, as if realizing
something for himself.

At that moment Tom Lomas looked in, saying heartily: "Right
you are, Percy! I'll have my car here in half a tick. I'm more
handy with it than yours."

"Thanks, old man! You're a Christian."

"Try to be—especially when you turn Turk! Well——" He
disappeared.

"I say, Lina," said Percy in his most amiable democratic way,
"would you mind leaving the moccasins for the next act? We
s'll be in a bit of a hole without them."

Miss M'Leod faced him and stared at him with the full blast
of her forget-me-not blue eyes, from her white face.

"Will you pardon me if I don't?" she said.

"What!" he exclaimed. "Why? Why not? It's nothing but
play, to amuse the people. I can't see how it can hurt the *moccasins*.
I understand you don't quite like seeing me make a fool of myself.
But anyhow, I'm a bit of a born fool. What?"—and his blackened
face laughed with a Turkish laugh. "Oh, yes, you have to realize
I rather enjoy playing the fool," he resumed. "And, after all, it
doesn't really hurt *you*, now does it? Shan't you leave us those
moccasins for the last act?"

She looked at him, then at the moccasins in her hand. No, it
was useless to yield to so ludicrous a person. The vulgarity of his
wheedling, the commonness of the whole performance! It was
useless to yield even the moccasins. It would be treachery to herself.

"I'm sorry," she said. "But I'd so much rather they weren't
used for this kind of thing. I never intended them to be." She
stood with her face averted from the ridiculous couple.

He changed as if she had slapped his face. He sat down on top
of the low pupils' desk, and gazed with glazed interest round the
class-room. Alice sat beside him, in her white gauze and her
bedizened face. They were like two rebuked sparrows on one twig,

he with his great, easy, intimate limbs, she so light and alert. And as he sat he sank into an unconscious physical sympathy with her. Miss M'Leod walked towards the door.

"You'll have to think of something as'll do instead," he muttered to Alice in a low voice, meaning the blue moccasins. And leaning down, he drew off one of the grey shoes she had on, caressing her foot with the slip of his hand over its slim bare shape. She hastily put the bare foot behind her other, shod foot.

Tom Lomas poked in his head, his overcoat collar turned up to his ears.

"Car's here," he said.

"Right-o! Tom! I'll chalk it up to thee, lad!" said Percy with heavy breeziness. Then, making a great effort with himself, he rose heavily and went across to the door, to his wife, saying to her, in the same stiff voice of false heartiness :

"You'll be as right as rain with Tom. You won't mind if I don't come out? No! I'd better not show myself to the audience. Well—I'm glad you came, if only for a while. Good-bye then! I'll be home after the service—but I shan't disturb you. Good-bye! Don't get wet now——" And his voice, falsely cheerful, stiff with anger, ended in a clang of indignation.

Alice Howells sat on the infants' bench in silence. She was ignored. And she was unhappy, uneasy, because of the scene.

Percy closed the door after his wife. Then he turned with a looming slowness to Alice, and said in a hoarse whisper : "Think o' that, now!"

She looked up at him anxiously. His face, in its dark pigment, was transfigured with indignant anger. His yellow-grey eyes blazed, and a great rush of anger seemed to be surging up volcanic in him. For a second his eyes rested on her upturned, troubled dark-blue eyes, then glanced away, as if he didn't want to look at her in his anger. Even so, she felt a touch of tenderness in his glance.

"And that's all she's ever cared about—her own things and her own way," he said, in the same hoarse whisper, hoarse with suddenly-released rage. Alice Howells hung her head in silence.

"Not another damned thing, but what's her own, her own—and her own holy way—damned holy-holy-holy, all to herself." His voice shook with hoarse, whispering rage, burst out at last.

Alice Howells looked up at him in distress.

"Oh, don't say it!" she said. "I'm sure she's fond of you."

"*Fond* of me! Fond of *me*!" he blazed, with a grin of transcendent irony. "It makes her sick to look at me. I am a hairy brute, I own it. Why, she's never once touched me to be fond of me—never once—though she pretends sometimes. But a man knows——" and he made a grimace of contempt. " He knows when a woman's just stroking him, good doggie !—and when she's really a bit woman-fond of him. That woman's never been real fond of anybody or anything, all her life—she couldn't, for all her show of kindness. She's limited to herself, that woman is ; and I've looked up to her as if she was God. More fool me ! If God's not good-natured and good-hearted, then what is He——? "

Alice sat with her head dropped, realizing once more that men aren't really fooled. She was upset, shaken by his rage, and frightened, as if she too were guilty. He had sat down blankly beside her. She glanced up at him.

" Never mind ! " she said soothingly. " You'll like her again to-morrow."

He looked down at her with a grin, a grey sort of grin. " Are you going to stroke me good doggie ! as well ? " he said.

" Why ? " she asked, blank.

But he did not answer. Then after a while he resumed : " Wouldn't even leave the moccasins ! And she'd hung them up in my room, left them there for years—any man'd consider they were his. And I did want this show to-night to be a success ! What are you going to do about it ? "

" I've sent over for a pair of pale-blue satin bed-slippers of mine —they'll do just as well," she replied.

" Aye ! For all that, it's done me in."

" You'll get over it."

" Happen so ! She's curdled my inside, for all that. I don't know how I'm going to be civil to her."

" Perhaps you'd better stay at the rectory to-night," she said softly.

He looked into her eyes. And in that look, he transferred his allegiance.

" *You* don't want to be drawn in, do you ? " he asked, with troubled tenderness.

But she only gazed with wide, darkened eyes into his eyes, so she was like an open, dark doorway to him. His heart beat thick, and the faint, breathless smile of passion came into his eyes again.

" You'll have to go on, Mrs. Howells. We can't keep them waiting any longer."

It was Jim Stokes, who was directing the show. They heard the clapping and stamping of the impatient audience.

" Goodness ! " cried Alice Howells, darting to the door.

PART I

THERE was a peasant near Jerusalem who acquired a young game-cock which looked a shabby little thing, but which put on brave feathers as spring advanced, and was resplendent with arched and orange neck by the time the fig-trees were letting out leaves from their end-tips.

This peasant was poor, he lived in a cottage of mud-brick, and had only a dirty little inner courtyard with a tough fig-tree for all his territory. He worked hard among the vines and olives and wheat of his master, then came home to sleep in the mud-brick cottage by the path. But he was proud of his young rooster. In the shut-in yard were three shabby hens which laid small eggs, shed the few feathers they had, and made a disproportionate amount of dirt. There was also, in a corner under a straw roof, a dull donkey that often went out with the peasant to work, but sometimes stayed at home. And there was the peasant's wife, a black-browed youngish woman who did not work too hard. She threw a little grain, or the remains of the porridge mess, to the fowls, and she cut green fodder with a sickle, for the ass.

The young cock grew to a certain splendour. By some freak of destiny, he was a dandy rooster, in that dirty little yard with three patchy hens. He learned to crane his neck and give shrill answers to the crowing of other cocks, beyond the walls, in a world he knew nothing of. But there was a special fiery colour to his crow, and the distant calling of the other cocks roused him to unexpected outbursts.

" How he sings," said the peasant, as he got up and pulled his day-shirt over his head.

" He is good for twenty hens," said the wife.

The peasant went out and looked with pride at his young rooster. A saucy, flamboyant bird, that has already made the final acquaintance of the three tattered hens. But the cockerel was tipping his head, listening to the challenge of far-off unseen cocks, in the unknown world. Ghost voices, crowing at him mysteriously out of limbo. He answered with a ringing defiance, never to be daunted.

" He will surely fly away one of these days," said the peasant's wife.

So they lured him with grain, caught him, though he fought with all his wings and feet, and they tied a cord round his shank, fastening it against the spur ; and they tied the other end of the cord to the post that held up the donkey's straw pent-roof.

The young cock, freed, marched with a prancing stride of indignation away from the humans, came to the end of his string, gave a tug and a hitch of his tied leg, fell over for a moment, scuffled frantically on the unclean earthen floor, to the horror of the shabby hens, then with a sickening lurch, regained his feet, and stood to think. The peasant and the peasant's wife laughed heartily, and the young cock heard them. And he knew, with a gloomy, foreboding kind of knowledge, that he was tied by the leg.

He no longer pranced and ruffled and forged his feathers. He walked within the limits of his tether sombrely. Still he gobbled up the best bits of food. Still, sometimes, he saved an extra-best bit for his favourite hen of the moment. Still he pranced with quivering, rocking fierceness upon such of his harem as came nonchalantly within range, and gave off the invisible lure. And still he crowed defiance to the cock-crows that showered up out of limbo, in the dawn.

But there was now a grim voracity in the way he gobbled his food, and a pinched triumph in the way he seized upon the shabby hens. His voice, above all, had lost the full gold of its clangour. He was tied by the leg and he knew it. Body, soul and spirit were tied by that string.

Underneath, however, the life in him was grimly unbroken. It was the cord that should break. So one morning, just before the light of dawn, rousing from his slumbers with a sudden wave of strength, he leaped forward on his wings, and the string snapped. He gave a wild strange squawk, rose in one lift to the top of the wall, and there he crowed a loud and splitting crow. So loud, it woke the peasant.

At the same time, at the same hour before dawn, on the same morning, a man awoke from a long sleep in which he was tied up. He woke numb and cold, inside a carved hole in the rock. Through all the long sleep his body had been full of hurt, and it was still full of hurt. He did not open his eyes. Yet he knew that he was awake, and numb, and cold, and rigid, and full of hurt, and tied up. His face was banded with cold bands, his legs were bandaged together. Only his hands were loose.

He could move if he wanted : he knew that. But he had no want. Who would want to come back from the dead ? A deep, deep nausea stirred in him, at the premonition of movement. He resented already the fact of the strange, incalculable moving that had already taken place in him : the moving back into consciousness. He had not wished it. He had wanted to stay outside, in the place where even memory is stone dead.

But now, something had returned to him, like a returned letter, and in that return he lay overcome with a sense of nausea. Yet suddenly his hands moved. They lifted up, cold, heavy and sore. Yet they lifted up, to drag away the cloth from his face, and push at the shoulder bands. Then they fell again, cold, heavy, numb, and sick with having moved even so much, unspeakably unwilling to move further.

With his face cleared, and his shoulders free, he lapsed again, and lay dead, resting on the cold nullity of being dead. It was the most desirable. And almost, he had it complete : the utter cold nullity of being outside.

Yet when he was most nearly gone, suddenly, driven by an ache at the wrists, his hands rose and began pushing at the bandages of his knees, his feet began to stir, even while his breast lay cold and dead still.

And at last, the eyes opened. On to the dark. The same dark ! yet perhaps there was a pale chink, of the all-disturbing night, prizing open the pure dark. He could not lift his head. The eyes closed. And again it was finished.

Then suddenly he leaned up, and the great world reeled. Bandages fell away. And narrow walls of rock closed upon him, and gave the new anguish of imprisonment. There were chinks of light. With a wave of strength that came from revulsion, he leaned forward, in that narrow well of rock, and leaned frail hands on the rock near the chinks of light.

Strength came from somewhere, from revulsion ; there was a crash and a wave of light, and the dead man was crouching in his lair, facing the animal onrush of light. Yet it was hardly dawn, and the strange, piercing keenness of daybreak's sharp breath was on him. It meant full awakening.

Slowly, slowly he crept down from the cell of rock, with the caution of the bitterly wounded. Bandages and linen and perfume fell away, and he crouched on the ground against the wall of rock, to recover oblivion. But he saw his hurt feet touching the earth again, with unspeakable pain, the earth they had meant to touch no more, and he saw his thin legs that had died, and pain unknowable, pain like utter bodily disillusion, filled him so full that he stood up, with one torn hand on the ledge of the tomb.

To be back ! To be back again, after all that ! He saw the linen swathing-bands fallen round his dead feet, and stooping, he picked them up, folded them, and laid them back in the rocky cavity from which he had emerged. Then he took the perfumed linen sheet, wrapped it round him as a mantle, and turned away, to the wanness of the chill dawn.

He was alone ; and having died, was even beyond loneliness.

Filled still with the sickness of unspeakable disillusion, the man stepped with wincing feet down the rocky slope, past the sleeping soldiers, who lay wrapped in their woollen mantles under the wild laurels. Silent, on naked, scarred feet, wrapped in a white linen shroud, he glanced down for a moment on the inert, heap-like bodies of the soldiers. They were repulsive, a slow squalor of limbs, yet he felt a certain compassion. He passed on towards the road, lest they should wake.

Having nowhere to go, he turned from the city that stood on her hills. He slowly followed the road away from the town, past the olives, under which purple anemones were drooping in the chill of dawn, and rich-green herbage was pressing thick. The world, the same as ever, the natural world, thronging with greenness, a nightingale winsomely, wistfully, coaxingly calling from the bushes beside a runnel of water, in the world, the natural world of morning and evening, forever undying, from which he had died.

He went on, on scarred feet, neither of this world nor of the next. Neither here nor there, neither seeing nor yet sightless, he passed dimly on, away from the city and its precincts, wondering why he should be travelling, yet driven by a dim, deep nausea of disillusion, and a resolution of which he was not even aware.

Advancing in a kind of half-consciousness under the dry stone wall of the olive orchard, he was roused by the shrill wild crowing of a cock just near him, a sound which made him shiver as if electricity had touched him. He saw a black and orange cock on a bough above the road, then running through the olives of the upper level, a peasant in a grey woollen shirt-tunic. Leaping out of greenness, came the black and orange cock with the red comb, his tail-feathers streaming lustrous.

" O stop him, Master ! " called the peasant. " My escaped cock ! "

The man addressed, with a sudden flicker of a smile, opened his great white wings of a shroud in front of the leaping bird. The

cock fell back with a squawk and a flutter, the peasant jumped
forward, there was a terrific beating of wings, and whirring of
feathers, then the peasant had the escaped cock safely under his
arm, its wings shut down, its face crazily craning forward, its round
eyes goggling from its white chops.

" It's my escaped cock ! " said the peasant, soothing the bird with
his left hand, as he looked perspiringly up into the face of the man
wrapped in white linen.

The peasant changed countenance, and stood transfixed, as he
looked into the dead-white face of the man who had died. That
dead-white face, so still, with the black beard growing on it as if in
death ; and those wide-open black sombre eyes, that had died,
and those washed scars on the waxy forehead ! The slow-blooded
man of the field let his jaw drop, in childish inability to meet the
situation.

" Don't be afraid," said the man in the shroud. " I am not dead.
They took me down too soon. So I have risen up. Yet if they
discover me, they will do it all over again. . . ."

He spoke in a voice of old disgust. Humanity ! Especially
humanity in authority ! There was only one thing it could do. He
looked with black, indifferent eyes into the quick, shifty eyes of the
peasant. The peasant quailed, and was powerless under the look of
deathly indifference, and strange cold resoluteness. He could only
say the one thing he was afraid to say :

" Will you hide in my house, Master ? "

" I will rest there. But if you tell any one, you know what will
happen. You will have to go before a judge."

" Me ! I shan't speak. Let us be quick ! "

The peasant looked round in fear, wondering sulkily why he had
let himself in for this doom. The man with scarred feet climbed
painfully up to the level of the olive garden, and followed the sullen,
hurrying peasant across the green wheat among the olive trees. He
felt the cool silkiness of the young wheat under his feet that had been
dead, and the roughishness of its separate life was apparent to him.
At the edges of rocks, he saw .the silky, silvery-haired buds of the
scarlet anemone bending downwards. And they too were in
another world. In his own world he was alone, utterly alone.
These things around him were in a world that had never died. But
he himself had died, or had been killed from out of it, and all that
remained now was the great void nausea of utter disillusion.

They came to a clay cottage, and the peasant waited dejectedly
for the other man to pass.

" Pass ! " he said. " Pass ! We have not been seen."

The man in white linen entered the earthen room, taking with him the aroma of strange perfumes. The peasant closed the door, and passed through the inner doorway into the yard, where the ass stood within the high walls, safe from being stolen. There the peasant, in great disquietude, tied up the cock. The man with the waxen face sat down on a mat near the hearth, for he was spent and barely conscious. Yet he heard outside the whispering of the peasant to his wife, for the woman had been watching from the roof.

Presently they came in, and the woman hid her face. She poured water, and put bread and dried figs on a wooden platter.

" Eat, Master ! " said the peasant. " Eat ! No one has seen."

But the stranger had no desire for food. Yet he moistened a little bread in the water, and ate it, since life must be. But desire was dead in him, even for food and drink. He had risen without desire, without even the desire to live, empty save for the all-overwhelming disillusion that lay like nausea where his life had been. Yet perhaps, deeper even than disillusion, was a desireless resoluteness, deeper even than consciousness.

The peasant and his wife stood near the door, watching. They saw with terror the livid wounds on the thin waxy hands and the thin feet of the stranger, and the small lacerations in the still dead forehead. They smelled with terror the scent of rich perfumes that came from him, from his body. And they looked at the fine, snowy, costly linen. Perhaps really he was a dead king, from the region of terrors. And he was still cold and remote in the region of death, with perfumes coming from his transparent body as if from some strange flower.

Having with difficulty swallowed some of the moistened bread, he lifted his eyes to them. He saw them as they were : limited, meagre in their life, without any splendour of gesture and of courage. But they were what they were, slow inevitable parts of the natural world. They had no nobility, but fear made them compassionate.

And the stranger had compassion on them again, for he knew that they would respond best to gentleness, giving back a clumsy gentleness again.

" Do not be afraid," he said to them gently. " Let me stay a little while with you. I shall not stay long. And then I shall go away forever. But do not be afraid. No harm will come to you through me."

They believed him at once, yet the fear did not leave them. And they said :

" Stay, Master, while ever you will. Rest ! Rest quietly ! "
But they were afraid.

So he let them be, and the peasant went away with the ass. The
sun had risen bright, and in the dark house with the door shut,
the man was again as if in the tomb. So he said to the woman,
" I would lie in the yard."

And she swept the yard for him, and laid him a mat, and he
lay down under the wall in the morning sun. There he saw the
first green leaves spurting like flames from the ends of the enclosed
fig-tree, out of the bareness to the sky of spring above. But the
man who had died could not look, he only lay quite still in the sun,
which was not yet too hot, and had no desire in him, not even to
move. But he lay with his thin legs in the sun, his black perfumed
hair falling into the hollows of his neck, and his thin colourless arms
utterly inert. As he lay there, the hens clucked and scratched, and
the escaped cock, caught and tied by the leg again, cowered in a
corner.

The peasant woman was frightened. She came peeping, and,
seeing him never move, feared to have a dead man in the yard.
But the sun had grown stronger, he opened his eyes and looked at
her. And now she was frightened of the man who was alive, but
spoke nothing.

He opened his eyes, and saw the world again bright as glass. It
was life, in which he had no share any more. But it shone outside
him, blue sky, and a bare fig-tree with little jets of green leaf.
Bright as glass, and he was not of it, for desire had failed.

Yet he was there, and not extinguished. The day passed in a
kind of coma, and at evening he went into the house. The peasant
man came home, but he was frightened, and had nothing to say.
The stranger too ate of the mess of beans, a little. Then he washed
his hands and turned to the wall, and was silent. The peasants
were silent too. They watched their guest sleep. Sleep was so near
death he could still sleep.

Yet when the sun came up, he went again to lie in the yard. The
sun was the one thing that drew him and swayed him, and he still
wanted to feel the cool air of the morning in his nostrils, see the
pale sky overhead. He still hated to be shut up.

As he came out, the young cock crowed. It was a diminished,
pinched cry, but there was that in the voice of the bird stronger
than chagrin. It was the necessity to live, and even to cry out the
triumph of life. The man who had died stood and watched the
cock who had escaped and been caught, ruffling himself up, rising

forward on his toes, throwing up his head, and parting his beak in another challenge from life to death. The brave sounds rang out, and though they were diminished by the cord round the bird's leg, they were not cut off. The man who had died looked nakedly on life, and saw a vast resoluteness everywhere flinging itself up in stormy or subtle wave-crests, foam-tips emerging out of the blue invisible, a black and orange cock or the green flame-tongues out of the extremes of the fig-tree. They came forth, these things and creatures of spring, glowing with desire and with assertion. They came like crests of foam, out of the blue flood of the invisible desire, out of the vast invisible sea of strength, and they came coloured and tangible, evanescent, yet deathless in their coming. The man who had died looked on the great swing into existence of things that had not died, but he saw no longer their tremulous desire to exist and to be. He heard instead their ringing, ringing, defiant challenge to all other things existing.

The man lay still, with eyes that had died now wide open and darkly still, seeing the everlasting resoluteness of life. And the cock, with the flat, brilliant glance, glanced back at him, with a bird's half-seeing look. And always the man who had died saw not the bird alone, but the short, sharp wave of life of which the bird was the crest. He watched the queer, beaky motion of the creature as it gobbled into itself the scraps of food ; its glancing of the eye of life, ever alert and watchful, overweening and cautious, and the voice of its life, crowing triumph and assertion, yet strangled by a cord of circumstance. He seemed to hear the queer speech of very life, as the cock triumphantly imitated the clucking of the favourite hen, when she had laid an egg, a clucking which still had, in the male bird the hollow chagrin of the cord round his leg. And when the man threw a bit of bread to the cock, it called with an extraordinary cooing tenderness, tousling and saving the morsel for the hens. The hens ran up greedily, and carried the morsel away beyond the reach of the string.

Then, walking complacently after them, suddenly the male bird's leg would hitch at the end of his tether, and he would yield with a kind of collapse. His flag fell, he seemed to diminish, he would huddle in the shade. And he was young, his tail-feathers, glossy as they were, were not fully grown. It was not till evening again that the tide of life in him made him forget. Then when his favourite hen came strolling unconcernedly near him, emitting the lure, he pounced on her with all his feathers vibrating. And the man who had died watched the unsteady, rocking vibration of the bent bird, and it was not the bird he saw, but one wave-tip of life overlapping for a minute another, in the tide of the swaying ocean of life. And the destiny of life seemed more fierce and compulsive to him even than the destiny of death. The doom of death was a shadow compared to the raging destiny of life, the determined surge of life.

At twilight the peasant came home with the ass, and he said : " Master ! It is said that the body was stolen from the garden, and the tomb is empty, and the soldiers are taken away, accursed Romans ! And the women are there to weep."

The man who had died looked at the man who had not died.

" It is well," he said.   " Say nothing, and we are safe."

And the peasant was relieved. He looked rather dirty and stupid, and even as much flaminess as that of the young cock, which he had tied by the leg, would never glow in him. He was without fire. But the man who had died thought to himself :

" Why, then, should he be lifted up ? Clods of earth are turned over for refreshment, they are not to be lifted up. Let the earth remain earthy, and hold its own against the sky. I was wrong to seek to lift it up. ·I was wrong to try to interfere. The ploughshare of devastation will be set in the soil of Judea, and the life of this peasant will be overturned like the sods of the field. No man can save the earth from tillage. It is tillage, not salvation. . . ."

So he saw the man, the peasant, with compassion ; but the man who had ·died no longer wished to interfere in the soul of the man who had not died, and who could never die, save to return to earth. Let him return to earth in his own good hour, and let no one try to interfere when the earth claims ·her own.

So the man with scars let the peasant go from him, for the peasant had no birth in him. Yet the man who had died said to himself : " He is my host."

And at dawn, when he was better, the man who had died rose up, and on slow, sore feet retraced his way to the garden. For he had been betrayed in a garden, and buried in a garden. And as he turned round the screen of laurels, near the rock-face, he saw a woman hovering by the tomb, a woman in blue and yellow. She peeped again into the mouth of the hole, that was like a deep cupboard. But still there was nothing. And she wrung her hands and wept. And as she turned away, she saw the man in white, standing by the laurels, and she gave a cry, thinking it might be a spy, and she said :

" They have taken him away ! "

So he said to her :

" Madeleine ! "

Then she reeled as if she would fall, for she knew him. And he said to her :

" Madeleine ! Do not be afraid. I am alive. They took me down too soon, so I came back to life. Then I was sheltered in a house."

She did not know what to say, but fell at his feet to kiss them.

" Don't touch me, Madeleine," he said. " Not yet ! I am not yet healed and in touch with men."

So she wept because she did not know what to do. And he said :

" Let us go aside, among the bushes, where we can speak unseen."

So in her blue mantle and her yellow robe, she followed him among the trees, and he sat down under a myrtle bush. And he said :

" I am not yet quite come to. Madeleine, what is to be done next ? "

" Master ! " she said. " Oh, we have wept for you ! And will you come back to us ? "

" What is finished is finished, and for me the end is past," he said. " The stream will run till no more rains fill it, then it will dry up. For me, that life is over."

" And will you give up your triumph ? " she said sadly.

" My triumph," he said, " is that I am not dead. I have outlived my mission, and know no more of it. It is my triumph. I have survived the day and the death of my interference, and am still a man. I am young still, Madeleine, not even come to middle age. I am glad all that is over. It had to be. But now I am glad it is over, and the day of my interference is done. The teacher and the saviour are dead in me ; now I can go about my business, into my own single life."

She heard him, and did not fully understand. But what he said made her feel disappointed.

" But you will come back to us ? " she said, insisting.

" I don't know what I shall do," he said. " When I am healed, I shall know better. But my mission is over, and my teaching is finished, and death has saved me from my own salvation. Oh, Madeleine, I want to take my single way in life, which is my portion. My public life is over, the life of my self-importance. Now I can wait on life, and say nothing, and have no one betray me. I wanted to be greater than the limits of my hands and feet, so I brought betrayal on myself. And I know I wronged Judas, my poor Judas. For I have died, and now I know my own limits. Now I can live

without striving to sway others any more. For my reach ends in
my finger-tips, and my stride is no longer than the ends of my toes.
Yet I would embrace multitudes, I who have never truly embraced
even one. But Judas and the high priests saved me from my own
salvation, and soon I can turn to my destiny like a bather in the sea
at dawn, who has just come down to the shore alone."

"Do you want to be alone henceforward?" she asked. "And
was your mission nothing? Was it all untrue?"

"Nay!" he said. "Neither were your lovers in the past nothing.
They were much to you, but you took more than you gave. Then
you came to me for salvation from your own excess. And I, in
my mission, I too ran to excess. I gave more than I took, and
that also is woe and vanity. So Pilate and the high priests saved me
from my own excessive salvation. Don't run to excess now in living,
Madeleine. It only means another death."

She pondered bitterly, for the need for excessive giving was in
her, and she could not bear to be denied.

"And will you not come back to us?" she said. "Have you
risen for yourself alone?"

He heard the sarcasm in her voice, and looked at her beautiful
face which still was dense with excessive need for salvation from the
woman she had been, the female who had caught men at her will.
The cloud of necessity was on her, to be saved from the old, wilful
Eve, who had embraced many men and taken more than she gave.
Now the other doom was on her. She wanted to give without
taking. And that too, is hard, and cruel to the warm body.

"I have not risen from the dead in order to seek death again,"
he said.

She glanced up at him, and saw the weariness settling again on
his waxy face, and the vast disillusion in his dark eyes, and the
underlying indifference. He felt her glance, and said to himself:
"Now my own followers will want to do me to death again, for
having risen up different from their expectation."

"But you will come to us, to see us, us who love you?" she said.

He laughed a little and said:

"Ah, yes." Then he added, "Have you a little money? Will
you give me a little money? I owe it."

She had not much, but it pleased her to give it to him.

"Do you think," he said to her, "that I might come and live
with you in your house?"

She looked up at him with large blue eyes, that gleamed strangely.

"Now?" she said with peculiar triumph.

And he, who shrank now from triumph of any sort, his own or another's, said :

" Not now ! Later, when I am healed, and . . . and I am in touch with the flesh."

The words faltered in him. And in his heart he knew he would never go to live in her house. For the flicker of triumph had gleamed in her eyes ; the greed of giving. But she murmured in a humming rapture :

" Ah, you know I would give up everything to you."

" Nay ! " he said. " I didn't ask that."

A revulsion from all the life he had known came over him again, the great nausea of disillusion, and the spear-thrust through his bowels. He crouched under the myrtle bushes, without strength. Yet his eyes were open. And she looked at him again, and she saw that it was not the Messiah. The Messiah had not risen. The enthusiasm and the burning purity were gone, and the rapt youth. His youth was dead. This man was middle-aged and disillusioned, with a certain terrible indifference, and a resoluteness which love would never conquer. This was not the Master she had so adored, the young, flamy, unphysical exalter of her soul. This was nearer to the lovers she had known of old, but with a greater indifference to the personal issue, and a lesser susceptibility.

She was thrown out of the balance of her rapturous, anguished adoration. This risen man was the death of her dream.

" You should go now," he said to her. " Do not touch me, I am in death. I shall come again here, on the third day. Come if you will, at dawn. And we will speak again."

She went away, perturbed and shattered. Yet as she went, her mind discarded the bitterness of the reality, and she conjured up rapture and wonder, that the Master was risen and was not dead. He was risen, the Saviour, the exalter, the wonder-worker ! He was risen, but not as man ; as pure God, who should not be touched by flesh, and who should be rapt away into Heaven. It was the most glorious and most ghostly of the miracles.

Meanwhile the man who had died gathered himself together at last, and slowly made his way to the peasant's house. He was glad to go back to them, and away from Madeleine and his own associates. For the peasants had the inertia of earth and would let him rest, and as yet, would put no compulsion on him.

The woman was on the roof, looking for him. She was afraid that he had gone away. His presence in the house had become like gentle wine to her. She hastened to the door, to him.

"Where have you been?" she said. "Why did you go away?"

"I have been to walk in a garden, and I have seen a friend, who gave me a little money. It is for you."

He held out his thin hand, with the small amount of money, all that Madeleine could give him. The peasant's wife's eyes glistened, for money was scarce, and she said:

"Oh, Master! And is it truly mine?"

"Take it!" he said. "It buys bread, and bread brings life."

So he lay down in the yard again, sick with relief at being alone again. For with the peasants he could be alone, but his own friends would never let him be alone. And in the safety of the yard, the young cock was dear to him, as it shouted in the helpless zest of life, and finished in the helpless humiliation of being tied by the leg. This day the ass stood swishing her tail under the shed. The man who had died lay down and turned utterly away from life, in the sickness of death in life.

But the woman brought wine and water, and sweetened cakes, and roused him, so that he ate a little, to please her. The day was hot, and as she crouched to serve him, he saw her breasts sway from her humble body, under her smock. He knew she wished he would desire her, and she was youngish, and not unpleasant. And he, who had never known a woman, would have desired her if he could. But he could not want her, though he felt gently towards her soft, crouching, humble body. But it was her thoughts, her consciousness, he could not mingle with. She was pleased with the money, and now she wanted to take more from him. She wanted the embrace of his body. But her little soul was hard, and short-sighted, and grasping, her body had its little greed, and no gentle reverence of the return gift. So he spoke a quiet, pleasant word to her, and turned away. He could not touch the little, personal body, the little, personal life of this woman, nor in any other. He turned away from it without hesitation.

Risen from the dead, he had realized at last that the body, too, has its little life, and beyond that, the greater life. He was virgin, in recoil from the little, greedy life of the body. But now he knew that virginity is a form of greed; and that the body rises again to give and to take, to take and to give, ungreedily. Now he knew that he had risen for the woman, or women, who knew the greater life of the body, not greedy to give, not greedy to take, and with whom he could mingle his body. But having died, he was patient, knowing there was time, an eternity of time. And he was driven by no greedy desire, either to give himself to others, or to grasp anything for himself. For he had died.

The peasant came home from work, and said :

" Master, I thank you for the money. But we did not want it. And all I have is yours."

But the man who had died was sad, because the peasant stood there in the little, personal body, and his eyes were cunning and sparkling with the hope of greater rewards in money, later on. True, the peasant had taken him in free, and had risked getting no reward. But the hope was cunning in him. Yet even this was as men are made. So when the peasant would have helped him to rise, for night had fallen, the man who had died said :

" Don't touch me, brother. I am not yet risen to the Father."

The sun burned with greater splendour, and burnished the young cock brighter. But the peasant kept the string renewed, and the bird was a prisoner. Yet the flame of life burned up to a sharp point in the cock, so that it eyed askance and haughtily the man who had died. And the man smiled and held the bird dear, and he said to it :

" Surely thou art risen to the Father, among birds."

And the young cock, answering, crowed.

When at dawn on the third morning the man went to the garden, he was absorbed, thinking of the greater life of the body, beyond the little, narrow, personal life. So he came through the thick screen of laurel and myrtle bushes, near the rock, suddenly, and he saw three women near the tomb. One was Madeleine, and one was the woman who had been his mother, and the third was a woman he knew, called Joan. He looked up, and saw them all, and they saw him, and they were all afraid.

He stood arrested in the distance, knowing they were there to claim him back, bodily. But he would in no wise return to them. Pallid, in the shadow of a grey morning that was blowing to rain, he saw them, and turned away. But Madeleine hastened towards him.

" I did not bring them," she said. " They have come of themselves. See, I have brought you money ! . . . Will you not speak to them ? "

She offered him some gold pieces, and he took them, saying :

" May I have this money ? I shall need it. I cannot speak to them, for I am not yet ascended to the Father. And I must leave you now."

" Ah ! Where will you go ? " she cried.

He looked at her, and saw she was clutching for the man in him who had died and was dead, the man of his youth and his mission, of his chastity and his fear, of his little life, his giving without taking.

" I must go to my Father ! " he said.

" And you will leave us ? There is your mother ! " she cried, turning round with the old anguish, which yet was sweet to her.

" But now I must ascend to my Father," he said, and he drew back into the bushes, and so turned quickly, and went away, saying to himself :

" Now I belong to no one and have no connection, and mission or gospel is gone from me. Lo ! I cannot make even my own life, and what have I to save ? . . . I can learn to be alone."

So he went back to the peasants' house, to the yard where the young cock was tied by the leg, with a string. And he wanted no one, for it was best to be alone ; for the presence of people made him lonely. The sun and the subtle salve of spring healed his wounds, even the gaping wound of disillusion through his bowels was closing up. And his need of men and women, his fever to have them and to be saved by them, this too was healing in him. Whatever came of touch between himself and the race of men, henceforth, should come without trespass or compulsion. For he said to himself :

" I tried to compel them to live, so they compelled me to die. It is always so, with compulsion. The recoil kills the advance. Now is my time to be alone."

Therefore he went no more to the garden, but lay still and saw the sun, or walked at dusk across the olive slopes, among the green wheat, that rose a palm-breadth higher every sunny day. And always he thought to himself :

" How good it is to have fulfilled my mission, and to be beyond it. Now I can be alone, and leave all things to themselves, and the fig-tree may be barren if it will, and the rich may be rich. My way is my own alone."

So the green jets of leaves unspread on the fig-tree, with the bright, translucent, green blood of the tree. And the young cock grew brighter, more lustrous with the sun's burnishing ; yet always tied by the leg with a string. And the sun went down more and more in pomp, out of the gold and red-flushed air. The man who had died was aware of it all, and he thought :

" The Word is but the midge that bites at evening. Man is tormented with words like midges, and they follow him right into the tomb. But beyond the tomb they cannot go. Now I have passed the place where words can bite no more and the air is clear, and there is nothing to say, and I am alone within my own skin, which is the walls of all my domain."

So he healed of his wounds, and enjoyed his immortality of being alive without fret. For in the tomb he had slipped that noose which we call care. For in the tomb he had left his striving self, which cares and asserts itself. Now his uncaring self healed and became whole within his skin, and he smiled to himself with pure aloneness, which is one sort of immortality.

Then he said to himself : " I will wander the earth, and say nothing. For nothing is so marvellous as to be alone in the phenomenal world, which is raging, and yet apart. And I have not seen it, I was too much blinded by my confusion within it. Now I will wander among the stirring of the phenomenal world, for it is the stirring of all things among themselves which leaves me purely alone."

So he communed with himself, and decided to be a physician. Because the power was still in him to heal any man or child who touched his compassion. Therefore he cut his hair and his beard after the right fashion, and smiled to himself. And he bought himself shoes, and the right mantle, and put the right cloth over his head, hiding all the little scars. And the peasant said :

" Master, will you go forth from us ? "

" Yes, for the time is come for me to return to men."

So he gave the peasant a piece of money, and said to him :

" Give me the cock that escaped and is now tied by the leg. For he shall go forth with me."

So for a piece of money the peasant gave the cock to the man who had died, and at dawn the man who had died set out into the phenomenal world, to be fulfilled in his own loneliness in the midst of it. For previously he had been too much mixed up in it. Then he had died. Now he must come back, to be alone in the midst. Yet even now he did not go quite alone, for under his arm, as he went, he carried the cock, whose tail fluttered gaily behind, and who craned his head excitedly, for he too was adventuring out for the first time into the wider phenomenal world, which is the stirring of the body of cocks also. And the peasant woman shed a few tears, but then went indoors, being a peasant, to look again at the pieces of money. And it seemed to her, a gleam came out of the pieces of money, wonderful.

The man who had died wandered on, and it was a sunny day. He looked around as he went, and stood aside as the pack-train passed by, towards the city. And he said to himself :

" Strange is the phenomenal world, dirty and clean together !
And I am the same. Yet I am apart ! And life bubbles variously.
Why should I have wanted it to bubble all alike ? What a pity I
preached to them ! A sermon is so much more likely to cake into
mud, and to close the fountains, than is a psalm or a song. I made
a mistake. I understand that they executed me for preaching to
them. Yet they could not finally execute me, for now I am risen
in my own aloneness, and inherit the earth, since I lay no claim
on it. And I will be alone in the seethe of all things ; first and
foremost, forever, I shall be alone. But I must toss this bird into
the seethe of phenomena, for he must ride his wave. How hot he
is with life ! Soon, in some place, I shall leave him among the
hens. And perhaps one evening, I shall meet a woman who can
lure my risen body, yet leave me my aloneness. For the body of
my desire has died, and I am not in touch anywhere. Yet how do
I know ! All at least is life. And this cock gleams with bright
aloneness, though he answers the lure of hens. And I shall hasten
on to that village on the hill ahead of me ; already I am tired and
weak, and want to close my eyes to everything."

Hastening a little with the desire to have finished going, he
overtook two men going slowly, and talking. And being soft-footed
he heard they were speaking of himself. And he remembered
them, for he had known them in his life, the life of his mission.
So he greeted them, but did not disclose himself in the dusk, and
they did not know him. He said to them :

" What then of him who would be king, and was put to death
for it ? "

They answered suspiciously : " Why ask you of him ? "

" I have known him, and thought much about him," he said.
So they replied : " He has risen."

" Yea ! And where is he, and how does he live ? "

" We know not, for it is not revealed. Yet he is risen, and in a
little while will ascend unto the Father."

" Yea ! And where then is his Father ? "

" Know ye not ? You are then of the Gentiles ! The Father is
in Heaven, above the cloud and the firmament."

" Truly ? Then how will he ascend ? "

" As Elijah the Prophet, he shall go up in a glory."

" Even into the sky."

" Into the sky."

" Then is he not risen in the flesh ? "

" He is risen in the flesh."

" And will he take flesh up into the sky ? "

" The Father in Heaven will take him up."

The man who had died said no more, for his say was over, and words beget words, even as gnats. But the man asked him : " Why do you carry a cock ? "

" I am a healer," he said, " and the bird hath virtue."

" You are not a believer ? "

" Yea ! I believe the bird is full of life and virtue."

They walked on in silence after this, and he felt they disliked his answer. So he smiled to himself, for a dangerous phenomenon in the world is a man of narrow belief, who denies the right of his neighbour to be alone. And as they came to the outskirts of the village, the man who had died stood still in the gloaming and said in his old voice :

" Know ye me not ? "

And they cried in fear : " Master ! "

" Yea ! " he said, laughing softly. And he turned suddenly away, down a side lane, and was gone under the wall before they knew.

So he came to an inn where the asses stood in the yard. And he called for fritters, and they were made for him. So he slept under a shed. But in the morning he was wakened by a loud crowing, and his cock's voice ringing in his ears. So he saw the rooster of the inn walking forth to battle, with his hens, a goodly number, behind him. Then the cock of the man who had died sprang forth, and a battle began between the birds. The man of the inn ran to save his rooster, but the man who had died said :

" If my bird wins I will give him thee. And if he lose, thou shalt eat him."

So the birds fought savagely, and the cock of the man who had died killed the common cock of the yard. Then the man who had died said to his young cock :

" Thou at least hast found thy kingdom, and the females to thy body. Thy aloneness can take on splendour, polished by the lure of thy hens."

And he left his bird there, and went on deeper into the phenomenal world, which is a vast complexity of entanglements and allurements. And he asked himself a last question :

" From what, and to what, could this infinite whirl be saved ? "

So he went his way, and was alone. But the way of the world was past belief, as he saw the strange entanglement of passions and circumstance and compulsion everywhere, but always the dread insomnia of compulsion. It was fear, the ultimate fear of death, that made men mad. So always he must move on, for if he stayed, his neighbours wound the strangling of their fear and bullying round him. There was nothing he could touch, for all, in a mad assertion of the ego, wanted to put a compulsion on him, and violate his intrinsic solitude. It was the mania of cities and societies and hosts, to lay a compulsion upon a man, upon all men. For men and women alike were mad with the egoistic fear of their own nothingness. And he thought of his own mission, how he had tried to lay the compulsion of love on all men. And the old nausea came back on him. For there was no contact without a subtle attempt to inflict a compulsion. And already he had been compelled even into death. The nausea of the old wound broke out afresh, and he looked again on the world with repulsion, dreading its mean contacts.

PART II

THE wind came cold and strong from inland, from the invisible snows of Lebanon. But the temple, facing south and west, towards Egypt, faced the splendid sun of winter as he curved down towards the sea, the warmth and radiance flooded in between the pillars of painted wood. But the sea was invisible, because of the trees, though its dashing sounded among the hum of pines. The air was turning golden to afternoon. The woman who served Isis stood in her yellow robe, and looked up at the steep slopes coming down to the sea, where the olive-trees silvered under the wind like water splashing. She was alone save for the goddess. And in the winter afternoon the light stood erect and magnificent off the invisible sea, filling the hills of the coast. She went towards the sun, through the grove of Mediterranean pine-trees and ever-green oaks, in the midst of which the temple stood, on a little, tree-covered tongue of land between two bays.

It was only a very little way, and then she stood among the dry trunks of the outermost pines, on the rocks under which the sea smote and sucked, facing the open where the bright sun gloried in winter. The sea was dark, almost indigo, running away from the land, and crested with white. The hand of the wind brushed it strangely with shadow, as it brushed the olives of the slopes with silver. And there was no boat out. The three boats were drawn high upon the steep shingle of the little bay, by the small grey tower. Along the edge of the shingle ran a high wall, inside which was a garden occupying the brief flat of the bay, then rising in terraces up the steep slope of the coast. And there, some little way up,

within another wall, stood the low white villa, white and alone as
the coast, overlooking the sea. But higher, much higher up, where
the olives had given way to pine-trees again, ran the coast road,
keeping to the height to be above the gullies that came down to the
bays.

Upon it all poured the royal sunshine of the January afternoon.
Or rather, all was part of the great sun, glow and substance and
immaculate loneliness of the sea, and pure brightness.

Crouching in the rocks above the dark water, which only swung
up and down, two slaves, half naked, were dressing pigeons for the
evening meal. They pierced the throat of a blue, live bird, and let
the drops of blood fall into the heaving sea, with curious concentration. They were performing some sacrifice, or working some
incantation. The woman of the temple, yellow and white and alone
like a winter narcissus, stood between the pines of the small, humped
peninsula where the temple secretly hid, and watched.

A black-and-white pigeon, vividly white, like a ghost escaped
over the low dark sea, sped out, caught the wind, tilted, rode,
soared, and swept over the pine-trees, and wheeled away, a speck,
inland. It had escaped. The priestess heard the cry of the boy
slave, a garden slave of about seventeen. He raised his arms to
heaven in anger as the pigeon wheeled away, naked and angry and
young he held out his arms. Then he turned and seized the girl
in an access of rage, and beat her with his fist that was stained
with pigeon's blood. And she lay down with her face hidden,
passive and quivering. The woman who owned them watched.
And as she watched, she saw another onlooker, a stranger, in a low,
broad hat, and a cloak of grey homespun, a dark bearded man standing on the little causeway of a rock that was the neck of her temple
peninsula. By the blowing of his dark-grey cloak she saw him.
And he saw her, on the rocks like a white-and-yellow narcissus,
because of the flutter of her white linen tunic, below the yellow
mantle of wool. And both of them watched the two slaves.

The boy suddenly left off beating the girl. He crouched over her,
touching her, trying to make her speak. But she lay quite inert,
face down on the smoothed rock. And he put his arms round her
and lifted her, but she slipped back to earth like one dead, yet far
too quickly for anything dead. The boy, desperate, caught her by
the hips and hugged her to him, turning her over there. There she
seemed inert, all her fight was in her shoulders. He twisted her
over, intent and unconscious, and pushed his hands between her
thighs, to push them apart. And in an instant he was covering her

in the blind, frightened frenzy of a boy's first passion. Quick and
frenzied his young body quivered naked on hers, blind, for a minute.
Then it lay quite still, as if dead.

And then, in terror, he peeped up. He peeped round, and drew
slowly to his feet, adjusting his loin-rag. He saw the stranger, and
then he saw, on the rocks beyond, the lady of Isis, his mistress.
And as he saw her, his whole body shrank and cowed, and with a
strange cringing motion he scuttled lamely towards the door in the
wall.

The girl sat up and looked after him. When she had seen him
disappear, she too looked round. And she saw the stranger and the
priestess. Then with a sullen movement she turned away, as if
she had seen nothing, to the four dead pigeons and the knife, which
lay there on the rock. And she began to strip the small feathers,
so that they rose on the wind like dust.

The priestess turned away. Slaves ! Let the overseer watch
them. She was not interested. She went slowly through the pines
again, back to the temple, which stood in the sun in a small clearing
at the centre of the tongue of land. It was a small temple of wood,
painted all pink and white and blue, having at the front four
wooden pillars rising like stems to the swollen lotus-bud of Egypt
at the top, supporting the roof and open, spiky lotus-flowers of the
outer frieze, which went round under the eaves. Two low steps of
stone led up to the platform before the pillars, and the chamber
behind the pillars was open. There a low stone altar stood, with
a few embers in its hollow, and the dark stain of blood in its end
groove.

She knew her temple so well, for she had built it at her own
expense, and tended it for seven years. There it stood, pink and
white, like a flower in the little clearing, backed by blackish ever-
green oaks ; and the shadow of afternoon was already washing over
its pillar-bases.

She entered slowly, passing through to the dark inner chamber,
lighted by a perfumed oil-flame. And once more she pushed shut
the door, and once more she threw a few grains of incense on a
brazier before the goddess, and once more she sat down before her
goddess, in the almost-darkness, to muse, to go away into the dreams
of the goddess.

It was Isis ; but not Isis, Mother of Horus. It was Isis Bereaved,
Isis in Search. The goddess, in painted marble, lifted her face and
strode, one thigh forward through the frail fluting of her robe, in
the anguish of bereavement and of search. She was looking for the

fragments of the dead Osiris, dead and scattered asunder, dead, torn apart, and thrown in fragments over the wide world. And she must find his hands and his feet, his heart, his thighs, his head, his belly, she must gather him together and fold her arms round the re-assembled body till it became warm again, and roused to life, and could embrace her, and could fecundate her womb. And the strange rapture and anguish of search went on through the years, as she lifted her throat and her hollowed eyes looked inward, in the tormented ecstasy of seeking, and the delicate navel of her bud-like belly showed through the frail, girdled robe with the eternal asking, asking, of her search. And through the years she found him bit by bit, heart and head and limbs and body. And yet she had not found the last reality, the final clue to him, that alone could bring him really back to her. For she was Isis of the subtle lotus, the womb which waits submerged and in bud, waits for the touch of that other inward sun that streams its rays from the loins of the male Osiris.

This was the mystery the woman had served alone for seven years, since she was twenty, till now she was twenty-seven. Before, when she was young, she had lived in the world, in Rome, in Ephesus, in Egypt. For her father had been one of Anthony's captains and comrades, had fought with Anthony and had stood with him when Cæsar was murdered, and through to the days of shame. Then he had come again across to Asia, out of favour with Rome, and had been killed in the mountains beyond Lebanon. The widow, having no favour to hope for from Octavius, had retired to her small property on the coast under Lebanon, taking her daughter from the world, a girl of nineteen, beautiful but unmarried.

When she was young the girl had known Cæsar, and had shrunk from his eagle-like rapacity. The golden Anthony had sat with her many a half-hour, in the splendour of his great limbs and glowing manhood, and talked with her of the philosophies and the gods. For he was fascinated as a child by the gods, though he mocked at them, and forgot them in his own vanity. But he said to her :

" I have sacrificed two doves for you, to Venus, for I am afraid you make no offering to the sweet goddess. Beware you will offend her. Come, why is the flower of you so cool within ? Does never a ray nor a glance find its way through ? Ah, come, a maid should open to the sun, when the sun leans towards her to caress her."

And the big, bright eyes of Anthony laughed down on her, bathing her in his glow. And she felt the lovely glow of his male beauty and his amorousness bathe all her limbs and her body. But it was as he said : the very flower of her womb was cool, was almost cold, like a bud in shadow of frost, for all the flooding of his sunshine. So Anthony, respecting her father, who loved her, had left her.

And it had always been the same. She saw many men, young and old. And on the whole, she liked the old ones best, for they talked to her still and sincere, and did not expect her to open like a flower to the sun of their maleness. Once she asked a philosopher : " Are all women born to be given to men ? " To which the old man answered slowly :

" Rare women wait for the re-born man. For the lotus, as you know, will not answer to all the bright heat of the sun. But she curves her dark, hidden head in the depths, and stirs not. Till, in the night, one of these rare, invisible suns that have been killed and shine no more, rises among the stars in unseen purple, and like the violet, sends its rare, purple rays out into the night. To these the lotus stirs as to a caress, and rises upwards through the flood, and lifts up her bent head, and opens with an expansion such as no other flower knows, and spreads her sharp rays of bliss, and offers her soft, gold depths such as no other flower possesses, to the penetration of the flooding, violet-dark sun that has died and risen and makes no show. But for the golden brief day-suns of show such as Anthony, and for the hard winter suns of power, such as Cæsar, the lotus stirs not, nor will ever stir. Those will only tear open the bud. Ah, I tell you, wait for the re-born and wait for the bud to stir."

So she had waited. For all the men were soldiers or politicians in the Roman spell, assertive, manly, splendid apparently, but of an inward meanness, an inadequacy. And Rome and Egypt alike, had left her alone, unroused. And she was a woman to herself, she would not give herself for a surface glow, nor marry for reasons. She would wait for the lotus to stir.

And then, in Egypt, she had found Isis, in whom she spelled her mystery. She had brought Isis to the shores of Sidon, and lived with her in the mystery of search ; whilst her mother, who loved affairs, controlled the small estate and the slaves with a free hand.

When the woman had roused from her muse and risen to perform the last brief ritual to Isis, she replenished the lamp and left the sanctuary, locking the door. In the outer world, the sun had already set, and twilight was chill among the humming trees, which hummed still, though the wind was abating.

A stranger in a dark, broad hat rose from the corner of the temple steps, holding his hat in the wind. He was dark-faced, with a black pointed beard. " O Madam, whose shelter may I implore ? " he said to the woman, who stood in her yellow mantle on a step above him, beside a pink-and-white painted pillar. Her face was rather long and pale, her dusky blonde hair was held under a thin gold net. She looked down on the vagabond with indifference. It was the same she had seen watching the slaves.

" Why come you down from the road ? " she asked.

" I saw the temple like a pale flower on the coast, and would rest among the trees of the precincts, if the lady of the goddess permits."

" It is Isis in Search," she said, answering his first question.

" The goddess is great," he replied.

She looked at him still with mistrust. There was a faint remote smile in the dark eyes lifted to her, though the face was hollow with suffering. The vagabond divined her hesitation, and was mocking her.

" Stay here upon the steps," she said. " A slave will show you the shelter."

" The lady of Egypt is gracious."

She went down the rocky path of the humped peninsula, in her gilded sandals. Beautiful were her ivory feet, beneath the white tunic, and above the saffron mantle her dusky-blonde head bent as with endless musings. A woman entangled in her own dream. The man smiled a little, half-bitterly, and sat again on the step to wait, drawing his mantle round him, in the cold twilight.

At length a slave appeared, also in hodden grey.

" Seek ye the shelter of our lady ? " he said insolently.

" Even so."

" Then come."

With the brusque insolence of a slave waiting on a vagabond, the young fellow led through the trees and down into a little gully in the rock, where, almost in darkness, was a small cave, with a litter of the tall heaths that grew on the waste places of the coast, under the stone-pines. The place was dark, but absolutely silent from the wind. There was still a faint odour of goats.

" Here sleep ! " said the slave. " For the goats come no more on this half-island. And there is water ! " He pointed to a little basin of rock where the maidenhair fern fringed a dripping mouthful of water.

Having scornfully bestowed his patronage, the slave departed. The man who had died climbed out to the tip of the peninsula, where the wave thrashed. It was rapidly getting dark, and the stars were coming out. The wind was abating for the night. Inland, the steep grooved upslope was dark to the long wavering outline of the crest against the translucent sky. Only now and then, a lantern flickered towards the villa.

The man who had died went back to the shelter. There he took bread from his leather pouch, dipped it in the water of the tiny spring, and slowly ate. Having eaten and washed his mouth, he looked once more at the bright stars in the pure windy sky, then settled the heath for his bed. Having laid his hat and his sandals aside, and put his pouch under his cheek for a pillow, he slept, for he was very tired. Yet during the night the cold woke him, pinching wearily through his weariness. Outside was brilliantly starry, and still windy. He sat and hugged himself in a sort of coma, and towards dawn went to sleep again.

In the morning the coast was still chill in shadow, though the sun was up behind the hills, when the woman came down from the villa towards the goddess. The sea was fair and pale blue, lovely in newness, and at last the wind was still. Yet the waves broke white in the many rocks, and tore in the shingle of the little bay. The woman came slowly, towards her dream. Yet she was aware of an interruption.

As she followed the little neck of rock on to her peninsula, and climbed the slope between the trees to the temple, a slave came down and stood, making his obeisance. There was a faint insolence in his humility. " Speak ! " she said.

" Lady, the man is there, he still sleeps. Lady, may I speak ? "

" Speak ! " she said, repelled by the fellow.

" Lady, the man is an escaped malefactor."

The slave seemed to triumph in imparting the unpleasant news.

" By what sign ? "

" Behold his hands and feet ! Will the lady look on him ? "

" Lead on ! "

The slave led quickly over the mound of the hill down to the tiny ravine. There he stood aside, and the woman went into the crack towards the cave. Her heart beat a little. Above all she must preserve her temple inviolate.

The vagabond was asleep with his cheek on his scrip, his mantle wrapped round him, but his bare, soiled feet curling side by side, to keep each other warm, and his hand lying loosely clenched in sleep. And in the pale skin of his feet usually covered by sandal-straps, she saw the scars, and in the palm of the loose hand.

She had no interest in men, particularly in the servile class. Yet she looked at the sleeping face. It was worn, hollow, and rather ugly. But, a true priestess, she saw the other kind of beauty in it, the sheer stillness of the deeper life. There was even a sort of majesty in the dark brows, over the still, hollow cheeks. She saw that his black hair, left long, in contrast to the Roman fashion, was touched with gray at the temples, and the black pointed beard had threads of gray. But that must be suffering or misfortune, for the man was young. His dusky skin had the silvery glisten of youth still.

There was a beauty of much suffering, and the strange calm candour of finer life in the whole delicate ugliness of the face. For the first time she was touched on the quick at the sight of a man, as if the tip of a fine flame of living had touched her. It was the first time. Men had roused all kinds of feeling in her, but never had touched her with the flame-tip of life.

She went back under the rock to where the slave waited.

" Know ! " she said. " This is no malefactor, but a free citizen of the east. Do not disturb him. But when he comes forth, bring him to me ; tell him I would speak with him."

She spoke coldly, for she found slaves invariably repellent, a little repulsive. They were so embedded in the lesser life, and their appetites and their small consciousness were a little disgusting. So she wrapped her dream round her, and went to the temple, where a slave-girl brought winter roses and jasmine, for the altar. But to-day, even in her ministrations, she was disturbed.

The sun rose over the hill, sparkling, the light fell triumphantly on the little pine-covered peninsula of the coast, and on the pink temple, in the pristine newness. The man who had died woke up, and put on his sandals. He put on his hat too, slung his scrip under his mantle, and went out, to see the morning in all its blue and its new gold. He glanced at the little yellow-and-white narcissus sparkling gaily in the rocks. And he saw the slave waiting for him like a menace.

" Master ! " said the slave. " Our lady would speak with you at the house of Isis."

" It is well," said the wanderer.

He went slowly, staying to look at the pale blue sea like a flower in unruffled bloom, and the white fringes among the rocks, like white rock-flowers, the hollow slopes sheering up high from the shore, grey with olive-trees and green with bright young wheat, and set with the white small villa. All fair and pure in the January morning.

The sun fell on the corner of the temple, he sat down on the step in the sunshine, in the infinite patience of waiting. He had come back to life, but not the same life that he had left, the life of little people and the little day. Re-born, he was in the other life, the greater day of the human consciousness. And he was alone and apart from the little day, and out of contact with the daily people. Not yet had he accepted the irrevocable *noli me tangere* which separates the re-born from the vulgar. The separation was absolute, as yet here at the temple he felt peace, the hard, bright pagan peace with hostility of slaves beneath.

The woman came into the dark inner doorway of the temple, from the shrine, and stood there, hesitating. She could see the dark figure of the man, sitting in that terrible stillness that was portentous to her, had something almost menacing in its patience.

She advanced across the outer chamber of the temple, and the man, becoming aware of her, stood up. She addressed him in Greek, but he said :

" Madam, my Greek is limited. Allow me to speak vulgar Syrian."

" Whence come you ? Whither go you ? " she asked, with a hurried preoccupation of a priestess.

" From the east beyond Damascus—and I go west as the road goes," he replied slowly.

She glanced at him with sudden anxiety and shyness.

" But why do you have the marks of a malefactor ? " she asked abruptly.

" Did the Lady of Isis spy upon me in my sleep ? " he asked, with a gray weariness.

" The slave warned me—your hands and feet——" she said.

He looked at her. Then he said :

" Will the Lady of Isis allow me to bid her farewell, and go up to the road ? "

The wind came in a sudden puff, lifting his mantle and his hat. He put up his hand to hold the brim, and she saw again the thin brown hand with its scar.

" See ! The scar ! " she said, pointing.

" Even so ! " he said. " But farewell, and to Isis my homage and my thanks for sleep."

He was going. But she looked up at him with her wondering blue eyes.

" Will you not look at Isis ? " she said, with sudden impulse. And something stirred in him, like pain.

" Where then ? " he said.

" Come ! "

He followed her into the inner shrine, into the almost-darkness.

When his eyes got used to the faint glow of the lamp, he saw the goddess striding like a ship, eager in the swirl of her gown, and he made his obeisance.

"Great is Isis!" he said. "In her search she is greater than death. Wonderful is such walking in a woman, wonderful the goal. All men praise thee, Isis, thou greater than the mother unto man."

The woman of Isis heard, and threw incense on the brazier. Then she looked at the man.

"Is it well with thee here?" she asked him. "Has Isis brought thee home to herself?"

He looked at the priestess in wonder and trouble.

"I know not," he said.

But the woman was pondering that this was the lost Osiris. She felt it in the quick of her soul. And her agitation was intense.

He would not stay in the close, dark, perfumed shrine. He went out again to the morning, to the cold air. He felt something approaching to touch him, and all his flesh was still woven with pain and the wild commandment: *Noli me tangere!* Touch me not! Oh, don't touch me!

The woman followed into the open with timid eagerness. He was moving away.

"O stranger, do not go! O stay awhile with Isis!"

He looked at her, at her face open like a flower, as if a sun had risen in her soul. And again his loins stirred.

"Would you detain me, girl of Isis?" he said.

"Stay! I am sure you are Osiris!" she said.

He laughed suddenly. "Not yet!" he said. Then he looked at her wistful face. "But I will sleep another night in the cave of the goats, if Isis wills it," he added.

She put her hands together with a priestess's childish happiness.

"Ah! Isis will be glad!" she said.

So he went down to the shore, in great trouble, saying to himself: "Shall I give myself into this touch? Shall I give myself into this touch? Men have tortured me to death with their touch. Yet this girl of Isis is a tender flame of healing. I am a physician, yet I have no healing like the flame of this tender girl. The flame of this tender girl! Like the first pale crocus of the spring. How could I have been blind to the healing and the bliss in the crocus-like body of a tender woman! Ah, tenderness! More terrible and lovely than the death I died——"

He pried small shell-fish from the rocks, and ate them with relish and wonder for the simple taste of the sea. And inwardly, he was tremulous, thinking: "Dare I come into touch? For this is further than death. I have dared to let them lay hands on me and put me to death. But dare I come into this tender touch of life? Oh, this is harder——"

But the woman went into the shrine again, and sat rapt in pure muse, through the long hours, watching the swirling stride of the yearning goddess, and the navel of the bud-like belly, like a seal on the virgin urge of the search. And she gave herself to the woman-flow and to the urge of Isis in Search.

Towards sundown she went on the peninsula to look for him. And she found him gone towards the sun, as she had gone the day before, and sitting on the pine-needles at the foot of the tree, where she had stood when first she saw him. Now she approached tremulously and slowly, afraid lest he did not want her. She stood near him unseen, till suddenly he glanced up at her from under his broad hat, and saw the westering sun in her netted hair. He was startled, yet he expected her.

"Is that your home?" he said, pointing to the white low villa on the slope of olives.

"It is my mother's house. She is a widow, and I am her only child."

"And are these all her slaves?"

"Except those that are mine."

Their eyes met for a moment.

"Will you too sit to see the sun go down?" he said.

He had not risen to speak to her. He had known too much pain. So she sat on the dry brown pine-needles, gathering her saffron mantle round her knees. A boat was coming in, out of the open glow into the shadow of the bay, and slaves were lifting small nets, their babble coming off the surface of the water.

"And this is home to you," he said.

"But I serve Isis in Search," she replied.

He looked at her. She was like a soft, musing cloud, somehow remote. His soul smote him with passion and compassion.

"Mayst thou find thy desire, maiden," he said, with sudden earnestness.

"And art thou not Osiris?" she asked.

He flushed suddenly.

"Yes, if thou wilt heal me!" he said. "For the death aloofness is still upon me, and I cannot escape it."

She looked at him for a moment in fear, from the soft blue sun of her eyes. Then she lowered her head, and they sat in silence in the warmth and glow of the western sun : the man who had died, and the woman of the pure search.

The sun was curving down to the sea, in grand winter splendour. It fell on the twinkling, naked bodies of the slaves, with their ruddy broad hams and their small black heads, as they ran spreading the nets on the pebble beach. The all-tolerant Pan watched over them. All-tolerant Pan should be their god for ever.

The woman rose as the sun's rim dipped, saying :

" If you will stay, I shall send down victual and covering."

" The lady your mother, what will she say ? "

The woman of Isis looked at him strangely, but with a tinge of misgiving.

" It is my own," she said.

" It is good," he said, smiling faintly, and foreseeing difficulties.

He watched her go, with her absorbed, strange motion of the self-dedicate. Her dun head was a little bent, the white linen swung about her ivory ankles. And he saw the naked slaves stand to look at her, with a certain wonder, and even a certain mischief. But she passed intent through the door in the wall, on the bay.

The man who had died sat on at the foot of the tree overlooking the strand, for on the little shore everything happened. At the small stream which ran in round the corner of the property wall, women slaves were still washing linen, and now and again came the hollow chock ! chock ! chock ! as they beat it against the smooth stones, in the dark little hollow of the pool. There was a smell of olive-refuse on the air ; and sometimes still the faint rumble of the grindstone that was milling the olives, inside the garden, and the sound of the slave calling to the ass at the mill. Then through the doorway a woman stepped, a gray-haired woman in a mantle of whitish wool, and there followed her a bare-headed man in a toga, a Roman : probably her steward or overseer. They stood on the high shingle above the sea, and cast round a rapid glance. The broad-hammed, ruddy-bodied slaves bent absorbed and abject over the nets, picking them clean, the women washing linen thrust their palms with energy down on the wash, the old slave bent absorbed at the water's edge, washing the fish and the polyps of the catch. And the woman and the overseer saw it all, in one glance. They also saw, seated at the foot of the tree on the rocks of the peninsula, the strange man silent and alone. And the man who had died saw that they spoke of him. Out of the little sacred world of the peninsula he looked on the common world, and saw it still hostile.

The sun was touching the sea, across the tiny bay stretched the shadow of the opposite humped headland. Over the shingle, now blue and cold in shadow, the elderly woman trod heavily, in shadow too, to look at the fish spread in the flat basket of the old man crouching at the water's edge : a naked old slave with fat hips and shoulders, on whose soft, fairish-orange body the last sun twinkled, then died. The old slave continued cleaning the fish absorbedly, not looking up : as if the lady were the shadow of twilight falling on him.

Then from the gateway stepped two slave-girls with flat baskets on their heads, and from one basket the terra-cotta wine-jar and the oil-jar poked up, leaning slightly. Over the massive shingle, under the wall, came the girls, and the woman of Isis in her saffron mantle stepped in twilight after them. Out at sea, the sun still shone. Here was shadow. The mother with gray head stood at the sea's edge and watched the daughter, all yellow and white, with dun blonde head, swinging unseeing and unheeding after the slave-girls, towards the neck of rock of the peninsula ; the daughter, travelling in her absorbed other-world. And not moving from her place, the elderly mother watched that procession of three file up the rise of the headland, between the trees, and disappear, shut in by trees. No slave had lifted a head to look. The gray-haired woman still watched the trees where her daughter had disappeared. Then she glanced again at the foot of the tree, where the man who had died was still sitting, inconspicuous now, for the sun had left him ; and only the far blade of the sea shone bright. It was evening. Patience ! Let destiny move !

The mother plodded with a stamping stride up the shingle : not long and swinging and rapt, like the daughter, but short and determined. Then down the rocks opposite came two naked slaves trotting with huge bundles of dark green on their shoulders, so that their broad, naked legs twinkled underneath like insects' legs, and their heads were hidden. They came trotting across the shingle, heedless and intent on their way, when suddenly the man, the Roman-looking overseer, addressed them, and they stopped dead. They stood invisible under their loads, as if they might disappear altogether, now they were arrested. Then a hand came out and pointed to the peninsula. Then the two green-heaped slaves trotted on, towards the temple precincts. The gray-haired woman joined the man, and slowly the two passed through the door again, from the shingle of the sea to the property of the villa. Then the old, fat-shouldered slave rose, pallid in the shadow, with his tray of fish from the sea, and the woman rose from the pool, dusky and alive, piling the wet linen in a heap on to the flat baskets, and the slaves who had cleaned the net gathered its whitish folds together. And the old slave with the fish basket on his shoulder, and the women slaves with the heaped baskets of wet linen on their heads, and the two slaves with the folded net, and the slave with oars on his shoulders, and the boy with the folded sail on his arm, gathered in a naked group near the door, and the man who had died heard the low buzz of their chatter. Then as the wind wafted cold, they began to pass through the door.

It was the life of the little day, the life of little people. And the man who had died said to himself : " Unless we encompass it in the greater day, and set the little life in the circle of the greater life, all is disaster."

Even the tops of the hills were in shadow. Only the sky was still upwardly radiant. The sea was a vast milky shadow. The man who had died rose a little stiffly, and turned into the grove.

There was no one at the temple. He went on to his lair in the rock. There, the slave-men had carried out the old heath of the bedding, swept the rock floor, and were spreading with nice art the myrtle, then the rougher heath, then the soft, bushy heath-tips on top, for a bed. Over it all they put a well-tanned white ox-skin. The maids had laid folded woollen covers at the head of the cave, and the wine-jar, the oil-jar, a terra-cotta drinking-cup, and a basket containing bread, salt, cheese, dried figs and eggs, stood neatly arranged. There was also a little brazier of charcoal. The cave was suddenly full, and a dwelling-place.

The woman of Isis stood in the hollow by the tiny spring.

Only one slave at a time could pass. The girl-slaves waited at the entrance to the narrow place. When the man who had died appeared, the woman sent the girls away. The men-slaves still arranged the bed, making the job as long as possible. But the woman of Isis dismissed them too. And the man who had died came to look at his house.

" Is it well ? " the woman asked him.

" It is very well," the man replied. " But the lady, your mother, and he who is no doubt the steward, watched while the slaves brought the goods. Will they not oppose you ? "

" I have my own portion ! Can I not give of my own ? Who is going to oppose me and the gods ? " she said, with a certain soft fury, touched with exasperation. So that he knew that her mother would oppose her, and that the spirit of the little life would fight

2 N *

against the spirit of the greater. And he thought : " Why did the woman of Isis relinquish her portion in the daily world ? She should have kept her goods fiercely ! "

" Will you eat and drink ? " she said. " On the ashes are warm eggs. And I will go up to the meal at the villa. But in the second hour of the night I shall come down to the temple. O, then, will you come too to Isis ? " She looked at him, and a queer glow dilated her eyes. This was her dream, and it was greater than herself. He could not bear to thwart her or hurt her in the least thing now. She was in the full glow of her woman's mystery.

" Shall I wait at the temple ? " he said.

" O, wait at the second hour and I shall come." He heard the humming supplication in her voice and his fibres quivered.

" But the lady, your mother ? " he said gently.

The woman looked at him, startled.

" She will not thwart me ! " she said.

So he knew that the mother would thwart the daughter, for the daughter had left her goods in the hands of her mother, who would hold fast to this power.

But she went, and the man who had died lay reclining on his couch, and ate the eggs from the ashes, and dipped his bread in oil, and ate it, for his flesh was dry : and he mixed wine and water, and drank. And so he lay still, and the lamp made a small bud of light.

He was absorbed and enmeshed in new sensations. The woman of Isis was lovely to him, not so much in form, as in the wonderful womanly glow of her. Suns beyond suns had dipped her in mysterious fire, the mysterious fire of a potent woman, and to touch her was like touching the sun. Best of all was her tender desire for him, like sunshine, so soft and still.

" She is like sunshine upon me," he said to himself, stretching his limbs. " I have never before stretched my limbs in such sunshine, as her desire for me. The greatest of all gods granted me this."

At the same time he was haunted by the fear of the outer world. " If they can, they will kill us," he said to himself. " But there is a law of the sun which protects us."

And again he said to himself : " I have risen naked and branded. But if I am naked enough for this contact, I have not died in vain. Before I was clogged."

He rose and went out. The night was chill and starry, and of a great wintry splendour. " There are destinies of splendour," he said to the night, " after all our doom of littleness and meanness and pain."

So he went up silently to the temple, and waited in darkness against the inner wall, looking out on a gray darkness, stars, and rims of trees. And he said again to himself : " There are destinies of splendour, and there is a greater power."

So at last he saw the light of her silk lanthorn swinging, coming intermittent between the trees, yet coming swiftly. She was alone, and near, the light softly swishing on her mantle-hem. And he trembled with fear and with joy, saying to himself : " I am almost more afraid of this touch than I was of death. For I am more nakedly exposed to it."

" I am here, Lady of Isis," he said softly out of the dark.

" Ah ! " she cried, in fear also, yet in rapture. For she was given to her dream.

She unlocked the door of the shrine, and he followed after her. Then she latched the door shut again. The air inside was warm and close and perfumed. The man who had died stood by the closed door, and watched the woman. She had come first to the goddess. And dim-lit, the goddess-statue stood surging forward, a little fearsome like a great woman-presence urging.

The priestess did not look at him. She took off her saffron mantle and laid it on a low couch. In the dim light she was bare armed, in her girdled white tunic. But she was still hiding herself away from him. He stood back in shadow, and watched her softly fan the brazier and fling on incense. Faint clouds of sweet aroma arose on the air. She turned to the statue in the ritual of approach, softly swaying forward with a slight lurch, liked a moored boat, tipping towards the goddess.

He watched the strange rapt woman, and he said to himself : " I must leave her alone in her rapture, her female mysteries." So she tipped in her strange forward-swaying rhythm before the goddess. Then she broke into a murmur of Greek, which he could not understand. And, as she murmured, her swaying softly subsided, like a boat on a sea that grows still. And as he watched her, he saw her soul in its aloneness, and its female difference. He said to himself : How different she is from me, how strangely different ! She is afraid of me, and my male difference. She is getting herself naked and clear of her fear. How sensitive and softly alive she is, with a life so different from mine ! How beautiful with a soft strange courage of life, so different from my courage of death ! What a beautiful thing, like the heart of a rose, like the core of a flame. She is making herself completely penetrable. Ah ! how terrible to fail her, or to trespass on her !

She turned to him, her face glowing from the goddess.

" You are Osiris, aren't you ? " she said naively.

" If you will," he said.

" Will you let Isis discover you ? Will you not take off your things ? "

He looked at the woman, and lost his breath. And his wounds, and especially the death-wound through his belly, began to cry again.

" It has hurt so much ! " he said. " You must forgive me if I am still held back."

But he took off his cloak and his tunic, and went naked towards the idol, his breast panting with the sudden terror of overwhelming pain, memory of overwhelming pain, and grief too bitter.

" They did me to death ! " he said in excuse of himself, turning his face to her for a moment.

And she saw the ghost of the death in him, as he stood there thin and stark before her, and suddenly she was terrified, and she felt robbed. She felt the shadow of the gray, grisly wing of death triumphant.

" Ah, Goddess," he said to the idol, in the vernacular. " I would be so glad to live, if you would give me my clue again."

For here again he felt desperate, faced by the demand of life, and burdened still by his death.

" Let me anoint you ! " the woman said to him softly. " Let me anoint the scars ! Show me, and let me anoint them ! "

He forgot his nakedness in this re-evoked old pain. He sat on the edge of the couch, and she poured a little ointment into the palm of his hand. And as she chafed his hand, it all came back, the nails, the holes, the cruelty, the unjust cruelty against him who had offered only kindness. The agony of injustice and cruelty came over him again, as in his death-hour. But she chafed the palm, murmuring : " What was torn becomes a new flesh, what was a wound is full of fresh life ; this scar is the eye of the violet."

And he could not help smiling at her, in her naive priestess's absorption. This was her dream, and he was only a dream-object to her. She would never know or understand what he was. Especially she would never know the death that was gone before in him. But what did it matter ? She was different. She was woman : her life and her death were different from his. Only she was good to him.

When she chafed his feet with oil and tender, tender healing, he could not refrain from saying to her :

"Once a woman washed my feet with tears, and wiped them with her hair, and poured on precious ointment."

The woman of Isis looked up at him from her earnest work, interrupted again.

"Were they hurt then ? " she said. " Your feet ? "

"No, no ! It was while they were whole."

"And did you love her ? "

"Love had passed in her. She only wanted to serve," he replied. "She had been a prostitute."

"And did you let her serve you ? " she asked.

"Yea."

"Did you let her serve you with the corpse of her love ? "

"Ay ! "

Suddenly it dawned on him : I asked them all to serve me with the corpse of their love. And in the end I offered them only the corpse of my love. This is my body—take and eat—my corpse——

A vivid shame went through him. " After all," he thought, " I wanted them to love with dead bodies. If I had kissed Judas with live love, perhaps he would never have kissed me with death. Perhaps he loved me in the flesh, and I willed that he should love me bodylessly, with the corpse of love——"

There dawned on him the reality of the soft warm love which is in touch, and which is full of delight. " And I told them, blessed are they that mourn," he said to himself. " Alas, if I mourned even this woman here, now I am in death, I should have to remain dead, and I want so much to live. Life has brought me to this woman with warm hands. And her touch is more to me now than all my words. For I want to live——"

"Go then to the goddess ! " she said softly, gently pushing him towards Isis. And as he stood there dazed and naked as an unborn thing, he heard the woman murmuring to the goddess, murmuring, murmuring with a plaintive appeal. She was stooping now, looking at the scar in the soft flesh of the socket of his side, a scar deep and like an eye sore with endless weeping, just in the soft socket above the hip. It was here that his blood had left him, and his essential seed. The woman was trembling softly and murmuring in Greek. And he in the recurring dismay of having died, and in the anguished perplexity of having tried to force life, felt his wounds crying aloud, and the deep places of the body howling again : " I have been murdered, and I lent myself to murder. They murdered me, but I lent myself to murder——"

The woman, silent now, but quivering, laid oil in her hand and put her palm over the wound in his right side. He winced, and the wound absorbed his life again, as thousands of times before. And in the dark, wild pain and panic of his consciousness rang only one cry : " Oh, how can she take this death out of me ? How can she take from me this death ? She can never know ! She can never understand ! She can never equal it ! . . ."

In silence, she softly rhythmically chafed the scar with oil. Absorbed now in her priestess's task, softly, softly gathering power, while the vitals of the man howled in panic. But as she gradually gathered power, and passed in a girdle round him to the opposite scar, gradually warmth began to take the place of the cold terror, and he felt : " I am going to be warm again, and I am going to be whole ! I shall be warm like the morning. I shall be a man. It doesn't need understanding. It needs newness. She brings me newness——"

And he listened to the faint, ceaseless wail of distress of his wounds, sounding as if for ever under the horizons of his consciousness. But the wail was growing dim, more dim.

He thought of the woman toiling over him : " She does not know ! She does not realize the death in me. But she has another consciousness. She comes to me from the opposite end of the night."

Having chafed all his lower body with oil, having worked with her slow intensity of a priestess, so that the sound of his wounds grew dimmer and dimmer, suddenly she put her breast against the wound in his left side, and her arms round him, folding over the wound in his right side, and she pressed him to her, in a power of living warmth, like the folds of a river. And the wailing died out altogether, and there was a stillness, and darkness in his soul, unbroken dark stillness, wholeness.

Then slowly, slowly, in the perfect darkness of his inner man, he felt the stir of something coming. A dawn, a new sun. A new sun was coming up in him, in the perfect inner darkness of himself. He waited for it breathless, quivering with a fearful hope. . . . " Now I am not myself. I am something new. . . ."

And as it rose, he felt, with a cold breath of disappointment, the girdle of the living woman slip down from him, the warmth and the glow slipped from him, leaving him stark. She crouched, spent, at the feet of the goddess, hiding her face.

Stooping, he laid his hand softly on her warm, bright shoulder, and the shock of desire went through him, shock after shock, so that he wondered if it were another sort of death : but full of magnificence.

Now all his consciousness was there in the crouching, hidden woman. He stooped beside her and caressed her softly, blindly, murmuring inarticulate things. And his death and his passion of sacrifice were all as nothing to him now, he knew only the crouching fulness of the woman there, the soft white rock of life. . . . " On this rock I built my life." The deep-folded, penetrable rock of the living woman ! The woman, hiding her face. Himself bending over, powerful and new like dawn.

He crouched to her, and he felt the blaze of his manhood and his power rise up in his loins, magnificent.

" I am risen ! "

Magnificent, blazing indomitable in the depths of his loins, his own sun dawned, and sent its fire running along his limbs, so that his face shone unconsciously.

He untied the string on the linen tunic, and slipped the garment down, till he saw the white glow of her white-gold breasts. And he touched them, and he felt his life go molten. " Father ! " he said, " why did you hide this from me ? " And he touched her with the poignancy of wonder, and the marvellous piercing transcendence of desire. " Lo ! " he said, " this is beyond prayer." It was the deep, interfolded warmth, warmth living and penetrable, the woman, the heart of the rose ! My mansion is the intricate warm rose, my joy is this blossom !

She looked up at him suddenly, her face like a lifted light, wistful, tender, her eyes like many wet flowers. And he drew her to his breast with a passion of tenderness and consuming desire, and the last thought : " My hour is upon me, I am taken unawares——"

So he knew her, and was one with her.

Afterwards, with a dim wonder, she touched the great scars in his sides with her finger-tips, and said :

" But they no longer hurt ? "

" They are suns ! " he said. " They shine from your touch. They are my atonement with you."

And when they left the temple, it was the coldness before dawn. As he closed the door, he looked again at the goddess, and he said : " Lo, Isis is a kindly goddess ; and full of tenderness. Great gods are warm-hearted, and have tender goddesses."

The woman wrapped herself in her mantle and went home in silence, sightless, brooding like the lotus softly shutting again, with its gold core full of fresh life. She saw nothing, for her own petals were a sheath to her. Only she thought : " I am full of Osiris. I am full of the risen Osiris ! . . ."

But the man looked at the vivid stars before dawn, as they rained down to the sea, and the dogstar green towards the sea's rim. And he thought : " How plastic it is, how full of curves and folds like an invisible rose of dark-petalled openness that shows where the dew touches its darkness ! How full it is, and great beyond all gods. How it leans around me, and I am part of it, the great rose of Space. I am like a grain of its perfume, and the woman is a grain of its beauty. Now the world is one flower of many petalled darknesses, and I am in its perfume as in a touch."

So, in the absolute stillness and fulness of touch, he slept in his cave while the dawn came. And after the dawn, the wind rose and brought a storm, with cold rain. So he stayed in his cave in the peace and the delight of being in touch, delighting to hear the sea, and the rain on the earth, and to see one white-and-gold narcissus bowing wet, and still wet. And he said : " This is the great atone-ment, the being in touch. The gray sea and the rain, the wet narcissus and the woman I wait for, the invisible Isis and the unseen sun are all in touch, and at one."

He waited at the temple for the woman, and she came in the rain. But she said to him :

" Let me sit awhile with Isis. And come to me, will you come to me, in the second hour of night ? "

So he went back to the cave and lay in stillness and in the joy of being in touch, waiting for the woman who would come with the night, and consummate again the contact. Then when night came the woman came, and came gladly, for her great yearning too was upon her, to be in touch, to be in touch with him, nearer.

So the days came, and the nights came, and days came again, and the contact was perfected and fulfilled. And he said : " I will ask her nothing, not even her name, for a name would set her apart."

And she said to herself : " He is Osiris. I wish to know no more."

Plum-blossom blew from the trees, the time of the narcissus was past, anemones lit up the ground and were gone, the perfume of bean-field was in the air. All changed, the blossom of the universe changed its petals and swung round to look another way. The spring was fulfilled, a contact was established, the man and the woman were fulfilled of one another, and departure was in the air.

One day he met her under the trees, when the morning sun was hot, and the pines smelled sweet, and on the hills the last pear-bloom was scattering. She came slowly towards him, and in her gentle lingering, her tender hanging back from him, he knew a change in her.

"Hast thou conceived?" he asked her.

"Why?" she said.

"Thou art like a tree whose green leaves follow the blossom, full of sap. And there is a withdrawing about thee."

"It is so," she said. "I am with young by thee. Is it good?"

"Yea!" he said. "How should it not be good? So the nightingale calls no more from the valley-bed. But where wilt thou bear the child, for I am naked of all but life."

"We will stay here," she said.

"But the lady, your mother?"

A shadow crossed her brow. She did not answer.

"What when she knows?" he said.

"She begins to know."

"And would she hurt you?"

"Ah, not me! What I have is all my own. And I shall be big with Osiris. . . . But thou, do you watch her slaves."

She looked at him, and the peace of her maternity was troubled by anxiety.

"Let not your heart be troubled!" he said. "I have died the death once."

So he knew the time was come again for him to depart. He would go alone, with his destiny. Yet not alone, for the touch would be upon him, even as he left his touch on her. And invisible suns would go with him.

Yet he must go. For here on the bay the little life of jealousy and property was resuming sway again, as the suns of passionate fecundity relaxed their sway. In the name of property, the widow and her slaves would seek to be revenged on him for the bread he had eaten, and the living touch he had established, the woman he had delighted in. But he said: "Not twice! They shall not now profane the touch in me. My wits against theirs."

So he watched. And he knew they plotted. So he moved from the little cave, and found another shelter, a tiny cove of sand by the sea, dry and secret under the rocks.

He said to the woman:

"I must go now soon. Trouble is coming to me from the slaves. But I am a man, and the world is open. But what is between us is good, and is established. Be at peace. And when the nightingale calls again from your valley-bed, I shall come again, sure as Spring."

She said: "O don't go! Stay with me on half the island, and

I will build a house for you and me under the pine-trees by the temple, where we can live apart."

Yet she knew that he would go. And even she wanted the coolness of her own air around her, and the release from anxiety.

" If I stay," he said, " they will betray me to the Romans and to their justice. But I will never be betrayed again. So when I am gone, live in peace with the growing child. And I shall come again : all is good between us, near or apart. The suns come back in their seasons : and I shall come again."

" Do not go yet," she said. " I have set a slave to watch at the neck of the peninsula. Do not go yet, till the harm shows."

But as he lay in his little cove, on a calm, still night, he heard the soft knock of oars, and the bump of a boat against the rock. So he crept out to listen. And he heard the Roman overseer say :

" Lead softly to the goat's den. And Lysippus shall throw the net over the malefactor while he sleeps, and we will bring him before justice, and the Lady of Isis shall know nothing of it. . . ."

The man who had died caught a whiff of flesh from the oiled and naked slaves as they crept up, then the faint perfume of the Roman. He crept nearer to the sea. The slave who sat in the boat sat motionless, holding the oars, for the sea was quite still. And the man who had died knew him.

So out of the deep cleft of a rock he said, in a clear voice :

" Art thou not that slave who possessed the maiden under the eyes of Isis ? Art thou not the youth ? Speak ! "

The youth stood up in the boat in terror. His movement sent the boat bumping against the rock. The slave sprang out in wild fear, and fled up the rocks. The man who had died quickly seized the boat and stepped in, and pushed off. The oars were yet warm with the unpleasant warmth of the hands of the slaves. But the man pulled slowly out, to get into the current which set down the coast, and would carry him in silence. The high coast was utterly dark against the starry night. There was no glimmer from the peninsula : the priestess came no more at night. The man who had died rowed slowly on, with the current, and laughed to himself : " I have sowed the seed of my life and my resurrection, and put my touch forever upon the choice woman of this day, and I carry her perfume in my flesh like essence of roses. She is dear to me in the middle of my being. But the gold and flowing serpent is coiling up again, to sleep at the root of my tree."

" So let the boat carry me. To-morrow is another day."

I

MR. LINDLEY was first vicar of Aldecross. The cottages of this tiny hamlet had nestled in peace since their beginning, and the country folk had crossed the lanes and farm-lands, two or three miles, to the parish church at Greymeed, on the bright Sunday mornings.

But when the pits were sunk, blank rows of dwellings started up beside the high roads, and a new population, skimmed from the floating scum of workmen, was filled in, the cottages and the country people almost obliterated.

To suit the convenience of these new collier-inhabitants, a church must be built at Aldecross. There was not too much money. And so the little building crouched like a humped stone-and-mortar mouse, with two little turrets at the west corners for ears, in the fields near the cottages and the apple trees, as far as possible from the dwellings down the high road. It had an uncertain, timid look about it. And so they planted big-leaved ivy, to hide its shrinking newness. So that now the little church stands buried in its greenery, stranded and sleeping among the fields, while the brick houses elbow nearer and nearer, threatening to crush it down. It is already obsolete.

The Reverend Ernest Lindley, aged twenty-seven, and newly married, came from his curacy in Suffolk to take charge of his church. He was just an ordinary young man, who had been to Cambridge and taken orders. His wife was a self-assured young woman, daughter of a Cambridgeshire rector. Her father had spent the whole of his thousand a year, so that Mrs. Lindley had nothing of her own. Thus the young married people came to Aldecross to live on a stipend of about a hundred and twenty pounds, and to keep up a superior position.

They were not very well received by the new, raw, disaffected population of colliers. Being accustomed to farm labourers, Mr. Lindley had considered himself as belonging indisputably to the upper or ordering classes. He had to be humble to the county families, but still, he was of their kind, whilst the common people were something different. He had no doubts of himself.

He found, however, that the collier population refused to accept this arrangement. They had no use for him in their lives, and they told him so, callously. The women merely said, " they were throng," or else, " Oh, it's no good you coming here, we're Chapel." The men were quite good-humoured so long as he did not touch them too nigh, they were cheerfully contemptuous of him, with a preconceived contempt he was powerless against.

At last, passing from indignation to silent resentment, even, if he dared have acknowledged it, to conscious hatred of the majority of his flock, and unconscious hatred of himself, he confined his activities to a narrow round of cottages, and he had to submit. He had no particular character, having always depended on his position in society to give him position among men. Now he was so poor, he had no social standing even among the common vulgar tradespeople of the district, and he had not the nature nor the wish to make his society agreeable to them, nor the strength to impose himself where he would have liked to be recognized. He dragged on, pale and miserable and neutral.

At first his wife raged with mortification. She took on airs and used a high hand. But her income was too small, the wrestling with tradesmen's bills was too pitiful, she only met with general, callous ridicule when she tried to be impressive.

Wounded to the quick of her pride, she found herself isolated in an indifferent, callous population. She raged indoors and out. But soon she learned that she must pay too heavily for her outdoor rages, and then she only raged within the walls of the rectory. There her feeling was so strong that she frightened herself. She saw herself hating her husband, and she knew that, unless she were careful, she would smash her form of life and bring catastrophe upon him and upon herself. So in very fear she went quiet. She hid, bitter and beaten by fear, behind the only shelter she had in the world, her gloomy, poor parsonage.

Children were born one every year ; almost mechanically, she continued to perform her maternal duty, which was forced upon her. Gradually, broken by the suppressing of her violent anger and misery and disgust, she became an invalid and took to her couch.

The children grew up healthy, but unwarmed and rather rigid. Their father and mother educated them at home, made them very proud and very genteel, put them definitely and cruelly in the upper classes, apart from the vulgar around them. So they lived quite isolated. They were good-looking, and had that curiously clean, semi-transparent look of the genteel, isolated poor.

Gradually Mr. and Mrs. Lindley lost all hold on life, and spent their hours, weeks and years merely haggling to make ends meet, and bitterly repressing and pruning their children into gentility, urging them to ambition, weighting them with duty. On Sunday morning the whole family, except the mother, went down the lane to church, the long-legged girls in skimpy frocks, the boys in black coats and long, grey, unfitting trousers. They passed by their father's parishioners with mute, clear faces, childish mouths closed in pride that was like a doom to them, and childish eyes already unseeing. Miss Mary, the eldest, was the leader. She was a long, slim thing with a fine profile and a proud, pure look of submission to a high fate. Miss Louisa, the second, was short and plump and obstinate-looking. She had more enemies than ideals. She looked after the lesser children, Miss Mary after the elder. The collier children watched this pale, distinguished procession of the vicar's family pass mutely by, and they were impressed by the air of gentility and distance, they made mock of the trousers of the small sons, they felt inferior in themselves, and hate stirred their hearts.

In her time, Miss Mary received as governess a few little daughters of tradesmen ; Miss Louisa managed the house and went among her father's church-goers, giving lessons on the piano to the colliers' daughters at thirteen shillings for twenty-six lessons.

II

One winter morning, when his daughter Mary was about twenty years old, Mr. Lindley, a thin, unobtrusive figure in his black overcoat and his wideawake, went down into Aldecross with a packet of white papers under his arm. He was delivering the parish almanacs.

A rather pale, neutral man of middle age, he waited while the train thumped over the level-crossing, going up to the pit which rattled busily just along the line. A wooden-legged man hobbled to open the gate, Mr. Lindley passed on. Just at his left hand, below the road and the railway, was the red roof of a cottage, showing through the bare twigs of apple trees. Mr. Lindley passed round the low wall, and descended the worn steps that led from the highway down to the cottage which crouched darkly and quietly away below the rumble of passing trains and the clank of coal-carts, in a quiet little underworld of its own. Snowdrops with tight-shut buds were hanging very still under the bare currant bushes.

The clergyman was just going to knock when he heard a clinking noise, and turning saw through the open door of a black shed just behind him an elderly woman in a black lace cap stooping among reddish big cans, pouring a very bright liquid into a tundish. There was a smell of paraffin. The woman put down her can, took the tundish and laid it on a shelf, then rose with a tin bottle. Her eyes met those of the clergyman.

"Oh, is it you, Mr. Lin'ley!" she said, in a complaining tone. "Go in."

The minister entered the house. In the hot kitchen sat a big, elderly man with a great grey beard, taking snuff. He grunted in a deep, muttering voice, telling the minister to sit down, and then took no more notice of him, but stared vacantly into the fire. Mr. Lindley waited.

The woman came in, the ribbons of her black lace cap, or bonnet, hanging on her shawl. She was of medium stature, everything about her was tidy. She went up a step out of the kitchen, carrying the paraffin tin. Feet were heard entering the room up the step. It was a little haberdashery shop, with parcels on the shelves of the walls, a big, old-fashioned sewing machine with tailor's work lying round it, in the open space. The woman went behind the counter, gave the child who had entered the paraffin bottle, and took from her a jug.

"My mother says shall yer put it down," said the child, and she was gone. The woman wrote in a book, then came into the kitchen with her jug. The husband, a very large man, rose and brought more coal to the already hot fire. He moved slowly and sluggishly. Already he was going dead ; being a tailor, his large form had become an encumbrance to him. In his youth he had been a great dancer and boxer. Now he was taciturn, and inert. The minister had nothing to say, so he sought for his phrases. But John Durant took no notice, existing silent and dull.

Mrs. Durant spread the cloth. Her husband poured himself beer into a mug, and began to smoke and drink.

"Shall you have some?" he growled through his beard at the clergyman, looking slowly from the man to the jug, capable of this one idea.

"No, thank you," replied Mr. Lindley, though he would have liked some beer. He must set the example in a drinking parish.

"We need a drop to keep us going," said Mrs. Durant.

She had rather a complaining manner. The clergyman sat on uncomfortably while she laid the table for the half-past ten lunch. Her husband drew up to eat. She remained in her little round arm-chair by the fire.

She was a woman who would have liked to be easy in her life, but to whose lot had fallen a rough and turbulent family, and a slothful husband who did not care what became of himself or anybody. So, her rather good-looking square face was peevish, she had that air of having been compelled all her life to serve unwillingly, and to control where she did not want to control. There was about her, too, that masterful *aplomb* of a woman who has brought up and ruled her sons : but even them she had ruled unwillingly. She had enjoyed managing her little haberdashery shop, riding in the carrier's cart to Nottingham, going through the big warehouses to buy her goods. But the fret of managing her sons she did not like. Only she loved her youngest boy, because he was her last, and she saw herself free.

This was one of the houses the clergyman visited occasionally. Mrs. Durant, as part of her regulation, had brought up all her sons in the Church. Not that she had any religion. Only, it was what she was used to. Mr. Durant was without religion. He read the fervently evangelical *Life of John Wesley* with a curious pleasure, getting from it a satisfaction as from the warmth of the fire, or a glass of brandy. But he cared no more about John Wesley, in fact, than about John Milton, of whom he had never heard.

Mrs. Durant took her chair to the table.

" I don't feel like eating," she sighed.

" Why—aren't you well ? " asked the clergyman, patronizing.

" It isn't that," she sighed. She sat with shut, straight mouth. " I don't know what's going to become of us."

But the clergyman had ground himself down so long that he could not easily sympathize.

" Have you any trouble ? " he asked.

" Ay, have I any trouble ! " cried the elderly woman. " I shall end my days in the workhouse."

The minister waited unmoved. What could she know of poverty, in her little house of plenty !

" I hope not," he said.

" And the one lad as I wanted to keep by me——" she lamented.

The minister listened without sympathy, quite neutral.

" And the lad as would have been a support to my old age ! What is going to become of us ? " she said.

The clergyman, justly, did not believe in the cry of poverty, but wondered what had become of the son.

"Has anything happened to Alfred?" he asked.

"We've got word he's gone for a Queen's sailor," she said sharply.

"He has joined the Navy!" exclaimed Mr. Lindley. "I think he could scarcely have done better—to serve his Queen and country on the sea . . ."

"He is wanted to serve *me*," she cried. "And I wanted my lad at home."

Alfred was her baby, her last, whom she had allowed herself the luxury of spoiling.

"You will miss him," said Mr. Lindley, "that is certain. But this is no regrettable step for him to have taken—on the con'rary."

"That's easy for you to say, Mr. Lindley," she replied tartly. "Do you think I want my lad climbing ropes at another man's bidding, like a monkey——?"

"There is no *dishonour*, surely, in serving in the Navy?"

"Dishonour this dishonour that," cried the angry old woman. "He goes and makes a slave of himself, and he'll rue it."

Her angry, scornful impatience nettled the clergyman, and silenced him for some moments.

"I do not see," he retorted at last, white at the gills and inadequate, "that the Queen's service is any more to be called slavery than working in a mine."

"At home he was at home, and his own master. *I* know he'll find a difference."

"It may be the making of him," said the clergyman. "It will take him away from bad companionship and drink."

Some of the Durants' sons were notorious drinkers, and Alfred was not quite steady.

"And why indeed shouldn't he have his glass?" cried the mother. "He picks no man's pocket to pay for it!"

The clergyman stiffened at what he thought was an allusion to his own profession, and his unpaid bills.

"With all due consideration, I am glad to hear he has joined the Navy," he said.

"Me with my old age coming on, and his father working very little! I'd thank you to be glad about something else besides that, Mr. Lindley."

The woman began to cry. Her husband, quite impassive, finished his lunch of meat-pie, and drank some beer. Then he turned to the fire, as if there were no one in the room but himself.

"I shall respect all men who serve God and their country on the sea, Mrs. Durant," said the clergyman stubbornly.

"That is very well, when they're not your sons who are doing the dirty work. It makes a difference," she replied tartly.

"I should be proud if one of my sons were to enter the Navy."

"Ay—well—we're not all of us made alike——"

The minister rose. He put down a large folded paper.

"I've brought the almanac," he said.

Mrs. Durant unfolded it.

"I do like a bit of colour in things," she said, petulantly.

The clergyman did not reply.

"There's that envelope for the organist's fund——" said the old woman, and rising, she took the thing from the mantelpiece, went into the shop, and returned sealing it up.

"Which is all I can afford," she said.

Mr. Lindley took his departure, in his pocket the envelope containing Mrs. Durant's offering for Miss Louisa's services. He went from door to door delivering the almanacs, in dull routine. Jaded with the monotony of the business, and with the repeated effort of greeting half-known people, he felt barren and rather irritable. At last he returned home.

In the dining-room was a small fire. Mrs. Lindley, growing very stout, lay on her couch. The vicar carved the cold mutton ; Miss Louisa, short and plump and rather flushed, came in from the kitchen ; Miss Mary, dark, with a beautiful white brow and grey eyes, served the vegetables ; the children chattered a little, but not exuberantly. The very air seemed starved.

"I went to the Durants," said the vicar, as he served out small portions of mutton ; "it appears Alfred has run away to join the Navy."

"Do him good," came the rough voice of the invalid.

Miss Louisa, attending to the youngest child, looked up in protest.

"Why has he done that ? " asked Mary's low, musical voice.

"He wanted some excitement, I suppose," said the vicar. "Shall we say grace ? "

The children were arranged, all bent their heads, grace was pronounced, at the last word every face was being raised to go on with the interesting subject.

"He's just done the right thing, for once," came the rather deep voice of the mother ; "save him from becoming a drunken sot, like the rest of them."

"They're not *all* drunken, mama," said Miss Louisa, stubbornly.

"It's no fault of their upbringing if they're not. Walter Durant is a standing disgrace."

"As I told Mrs. Durant," said the vicar, eating hungrily, "it is the best thing he could have done. It will take him away from temptation during the most dangerous years of his life—how old is he—nineteen?"

"Twenty," said Miss Louisa.

"Twenty!" repeated the vicar. "It will give him wholesome discipline and set before him some sort of standard of duty and honour—nothing could have been better for him. But——"

"We shall miss him from the choir," said Miss Louisa, as if taking opposite sides to her parents.

"That is as it may be," said the vicar. "I prefer to know he is safe in the Navy than running the risk of getting into bad ways here."

"Was he getting into bad ways?" asked the stubborn Miss Louisa.

"You know, Louisa, he wasn't quite what he used to be," said Miss Mary gently and steadily. Miss Louisa shut her rather heavy jaw sulkily. She wanted to deny it, but she knew it was true.

For her he had been a laughing, warm lad, with something kindly and something rich about him. He had made her feel warm. It seemed the days would be colder since he had gone.

"Quite the best thing he could do," said the mother with emphasis.

"I think so," said the vicar. "But his mother was almost abusive because I suggested it."

He spoke in an injured tone.

"What does she care for her children's welfare?" said the invalid. "Their wages is all her concern."

"I suppose she wanted him at home with her," said Miss Louisa.

"Yes, she did—at the expense of his learning to be a drunkard like the rest of them," retorted her mother.

"George Durant doesn't drink," defended her daughter.

"Because he got burned so badly when he was nineteen—in the pit—and that frightened him. The Navy is a better remedy than that, at least."

"Certainly," said the vicar. "Certainly."

And to this Miss Louisa agreed. Yet she could not but feel angry that he had gone away for so many years. She herself was only nineteen.

III

It happened when Miss Mary was twenty-three years old that Mr. Lindley was very ill. The family was exceedingly poor at the time, such a lot of money was needed, so little was forthcoming. Neither Miss Mary nor Miss Louisa had suitors. What chance had they? They met no eligible young men in Aldecross. And what they earned was a mere drop in a void. The girls' hearts were chilled and hardened with fear of this perpetual, cold penury, this narrow struggle, this horrible nothingness of their lives.

A clergyman had to be found for the church work. It so happened the son of an old friend of Mr. Lindley's was waiting three months before taking up his duties. He would come and officiate, for nothing. The young clergyman was keenly expected. He was not more than twenty-seven, a Master of Arts of Oxford, had written his thesis on Roman Law. He came of an old Cambridgeshire family, had some private means, was going to take a church in Northamptonshire with a good stipend, and was not married. Mrs. Lindley incurred new debts, and scarcely regretted her husband's illness.

But when Mr. Massy came there was a shock of disappointment in the house. They had expected a young man with a pipe and a deep voice, but with better manners than Sidney, the eldest of the Lindleys. There arrived instead a small, chétif man, scarcely larger than a boy of twelve, spectacled, timid in the extreme, without a word to utter at first ; yet with a certain inhuman self-sureness.

" What a little abortion ! " was Mrs. Lindley's exclamation to herself on first seeing him, in his buttoned-up clerical coat. And for the first time for many days she was profoundly thankful to God that all her children were decent specimens.

He had not normal powers of perception. They soon saw that he lacked the full range of human feelings, but had rather a strong, philosophical mind, from which he lived. His body was almost unthinkable, in intellect he was something definite. The conversation at once took a balanced, abstract tone when he participated. There was no spontaneous exclamation, no violent assertion or expression of personal conviction, but all cold, reasonable assertion. This was very hard on Mrs. Lindley. The little man would look at her, after one of her pronouncements, and then give, in his thin voice, his own calculated version, so that she felt as if she were tumbling into thin air through a hole in the flimsy floor on which their conversation stood. It was she who felt a fool. Soon she was reduced to a hardy silence.

Still, at the back of her mind, she remembered that he was an unattached gentleman, who would shortly have an income altogether of six or seven hundred a year. What did the man matter, if there were pecuniary ease ! The man was a trifle thrown in. After twenty-two years her sentimentality was ground away, and only the millstone of poverty mattered to her. So she supported the little man as a representative of a decent income.

His most irritating habit was that of a sneering little giggle, all on his own, which came when he perceived or related some illogical absurdity on the part of another person. It was the only form of humour he had. Stupidity in thinking seemed to him exquisitely funny. But any novel was unintelligibly meaningless and dull, and to an Irish sort of humour he listened curiously, examining it like mathematics, or else simply not hearing. In normal human relationship he was not there. Quite unable to take part in simple everyday talk, he padded silently round the house, or sat in the dining-room looking nervously from side to side, always apart in a cold, rarefied little world of his own. Sometimes he made an ironic remark, that did not seem humanly relevant, or he gave his little laugh, like a sneer. He had to defend himself and his own insufficiency. And he answered questions grudgingly, with a yes or no, because he did not see their import and was nervous. It seemed to Miss Louisa he scarcely distinguished one person from another, but that he liked to be near to her, or to Miss Mary, for some sort of contact which stimulated him unknown.

Apart from all this, he was the most admirable workman. He was unremittingly shy, but perfect in his sense of duty : as far as he could conceive Christianity, he was a perfect Christian. Nothing that he realized he could do for any one did he leave undone, although he was so incapable of coming into contact with another being that he could not proffer help. Now he attended assiduously to the sick man, investigated all the affairs of the parish or the church which Mr. Lindley had in control, straightened out accounts, made lists of the sick and needy, padded round with help and to see what he could do. He heard of Mrs. Lindley's anxiety about her sons, and began to investigate means of sending them to Cambridge. His kindness almost frightened Miss Mary. She honoured it so, and yet she shrank from it. For, in it all Mr. Massy seemed to have no sense of any person, any human being whom he was helping : he only realized a kind of mathematical working out, solving of given situations, a calculated well-doing. And it was as if he had accepted the Christian tenets as axioms. His religion consisted in what his scrupulous, abstract mind approved of.

Seeing his acts, Miss Mary must respect and honour him. In consequence she must serve him. To this she had to force herself, shuddering and yet desirous, but he did not perceive it. She accompanied him on his visiting in the parish, and whilst she was cold with admiration for him, often she was touched with pity for the little padding figure with bent shoulders, buttoned up to the chin in his overcoat. She was a handsome, calm girl, tall, with a beautiful repose. Her clothes were poor, and she wore a black silk scarf, having no furs. But she was a lady. As the people saw her walking down Aldecross beside Mr. Massy they said :

" My word, Miss Mary's got a catch. Did ever you see such a sickly little shrimp ! "

She knew they were talking so, and it made her heart grow hot against them, and she drew herself as it were protectively towards the little man beside her. At any rate, she could see and give honour to his genuine goodness.

He could not walk fast, or far.

" You have not been well ? " she asked, in her dignified way.

" I have an internal trouble."

He was not aware of her slight shudder. There was silence, whilst she bowed to recover her composure, to resume her gentle manner towards him.

He was fond of Miss Mary. She had made it a rule of hospitality that he should always be escorted by herself or by her sister on his visits in the parish, which were not many. But some mornings she was engaged. Then Miss Louisa took her place. It was no good Miss Louisa's trying to adopt to Mr. Massy an attitude of queenly service. She was unable to regard him save with aversion. When she saw him from behind, thin and bent-shouldered, looking like a sickly lad of thirteen, she disliked him exceedingly, and felt a desire to put him out of existence. And yet a deeper justice in Mary made Louisa humble before her sister.

They were going to see Mr. Durant, who was paralysed and not expected to live. Miss Louisa was crudely ashamed at being admitted to the cottage in company with the little clergyman.

Mrs. Durant was, however, much quieter in the face of her real trouble.

" How is Mr. Durant ? " asked Louisa.

" He is no different—and we don't expect him to be," was the reply. The little clergyman stood looking on.

They went upstairs. The three stood for some time looking at the bed, at the grey head of the old man on the pillow, the grey beard over the sheet. Miss Louisa was shocked and afraid.

" It is so dreadful," she said, with a shudder.

" It is how I always thought it would be," replied Mrs. Durant.

Then Miss Louisa was afraid of her. The two women were uneasy, waiting for Mr. Massy to say something. He stood, small and bent, too nervous to speak.

" Has he any understanding ? " he asked at length.

" Maybe," said Mrs. Durant. " Can you hear, John ? " she asked loudly. The dull blue eye of the inert man looked at her feebly.

" Yes, he understands," said Mrs. Durant to Mr. Massy. Except for the dull look in his eyes, the sick man lay as if dead. The three stood in silence. Miss Louisa was obstinate but heavy-hearted under the load of unlivingness. It was Mr. Massy who kept her there in discipline. His non-human will dominated them all.

Then they heard a sound below, a man's footsteps, and a man's voice called subduedly :

" Are you upstairs, mother ? "

Mrs. Durant started and moved to the door. But already a quick, firm step was running up the stairs.

" I'm a bit early, mother," a troubled voice said, and on the landing they saw the form of the sailor. His mother came and clung to him. She was suddenly aware that she needed something to hold on to. He put his arms round her, and bent over her, kissing her.

" He's not gone, mother ? " he asked anxiously, struggling to control his voice.

Miss Louisa looked away from the mother and son who stood together in the gloom on the landing. She could not bear it that she and Mr. Massy should be there. The latter stood nervously, as if ill at ease before the emotion that was running. He was a witness nervous, unwilling, but dispassionate. To Miss Louisa's hot heart it seemed all, all wrong that they should be there.

Mrs. Durant entered the bedroom, her face wet.

" There's Miss Louisa and the vicar," she said, out of voice and quavering.

Her son, red-faced and slender, drew himself up to salute. But Miss Louisa held out her hand. Then she saw his hazel eyes recognize her for a moment, and his small white teeth showed in a glimpse of the greeting she used to love. She was covered with confusion. He went round to the bed ; his boots clicked on the plaster floor, he bowed his head with dignity.

"How are you, dad?" he said, laying his hand on the sheet, faltering. But the old man stared fixedly and unseeing. The son stood perfectly still for a few minutes, then slowly recoiled. Miss Louisa saw the fine outline of his breast, under the sailor's blue blouse, as his chest began to heave.

"He doesn't know me," he said, turning to his mother. He gradually went white.

"No, my boy!" cried the mother, pitiful, lifting her face. And suddenly she put her face against his shoulder, he was stooping down to her, holding her against him, and she cried aloud for a moment or two. Miss Louisa saw his sides heaving, and heard the sharp hiss of his breath. She turned away, tears streaming down her face. The father lay inert upon the white bed, Mr. Massy looked queer and obliterated, so little now that the sailor with his sun-burned skin was in the room. He stood waiting. Miss Louisa wanted to die, she wanted to have done. She dared not turn round again to look.

"Shall I offer a prayer?" came the frail voice of the clergyman, and all kneeled down.

Miss Louisa was frightened of the inert man upon the bed. Then she felt a flash of fear of Mr. Massy, hearing his thin, detached voice. And then, calmed, she looked up. On the far side of the bed were the heads of the mother and son, the one in the black lace cap, with the small white nape of the neck beneath, the other, with brown, sun-scorched hair too close and wiry to allow of a parting, and neck tanned firm, bowed as if unwillingly. The great grey beard of the old man did not move, the prayer continued. Mr. Massy prayed with a pure lucidity that they all might conform to the higher Will. He was like something that dominated the bowed heads, something dispassionate that governed them inexorably. Miss Louisa was afraid of him. And she was bound, during the course of the prayer, to have a little reverence for him. It was like a foretaste of inexor-able, cold death, a taste of pure justice.

That evening she talked to Mary of the visit. Her heart, her veins were possessed by the thought of Alfred Durant as he held his mother in his arms ; then the break in his voice, as she remembered it again and again, was like a flame through her ; and she wanted to see his face more distinctly in her mind, ruddy with the sun, and his golden-brown eyes, kind and careless, strained now with a natural fear, the fine nose tanned hard by the sun, the mouth that could not help smiling at her. And it went through her with pride, to think of his figure, a straight, fine jet of life.

" He is a handsome lad," said she to Miss Mary, as if he had not been a year older than herself. Underneath was the deeper dread, almost hatred, of the inhuman being of Mr. Massy. She felt she must protect herself and Alfred from him.

" When I felt Mr. Massy there," she said, " I almost hated him. What right had he to be there ! "

" Surely he has all right," said Miss Mary after a pause. " He is *really* a Christian."

" He seems to me nearly an imbecile," said Miss Louisa.

Miss Mary, quiet and beautiful, was silent for a moment :

" Oh, no," she said. " Not *imbecile*——"

" Well then—he reminds me of a six months' child—or a five months' child—as if he didn't have time to get developed enough before he was born."

" Yes," said Miss Mary, slowly. " There is something lacking. But there is something wonderful in him : and he is really *good*——"

" Yes," said Miss Louisa, " it doesn't seem right that he should be. What right has *that* to be called goodness ! "

" But it *is* goodness," persisted Mary. Then she added, with a laugh : " And come, you wouldn't deny that as well."

There was a doggedness in her voice. She went about very quietly. In her soul, she knew what was going to happen. She knew that Mr. Massy was stronger than she, and that she must submit to what he was. Her physical self was prouder, stronger than he, her physical self disliked and despised him. But she was in the grip of his moral, mental being. And she felt the days allotted out to her. And her family watched.

IV

A few days after, old Mr. Durant died. Miss Louisa saw Alfred once more, but he was stiff before her now, treating her not like a person, but as if she were some sort of will in command and he a separate, distinct will waiting in front of her. She had never felt such utter steel-plate separation from any one. It puzzled her and frightened her. What had become of him ? And she hated the military discipline—she was antagonistic to it. Now he was not himself. He was the will which obeys set over against the will which commands. She hesitated over accepting this. He had put himself out of her range. He had ranked himself inferior, subordinate to her. And that was how he would get away from her, that was how he would avoid all connection with her : by fronting her impersonally from the opposite camp, by taking up the abstract position of an inferior.

She went brooding steadily and sullenly over this, brooding and brooding. Her fierce, obstinate heart could not give way. It clung to its own rights. Sometimes she dismissed him. Why should he, her inferior, trouble her ?

Then she relapsed to him, and almost hated him. It was his way of getting out of it. She felt the cowardice of it, his calmly placing her in a superior class, and placing himself inaccessibly apart, in an inferior, as if she, the sentient woman who was fond of him, did not count. But she was not going to submit. Dogged in her heart she held on to him.

V

In six months' time Miss Mary had married Mr. Massy. There had been no love-making, nobody had made any remark. But everybody was tense and callous with expectation. When one day Mr. Massy asked for Mary's hand, Mr. Lindley started and trembled from the thin, abstract voice of the little man. Mr. Massy was very nervous, but so curiously absolute.

" I shall be very glad," said the vicar, " but of course the decision lies with Mary herself." And his still feeble hand shook as he moved a Bible on his desk.

The small man, keeping fixedly to his idea, padded out of the room to find Miss Mary. He sat a long time by her, while she made some conversation, before he had readiness to speak. She was afraid of what was coming, and sat stiff in apprehension. She felt as if her body would rise and fling him aside. But her spirit quivered and wait d. Almost in expectation she waited, almost wanting him. And then she knew he would speak.

" I have already asked Mr. Lindley," said the clergyman, while suddenly she looked with aversion at his little knees, " if he would consent to my proposal." He was aware of his own disadvantage, but his will was set.

She went cold as she sat, and impervious, almost as if she had become stone. He waited a moment nervously. He would not persuade her. He himself never even heard persuasion, but pursued his own course.   He looked at her, sure of himself, unsure of her, and said :

"Will you become my wife, Mary ? "

Still her heart was hard and cold.   She sat proudly.

"I should like to speak to mama first," she said.

"Very well," replied Mr. Massy.   And in a moment he padded away. Mary went to her mother.   She was cold and reserved.

"Mr. Massy has asked me to marry him, mama," she said.   Mrs. Lindley went on staring at her book.   She was cramped in her feeling.

"Well, and what did you say ? "

They were both keeping calm and cold.

"I said I would speak to you before answering him."

This was equivalent to a question.   Mrs. Lindley did not want to reply to it.   She shifted her heavy form irritably on the couch. Miss Mary sat calm and straight, with closed mouth.

"Your father thinks it would not be a bad match," said the mother, as if casually.

Nothing more was said.   Everybody remained cold and shut-off. Miss Mary did not speak to Miss Louisa, the Reverend Ernest Lindley kept out of sight.

At evening Miss Mary accepted Mr. Massy.

"Yes, I will marry you," she said, with even a little movement of tenderness towards him.   He was embarrassed, but satisfied. She could see him making some movement towards her, could feel the male in him, something cold and triumphant, asserting itself. She sat rigid, and waited.

When Miss Louisa knew, she was silent with bitter anger against everybody, even against Mary.   She felt her faith wounded.   Did the real things to her not matter after all ?   She wanted to get away. She thought of Mr. Massy.   He had some curious power, some unanswerable right.   He was a will that they could not controvert. Suddenly a flush started in her.   If he had come to her she would have flipped him out of the room.   He was never going to touch *her*.   And she was glad.   She was glad that her blood would rise and exterminate the little man, if he came too near to her, no matter how her judgment was paralysed by him, no matter how he moved in abstract goodness.   She thought she was perverse to be glad, but glad she was.   "I would just flip him out of the room," she said, and she derived great satisfaction from the open statement. Nevertheless, perhaps she ought still to feel that Mary, on her plane, was a higher being than herself.   But then Mary was Mary, and she was Louisa, and that also was inalterable.

Mary, in marrying him, tried to become a pure reason such as he was, without feeling or impulse. She shut herself up, she shut herself rigid against the agonies of shame and the terror of violation which came at first. She *would* not feel, and she *would* not feel. She was a pure will acquiescing to him. She elected a certain kind of fate. She would be good and purely just, she would live in a higher freedom than she had ever known, she would be free of mundane care, she was a pure will towards right. She had sold herself, but she had a new freedom. She had got rid of her body. She had sold a lower thing, her body, for a higher thing, her freedom from material things. She considered that she paid for all she got from her husband. So, in a kind of independence, she moved proud and free. She had paid with her body : that was henceforward out of consideration. She was glad to be rid of it. She had bought her position in the world—that henceforth was taken for granted. There remained only the direction of her activity towards charity and high-minded living.

She could scarcely bear other people to be present with her and her husband. Her private life was her shame. But then, she could keep it hidden. She lived almost isolated in the rectory of the tiny village miles from the railway. She suffered as if it were an insult to her own flesh, seeing the repulsion which some people felt for her husband, or the special manner they had of treating him, as if he were a " case." But most people were uneasy before him, which restored her pride.

If she had let herself, she would have hated him, hated his padding round the house, his thin voice devoid of human understanding, his bent little shoulders and rather incomplete face that reminded her of an abortion. But rigorously she kept to her position. She took care of him and was just to him. There was also a deep, craven fear of him, something slave-like.

There was not much fault to be found with his behaviour. He was scrupulously just and kind according to his lights. But the male in him was cold and self-complete, and utterly domineering. Weak, insufficient little thing as he was, she had not expected this of him. It was something in the bargain she had not understood. It made her hold her head, to keep still. She knew, vaguely, that she was murdering herself. After all, her body was not quite so easy to get rid of. And this manner of disposing of it—ah, sometimes she felt she must rise and bring about death, lift her hand for utter denial of everything, by a general destruction.

He was almost unaware of the conditions about him. He did not fuss in the domestic way, she did as she liked in the house. Indeed, she was a great deal free of him. He would sit obliterated for hours. He was kind, and almost anxiously considerate. But when he considered he was right, his will was just blindly male, like a cold machine. And on most points he was logically right, or he had with him the right of the creed they both accepted. It was so. There was nothing for her to go against.

Then she found herself with child, and felt for the first time horror, afraid before God and man. This also she had to go through —it was the right. When the child arrived, it was a bonny, healthy lad. Her heart hurt in her body, as she took the baby between her hands. The flesh that was trampled and silent in her must speak again in the boy. After all, she had to live—it was not so simple after all. Nothing was finished completely. She looked and looked at the baby, and almost hated it, and suffered an anguish of love for it. She hated it because it made her live again in the flesh, when she *could* not live in the flesh, she could not. She wanted to trample her flesh down, down, extinct, to live in the mind. And now there was this child. It was too cruel, too racking. For she must love the child. Her purpose was broken in two again. She had to become amorphous, purposeless, without real being. As a mother, she was a fragmentary, ignoble thing.

Mr. Massy, blind to everything else in the way of human feeling, became obsessed by the idea of his child. When it arrived, suddenly it filled the whole world of feeling for him. It was his obsession, his terror was for its safety and well-being. It was something new, as if he himself had been born a naked infant, conscious of his own exposure, and full of apprehension. He who had never been aware of any one else, all his life, now was aware of nothing but the child. Not that he ever played with it, or kissed it, or tended it. He did nothing for it. But it dominated him, it filled, and at the same time emptied his mind. The world was all baby for him.

This his wife must also bear, his question : " What is the reason that he cries ? "—his reminder, at the first sound : " Mary, that is the child,"—his restlessness if the feeding-time were five minutes past. She had bargained for this—now she must stand by her bargain.

VI

Miss Louisa, at home in the dingy vicarage, had suffered a great deal over her sister's wedding. Having once begun to cry out against it, during the engagement, she had been silenced by Mary's quiet : " I don't agree with you about him, Louisa, I *want* to marry him." Then Miss Louisa had been angry deep in her heart, and therefore silent. This dangerous state started the change in her. Her own revulsion made her recoil from the hitherto undoubted Mary.

" I'd beg the streets barefoot first," said Miss Louisa, thinking of Mr. Massy.

But evidently Mary could perform a different heroism. So she, Louisa the practical, suddenly felt that Mary, her ideal, was questionable after all. How could she be pure—one cannot be dirty in act and spiritual in being. Louisa distrusted Mary's high spirituality. It was no longer genuine for her. And if Mary were spiritual and misguided, why did not her father protect her? Because of the money. He disliked the whole affair, but he backed away, because of the money. And the mother frankly did not care : her daughters could do as they liked. Her mother's pronouncement :

" Whatever happens to *him*, Mary is safe for life,"—so evidently and shallowly a calculation, incensed Louisa.

" I'd rather be safe in the workhouse," she cried.

" Your father will see to that," replied her mother brutally. This speech, in its indirectness, so injured Miss Louisa that she hated her mother deep, deep in her heart, and almost hated herself. It was a long time resolving itself out, this hate. But it worked and worked, and at last the young woman said :

" They are wrong—they are all wrong. They have ground out their souls for what isn't worth anything, and there isn't a grain of love in them anywhere. And I *will* have love. They want us to deny it. They've never found it, so they want to say it doesn't exist. But I *will* have it. I *will* love—it is my birthright. I will love the man I marry—that is all I care about."

So Miss Louisa stood isolated from everybody. She and Mary had parted over Mr. Massy. In Louisa's eyes, Mary was degraded, married to Mr. Massy. She could not bear to think of her lofty, spiritual sister degraded in the body like this. Mary was wrong, wrong, wrong : she was not superior, she was flawed, incomplete. The two sisters stood apart. They still loved each other, they would love each other as long as they lived. But they had parted ways. A new solitariness came over the obstinate Louisa, and her heavy jaw set stubbornly. She was going on her own way. But which way ? She was quite alone, with a blank world before her. How could she be said to have any way ? Yet she had her fixed will to love, to have the man she loved.

c

VII

When her boy was three years old, Mary had another baby, a girl. The three years had gone by monotonously. They might have been an eternity, they might have been brief as a sleep. She did not know. Only, there was always a weight on top of her, something that pressed down her life. The only thing that had happened was that Mr. Massy had had an operation. He was always exceedingly fragile. His wife had soon learned to attend to him mechanically, as part of her duty.

But this third year, after the baby girl had been born, Mary felt oppressed and depressed. Christmas drew near : the gloomy, unleavened Christmas of the rectory, where all the days were of the same dark fabric. And Mary was afraid. It was as if the darkness were coming upon her.

"Edward, I should like to go home for Christmas," she said, and a certain terror filled her as she spoke.

"But you can't leave baby," said her husband, blinking.

"We can all go."

He thought, and stared in his collective fashion.

"Why do you wish to go ? " he asked.

"Because I need a change. A change would do me good, and it would be good for the milk."

He heard the will in his wife's voice, and was at a loss. Her language was unintelligible to him. But somehow he felt that Mary was set upon it. And while she was breeding, either about to have a child, or nursing, he regarded her as a special sort of being.

"Wouldn't it hurt baby to take her by the train ? " he said.

"No," replied the mother, "why should it ? "

They went. When they were in the train it began to snow. From the window of his first-class carriage the little clergyman watched the big flakes sweep by, like a blind drawn across the country. He was obsessed by thought of the baby, and afraid of the draughts of the carriage.

"Sit right in the corner," he said to his wife, "and hold baby close back."

She moved at his bidding, and stared out of the window. His eternal presence was like an iron weight on her brain. But she was going partially to escape for a few days.

"Sit on the other side, Jack," said the father. "It is less draughty. Come to this window."

He watched the boy in anxiety. But his children were the

only beings in the world who took not the slightest notice of him.

"Look, mother, look!" cried the boy. "They fly right in my face"—he meant the snowflakes.

"Come into this corner," repeated his father, out of another world.

"He's jumped on this one's back, mother, an' they're riding to the bottom!" cried the boy, jumping with glee.

"Tell him to come on this side," the little man bade his wife.

"Jack, kneel on this cushion," said the mother, putting her white hand on the place.

The boy slid over in silence to the place she indicated, waited still for a moment, then almost deliberately, stridently cried:

"Look at all those in the corner, mother, making a heap," and he pointed to the cluster of snowflakes with finger pressed dramatically on the pane, and he turned to his mother a bit ostentatiously.

"All in a heap!" she said.

He had seen her face, and had her response, and he was somewhat assured. Vaguely uneasy, he was reassured if he could win her attention.

They arrived at the vicarage at half-past two, not having had lunch.

"How are you, Edward?" said Mr. Lindley, trying on his side to be fatherly. But he was always in a false position with his son-in-law, frustrated before him, therefore, as much as possible, he shut his eyes and ears to him. The vicar was looking thin and pale and ill-nourished. He had gone quite grey. He was, however, still haughty; but, since the growing-up of his children, it was a brittle haughtiness, that might break at any moment and leave the vicar only an impoverished, pitiable figure. Mrs. Lindley took all the notice of her daughter, and of the children. She ignored her son-in-law. Miss Louisa was clucking and laughing and rejoicing over the baby. Mr. Massy stood aside, a bent, persistent little figure.

"Oh a pretty!—a little pretty! oh a cold little pretty come in a railway-train!" Miss Louisa was cooing to the infant, crouching on the hearthrug, opening the white woollen wraps and exposing the child to the fireglow.

"Mary," said the little clergyman, "I think it would be better to give baby a warm bath; she may take a cold."

"I think it is not necessary," said the mother, coming and closing her hand judiciously over the rosy feet and hands of the mite. "She is not chilly."

"Not a bit," cried Miss Louisa. "She's not caught cold."

" I'll go and bring her flannels," said Mr. Massy, with one idea.

" I can bath her in the kitchen then," said Mary, in an altered, cold tone.

" You can't, the girl is scrubbing there," said Miss Louisa. " Besides, she doesn't want a bath at this time of day."

" She'd better have one," said Mary, quietly, out of submission. Miss Louisa's gorge rose, and she was silent. When the little man padded down with the flannels on his arm, Mrs. Lindley asked :

" Hadn't *you* better take a hot bath, Edward ? "

But the sarcasm was lost on the little clergyman. He was absorbed in the preparations round the baby.

The room was dull and threadbare, and the snow outside seemed fairy-like by comparison, so white on the lawn and tufted on the bushes. Indoors the heavy pictures hung obscurely on the walls, everything was dingy with gloom.

Except in the fireglow, where they had laid the bath on the hearth. Mrs. Massy, her black hair always smoothly coiled and queenly, kneeled by the bath, wearing a rubber apron, and holding the kicking child. Her husband stood holding the towels and the flannels to warm. Louisa, too cross to share in the joy of the baby's bath, was laying the table. The boy was hanging on the door-knob, wrestling with it to get out. His father looked round.

" Come away from the door, Jack," he said ineffectually. Jack tugged harder at the knob as if he did not hear. Mr. Massy blinked at him.

" He must come away from the door, Mary," he said. " There will be a draught if it is opened."

" Jack, come away from the door, dear," said the mother, dexterously turning the shiny wet baby on to her towelled knee. then glancing round : " Go and tell Auntie Louisa about the train."

Louisa, also afraid to open the door, was watching the scene on the hearth. Mr. Massy stood holding the baby's flannel, as if assisting at some ceremonial. If everybody had not been subduedly angry, it would have been ridiculous.

" I want to see out of the window," Jack said. His father turned hastily.

" Do *you* mind lifting him on to a chair, Louisa," said Mary hastily. The father was too delicate.

When the baby was flannelled, Mr. Massy went upstairs and returned with four pillows, which he set in the fender to warm. Then he stood watching the mother feed her child, obsessed by the idea of his infant.

Louisa went on with her preparations for the meal. She could not have told why she was so sullenly angry. Mrs. Lindley, as usual, lay silently watching.

Mary carried her child upstairs, followed by her husband with the pillows. After a while he came down again.

" What is Mary doing ? Why doesn't she come down to eat ? " asked Mrs. Lindley.

" She is staying with baby. The room is rather cold. I will ask the girl to put in a fire." He was going absorbedly to the door.

" But Mary has had nothing to eat. It is *she* who will catch cold," said the mother, exasperated.

Mr. Massy seemed as if he did not hear. Yet he looked at his mother-in-law, and answered :

" I will take her something."

He went out. Mrs. Lindley shifted on her couch with anger. Miss Louisa glowered. But no one said anything, because of the money that came to the vicarage from Mr. Massy.

Louisa went upstairs. Her sister was sitting by the bed, reading a scrap of paper.

" Won't you come down and eat ? " the younger asked.

" In a moment or two," Mary replied, in a quiet, reserved voice, that forbade any one to approach her.

It was this that made Miss Louisa most furious. She went downstairs, and announced to her mother :

" I am going out. I may not be home to tea."

VIII

No one remarked on her exit. She put on her fur hat, that the village people knew so well, and the old Norfolk jacket. Louisa was short and plump and plain. She had her mother's heavy jaw, her father's proud brow, and her own grey, brooding eyes that were very beautiful when she smiled. It was true, as the people said, that she looked sulky. Her chief attraction was her glistening, heavy, deep-blonde hair, which shone and gleamed with a richness that was not entirely foreign to her.

" Where am I going ? " she said to herself, when she got outside in the snow. She did not hesitate, however, but by mechanical walking found herself descending the hill towards Old Aldecross. In the valley that was black with trees, the colliery breathed in stertorous pants, sending out high conical columns of steam that remained upright, whiter than the snow on the hills, yet shadowy, in the dead air. Louisa would not acknowledge to herself whither she was making her way, till she came to the railway crossing. Then the bunches of snow in the twigs of the apple tree that leaned towards the fence told her she must go and see Mrs. Durant. The tree was in Mrs. Durant's garden.

Alfred was now at home again, living with his mother in the cottage below the road. From the highway hedge, by the railway crossing, the snowy garden sheered down steeply, like the side of a hole, then dropped straight in a wall. In this depth the house was snug, its chimney just level with the road. Miss Louisa descended the stone stairs, and stood below in the little backyard, in the dimness and the semi-secrecy. A big tree leaned overhead, above the paraffin hut. Louisa felt secure from all the world down there. She knocked at the open door, then looked round. The tongue of garden narrowing in from the quarry bed was white with snow : she thought of the thick fringes of snowdrops it would show beneath the currant bushes in a month's time. The ragged fringe of pinks hanging over the garden brim behind her was whitened now with snowflakes, that in summer held white blossom to Louisa's face. It was pleasant, she thought, to gather flowers that stooped to one's face from above.

She knocked again. Peeping in, she saw the scarlet glow of the kitchen, red firelight falling on the brick floor and on the bright chintz cushions. It was alive and bright as a peep-show. She crossed the scullery, where still an almanac hung. There was no one about. "Mrs. Durant," called Louisa softly, "Mrs. Durant."

She went up the brick step into the front room, that still had its little shop counter and its bundles of goods, and she called from the stair-foot. Then she knew Mrs. Durant was out.

She went into the yard, to follow the old woman's footsteps up the garden path.

She emerged from the bushes and raspberry canes. There was the whole quarry bed, a wide garden white and dimmed, brindled with dark bushes, lying half submerged. On the left, overhead, the little colliery train rumbled by. Right away at the back was a mass of trees.

Louisa followed the open path, looking from right to left, and then she gave a cry of concern. The old woman was sitting rocking slightly among the ragged snowy cabbages. Louisa ran to her, found her whimpering with little, involuntary cries.

" Whatever have you done ? " cried Louisa, kneeling in the snow.

" I've—I've—I was pulling a brussel-sprout stalk—and—oh-h !—

something tore inside me. I've had a pain," the old woman wept from shock and suffering, gasping between her whimpers,—" I've had a pain there—a long time—and now—oh—oh ! " She panted, pressed her hand on her side, leaned as if she would faint, looking yellow against the snow. Louisa supported her.

" Do you think you could walk now ? " she asked.

" Yes," gasped the old woman.

Louisa helped her to her feet.

" Get the cabbage—I want it for Alfred's dinner," panted Mrs. Durant. Louisa picked up the stalk of brussel-sprouts, and with difficulty got the old woman indoors. She gave her brandy, laid her on the couch, saying :

" I'm going to send for a doctor—wait just a minute."

The young woman ran up the steps to the public-house a few yards away. The landlady was astonished to see Miss Louisa.

" Will you send for a doctor at once to Mrs. Durant," she said, with some of her father in her commanding tone.

" Is something the matter ? " fluttered the landlady in concern.

Louisa, glancing out up the road, saw the grocer's cart driving to Eastwood. She ran and stopped the man, and told him.

Mrs. Durant lay on the sofa, her face turned away, when the young woman came back.

" Let me put you to bed," Louisa said. Mrs. Durant did not resist.

Louisa knew the ways of the working people. In the bottom drawer of the dresser she found dusters and flannels. With the old pit-flannel she snatched out the oven shelves, wrapped them up, and put them in the bed. From the son's bed she took a blanket, and, running down, set it before the fire. Having undressed the little old woman, Louisa carried her upstairs.

" You'll drop me, you'll drop me ! " cried Mrs. Durant.

Louisa did not answer, but bore her burden quickly. She could not light a fire, because there was no fire-place in the bedroom. And the floor was plaster. So she fetched the lamp, and stood it lighted in one corner.

" It will air the room," she said.

" Yes," moaned the old woman.

Louisa ran with more hot flannels, replacing those from the oven shelves. Then she made a bran-bag and laid it on the woman's side. There was a big lump on the side of the abdomen.

" I've felt it coming a long time," moaned the old lady, when the pain was easier, " but I've not said anything ; I didn't want to upset our Alfred."

Louisa did not see why " our Alfred " should be spared.

" What time is it ? " came the plaintive voice.

" A quarter to four."

" Oh ! " wailed the old lady, " he'll be here in half an hour, and no dinner ready for him."

" Let me do it ? " said Louisa, gently.

" There's that cabbage—and you'll find the meat in the pantry—and there's an apple pie you can hot up. But *don't you* do it—— ! "

" Who will, then ? " asked Louisa.

" I don't know," moaned the sick woman, unable to consider.

Louisa did it. The doctor came and gave serious examination. He looked very grave.

" What is it, doctor ? " asked the old lady, looking up at him with old, pathetic eyes in which already hope was dead.

" I think you've torn the skin in which a tumour hangs," he replied.

" Ay ! " she murmured, and she turned away.

" You see, she may die any minute—and it *may* be swaled away," said the old doctor to Louisa.

The young woman went upstairs again.

" He says the lump may be swaled away, and you may get quite well again," she said.

" Ay ! " murmured the old lady. It did not deceive her. Presently she asked :

" Is there a good fire ? "

" I think so," answered Louisa.

" He'll want a good fire," the mother said. Louisa attended to it.

Since the death of Durant, the widow had come to church occasionally, and Louisa had been friendly to her. In the girl's heart the purpose was fixed. No man had affected her as Alfred Durant had done, and to that she kept. In her heart, she adhered to him. A natural sympathy existed between her and his rather hard, materialistic mother.

Alfred was the most lovable of the old woman's sons. He had grown up like the rest, however, headstrong and blind to everything but his own will. Like the other boys, he had insisted on going into the pit as soon as he left school, because that was the only way speedily to become a man, level with all the other men. This was a great chagrin to his mother, who would have liked to have this last of her sons a gentleman.

But still he remained constant to her. His feeling for her was deep and unexpressed. He noticed when she was tired, or when she had a new cap. And he bought little things for her occasionally. She was not wise enough to see how much he lived by her.

At the bottom he did not satisfy her, he did not seem manly enough. He liked to read books occasionally, and better still he liked to play the piccolo. It amused her to see his head nod over the instrument as he made an effort to get the right note. It made her fond of him, with tenderness, almost pity, but not with respect. She wanted a man to be fixed, going his own way without knowledge of women. Whereas she knew Alfred depended on her. He sang in the choir because he liked singing. In the summer he worked in the garden, attended to the fowls and pigs. He kept pigeons. He played on Saturday in the cricket or football team. But to her he did not seem the man, the independent man her other boys had been. He was her baby—and whilst she loved him for it, she was a little bit contemptuous of him.

There grew up a little hostility between them. Then he began to drink, as the others had done ; but not in their blind, oblivious way. He was a little self-conscious over it. She saw this, and she pitied it in him. She loved him most, but she was not satisfied with him because he was not free of her. He could not quite go his own way.

Then at twenty he ran away and served his time in the Navy. This had made a man of him. He had hated it bitterly, the service, the subordination. For years he fought with himself under the military discipline, for his own self-respect, struggling through blind anger and shame and a cramping sense of inferiority. Out of humiliation and self-hatred he rose into a sort of inner freedom. And his love for his mother, whom he idealized, remained the fact of hope and of belief.

He came home again, nearly thirty years old, but naïve and inexperienced as a boy, only with a silence about him that was new : a sort of dumb humility before life, a fear of living. He was almost quite chaste. A strong sensitiveness had kept him from women. Sexual talk was all very well among men, but somehow it had no application to living women. There were two things for him, the *idea* of women, with which he sometimes debauched himself, and real women, before whom he felt a deep uneasiness, and a need to draw away. He shrank and defended himself from the approach of any woman. And then he felt ashamed. In his innermost soul he felt he was not a man, he was less than the normal man. In Genoa he went with an under-officer to a drinking house where

c *

the cheaper sort of girl came in to look for lovers. He sat there with his glass, the girls looked at him, but they never came to him. He knew that if they did come he could only pay for food and drink for them, because he felt a pity for them, and was anxious lest they lacked good necessities. He could not have gone with one of them ; he knew it, and was ashamed, looking with curious envy at the swaggering, easy-passionate Italian whose body went to a woman by instinctive impersonal attraction. They were men, he was not a man. He sat feeling short, feeling like a leper. And he went away imagining sexual scenes between himself and a woman, walking wrapt in this indulgence. But when the ready woman presented herself, the very fact that she was a palpable woman made it impossible for him to touch her. And this incapacity was like a core of rottenness in him.

So several times he went, drunk, with his companions, to the licensed prostitute houses abroad. But the sordid insignificance of the experience appalled him. It had not been anything really : it meant nothing. He felt as if he were, not physically, but spiritually impotent : not actually impotent, but intrinsically so.

He came home with this secret, never changing burden of his unknown, unbestowed self torturing him. His Navy training left him in perfect physical condition. He was sensible of, and proud of his body. He bathed and used dumb-bells, and kept himself fit. He played cricket and football. He read books and began to hold fixed ideas which he got from the Fabians. He played his piccolo, and was considered an expert. But at the bottom of his soul was always this canker of shame and incompleteness : he was miserable beneath all his healthy cheerfulness, he was uneasy and felt despicable among all his confidence and superiority of ideas. He would have changed with any mere brute, just to be free of himself, to be free of this shame of self-consciousness. He saw some collier lurching straight forward without misgiving, pursuing his own satisfactions, and he envied him. Anything, he would have given anything for this spontaneity and this blind stupidity which went to its own satisfaction direct.

IX

He was not unhappy in the pit. He was admired by the men, and well enough liked. It was only he himself who felt the difference between himself and the others. He seemed to hide his own stigma. But he was never sure that the others did not really despise him for a ninny, as being less a man than they were. Only he pretended to be more manly, and was surprised by the ease with which they were deceived. And, being naturally cheerful, he was happy at work. He was sure of himself there. Naked to the waist, hot and grimy with labour, they squatted on their heels for a few minutes and talked, seeing each other dimly by the light of the safety lamps, while the black coal rose jutting round them, and the props of wood stood like little pillars in the low, black, very dark temple. Then the pony came and the gang-lad with a message from Number 7, or with a bottle of water from the horse-trough or some news of the world above. The day passed pleasantly enough. There was an ease, a go-as-you-please about the day underground, a delightful camaraderie of men shut off alone from the rest of the world, in a dangerous place, and a variety of labour, holing, loading, timbering, and a glamour of mystery and adventure in the atmosphere, that made the pit not unattractive to him when he had again got over his anguish of desire for the open air and the sea.

This day there was much to do and Durant was not in humour to talk. He went on working in silence through the afternoon.

" Loose-all " came, and they tramped to the bottom. The whitewashed underground office shone brightly. Men were putting out their lamps. They sat in dozens round the bottom of the shaft, down which black, heavy drops of water fell continuously into the sumph. The electric lights shone away down the main underground road.

" Is it raining ? " asked Durant.

" Snowing," said an old man, and the younger was pleased. He liked to go up when it was snowing.

" It'll just come right for Christmas ? " said the old man.

" Ay," replied Durant.

" A green Christmas, a fat churchyard," said the other sententiously.

Durant laughed, showing his small, rather pointed teeth.

The cage came down, a dozen men lined on. Durant noticed tufts of snow on the perforated, arched roof of the chain, and he was pleased. He wondered how it liked its excursion underground. But already it was getting soppy with black water.

He liked things about him. There was a little smile on his face. But underlying it was the curious consciousness he felt in himself.

The upper world came almost with a flash, because of the glimmer of snow. Hurrying along the bank, giving up his lamp at the office, he smiled to feel the open about him again, all glimmering round him with snow. The hills on either hand were pale blue in the dusk, and the hedges looked savage and dark. The snow was trampled between the railway lines. But far ahead, beyond the black figures of miners moving home, it became smooth again, spreading right up to the dark wall of the coppice.

To the west there was a pinkness, and a big star hovered half revealed. Below, the lights of the pit came out crisp and yellow among the darkness of the buildings, and the lights of Old Aldecross twinkled in rows down the bluish twilight.

Durant walked glad with life among the miners, who were all talking animatedly because of the snow. He liked their company, he liked the white dusky world. It gave him a little thrill to stop at the garden gate and see the light of home down below, shining on the silent blue snow.

X

By the big gate of the railway, in the fence, was a little gate, that he kept locked. As he unfastened it, he watched the kitchen light that shone on to the bushes and the snow outside. It was a candle burning till night set in, he thought to himself. He slid down the steep path to the level below. He liked making the first marks in the smooth snow. Then he came through the bushes to the house. The two women heard his heavy boots ring outside on the scraper, and his voice as he opened the door :

" How much worth of oil do you reckon to save by that candle, mother ? " He liked a good light from the lamp.

He had just put down his bottle and snap-bag and was hanging his coat behind the scullery door, when Miss Louisa came upon him. He was startled, but he smiled.

His eyes began to laugh—then his face went suddenly straight, and he was afraid.

" Your mother's had an accident," she said.

" How ? " he exclaimed.

" In the garden," she answered. He hesitated with his coat in his hands. Then he hung it up and turned to the kitchen.

" Is she in bed ? " he asked.

" Yes," said Miss Louisa, who found it hard to deceive him. He was silent. He went into the kitchen, sat down heavily in his father's old chair, and began to pull off his boots. His head was small, rather finely shapen. His brown hair, close and crisp, would look jolly whatever happened. He wore heavy, moleskin trousers that gave off the stale, exhausted scent of the pit. Having put on his slippers, he carried his boots into the scullery.

" What is it ? " he asked, afraid.

" Something internal," she replied.

He went upstairs. His mother kept herself calm for his coming. Louisa felt his tread shake the plaster floor of the bedroom above.

" What have you done ? " he asked.

" It's nothing, my lad," said the old woman, rather hard. " It's nothing. You needn't fret, my boy, it's nothing more the matter with me than I had yesterday, or last week. The doctor said I'd done nothing serious."

" What were you doing ? " asked her son.

" I was pulling up a cabbage, and I suppose I pulled too hard ; for, oh—there was such a pain——"

Her son looked at her quickly. She hardened herself.

" But who doesn't have a sudden pain sometimes, my boy? We all do."

" And what's it done ? "

" I don't know," she said, " but I don't suppose it's anything."

The big lamp in the corner was screened with a dark green screen, so that he could scarcely see her face. He was strung tight with apprehension and many emotions. Then his brow knitted.

" What did you go pulling your inside out at cabbages for," he asked, " and the ground frozen ? You'd go on dragging and dragging, if you killed yourself."

" Somebody's got to get them," she said.

" You needn't do yourself harm."

But they had reached futility.

Miss Louisa could hear plainly downstairs. Her heart sank. It seemed so hopeless between them.

" Are you sure it's nothing much, mother ? " he asked, appealing, after a little silence.

" Ay, it's nothing," said the old woman, rather bitter.

" I don't want you to—to—to be badly—you know."

" Go an' get your dinner," she said. She knew she was going to die : moreover, the pain was torture just then. " They're only cosseting me up a bit because I'm an old woman. Miss Louisa's *very* good—and she'll have got your dinner ready, so you'd better go and eat it."

He felt stupid and ashamed. His mother put him off. He had to turn away. The pain burned in his bowels. He went downstairs. The mother was glad he was gone, so that she could moan with pain.

He had resumed the old habit of eating before he washed himself. Miss Louisa served his dinner. It was strange and exciting to her.

She was strung up tense, trying to understand him and his mother. She watched him as he sat. He was turned away from his food, looking in the fire. Her soul watched him, trying to see what he was. His black face and arms were uncouth, he was foreign. His face was masked black with coal-dust. She could not see him, she could not know him. The brown eyebrows, the steady eyes, the coarse, small moustache above the closed mouth—these were the only familiar indications. What was he, as he sat there in his pit-dirt? She could not see him, and it hurt her.

She ran upstairs, presently coming down with the flannels and the bran-bag, to heat them, because the pain was on again.

He was half-way through his dinner. He put down the fork, suddenly nauseated.

"They will soothe the wrench," she said. He watched, useless and left out.

"Is she bad?" he asked.

"I think she is," she answered.

It was useless for him to stir or comment. Louisa was busy. She went upstairs. The poor old woman was in a white, cold sweat of pain. Louisa's face was sullen with suffering as she went about to relieve her. Then she sat and waited. The pain passed gradually, the old woman sank into a state of coma. Louisa still sat silent by the bed. She heard the sound of water downstairs. Then came the voice of the old mother, faint but unrelaxing:

"Alfred's washing himself—he'll want his back washing——"

Louisa listened anxiously, wondering what the sick woman wanted.

"He can't bear if his back isn't washed——" the old woman persisted, in a cruel attention to his needs. Louisa rose and wiped the sweat from the yellowish brow.

"I will go down," she said soothingly.

"If you would," murmured the sick woman.

Louisa waited a moment. Mrs. Durant closed her eyes, having discharged her duty. The young woman went downstairs. Herself, or the man, what did they matter? Only the suffering woman must be considered.

Alfred was kneeling on the hearthrug, stripped to the waist, washing himself in a large panchion of earthenware. He did so every evening, when he had eaten his dinner; his brothers had done so before him. But Miss Louisa was strange in the house.

He was mechanically rubbing the white lather on his head, with a repeated, unconscious movement, his hand every now and then passing over his neck. Louisa watched. She had to brace herself to this also. He bent his head into the water, washed it free of soap, and pressed the water out of his eyes.

"Your mother said you would want your back washing," she said.

Curious how it hurt her to take part in their fixed routine of life ! Louisa felt the almost repulsive intimacy being forced upon her. It was all so common, so like herding. She lost her own distinctness.

He ducked his face round, looking up at her in what was a very comical way. She had to harden herself.

"How funny he looks with his face upside down," she thought. After all, there was a difference between her and the common people. The water in which his arms were plunged was quite black, the soap-froth was darkish. She could scarcely conceive him as human. Mechanically, under the influence of habit, he groped in the black water, fished out soap and flannel, and handed them backward to Louisa. Then he remained rigid and submissive, his two arms thrust straight in the panchion, supporting the weight of his shoulders. His skin was beautifully white and unblemished, of an opaque, solid whiteness. Gradually Louisa saw it : this also was what he was. It fascinated her. Her feeling of separateness passed away : she ceased to draw back from contact with him and his mother. There was this living centre. Her heart ran hot. She had reached some goal in this beautiful, clear, male body. She loved him in a white, impersonal heat. But the sun-burnt, reddish neck and ears : they were more personal, more curious. A tenderness rose in her, she loved even his queer ears. A person—an intimate being he was to her. She put down the towel and went upstairs again, troubled in her heart. She had only seen one human being in her life—and that was Mary. All the rest were strangers. Now her soul was going to open, she was going to see another. She felt strange and pregnant.

"He'll be more comfortable," murmured the sick woman abstractedly, as Louisa entered the room. The latter did not answer. Her own heart was heavy with its own responsibility. Mrs. Durant lay silent awhile, then she murmured plaintively :

"You mustn't mind, Miss Louisa."

"Why should I ? " replied Louisa, deeply moved.

"It's what we're used to," said the old woman.

And Louisa felt herself excluded again from their life. She sat in pain, with the tears of disappointment distilling in her heart. Was that all ?

Alfred came upstairs. He was clean, and in his shirt-sleeves. He looked a workman now. Louisa felt that she and he were foreigners, moving in different lives. It dulled her again. Oh, if she could only find some fixed relations, something sure and abiding.

"How do you feel?" he said to his mother.

"It's a bit better," she replied wearily, impersonally. This strange putting herself aside, this abstracting herself and answering him only what she thought good for him to hear, made the relations between mother and son poignant and cramping to Miss Louisa. It made the man so ineffectual, so nothing. Louisa groped as if she had lost him. The mother was real and positive—he was not very actual. It puzzled and chilled the young woman.

"I'd better fetch Mrs. Harrison?" he said, waiting for his mother to decide.

"I suppose we shall have to have somebody," she replied.

Miss Louisa stood by, afraid to interfere in their business. They did not include her in their lives, they felt she had nothing to do with them, except as a help from outside. She was quite external to them. She felt hurt and powerless against this unconscious difference. But something patient and unyielding in her made her say:

"I will stay and do the nursing: you can't be left."

The other two were shy, and at a loss for an answer.

"We s'll manage to get somebody," said the old woman wearily. She did not care very much what happened, now.

"I will stay until to-morrow, in any case," said Louisa. "Then we can see."

"I'm sure you've no right to trouble yourself," moaned the old woman. But she must leave herself in my hands.

Miss Louisa felt glad that she was admitted, even in an official capacity. She wanted to share their lives. At home they would need her, now Mary had come. But they must manage without her.

"I must write a note to the vicarage," she said.

Alfred Durant looked at her inquiringly, for her service. He had always that intelligent readiness to serve, since he had been in the Navy. But there was a simple independence in his willingness, which she loved. She felt nevertheless it was hard to get at him. He was so deferential, quick to take the slightest suggestion of an order from her, implicitly, that she could not get at the man in him.

He looked at her very keenly. She noticed his eyes were golden brown, with a very small pupil, the kind of eyes that can see a long way off. He stood alert, at military attention. His face was still rather weather-reddened.

"Do you want pen and paper?" he asked, with deferential suggestion to a superior, which was more difficult for her than reserve.

"Yes, please," she said.

He turned and went downstairs. He seemed to her so self-contained, so utterly sure in his movement. How was she to approach him? For he would take not one step towards her. He would only put himself entirely and impersonally at her service, glad to serve her, but keeping himself quite removed from her. She could see he felt real joy in doing anything for her, but any recognition would confuse him and hurt him. Strange it was to her, to have a man going about the house in his shirt-sleeves, his waistcoat unbuttoned, his throat bare, waiting on her. He moved well, as if he had plenty of life to spare. She was attracted by his completeness. And yet, when all was ready, and there was nothing more for him to do, she quivered, meeting his questioning look.

As she sat writing, he placed another candle near her. The rather dense light fell in two places on the overfoldings of her hair till it glistened heavy and bright, like a dense golden plumage folded up. Then the nape of her neck was very white, with fine down and pointed wisps of gold. He watched it as it were a vision, losing himself. She was all that was beyond him, of revelation and exquisiteness. All that was ideal and beyond him, she was that—and he was lost to himself in looking at her. She had no connection with him. He did not approach her. She was there like a wonderful distance. But it was a treat, having her in the house. Even with this anguish for his mother tightening about him, he was sensible of the wonder of living this evening. The candles glistened on her hair, and seemed to fascinate him. He felt a little awe of her, and a sense of uplifting, that he and she and his mother should be together for a time, in the strange, unknown atmosphere. And, when he got out of the house, he was afraid. He saw the stars above ringing with fine brightness, the snow beneath just visible, and a new night was gathering round him. He was afraid almost with obliteration. What was this new night ringing about him, and what was he? He could not recognize himself nor any of his surroundings. He was afraid to think of his mother. And yet his chest was conscious of her, and of what was happening to her. He could not escape from her, she carried him with her into an unformed, unknown chaos.

XI

He went up the road in an agony, not knowing what it was all about, but feeling as if a red-hot iron were gripped round his chest. Without thinking, he shook two or three tears on to the snow. Yet in his mind he did not believe his mother would die. He was in the grip of some greater consciousness. As he sat in the hall of the vicarage, waiting whilst Mary put things for Louisa into a bag, he wondered why he had been so upset. He felt abashed and humbled by the big house, he felt again as if he were one of the rank and file. When Miss Mary spoke to him, he almost saluted.

" An honest man," thought Mary. And the patronage was applied as salve to her own sickness. She had station, so she could patronize : it was almost all that was left to her. But she could not have lived without having a certain position. She could never have trusted herself outside a definite place, nor respected herself except as a woman of superior class.

As Alfred came to the latch-gate, he felt the grief at his heart again, and saw the new heavens. He stood a moment looking northward to the Plough climbing up the night, and at the far glimmer of snow in distant fields. Then his grief came on like physical pain. He held tight to the gate, biting his mouth, whispering " Mother ! " It was a fierce, cutting, physical pain of grief, that came on in bouts, as his mother's pain came on in bouts, and was so acute he could scarcely keep erect. He did not know where it came from, the pain, nor why. It had nothing to do with his thoughts. Almost it had nothing to do with him. Only it gripped him and he must submit. The whole tide of his soul, gathering in its unknown towards this expansion into death, carried him with it helplessly, all the fritter of his thought and consciousness caught up as nothing, the heave passing on towards its breaking, taking him further than he had ever been. When the young man had regained himself, he went indoors, and there he was almost gay. It seemed to excite him. He felt in high spirits : he made whimsical fun of things. He sat on one side of his mother's bed, Louisa on the other, and a certain gaiety seized them all. But the night and the dread was coming on.

Alfred kissed his mother and went to bed. When he was half undressed the knowledge of his mother came upon him, and the suffering seized him in its grip like two hands, in agony. He lay on the bed screwed up tight. It lasted so long, and exhausted him so much, that he fell asleep, without having the energy to get up and finish undressing. He awoke after midnight to find himself stone cold. He undressed and got into bed, and was soon asleep again.

At a quarter to six he woke, and instantly remembered. Having pulled on his trousers and lighted a candle, he went into his mother's room. He put his hand before the candle flame so that no light fell on the bed.

" Mother ! " he whispered.

" Yes," was the reply.

There was a hesitation.

" Should I go to work ? "

He waited, his heart was beating heavily.

" I think I'd go, my lad."

His heart went down in a kind of despair.

" You want me to ? "

He let his hand down from the candle flame. The light fell on the bed. There he saw Louisa lying looking up at him. Her eyes were upon him. She quickly shut her eyes and half buried her face in the pillow, her back turned to him. He saw the rough hair like bright vapour about her round head, and the two plaits flung coiled among the bedclothes. It gave him a shock. He stood almost himself, determined. Louisa cowered down. He looked, and met his mother's eyes. Then he gave way again, and ceased to be sure, ceased to be himself.

" Yes, go to work, my boy," said the mother.

" All right," replied he, kissing her. His heart was down at despair, and bitter. He went away.

" Alfred ! " cried his mother faintly.

He came back with beating heart.

" What, mother ? "

" You'll always do what's right, Alfred ? " the mother asked, beside herself in terror now he was leaving her. He was too terrified and bewildered to know what she meant.

" Yes," he said.

She turned her cheek to him. He kissed her, then went away, in bitter despair. He went to work.

XII

By midday his mother was dead. The word met him at the pit-mouth. As he had known, inwardly, it was not a shock to him, and yet he trembled. He went home quite calmly, feeling only heavy in his breathing.

Miss Louisa was still at the house. She had seen to everything possible. Very succinctly, she informed him of what he needed to know. But there was one point of anxiety for her.

" You *did* half expect it—it's not come as a blow to you ? " she asked, looking up at him. Her eyes were dark and calm and searching. She too felt lost. He was so dark and inchoate.

" I suppose—yes," he said stupidly. He looked aside, unable to endure her eyes on him.

" I could not bear to think you might not have guessed," she said.

He did not answer.

He felt it a great strain to have her near him at this time. He wanted to be alone. As soon as the relatives began to arrive, Louisa departed and came no more. While everything was arranging, and a crowd was in the house, whilst he had business to settle, he went well enough, with only those uncontrollable paroxysms of grief. For the rest, he was superficial. By himself, he endured the fierce, almost insane bursts of grief which passed again and left him calm, almost clear, just wondering. He had not known before that everything could break down, that he himself could break down, and all be a great chaos, very vast and wonderful. It seemed as if life in him had burst its bounds, and he was lost in a great, bewildering flood, immense and unpeopled. He himself was broken and spilled out amid it all. He could only breathe panting in silence. Then the anguish came on again.

When all the people had gone from the Quarry Cottage, leaving the young man alone with an elderly housekeeper, then the long trial began. The snow had thawed and frozen, a fresh fall had whitened the grey, this then began to thaw. The world was a place of loose grey slosh. Alfred had nothing to do in the evenings. He was a man whose life had been filled up with small activities. Without knowing it, he had been centralized, polarized in his mother. It was she who had kept him. Even now, when the old housekeeper had left him, he might still have gone on in his old way. But the force and balance of his life was lacking. He sat pretending to read, all the time holding his fists clenched, and holding himself in, enduring he did not know what. He walked the black and sodden miles of field-paths, till he was tired out : but all this was only running away from whence he must return. At work he was all right. If it had been summer he might have escaped by working in the garden till bedtime. But now, there was no escape, no relief, no help. He, perhaps, was made for action rather than for understanding ; for doing than for being. He was shocked out of his activities, like a swimmer who forgets to swim.

For a week, he had the force to endure this suffocation and struggle, then he began to get exhausted, and knew it must come out. The instinct of self-preservation became strongest. But there was the question : Where was he to go ? The public-house really meant nothing to him, it was no good going there. He began to think of emigration. In another country he would be all right. He wrote to the emigration offices.

On the Sunday after the funeral, when all the Durant people had attended church, Alfred had seen Miss Louisa, impassive and reserved, sitting with Miss Mary, who was proud and very distant, and with the other Lindleys, who were people removed. Alfred saw them as people remote. He did not think about it. They had nothing to do with his life. After service Louisa had come to him and shaken hands.

" My sister would like you to come to supper one evening, if you would be so good."

He looked at Miss Mary, who bowed. Out of kindness, Mary had proposed this to Louisa, disapproving of herself even as she did so. But she did not examine herself closely.

" Yes," said Durant awkwardly, " I'll come if you want me." But he vaguely felt that it was misplaced.

" You'll come to-morrow evening, then, about half-past six."

He went. Miss Louisa was very kind to him. There could be no music, because of the babies. He sat with his fists clenched on his thighs, very quiet and unmoved, lapsing, among all those people, into a kind of muse or daze. There was nothing between him and them. They knew it as well as he. But he remained very steady in himself, and the evening passed slowly. Mrs. Lindley called him " young man."

" Will you sit here, young man ? "

He sat there. One name was as good as another. What had they to do with him ?

Mr. Lindley kept a special tone for him, kind, indulgent, but patronizing. Durant took it all without criticism or offence, just submitting. But he did not want to eat—that troubled him, to have to eat in their presence. He knew he was out of place. But it was his duty to stay yet awhile. He answered precisely, in mono-syllables.

When he left he winced with confusion. He was glad it was

finished. He got away as quickly as possible. And he wanted still more intensely to go right away, to Canada.

Miss Louisa suffered in her soul, indignant with all of them, with him too, but quite unable to say why she was indignant.

XIII

Two evenings after, Louisa tapped at the door of the Quarry Cottage, at half-past six. He had finished dinner, the woman had washed up and gone away, but still he sat in his pit dirt. He was going later to the New Inn. He had begun to go there because he must go somewhere. The mere contact with other men was necessary to him, the noise, the warmth, the forgetful flight of the hours. But still he did not move. He sat alone in the empty house till it began to grow on him like something unnatural.

He was in his pit dirt when he opened the door.

" I have been wanting to call—I thought I would," she said, and she went to the sofa. He wondered why she wouldn't use his mother's round arm-chair. Yet something stirred in him, like anger, when the housekeeper placed herself in it.

" I ought to have been washed by now," he said, glancing at the clock, which was adorned with butterflies and cherries, and the name of " T. Brooks, Mansfield." He laid his black hands along his mottled dirty arms. Louisa looked at him. There was the reserve, and the simple neutrality towards her, which she dreaded in him. It made it impossible for her to approach him.

" I am afraid," she said, " that I wasn't kind in asking you to supper."

" I'm not used to it," he said, smiling with his mouth, showing the interspaced white teeth. His eyes, however, were steady and unseeing.

" It's not *that*," she said hastily. Her repose was exquisite and her dark grey eyes rich with understanding. He felt afraid of her as she sat there, as he began to grow conscious of her.

" How do you get on alone ? " she asked.

He glanced away to the fire.

" Oh—— " he answered, shifting uneasily, not finishing his answer.

Her face settled heavily.

" How close it is in this room. You have such immense fires. I will take off my coat," she said.

He watched her take off her hat and coat. She wore a cream

cashmir blouse embroidered with gold silk. It seemed to him a very fine garment, fitting her throat and wrists close. It gave him a feeling of pleasure and cleanness and relief from himself.

" What were you thinking about, that you didn't get washed ? " she asked, half intimately. He laughed, turning aside his head. The whites of his eyes showed very distinct in his black face.

" Oh," he said, " I couldn't tell you."

There was a pause.

" Are you going to keep this house on ? " she asked.

He stirred in his chair, under the question.

" I hardly know," he said. " I'm very likely going to Canada."

Her spirit became very quiet and attentive.

" What for ? " she asked.

Again he shifted restlessly on his seat.

" Well "—he said slowly—" to try the life."

" But which life ? "

" There's various things—farming or lumbering or mining. I don't mind much what it is."

" And is that what you want ? "

He did not think in these times, so he could not answer.

" I don't know," he said, " till I've tried."

She saw him drawing away from her for ever.

" Aren't you sorry to leave this house and garden ? " she asked.

" I don't know," he answered reluctantly. " I suppose our Fred would come in—that's what he's wanting."

" You don't want to settle down ? " she asked.

He was leaning forward on the arms of his chair. He turned to her. Her face was pale and set. It looked heavy and impassive, her hair shone richer as she grew white. She was to him something steady and immovable and eternal presented to him. His heart was hot in an anguish of suspense. Sharp twitches of fear and pain were in his limbs. He turned his whole body away from her. The silence was unendurable. He could not bear her to sit there any more. It made his heart go hot and stifled in his breast.

" Were you going out to-night ? " she asked.

" Only to the New Inn," he said.

Again there was silence.

She reached for her hat. Nothing else was suggested to her. She *had* to go. He sat waiting for her to be gone, for relief. And she knew that if she went out of that house as she was, she went out a failure. Yet she continued to pin on her hat ; in a moment she would have to go. Something was carrying her.

Then suddenly a sharp pang, like lightning, seared her from head to foot, and she was beyond herself.

" Do you want me to go ? " she asked, controlled, yet speaking out of a fiery anguish, as if the words were spoken from her without her intervention.

He went white under his dirt.

" Why ? " he asked, turning to her in fear, compelled.

" Do you want me to go ? " she repeated.

" Why ? " he asked again.

" Because I wanted to stay with you," she said, suffocated, with her lungs full of fire.

His face worked, he hung forward a little, suspended, staring straight into her eyes, in torment, in an agony of chaos, unable to collect himself. And as if turned to stone, she looked back into his eyes. Their souls were exposed bare for a few moments. It was agony. They could not bear it. He dropped his head, whilst his body jerked with little sharp twitchings.

She turned away for her coat. Her soul had gone dead in her. Her hands trembled, but she could not feel any more. She drew on her coat. There was a cruel suspense in the room. The moment had come for her to go. He lifted his head. His eyes were like agate, expressionless, save for the black points of torture. They held her, she had no will, no life any more. She felt broken.

" Don't you want me ? " she said helplessly.

A spasm of torture crossed his eyes, which held her fixed.

" I—I——" he began, but he could not speak. Something drew him from his chair to her. She stood motionless, spellbound, like a creature given up as prey. He put his hand tentatively, uncertainly, on her arm. The expression of his face was strange and inhuman. She stood utterly motionless. Then clumsily he put his arms round her, and took her, cruelly, blindly, straining her till she nearly lost consciousness, till he himself had almost fallen.

Then, gradually, as he held her gripped, and his brain reeled round, and he felt himself falling, falling from himself, and whilst she, yielded up, swooned to a kind of death of herself, a moment of utter darkness came over him, and they began to wake up again as if from a long sleep. He was himself.

After a while his arms slackened, she loosened herself a little, and put her arms round him, as he held her. So they held each other close, and hid each against the other for assurance, helpless in speech. And it was ever her hands that trembled more closely upon him, drawing him nearer into her, with love.

And at last she drew back her face and looked up at him, her eyes wet, and shining with light. His heart, which saw, was silent with fear. He was with her. She saw his face all sombre and inscrutable, and he seemed eternal to her. And all the echo of pain came back into the rarity of bliss, and all her tears came up.

" I love you," she said, her lips drawn to sobbing. He put down his head against her, unable to hear her, unable to bear the sudden coming of the peace and passion that almost broke his heart. They stood together in silence whilst the thing moved away a little.

At last she wanted to see him. She looked up. His eyes were strange and glowing, with a tiny black pupil. Strange, they were, and powerful over her. And his mouth came to hers, and slowly her eyelids closed, as his mouth sought hers closer and closer, and took possession of her.

They were silent for a long time, too much mixed up with passion and grief and death to do anything but hold each other in pain and kiss with long, hurting kisses wherein fear was transfused into desire. At last she disengaged herself. He felt as if his heart were hurt, but glad, and he scarcely dared look at her.

" I'm glad," she said also.

He held her hands in passionate gratitude and desire. He had not yet the presence of mind to say anything. He was dazed with relief.

" I ought to go," she said.

He looked at her. He could not grasp the thought of her going, he knew he could never be separated from her any more. Yet he dared not assert himself. He held her hands tight.

" Your face is black," she said.

He laughed.

" Yours is a bit smudged," he said.

They were afraid of each other, afraid to talk. He could only keep her near to him. After a while she wanted to wash her face. He brought her some warm water, standing by and watching her. There was something he wanted to say, that he dared not. He watched her wiping her face, and making tidy her hair.

" They'll see your blouse is dirty," he said.

She looked at her sleeves and laughed for joy.

He was sharp with pride.

" What shall you do ? " he asked.

" How ? " she said.

He was awkward at a reply.

" About me," he said.

" What do you want me to do ? " she laughed.
He put his hand out slowly to her. What did it matter !
" But make yourself clean," she said.

XIV

As they went up the hill, the night seemed dense with the unknown.
They kept close together, feeling as if the darkness were alive and
full of knowledge, all around them. In silence they walked up the
hill. At first the street lamps went their way. Several people
passed them. He was more shy than she, and would have let her
go had she loosened in the least. But she held firm.

Then they came into the true darkness, between the fields. They
did not want to speak, feeling closer together in silence. So they
arrived at the vicarage gate. They stood under the naked horse-
chestnut tree.

" I wish you didn't have to go," he said.

She laughed a quick little laugh.

" Come to-morrow," she said, in a low tone, " and ask father."

She felt his hand close on hers.

She gave the same sorrowful little laugh of sympathy. Then she
kissed him, sending him home.

At home, the old grief came on in another paroxysm, obliterating
Louisa, obliterating even his mother for whom the stress was raging
like a burst of fever in a wound. But something was sound in his
heart.

XV

The next evening he dressed to go to the vicarage, feeling it was
to be done, not imagining what it would be like. He would not
take this seriously. He was sure of Louisa, and this marriage was
like fate to him. It filled him also with a blessed feeling of fatality.
He was not responsible, neither had her people anything really to
do with it.

They ushered him into the little study, which was fireless. By
and by the vicar came in. His voice was cold and hostile as he
said :

" What can I do for you, young man ? "

He knew already, without asking.

Durant looked up at him, again like a sailor before a superior.
He had the subordinate manner. Yet his spirit was clear.

" I wanted, Mr. Lindley——" he began respectfully, then all the colour suddenly left his face. It seemed now a violation to say what he had to say. What was he doing there? But he stood on, because it had to be done. He held firmly to his own independence and self-respect. He must not be indecisive. He must put himself aside : the matter was bigger than just his personal self. He must not feel. This was his highest duty.

" You wanted——" said the vicar.

Durant's mouth was dry, but he answered with steadiness :

" Miss Louisa—Louisa—promised to marry me——"

" You asked Miss Louisa if she would marry you—yes——" corrected the vicar. Durant reflected he had not asked her this :

" If she would marry me, sir. I hope you—don't mind."

He smiled. He was a good-looking man, and the vicar could not help seeing it.

" And my daughter was willing to marry you ? " said Mr. Lindley.

" Yes," said Durant seriously. It was pain to him, nevertheless. He felt the natural hostility between himself and the elder man.

" Will you come this way ? " said the vicar. He led into the dining-room, where were Mary, Louisa, and Mrs. Lindley. Mr. Massy sat in a corner with a lamp.

" This young man has come on your account, Louisa ? " said Mr. Lindley.

" Yes," said Louisa, her eyes on Durant, who stood erect, in discipline. He dared not look at her, but he was aware of her.

" You don't want to marry a collier, you little fool," cried Mrs. Lindley harshly. She lay obese and helpless upon the couch, swathed in a loose dove-grey gown.

" Oh, hush, mother," cried Mary, with quiet intensity and pride.

" What means have you to support a wife ? " demanded the vicar's wife roughly.

" I ! " Durant replied, starting. " I think I can earn enough."

" Well, and how much ? " came the rough voice.

" Seven and six a day," replied the young man.

" And will it get to be any more ? "

" I hope so."

" And are you going to live in that poky little house ? "

" I think so," said Durant, " if it's all right."

He took small offence, only was upset, because they would not think him good enough. He knew that, in their sense, he was not.

" Then she's a fool, I tell you, if she marries you," cried the mother roughly, casting her decision.

" After all, mama, it is Louisa's affair," said Mary distinctly,
" and we must remember——"

" As she makes her bed, she must lie—but she'll repent it,"
interrupted Mrs. Lindley.

" And after all," said Mr. Lindley, " Louisa cannot quite hold
herself free to act entirely without consideration for her family."

" What do you want, papa ? " asked Louisa sharply.

" I mean that if you marry this man, it will make my position
very difficult for me, particularly if you stay in this parish. If you
were moving quite away, it would be simpler. But living here in
a collier's cottage, under my nose, as it were—it would be almost
unseemly. I have my position to maintain, and a position which
may not be taken lightly."

" Come over here, young man," cried the mother, in her rough
voice, " and let us look at you."

Durant, flushing, went over and stood—not quite at attention, so
that he did not know what to do with his hands. Miss Louisa was
angry to see him standing there, obedient and acquiescent. He
ought to show himself a man.

" Can't you take her away and live out of sight ? " said the mother.
" You'd both of you be better off."

" Yes, we can go away," he said.

" Do you want to ? " asked Miss Mary clearly.

He faced round. Mary looked very stately and impressive. He
flushed.

" I do if it's going to be a trouble to anybody," he said.

" For yourself, you would rather stay ? " said Mary.

" It's my home," he said, " and that's the house I was born in."

" Then "—Mary turned clearly to her parents, " I really don't
see how you can make the conditions, papa. He has his own rights,
and if Louisa wants to marry him——"

" Louisa, Louisa ! " cried the father impatiently. " I cannot
understand why Louisa should not behave in the normal way. I
cannot see why she should only think of herself, and leave her family
out of count. The thing is enough in itself, and she ought to try to
ameliorate it as much as possible. And if——"

" But I love the man, papa," said Louisa.

" And I hope you love your parents, and I hope you want to
spare them as much of the—the loss of prestige, as possible."

" We *can* go away to live," said Louisa, her face breaking to tears.
At last she was really hurt.

" Oh, yes, easily," Durant replied hastily, pale, distressed.

There was dead silence in the room.

" I think it would really be better," murmured the vicar, mollified.

" Very likely it would," said the rough-voiced invalid.

" Though I think we ought to apologize for asking such a thing," said Mary haughtily.

" No," said Durant. " It will be best all round." He was glad there was no more bother.

" And shall we put up the banns here or go to the registrar ? " he asked clearly, like a challenge.

" We will go to the registrar," replied Louisa decidedly.

Again there was a dead silence in the room.

" Well, if you will have your own way, you must go your own way," said the mother emphatically.

All the time Mr. Massy had sat obscure and unnoticed in a corner of the room. At this juncture he got up, saying :

" There is baby, Mary."

Mary rose and went out of the room, stately ; her little husband padded after her. Durant watched the fragile, small man go, wondering.

" And where," asked the vicar, almost genial, " do you think you will go when you are married ? "

Durant started.

" I was thinking of emigrating," he said.

" To Canada ? Or where ? "

" I think to Canada."

" Yes, that would be very good."

Again there was a pause.

" We shan't see much of you then, as a son-in-law," said the mother, roughly but amicably.

" Not much," he said.

Then he took his leave. Louisa went with him to the gate. She stood before him in distress.

" You won't mind them, will you ? " she said humbly.

" I don't mind them, if they don't mind me ! " he said. Then he stooped and kissed her.

" Let us be married soon," she murmured, in tears.

" All right," he said. " I'll go to-morrow to Barford."

THE two girls were usually known by their surnames, Banford and March. They had taken the farm together, intending to work it all by themselves : that is, they were going to rear chickens, make a living by poultry, and add to this by keeping a cow, and raising one or two young beasts. Unfortunately, things did not turn out well. Banford was a small, thin, delicate thing with spectacles. She, however, was the principal investor, for March had little or no money. Banford's father, who was a tradesman in Islington, gave his daughter the start, for her health's sake, and because he loved her, and because it did not look as if she would marry. March was more robust. She had learned carpentry and joinery at the evening classes in Islington. She would be the man about the place. They had, moreover, Banford's old grandfather living with them at the start. He had been a farmer. But unfortunately the old man died after he had been at Bailey Farm for a year. Then the two girls were left alone.

They were neither of them young : that is, they were near thirty. But they certainly were not old. They set out quite gallantly with their enterprise. They had numbers of chickens, black Leghorns and white Leghorns, Plymouths and Wyandottes ; also some ducks ; also two heifers in the fields. One heifer, unfortunately, refused absolutely to stay in the Bailey Farm closes. No matter how March made up the fences, the heifer was out, wild in the woods, or trespassing on the neighbouring pasture, and March and Banford were away, flying after her, with more haste than success. So this heifer they sold in despair. Then, just before the other beast was expecting her first calf, the old man died, and the girls, afraid of the coming event, sold her in a panic, and limited their attentions to fowls and ducks.

In spite of a little chagrin, it was a relief to have no more cattle on hand. Life was not made merely to be slaved away. Both girls agreed in this. The fowls were quite enough trouble. March had set up her carpenter's bench at the end of the open shed. Here she worked, making coops and doors and other appurtenances. The

fowls were housed in the bigger building, which had served as barn
and cowshed in old days. They had a beautiful home, and should
have been perfectly content. Indeed, they looked well enough.
But the girls were disgusted at their tendency to strange illnesses,
at their exacting way of life, and at their refusal, obstinate refusal
to lay eggs.

March did most of the outdoor work. When she was out and
about, in her puttees and breeches, her belted coat and her loose
cap, she looked almost like some graceful, loose-balanced young
man, for her shoulders were straight, and her movements easy and
confident, even tinged with a little indifference, or irony. But her
face was not a man's face, ever. The wisps of her crisp dark hair
blew about her as she stooped, her eyes were big and wide and dark,
when she looked up again, strange, startled, shy and sardonic at
once. Her mouth, too, was almost pinched as if in pain and irony.
There was something odd and unexplained about her. She would
stand balanced on one hip, looking at the fowls pattering about in
the obnoxious fine mud of the sloping yard, and calling to her
favourite white hen, which came in answer to her name. But there
was an almost satirical flicker in March's big, dark eyes as she
looked at her three-toed flock pottering about under her gaze, and
the same slight dangerous satire in her voice as she spoke to the
favoured Patty, who pecked at March's boot by way of friendly
demonstration.

Fowls did not flourish at Bailey Farm, in spite of all that March
did for them. When she provided hot food for them in the morning,
according to rule, she noticed that it made them heavy and dozy for
hours. She expected to see them lean against the pillars of the shed
in their languid processes of digestion. And she knew quite well
that they ought to be busily scratching and foraging about, if they
were to come to any good. So she decided to give them their hot
food at night, and let them sleep on it. Which she did. But it
made no difference.

War conditions, again, were very unfavourable to poultry keeping. Food was scarce and bad. And when the Daylight Saving Bill
was passed, the fowls obstinately refused to go to bed as usual, about
nine o'clock in the summer-time. That was late enough, indeed, for
there was no peace till they were shut up and asleep. Now they
cheerfully walked around, without so much as glancing at the barn,
until ten o'clock or later. Both Banford and March disbelieved in
living for work alone. They wanted to read or take a cycle-ride in
the evening, or perhaps March wished to paint curvilinear swans on

porcelain, with green background, or else make a marvellous fire-screen by processes of elaborate cabinet work. For she was a creature of odd whims and unsatisfied tendencies. But from all these things she was prevented by the stupid fowls.

One evil there was greater than any other. Bailey Farm was a little homestead, with ancient wooden barn and low-gabled farm-house, lying just one field removed from the edge of the wood. Since the war the fox was a demon. He carried off the hens under the very noses of March and Banford. Banford would start and stare through her big spectacles with all her eyes, as another squawk and flutter took place at her heels. Too late ! Another white Leghorn gone. It was disheartening.

They did what they could to remedy it. When it became per-mitted to shoot foxes, they stood sentinel with their guns, the two of them, at the favoured hours. But it was no good. The fox was too quick for them. So another year passed, and another, and they were living on their losses, as Banford said. They let their farm-house one summer, and retired to live in a railway-carriage that was deposited as a sort of out-house in a corner of the field. This amused them, and helped their finances. None the less, things looked dark.

Although they were usually the best of friends, because Banford, though nervous and delicate, was a warm, generous soul, and March, though so odd and absent in herself, had a strange magna-nimity, yet, in the long solitude, they were apt to become a little irritable with one another, tired of one another. March had four-fifths of the work to do, and though she did not mind, there seemed no relief, and it made her eyes flash curiously sometimes. Then Banford, feeling more nerve-worn than ever, would become despon-dent, and March would speak sharply to her. They seemed to be losing ground, somehow, losing hope as the months went by. There alone in the fields by the wood, with the wide country stretching hollow and dim to the round hills of the White Horse, in the far distance, they seemed to have to live too much off themselves. There was nothing to keep them up—and no hope.

The fox really exasperated them both. As soon as they had let the fowls out, in the early summer mornings, they had to take their guns and keep guard : and then again, as soon as evening began to mellow, they must go once more. And he was so sly. He slid along in the deep grass ; he was difficult as a serpent to see. And he seemed to circumvent the girls deliberately. Once or twice March had caught sight of the white tip of his brush, or the ruddy shadow of him in the deep grass, and she had let fire at him. But he made no account of this.

One evening March was standing with her back to the sunset, her gun under her arm, her hair pushed under her cap. She was half watching, half musing. It was her constant state. Her eyes were keen and observant, but her inner mind took no notice of what she saw. She was always lapsing into this odd, rapt state, her mouth rather screwed up. It was a question whether she was there, actually conscious present, or not.

The trees on the wood-edge were a darkish, brownish green in the full light—for it was the end of August. Beyond, the naked, copper-like shafts and limbs of the pine-trees shone in the air. Nearer the rough grass, with its long brownish stalks all agleam, was full of light. The fowls were round about—the ducks were still swimming on the pond under the pine-trees. March looked at it all, saw it all, and did not see it. She heard Banford speaking to the fowls in the distance—and she did not hear. What was she thinking about? Heaven knows. Her consciousness was, as it were, held back.

She lowered her eyes, and suddenly saw the fox. He was looking up at her. His chin was pressed down, and his eyes were looking up. They met her eyes. And he knew her. She was spellbound—she knew he knew her. So he looked into her eyes, and her soul failed her. He knew her, he was not daunted.

She struggled, confusedly she came to herself, and saw him making off, with slow leaps over some fallen boughs, slow, impudent jumps. Then he glanced over his shoulder, and ran smoothly away. She saw his brush held smooth like a feather, she saw his white buttocks twinkle. And he was gone, softly, soft as the wind.

She put her gun to her shoulder, but even then pursed her mouth, knowing it was nonsense to pretend to fire. So she began to walk slowly after him, in the direction he had gone, slowly, pertinaciously. She expected to find him. In her heart she was determined to find him. What she would do when she saw him again she did not consider. But she was determined to find him. So she walked abstractedly about on the edge of the wood, with wide, vivid dark eyes, and a faint flush in her cheeks. She did not think. In strange mindlessness she walked hither and thither.

At last she became aware that Banford was calling her. She made an effort of attention, turned, and gave some sort of screaming call in answer. Then again she was striding off towards the homestead. The red sun was setting, the fowls were retiring towards their roost. She watched them, white creatures, black creatures, gathering to the barn. She watched them spellbound, without seeing them. But her automatic intelligence told her when it was time to shut the door.

She went indoors to supper, which Banford had set on the table. Banford chatted easily. March seemed to listen, in her distant, manly way. She answered a brief word now and then. But all the time she was as if spellbound. And as soon as supper was over, she rose again to go out, without saying why.

She took her gun again and went to look for the fox. For he had lifted his eyes upon her, and his knowing look seemed to have entered her brain. She did not so much think of him : she was possessed by him. She saw his dark, shrewd, unabashed eye looking into her, knowing her. She felt him invisibly master her spirit. She knew the way he lowered his chin as he looked up, she knew his muzzle, the golden brown, and the greyish white. And again, she saw him glance over his shoulder at her, half inviting, half contemptuous, and cunning. So she went, with her great startled eyes glowing, her gun under her arm, along the wood edge. Meanwhile the night fell, and a great moon rose above the pine-trees. And again Banford was calling.

So she went indoors. She was silent and busy. She examined her gun, and cleaned it, musing abstractedly by the lamp-light. Then she went out again, under the great moon, to see if everything was right. When she saw the dark crests of the pine-trees against the blood-red sky, again her heart beat to the fox, the fox. She wanted to follow him, with her gun.

It was some days before she mentioned the affair to Banford. Then suddenly one evening she said :

" The fox was right at my feet on Saturday night."

" Where ? " said Banford, her eyes opening behind her spectacles.

" When I stood just above the pond."

" Did you fire ? " cried Banford.

" No, I didn't."

" Why not ? "

" Why, I was too much surprised, I suppose."

It was the same old, slow, laconic way of speech March always had. Banford stared at her friend for a few moments.

" You saw him ? " she cried.

" Oh yes ! He was looking up at me, cool as anything."

" I tell you," cried Banford—" the cheek ! They're not afraid of us, Nellie."

" Oh no," said March.

" Pity you didn't get a shot at him," said Banford.

" Isn't it a pity ! I've been looking for him ever since. But I
don't suppose he'll come so near again."

" I don't suppose he will," said Banford.

And she proceeded to forget about it, except that she was more
indignant than ever at the impudence of the beggar. March also
was not conscious that she thought of the fox. But whenever she fell
into her half-musing, when she was half rapt and half intelligently
aware of what passed under her vision, then it was the fox which
somehow dominated her unconsciousness, possessed the blank half
of her musing. And so it was for weeks, and months. No matter
whether she had been climbing the trees for the apples, or beating
down the last of the damsons, or whether she had been digging out
the ditch from the duck-pond, or clearing out the barn, when she
had finished, or when she straightened herself, and pushed the wisps
of hair away again from her forehead, and pursed up her mouth
again in an odd, screwed fashion, much too old for her years, there
was sure to come over her mind the old spell of the fox, as it came
when he was looking at her. It was as if she could smell him at these
times. And it always recurred, at unexpected moments, just as she
was going to sleep at night, or just as she was pouring the water into
the teapot to make tea—it was the fox, it came over her like a spell.

So the months passed. She still looked for him unconsciously when
she went towards the wood. He had become a settled effect in her
spirit, a state permanently established, not continuous, but always
recurring. She did not know what she felt or thought : only the
state came over her, as when he looked at her.

The months passed, the dark evenings came, heavy, dark
November, when March went about in high boots, ankle deep in
mud, when the night began to fall at four o'clock, and the day never
properly dawned. Both girls dreaded these times. They dreaded
the almost continuous darkness that enveloped them on their
desolate little farm near the wood. Banford was physically afraid.
She was afraid of tramps, afraid lest someone should come prowling
round. March was not so much afraid as uncomfortable, and disturbed. She felt discomfort and gloom in all her physique.

Usually the two girls had tea in the sitting-room. March lighted
a fire at dusk, and put on the wood she had chopped and sawed
during the day. Then the long evening was in front, dark, sodden,
black outside, lonely and rather oppressive inside, a little dismal.
March was content not to talk, but Banford could not keep still.
Merely listening to the wind in the pines outside, or the drip of
water, was too much for her.

One evening the girls had washed up the tea-things in the kitchen, and March had put on her house-shoes, and taken up a roll of crochet-work, which she worked at slowly from time to time. So she lapsed into silence. Banford stared at the red fire, which, being of wood, needed constant attention. She was afraid to begin to read too early, because her eyes would not bear any strain. So she sat staring at the fire, listening to the distant sounds, sound of cattle lowing, of a dull, heavy, moist wind, of the rattle of the evening train on the little railway not far off. She was almost fascinated by the red glow of the fire.

Suddenly both girls started, and lifted their heads. They heard a footstep—distinctly a footstep. Banford recoiled in fear. March stood listening. Then rapidly she approached the door that led into the kitchen. At the same time they heard the footsteps approach the back door. They waited a second. The back door opened softly. Banford gave a loud cry. A man's voice said softly :

" Hello ! "

March recoiled, and took a gun from a corner.

" What do you want ? " she cried, in a sharp voice.

Again the soft, softly vibrating man's voice said :

" Hello ! What's wrong ? "

" I shall shoot ! " cried March. " What do you want ? "

" Why, what's wrong ? What's wrong ? " came the soft, wondering, rather scared voice : and a young soldier, with his heavy kit on his back, advanced into the dim light.

" Why," he said, " who lives here then ? "

" We live here," said March. " What do you want ? "

" Oh ! " came the long, melodious, wonder-note from the young soldier. " Doesn't William Grenfel live here then ? "

" No—you know he doesn't."

" Do I ? Do I ? I don't, you see. He *did* live here, because he was my grandfather, and I lived here myself five years ago. What's become of him then ? "

The young man—or youth, for he would not be more than twenty—now advanced and stood in the inner doorway. March, already under the influence of his strange, soft, modulated voice, stared at him spellbound. He had a ruddy, roundish face, with fairish hair, rather long, flattened to his forehead with sweat. His eyes were blue, and very bright and sharp. On his cheeks, on the fresh ruddy skin were fine, fair hairs, like a down, but sharper. It gave him a slightly glistening look. Having his heavy sack on his shoulders, he stooped, thrusting his head forward. His hat was loose in one hand. He stared brightly, very keenly from girl to girl, particularly at March, who stood pale, with great dilated eyes, in her belted coat and puttees, her hair knotted in a big crisp knot behind. She still had the gun in her hand. Behind her, Banford, clinging to the sofa-arm, was shrinking away, with half-averted head.

"I thought my grandfather still lived here? I wonder if he's dead."

"We've been here for three years," said Banford, who was beginning to recover her wits, seeing something boyish in the round head with its rather long sweaty hair.

"Three years! You don't say so! And you don't know who was here before you?"

"I know it was an old man, who lived by himself."

"Ay! Yes, that's him! And what became of him then?"

"He died. I know he died."

"Ay! He's dead then!"

The youth stared at them without changing colour or expression. If he had any expression, besides a slight baffled look of wonder, it was one of sharp curiosity concerning the two girls; sharp, impersonal curiosity, the curiosity of that round young head.

But to March he was the fox. Whether it was the thrusting forward of his head, or the glisten of fine whitish hairs on the ruddy cheekbones, or the bright, keen eyes, that can never be said : but the boy was to her the fox, and she could not see him otherwise.

"How is it you didn't know if your grandfather was alive or dead?" asked Banford, recovering her natural sharpness.

"Ay, that's it," replied the softly-breathing youth. "You see I joined up in Canada, and I hadn't heard for three or four years. I ran away to Canada."

"And now have you just come from France?"

"Well—from Salonika really."

There was a pause, nobody knowing quite what to say.

"So you've nowhere to go now?" said Banford rather lamely.

"Oh, I know some people in the village. Anyhow, I can go to the Swan."

"You came on the train, I suppose. Would you like to sit down a bit?"

"Well—I don't mind."

He gave an odd little groan as he swung off his kit. Banford looked at March.

"Put the gun down," she said. "We'll make a cup of tea."

"Ay," said the youth. "We've seen enough of rifles."

He sat down rather tired on the sofa, leaning forward.

o *

March recovered her presence of mind, and went into the kitchen. There she heard the soft young voice musing :

" Well, to think I should come back and find it like this ! " He did not seem sad, not at all—only rather interestedly surprised.

" And what a difference in the place, eh ? " he continued, looking round the room.

" You see a difference, do you ? " said Banford.

" Yes—don't I ! "

His eyes were unnaturally clear and bright, though it was the brightness of abundant health.

March was busy in the kitchen preparing another meal. It was about seven o'clock. All the time, while she was active, she was attending to the youth in the sitting-room, not so much listening to what he said as feeling the soft run of his voice. She primmed up her mouth tighter and tighter, puckering it as if it were sewed, in her effort to keep her will uppermost. Yet her large eyes dilated and glowed in spite of her ; she lost herself. Rapidly and carelessly she prepared the meal, cutting large chunks of bread and margarine— for there was no butter. She racked her brain to think of something else to put on the tray—she had only bread, margarine, and jam, and the larder was bare. Unable to conjure anything up, she went into the sitting-room with her tray.

She did not want to be noticed. Above all, she did not want him to look at her. But when she came in, and was busy setting the table just behind him, he pulled himself up from his sprawling, and turned and looked over his shoulder. She became pale and wan.

The youth watched her as she bent over the table, looked at her slim, well-shaped legs, at the belted coat dropping around her thighs, at the knot of dark hair, and his curiosity, vivid and widely alert, was again arrested by her.

The lamp was shaded with a dark-green shade, so that the light was thrown downwards and the upper half of the room was dim. His face moved bright under the light, but March loomed shadowy in the distance.

She turned round, but kept her eyes sideways, dropping and lifting her dark lashes. Her mouth unpuckered as she said to Banford :

" Will you pour out ? "

Then she went into the kitchen again.

" Have your tea where you are, will you ? " said Banford to the youth—" unless you'd rather come to the table."

" Well," said he, " I'm nice and comfortable here, aren't I ? I will have it here, if you don't mind."

" There's nothing but bread and jam," she said. And she put his plate on a stool by him. She was very happy now, waiting on him. For she loved company. And now she was no more afraid of him than if he were her own younger brother. He was such a boy.

" Nellie," she called. " I've poured you a cup out."

March appeared in the doorway, took her cup, and sat down in a corner, as far from the light as possible. She was very sensitive in her knees. Having no skirts to cover them, and being forced to sit with them boldly exposed, she suffered. She shrank and shrank, trying not to be seen. And the youth, sprawling low on the couch, glanced up at her, with long, steady, penetrating looks, till she was almost ready to disappear. Yet she held her cup balanced, she drank her tea, screwed up her mouth and held her head averted. Her desire to be invisible was so strong that it quite baffled the youth. He felt he could not see her distinctly. She seemed like a shadow within the shadow. And ever his eyes came back to her, searching, unremitting, with unconscious fixed attention.

Meanwhile he was talking softly and smoothly to Banford, who loved nothing so much as gossip, and who was full of perky interest, like a bird. Also he ate largely and quickly and voraciously, so that March had to cut more chunks of bread and margarine, for the roughness of which Banford apologized.

" Oh well," said March, suddenly speaking, " if there's no butter to put on it, it's no good trying to make dainty pieces."

Again the youth watched her, and he laughed, with a sudden, quick laugh, showing his teeth and wrinkling his nose.

" It isn't, is it," he answered, in his soft, near voice.

It appeared he was Cornish by birth and upbringing. When he was twelve years old he had come to Bailey Farm with his grand-father, with whom he had never agreed very well. So he had run away to Canada, and worked far away in the West. Now he was here—and that was the end of it.

He was very curious about the girls, to find out exactly what they were doing. His questions were those of a farm youth ; acute, practical, a little mocking. He was very much amused by their attitude to their losses : for they were amusing on the score of heifers and fowls.

" Oh well," broke in March, " we don't believe in living for nothing but work."

" Don't you ? " he answered. And again the quick young laugh came over his face. He kept his eyes steadily on the obscure woman in the corner.

" But what will you do when you've used up all your capital ? "
he said.

" Oh, I don't know," answered March laconically. " Hire ourselves out for land-workers, I suppose."

" Yes, but there won't be any demand for women land-workers
now the war's over," said the youth.

" Oh, we'll see. We shall hold on a bit longer yet," said March,
with a plangent, half-sad, half-ironical indifference.

" There wants a man about the place," said the youth softly.

Banford burst out laughing.

" Take care what you say," she interrupted. " We consider
ourselves quite efficient."

" Oh," came March's slow plangent voice, " it isn't a case of
efficiency, I'm afraid. If you're going to do farming you must be at
it from morning till night, and you might as well be a beast yourself."

" Yes, that's it," said the youth. " You aren't willing to put
yourselves into it."

" We aren't," said March, " and we know it."

" We want some of our time for ourselves," said Banford.

The youth threw himself back on the sofa, his face tight with
laughter, and laughed silently but thoroughly. The calm scorn of
the girls tickled him tremendously.

" Yes," he said, " but why did you begin then ? "

" Oh," said March, " we had a better opinion of the nature of
fowls then than we have now."

" Of Nature altogether, I'm afraid," said Banford. " Don't talk
to me about Nature."

Again the face of the youth tightened with delighted laughter.

" You haven't a very high opinion of fowls and cattle, haven't
you ? " he said.

" Oh no—quite a low one," said March.

He laughed out.

" Neither fowls nor heifers," said Banford, " nor goats nor the
weather."

The youth broke into a sharp yap of laughter, delighted. The
girls began to laugh too, March turning aside her face and wrinkling
her mouth in amusement.

" Oh, well," said Banford, " we don't mind, do we, Nellie ? "

" No," said March, " we don't mind."

The youth was very pleased. He had eaten and drunk his fill.
Banford began to question him. His name was Henry Grenfel—no,
he was not called Harry, always Henry. He continued to answer

with courteous simplicity, grave and charming. March, who was not included, cast long, slow glances at him from her recess, as he sat there on the sofa, his hands clasping his knees, his face under the lamp bright and alert, turned to Banford. She became almost peaceful at last. He was identified with the fox—and he was here in full presence. She need not go after him any more. There in the shadow of her corner she gave herself up to a warm, relaxed peace, almost like sleep, accepting the spell that was on her. But she wished to remain hidden. She was only fully at peace whilst he forgot her, talking to Banford. Hidden in the shadow of the corner, she need not any more be divided in herself, trying to keep up two planes of consciousness. She could at last lapse into the odour of the fox.

For the youth, sitting before the fire in his uniform, sent a faint but distinct odour into the room, indefinable, but something like a wild creature. March no longer tried to reserve herself from it. She was still and soft in her corner like a passive creature in its cave.

At last the talk dwindled. The youth relaxed his clasp of his knees, pulled himself together a little, and looked round. Again he became aware of the silent, half-invisible woman in the corner.

"Well," he said, unwillingly, "I suppose I'd better be going, or they'll be in bed at the Swan."

"I'm afraid they're in bed anyhow," said Banford. "They've all got this influenza."

"Have they!" he exclaimed. And he pondered. "Well," he continued, "I shall find a place somewhere."

"I'd say you could stay here, only——" Banford began.

He turned and watched her, holding his head forward.

"What?" he asked.

"Oh, well," she said, "propriety, I suppose." She was rather confused.

"It wouldn't be improper, would it?" he said, gently surprised.

"Not as far as we're concerned," said Banford.

"And not as far as *I'm* concerned," he said, with grave *naïveté*. "After all, it's my own home, in a way."

Banford smiled at this.

"It's what the village will have to say," she said.

There was a moment's blank pause.

"What do you say, Nellie?" asked Banford.

"I don't mind," said March, in her distinct tone. "The village doesn't matter to me, anyhow."

"No," said the youth, quick and soft. "Why should it? I mean, what should they say?"

" Oh, well," came March's plangent, laconic voice, " they'll easily find something to say. But it makes no difference what they say. We can look after ourselves."

" Of course you can," said the youth.

" Well, then, stop if you like," said Banford. " The spare room is quite ready."

His face shone with pleasure.

" If you're quite sure it isn't troubling you too much," he said, with that soft courtesy which distinguished him.

" Oh, it's no trouble," they both said.

He looked, smiled with delight, from one to another.

" It's awfully nice not to have to turn out again, isn't it ? " he said gratefully.

" I suppose it is," said Banford.

March disappeared to attend to the room. Banford was as pleased and thoughtful as if she had her own young brother home from France. It gave her just the same kind of gratification to attend on him, to get out the bath for him, and everything. Her natural warmth and kindliness had now an outlet. And the youth luxuriated in her sisterly attention. But it puzzled him slightly to know that March was silently working for him too. She was so curiously silent and obliterated. It seemed to him he had not really seen her. He felt he should not know her if he met her in the road.

That night March dreamed vividly. She dreamed she heard a singing outside which she could not understand, a singing that roamed round the house, in the fields, and in the darkness. It moved her so that she felt she must weep. She went out, and suddenly she knew it was the fox singing. He was very yellow and bright, like corn. She went nearer to him, but he ran away and ceased singing. He seemed near, and she wanted to touch him. She stretched out her hand, but suddenly he bit her wrist, and at the same instant, as she drew back, the fox, turning round to bound away, whisked his brush across her face, and it seemed his brush was on fire, for it seared and burned her mouth with a great pain. She awoke with the pain of it, and lay trembling as if she were really seared.

In the morning, however, she only remembered it as a distant memory. She arose and was busy preparing the house and attending to the fowls. Banford flew into the village on her bicycle to try and buy food. She was a hospitable soul. But alas, in the year 1918 there was not much food to buy. The youth came downstairs in his shirt-sleeves. He was young and fresh, but he walked with his head thrust forward, so that his shoulders seemed raised and rounded, as if he had a slight curvature of the spine. It must have been only a manner of bearing himself, for he was young and vigorous. He washed himself and went outside, whilst the women were preparing breakfast.

He saw everything, and examined everything. His curiosity was quick and insatiable. He compared the state of things with that which he remembered before, and cast over in his mind the effect of the changes. He watched the fowls and the ducks, to see their condition ; he noticed the flight of wood-pigeons overhead : they were very numerous ; he saw the few apples high up, which March had not been able to reach ; he remarked that they had borrowed a draw-pump, presumably to empty the big soft-water cistern which was on the north side of the house.

"It's a funny, dilapidated old place," he said to the girls as he sat at breakfast.

His eyes were wise and childish, with thinking about things. He did not say much, but ate largely. March kept her face averted. She, too, in the early morning could not be aware of him, though something about the glint of his khaki reminded her of the brilliance of her dream-fox.

During the day the girls went about their business. In the morning he attended to the guns, shot a rabbit and a wild duck that was flying high towards the wood. That was a great addition to the empty larder. The girls felt that already he had earned his keep. He said nothing about leaving, however. In the afternoon he went to the village. He came back at tea-time. He had the same alert, forward-reaching look on his roundish face. He hung his hat on a peg with a little swinging gesture. He was thinking about something.

"Well," he said to the girls, as he sat at table. "What am I going to do ? "

"How do you mean—what are you going to do ? " said Banford.

"Where am I going to find a place in the village to stay ? " he said.

"I don't know," said Banford. "Where do you think of staying ? "

"Well "—he hesitated—" at the Swan they've got this flu, and at the Plough and Harrow they've got the soldiers who are collecting the hay for the army : besides, in the private houses, there's ten men and a corporal altogether billeted in the village, they tell me. I'm not sure where I could get a bed."

He left the matter to them. He was rather calm about it. March sat with her elbows on the table, her two hands supporting her chin, looking at him unconsciously. Suddenly he lifted his clouded blue eyes, and unthinking looked straight into March's eyes. He was

startled as well as she. He, too, recoiled a little. March felt the
same sly, taunting, knowing spark leap out of his eyes, as he turned
his head aside, and fall into her soul, as it had fallen from the dark
eyes of the fox. She pursed her mouth as if in pain, as if asleep too.

"Well, I don't know," Banford was saying. She seemed reluctant,
as if she were afraid of being imposed upon. She looked at March.
But, with her weak, troubled sight, she only saw the usual semi-
abstraction on her friend's face. "Why don't you speak, Nellie ? "
she said.

But March was wide-eyed and silent, and the youth, as if fascinated, was watching her without moving his eyes.

"Go on—answer something," said Banford. And March turned
her head slightly aside, as if coming to consciousness, or trying to
come to consciousness.

"What do you expect me to say ? " she asked automatically.

"Say what you think," said Banford.

"It's all the same to me," said March.

And again there was silence. A pointed light seemed to be on the
boy's eyes, penetrating like a needle.

"So it is to me," said Banford. "You can stop on here if you like."

A smile like a cunning little flame came over his face, suddenly
and involuntarily. He dropped his head quickly to hide it, and
remained with his head dropped, his face hidden.

"You can stop on here if you like. You can please yourself,
Henry," Banford concluded.

Still he did not reply, but remained with his head dropped. Then
he lifted his face. It was bright with a curious light, as if exultant,
and his eyes were strangely clear as he watched March. She turned
her face aside, her mouth suffering as if wounded, and her consciousness dim.

Banford became a little puzzled. She watched the steady,
pellucid gaze of the youth's eyes as he looked at March, with the
invisible smile gleaming on his face. She did not know how he was
smiling, for no feature moved. It seemed only in the gleam, almost
the glitter of the fine hairs on his cheeks. Then he looked with quite
a changed look at Banford.

"I'm sure," he said in his soft, courteous voice, "you're awfully
good. You're too good. You don't want to be bothered with me,
I'm sure."

"Cut a bit of bread, Nellie," said Banford uneasily, adding : "It's
no bother, if you like to stay. It's like having my own brother here
for a few days. He's a boy like you are."

"That's awfully kind of you," the lad repeated. "I should like to stay ever so much, if you're sure I'm not a trouble to you."

"No, of course you're no trouble. I tell you, it's a pleasure to have somebody in the house besides ourselves," said warm-hearted Banford.

"But Miss March?" he said in his soft voice, looking at her.

"Oh, it's quite all right as far as I'm concerned," said March vaguely.

His face beamed, and he almost rubbed his hands with pleasure. "Well then," he said, "I should love it, if you'd let me pay my board and help with the work."

"You've no need to talk about board," said Banford.

One or two days went by, and the youth stayed on at the farm. Banford was quite charmed by him. He was so soft and courteous in speech, not wanting to say much himself, preferring to hear what she had to say, and to laugh in his quick, half-mocking way. He helped readily with the work—but not too much. He loved to be out alone with the gun in his hands, to watch, to see. For his sharp-eyed, impersonal curiosity was insatiable, and he was most free when he was quite alone, half-hidden, watching.

Particularly he watched March. She was a strange character to him. Her figure, like a graceful young man's, piqued him. Her dark eyes made something rise in his soul, with a curious elate excitement, when he looked into them, an excitement he was afraid to let be seen, it was so keen and secret. And then her odd, shrewd speech made him laugh outright. He felt he must go further, he was inevitably impelled. But he put away the thought of her and went off towards the wood's edge with the gun.

The dusk was falling as he came home, and with the dusk, a fine, late November rain. He saw the fire-light leaping in the window of the sitting-room, a leaping light in the little cluster of the dark buildings. And he thought to himself it would be a good thing to have this place for his own. And then the thought entered him shrewdly: why not marry March? He stood still in the middle of the field for some moments, the dead rabbit hanging still in his hand, arrested by this thought. His mind waited in amazement—it seemed to calculate—and then he smiled curiously to himself in acquiescence. Why not? Why not indeed? It was a good idea. What if it was rather ridiculous? What did it matter? What if she was older than he? It didn't matter. When he thought of her dark, startled, vulnerable eyes he smiled subtly to himself. He was older than she, really. He was master of her.

He scarcely admitted his intention even to himself. He kept it as
a secret even from himself. It was all too uncertain as yet. He
would have to see how things went. Yes, he would have to see how
things went. If he wasn't careful, she would just simply mock at the
idea. He knew, sly and subtle as he was, that if he went to her
plainly and said : " Miss March, I love you and want you to marry
me," her inevitable answer would be : " Get out. I don't want any
of that tomfoolery." This was her attitude to men and their " tomfoolery." If he was not careful, she would turn round on him with her
savage, sardonic ridicule, and dismiss him from the farm and from
her own mind for ever. He would have to go gently. He would
have to catch her as you catch a deer or a woodcock when you go out
shooting. It's no good walking out into the forest and saying to the
deer : " Please fall to my gun." No, it is a slow, subtle battle.
When you really go out to get a deer, you gather yourself together,
you coil yourself inside yourself, and you advance secretly, before
dawn, into the mountains. It is not so much what you do, when you
go out hunting, as how you feel. You have to be subtle and cunning
and absolutely fatally ready. It becomes like a fate. Your own fate
overtakes and determines the fate of the deer you are hunting.
First of all, even before you come in sight of your quarry, there is a
strange battle, like mesmerism. Your own soul, as a hunter, has
gone out to fasten on the soul of the deer, even before you see any
deer. And the soul of the deer fights to escape. Even before the deer
has any wind of you, it is so. It is a subtle, profound battle of wills
which takes place in the invisible. And it is a battle never finished
till your bullet goes home. When you are *really* worked up to the
true pitch, and you come at last into range, you don't then aim as
you do when you are firing at a bottle. It is your own *will* which
carries the bullet into the heart of your quarry. The bullet's flight
home is a sheer projection of your own fate into the fate of the deer.
It happens like a supreme wish, a supreme act of volition, not as a
dodge of cleverness.

He was a huntsman in spirit, not a farmer, and not a soldier stuck
in a regiment. And it was as a young hunter that he wanted to bring
down March as his quarry, to make her his wife. So he gathered
himself subtly together, seemed to withdraw into a kind of invisibility.
He was not quite sure how he would go on. And March was
suspicious as a hare. So he remained in appearance just the nice,
odd stranger-youth, staying for a fortnight on the place.

He had been sawing logs for the fire in the afternoon. Darkness
came very early. It was still a cold, raw mist. It was getting almost

too dark to see. A pile of short sawed logs lay beside the trestle. March came to carry them indoors, or into the shed, as he was busy sawing the last log. He was working in his shirt-sleeves, and did not notice her approach ; she came unwillingly, as if shy. He saw her stooping to the bright-ended logs, and he stopped sawing. A fire like lightning flew down his legs in the nerves.

" March ? " he said, in his quiet, young voice.

She looked up from the logs she was piling.

" Yes ! " she said.

He looked down on her in the dusk. He could see her not too distinctly.

" I wanted to ask you something," he said.

" Did you ? What was it ? " she said. Already the fright was in her voice. But she was too much mistress of herself.

" Why "—his voice seemed to draw out soft and subtle, it penetrated her nerves—" why, what do you think it is ? "

She stood up, placed her hands on her hips, and stood looking at him transfixed, without answering. Again he burned with a sudden power.

" Well," he said, and his voice was so soft it seemed rather like a subtle touch, like the merest touch of a cat's paw, a feeling rather than a sound. " Well—I wanted to ask you to marry me."

March felt rather than heard him. She was trying in vain to turn aside her face. A great relaxation seemed to have come over her. She stood silent, her head slightly on one side. He seemed to be bending towards her, invisibly smiling. It seemed to her fine sparks came out of him.

Then very suddenly she said :

" Don't try any of your tomfoolery on me."

A quiver went over his nerves. He had missed. He waited a moment to collect himself again. Then he said, putting all the strange softness into his voice, as if he were imperceptibly stroking her :

" Why, it's not tomfoolery. It's not tomfoolery. I mean it. I mean it. What makes you disbelieve me ? "

He sounded hurt. And his voice had such a curious power over her ; making her feel loose and relaxed. She struggled somewhere for her own power. She felt for a moment that she was lost—lost— lost. The word seemed to rock in her as if she were dying. Suddenly again she spoke.

" You don't know what you are talking about," she said, in a brief and transient stroke of scorn. " What nonsense ! I'm old enough to be your mother."

" Yes, I do know what I'm talking about. Yes, I do," he persisted softly, as if he were producing his voice in her blood. " I know quite well what I'm talking about. You're not old enough to be my mother. That isn't true. And what does it matter even if it was. You can marry me whatever age we are. What is age to me? And what is age to you! Age is nothing."

A swoon went over her as he concluded. He spoke rapidly—in the rapid Cornish fashion—and his voice seemed to sound in her somewhere where she was helpless against it. " Age is nothing!" The soft, heavy insistence of it made her sway dimly out there in the darkness. She could not answer.

A great exultance leaped like fire over his limbs. He felt he had won.

" I want to marry you, you see. Why shouldn't I?" he proceeded, soft and rapid. He waited for her to answer. In the dusk he saw her almost phosphorescent. Her eyelids were dropped, her face half-averted and unconscious. She seemed to be in his power. But he waited, watchful. He dared not yet touch her.

" Say then," he said, " say then you'll marry me. Say—say!" He was softly insistent.

" What?" she asked, faint, from a distance, like one in pain. His voice was now unthinkably near and soft. He drew very near to her. " Say yes."

" Oh, I can't," she wailed helplessly, half-articulate, as if semi-conscious, and as if in pain, like one who dies. " How can I?"

" You can," he said softly, laying his hand gently on her shoulder as she stood with her head averted and dropped, dazed. " You can. Yes, you can. What makes you say you can't? You can. You can." And with awful softness he bent forward and just touched her neck with his mouth and his chin.

" Don't!" she cried, with a faint mad cry like hysteria, starting away and facing round on him. " What do you mean?" But she had no breath to speak with. It was as if she was killed.

" I mean what I say," he persisted softly and cruelly. " I want you to marry me. I want you to marry me. You know that, now, don't you? You know that, now? Don't you? Don't you?"

" What?" she said.

" Know," he replied.

" Yes," she said. " I know you say so."

" And you know I mean it, don't you?"

" I know you say so."

" You believe me?" he said.

She was silent for some time. Then she pursed her lips.

"I don't know what I believe," she said.

"Are you out there?" came Banford's voice, calling from the house.

"Yes, we're bringing in the logs," he answered.

"I thought you'd gone lost," said Banford disconsolately. "Hurry up, do, and come and let's have tea. The kettle's boiling."

He stooped at once, to take an armful of little logs and carry them into the kitchen, where they were piled in a corner. March also helped, filling her arms and carrying the logs on her breast as if they were some heavy child. The night had fallen cold.

When the logs were all in, the two cleaned their boots noisily on the scraper outside, then rubbed them on the mat. March shut the door and took off her old felt hat—her farm-girl hat. Her thick, crisp black hair was loose, her face was pale and strained. She pushed back her hair vaguely, and washed her hands. Banford came hurrying into the dimly lighted kitchen, to take from the oven the scones she was keeping hot.

"Whatever have you been doing all this time?" she asked fretfully. "I thought you were never coming in. And it's ages since you stopped sawing. What were you doing out there?"

"Well," said Henry, "we had to stop that hole in the barn, to keep the rats out."

"Why, I could see you standing there in the shed. I could see your shirt-sleeves," challenged Banford.

"Yes, I was just putting the saw away."

They went in to tea. March was quite mute. Her face was pale and strained and vague. The youth, who always had the same ruddy, self-contained look on his face, as though he were keeping himself to himself, had come to tea in his shirt-sleeves as if he were at home. He bent over his plate as he ate his food.

"Aren't you cold?" said Banford spitefully. "In your shirt-sleeves."

He looked up at her, with his chin near his plate, and his eyes very clear, pellucid, and unwavering as he watched her.

"No, I'm not cold," he said with his usual soft courtesy. "It's much warmer in here than it is outside, you see."

"I hope it is," said Banford, feeling nettled by him. He had a strange suave assurance, and a wide-eyed bright look that got on her nerves this evening.

"But perhaps," he said softly and courteously, "you don't like me coming to tea without my coat. I forgot that."

" Oh, I don't mind," said Banford : although she *did*.

" I'll go and get it, shall I ? " he said.

March's dark eyes turned slowly down to him.

" No, don't you bother," she said in her queer, twanging tone. " If you feel all right as you are, stop as you are." She spoke with a crude authority.

" Yes," said he, " I *feel* all right, if I'm not rude."

" It's usually considered rude," said Banford. " But we don't mind."

" Go along, ' considered rude,' " ejaculated March. " Who considers it rude ? "

" Why you do, Nellie, in anybody else," said Banford, bridling a little behind her spectacles, and feeling her food stick in her throat.

But March had again gone vague and unheeding, chewing her food as if she did not know she was eating at all. And the youth looked from one to another, with bright, watchful eyes.

Banford was offended. For all his suave courtesy and soft voice, the youth seemed to her impudent. She did not like to look at him. She did not like to meet his clear, watchful eyes, she did not like to see the strange glow in his face, his cheeks with their delicate fine hair, and his ruddy skin that was quite dull and yet which seemed to burn with a curious heat of life. It made her feel a little ill to look at him : the quality of his physical presence was too penetrating, too hot.

After tea the evening was very quiet. The youth rarely went into the village. As a rule he read : he was a great reader, in his own hours. That is, when he did begin, he read absorbedly. But he was not very eager to begin. Often he walked about the fields and along the hedges alone in the dark at night, prowling with a queer instinct for the night, and listening to the wild sounds.

To-night, however, he took a Captain Mayne Reid book from Banford's shelf and sat down with knees wide apart and immersed himself in his story. His brownish fair hair was long, and lay on his head like a thick cap, combed sideways. He was still in his shirt-sleeves, and bending forward under the lamp-light, with his knees stuck wide apart and the book in his hand and his whole figure absorbed in the rather strenuous business of reading, he gave Banford's sitting-room the look of a lumber-camp. She resented this. For on her sitting-room floor she had a red Turkey rug and dark stain round, the fire-place had fashionable green tiles, the piano stood open with the latest dance-music—she played quite well : and on the walls were March's hand-painted swans and water-lilies. Moreover, with the logs nicely, tremulously burning in the grate, the thick curtains drawn, the doors all shut, and the pine-trees hissing and shuddering in the wind outside, it was cosy, it was refined and nice. She resented the big, raw, long-legged youth sticking his khaki knees out and sitting there with his soldier's shirt-cuffs buttoned on his thick red wrists. From time to time he turned a page, and from time to time he gave a sharp look at the fire, settling the logs. Then he immersed himself again in the intense and isolated business of reading.

March, on the far side of the table, was spasmodically crocheting. Her mouth was pursed in an odd way, as when she had dreamed the fox's brush burned it, her beautiful, crisp black hair strayed in wisps. But her whole figure was absorbed in its bearing, as if she herself was miles away. In a sort of semi-dream she seemed to be hearing the fox singing round the house in the wind, singing wildly and sweetly and like a madness. With red but well-shaped hands she slowly crocheted the white cotton, very slowly, awkwardly.

Banford was also trying to read, sitting in her low chair. But between those two she felt fidgety. She kept moving and looking round and listening to the wind, and glancing secretly from one to the other of her companions. March, seated on a straight chair, with her knees in their close breeches crossed, and slowly, laboriously crocheting, was also a trial.

"Oh dear!" said Banford. "My eyes are bad to-night." And she pressed her fingers on her eyes.

The youth looked up at her with his clear, bright look, but did not speak.

"Are they, Jill?" said March absently.

Then the youth began to read again, and Banford perforce returned to her book. But she could not keep still. After a while she looked up at March, and a queer, almost malignant little smile was on her thin face.

"A penny for them, Nell," she said suddenly.

March looked round with big, startled black eyes, and went pale as if with terror. She had been listening to the fox singing so tenderly, so tenderly, as he wandered round the house.

"What?" she said vaguely.

"A penny for them," said Banford sarcastically. "Or twopence, if they're as deep as all that."

The youth was watching with bright, clear eyes from beneath the lamp.

"Why," came March's vague voice, "what do you want to waste your money for?"

" I thought it would be well spent," said Banford.

" I wasn't thinking of anything except the way the wind was blowing," said March.

" Oh dear," replied Banford, " I could have had as original thoughts as that myself. I'm afraid I *have* wasted my money this time."

" Well, you needn't pay," said March.

The youth suddenly laughed. Both women looked at him : March rather surprised-looking, as if she had hardly known he was there.

" Why, do you ever pay up on these occasions ? " he asked.

" Oh yes," said Banford. " We always do. I've sometimes had to pass a shilling a week to Nellie, in the winter-time. It costs much less in summer.

" What, paying for each other's thoughts ? " he laughed.

" Yes, when we've absolutely come to the end of everything else."

He laughed quickly, wrinkling his nose sharply like a puppy and laughing with quick pleasure, his eyes shining.

" It's the first time I ever heard of that," he said.

" I guess you'd hear of it often enough if you stayed a winter on Bailey Farm," said Banford lamentably.

" Do you get so tired, then ? " he asked.

" So bored," said Banford.

" Oh ! " he said gravely. " But why should you be bored ? "

" Who wouldn't be bored ? " said Banford.

" I'm sorry to hear that," he said gravely.

" You must be, if you were hoping to have a lively time here," said Banford.

He looked at her long and gravely.

" Well," he said, with his odd, young seriousness, " it's quite lively enough for me."

" I'm glad to hear it," said Banford.

And she returned to her book. In her thin, frail hair were already many threads of grey, though she was not yet thirty. The boy did not look down, but turned his eyes to March, who was sitting with pursed mouth laboriously crocheting, her eyes wide and absent. She had a warm, pale, fine skin, and a delicate nose. Her pursed mouth looked shrewish. But the shrewish look was contradicted by the curious lifted arch of her dark brows, and the wideness of her eyes ; a look of startled wonder and vagueness. She was listening again for the fox, who seemed to have wandered farther off into the night.

From under the edge of the lamp-light the boy sat with his face looking up, watching her silently, his eyes round and very clear and intent. Banford, biting her fingers irritably, was glancing at him under her hair. He sat there perfectly still, his ruddy face tilted up from the low level under the light, on the edge of the dimness, and watching with perfect abstract intentness. March suddenly lifted her great, dark eyes from her crocheting, and saw him. She started, giving a little exclamation.

"There he is!" she cried, involuntarily, as if terribly startled.

Banford looked around in amazement, sitting up straight.

"Whatever has got you, Nellie?" she cried.

But March, her face flushed a delicate rose colour, was looking away to the door.

"Nothing! Nothing!" she said crossly. "Can't one speak?"

"Yes, if you speak sensibly," said Banford. "Whatever did you mean?"

"I don't know what I meant," cried March testily.

"Oh, Nellie, I hope you aren't going jumpy and nervy. I feel I can't stand another *thing*! Whoever did you mean? Did you mean Henry?" cried poor, frightened Banford.

"Yes. I suppose so," said March laconically. She would never confess to the fox.

"Oh dear, my nerves are all gone for to-night," wailed Banford.

At nine o'clock March brought in a tray with bread and cheese and tea—Henry had confessed that he liked a cup of tea. Banford drank a glass of milk, and ate a little bread. And soon she said:

"I'm going to bed, Nellie. I'm all nerves to-night. Are you coming?"

"Yes, I'm coming the minute I've taken the tray away," said March.

"Don't be long then," said Banford fretfully. "Good night, Henry. You'll see the fire is safe, if you come up last, won't you?"

"Yes, Miss Banford, I'll see it's safe," he replied in his reassuring way.

March was lighting the candle to go to the kitchen. Banford took her candle and went upstairs. When March came back to the fire, she said to him:

"I suppose we can trust you to put out the fire and everything?" She stood there with her hand on her hip, and one knee loose, her head averted shyly, as if she could not look at him. He had his face lifted, watching her.

"Come and sit down a minute," he said softly.

" No, I'll be going. Jill will be waiting, and she'll get upset if I don't come."

" What made you jump like that this evening ? " he asked.

" When did I jump ? " she retorted, looking at him.

" Why, just now you did," he said. " When you cried out."

" Oh ! " she said. " Then ! Why, I thought you were the fox ! " And her face screwed into a queer smile, half-ironic.

" The fox ! Why the fox ? " he asked softly.

" Why, one evening last summer when I was out with the gun I saw the fox in the grass nearly at my feet, looking straight up at me. I don't know—I suppose he made an impression on me." She turned aside her head again, and let one foot stray loose, self-consciously.

" And did you shoot him ? " asked the boy.

" No, he gave me such a start, staring straight at me as he did, and then stopping to look back at me over his shoulder with a laugh on his face."

" A laugh on his face ! " repeated Henry, also laughing. " He frightened you, did he ? "

" No, he didn't frighten me. He made an impression on me, that's all."

" And you thought I was the fox, did you ? " he laughed, with the same queer, quick little laugh, like a puppy wrinkling its nose.

" Yes, I did, for the moment," she said. " Perhaps he'd been in my mind without my knowing."

" Perhaps you think I've come to steal your chickens or something," he said, with the same young laugh.

But she only looked at him with a wide, dark, vacant eye.

" It's the first time," he said, " that I've ever been taken for a fox. Won't you sit down for a minute ? " His voice was very soft and cajoling.

" No," she said. " Jill will be waiting." But still she did not go, but stood with one foot loose and her face turned aside, just outside the circle of light.

" But won't you answer my question ? " he said, lowering his voice still more.

" I don't know what question you mean."

" Yes, you do. Of course you do. I mean the question of you marrying me."

" No, I shan't answer that question," she said flatly.

" Won't you ? " The queer, young laugh came on his nose again.

"Is it because I'm like the fox? Is that why?" And still he laughed.

She turned and looked at him with a long, slow look.

"I wouldn't let that put you against me," he said. "Let me turn the lamp low, and come and sit down a minute."

He put his red hand under the glow of the lamp, and suddenly made the light very dim. March stood there in the dimness quite shadowy, but unmoving. He rose silently to his feet, on his long legs. And now his voice was extraordinarily soft and suggestive, hardly audible.

"You'll stay a moment," he said. "Just a moment." And he put his hand on her shoulder. She turned her face from him. "I'm sure you don't really think I'm like the fox," he said, with the same softness and with a suggestion of laughter in his tone, a subtle mockery. "Do you now?" And he drew her gently towards him and kissed her neck, softly. She winced and trembled and hung away. But his strong, young arm held her, and he kissed her softly again, still on the neck, for her face was averted.

"Won't you answer my question? Won't you now?" came his soft, lingering voice. He was trying to draw her near to kiss her face. And he kissed her cheek softly, near the ear.

At that moment Banford's voice was heard calling fretfully, crossly from upstairs.

"There's Jill!" cried March, starting and drawing erect.

And as she did so, quick as lightning he kissed her on the mouth, with a quick brushing kiss. It seemed to burn through her every fibre. She gave a queer little cry.

"You will, won't you? You will?" he insisted softly.

"Nellie! *Nellie!* Whatever are you so long for?" came Banford's faint cry from the outer darkness.

But he held her fast, and was murmuring with that intolerable softness and insistency:

"You will, won't you? Say yes! Say yes!"

March, who felt as if the fire had gone through her and scathed her, and as if she could do no more, murmured:

"Yes! Yes! Anything you like! Anything you like! Only let me go! Only let me go! Jill's calling."

"You know you've promised," he said insidiously.

"Yes! Yes! I do!" Her voice suddenly rose into a shrill cry. "All right, Jill I'm coming."

Startled, he let her go, and she went straight upstairs.

In the morning at breakfast, after he had looked round the place and attended to the stock and thought to himself that one could live easily enough here, he said to Banford :

" Do you know what, Miss Banford ? "

" Well, what ? " said the good-natured, nervy Banford.

He looked at March, who was spreading jam on her bread.

" Shall I tell ? " he said to her.

She looked up at him, and a deep pink colour flushed over her face.

" Yes, if you mean Jill," she said. " I hope you won't go talking all over the village, that's all." And she swallowed her dry bread with difficulty.

" Whatever's coming ? " said Banford, looking up with wide, tired, slightly reddened eyes. She was a thin, frail little thing, and her hair, which was delicate and thin, was bobbed, so it hung softly by her worn face in its faded brown and grey.

" Why, what do you think ? " he said, smiling like one who has a secret.

" How do I know ! " said Banford.

" Can't you guess ? " he said, making bright eyes, and smiling, pleased with himself.

" I'm sure I can't. What's more, I'm not going to try."

" Nellie and I are going to be married."

Banford put down her knife out of her thin, delicate fingers, as if she would never take it up to eat any more. She stared with blank, reddened eyes.

" You what ? " she exclaimed.

" We're going to get married. Aren't we, Nellie ? " and he turned to March.

" You say so, anyway," said March laconically. But again she flushed with an agonized flush. She, too, could swallow no more.

Banford looked at her like a bird that has been shot : a poor, little sick bird. She gazed at her with all her wounded soul in her face, at the deep-flushed March.

" Never ! " she exclaimed, helpless.

" It's quite right," said the bright and gloating youth.

Banford turned aside her face, as if the sight of the food on the table made her sick. She sat like this for some moments, as if she were sick. Then, with one hand on the edge of the table, she rose to her feet.

" I'll *never* believe it, Nellie," she cried. " It's absolutely impossible ! "

Her plaintive, fretful voice had a thread of hot anger and despair.

"Why? Why shouldn't you believe it?" asked the youth, with all his soft, velvety impertinence in his voice.

Banford looked at him from her wide, vague eyes, as if he were some creature in a museum.

"Oh," she said languidly, "because she can never be such a fool. She can't lose her self-respect to such an extent." Her voice was cold and plaintive, drifting.

"In what way will she lose her self-respect?" asked the boy.

Banford looked at him with vague fixity from behind her spectacles.

"If she hasn't lost it already," she said.

He became very red, vermilion, under the slow, vague stare from behind the spectacles.

"I don't see it at all," he said.

"Probably you don't. I shouldn't expect you would," said Banford, with that straying mild tone of remoteness which made her words even more insulting.

He sat stiff in his chair, staring with hot, blue eyes from his scarlet face. An ugly look had come on his brow.

"My word, she doesn't know what she's letting herself in for," said Banford, in her plaintive, drifting, insulting voice.

"What has it got to do with you, anyway?" said the youth, in a temper.

"More than it has to do with you, probably," she replied, plaintive and venomous.

"Oh, has it! I don't see that at all," he jerked out.

"No, you wouldn't," she answered, drifting.

"Anyhow," said March, pushing back her chair and rising uncouthly. "It's no good arguing about it." And she seized the bread and the teapot, and strode away to the kitchen.

Banford let her fingers stray across her brow and along her hair, like one bemused. Then she turned and went away upstairs.

Henry sat stiff and sulky in his chair, with his face and his eyes on fire. March came and went, clearing the table. But Henry sat on, stiff with temper. He took no notice of her. She had regained her composure and her soft, even, creamy complexion. But her mouth was pursed up. She glanced at him each time as she came to take things from the table, glanced from her large, curious eyes, more in curiosity than anything. Such a long, red-faced, sulky boy! That was all he was. He seemed as remote from her as if his red face were a red chimney-pot on a cottage across the fields, and she looked at him just as objectively, as remotely.

At length he got up and stalked out into the fields with the gun. He came in only at dinner-time, with the devil still in his face, but his manners quite polite. Nobody said anything particular ; they sat each one at the sharp corner of a triangle, in obstinate remoteness. In the afternoon he went out again at once with the gun. He came in at nightfall with a rabbit and a pigeon. He stayed in all the evening, but hardly opened his mouth. He was in the devil of a temper, feeling he had been insulted.

Banford's eyes were red, she had evidently been crying. But her manner was more remote and supercilious than ever ; the way she turned her head if he spoke at all, as if he were some tramp or inferior intruder of that sort, made his blue eyes go almost black with rage. His face looked sulkier. But he never forgot his polite intonation, if he opened his mouth to speak.

March seemed to flourish in this atmosphere. She seemed to sit between the two antagonists with a little wicked smile on her face, enjoying herself. There was even a sort of complacency in the way she laboriously crocheted this evening.

When he was in bed, the youth could hear the two women talking and arguing in their room. He sat up in bed and strained his ears to hear what they said. But he could hear nothing, it was too far off. Yet he could hear the soft, plaintive drip of Banford's voice, and March's deeper note.

The night was quiet, frosty. Big stars were snapping outside, beyond the ridge-tops of the pine-trees. He listened and listened. In the distance he heard a fox yelping : and the dogs from the farms barking in answer. But it was not that he wanted to hear. It was what the two women were saying.

He got stealthily out of bed, and stood by his door. He could hear no more than before. Very, very carefully he began to lift the door latch. After quite a time he had his door open. Then he stepped stealthily out into the passage. The old oak planks were cold under his feet, and they creaked preposterously. He crept very, very gently up the one step, and along by the wall, till he stood outside their door. And there he held his breath and listened. Banford's voice :

" No, I simply couldn't stand it. I should be dead in a month. Which is just what he would be aiming at, of course. That would just be his game, to see me in the churchyard. No, Nellie, if you were to do such a thing as to marry him, you could never stop here. I couldn't, I couldn't live in the same house with him. Oh—h ! I feel quite sick with the smell of his clothes. And his red face simply turns me over. I can't eat my food when he's at the table. What a fool I was ever to let him stop. One ought *never* to try to do a kind action. It always flies back in your face like a boomerang."

" Well, he's only got two more days," said March.

" Yes, thank heaven. And when he's gone he'll never come in this house again. I feel so bad while he's here. And I know, I know he's only counting what he can get out of you. I *know* that's all it is. He's just a good-for-nothing, who doesn't want to work, and who thinks he'll live on us. But he won't live on me. If you're such a fool, then it's your own look-out. Mrs. Burgess knew him all the time he was here. And the old man could never get him to do any steady work. He was off with the gun on every occasion, just as he is now. Nothing but the gun ! Oh, I do hate it. You don't know what you're doing, Nellie, you don't. If you marry him he'll just make a fool of you. He'll go off and leave you stranded. I know he will, if he can't get Bailey Farm out of us—and he's not going to, while I live. While I live he's never going to set foot here. I know what it would be. He'd soon think he was master of both of us, as he thinks he's master of you already."

" But he isn't," said Nellie.

" He thinks he is, anyway. And that's what he wants : to come and be master here. Yes, imagine it ! That's what we've got the place together for, is it, to be bossed and bullied by a hateful red-faced boy, a beastly labourer. Oh, we *did* make a mistake when we let him stop. We ought never to have lowered ourselves. And I've had such a fight with all the people here, not to be pulled down to their level. No, he's not coming here. And then you see—if he can't have the place, he'll run off to Canada or somewhere again, as if he'd never known you. And here you'll be, absolutely ruined and made a fool of. I know I shall never have any peace of mind again."

" We'll tell him he can't come here. We'll tell him that," said March.

" Oh, don't you bother ; I'm going to tell him that, and other things as well, before he goes. He's not going to have all his own way while I've got the strength left to speak. Oh, Nellie, he'll despise you, he'll despise you, like the awful little beast he is, if you give way to him. I'd no more trust him than I'd trust a cat not to steal. He's deep, he's deep, and he's bossy, and he's selfish through and through, as cold as ice. All he wants is to make use of you. And when you're no more use to him, then I pity you."

" I don't think he's as bad as all that," said March.

" No, because he's been playing up to you. But you'll find out, if you see much more of him. Oh, Nellie, I can't bear to think of it."

" Well, it won't hurt you, Jill, darling."

" Won't it ! Won't it ! I shall never know a moment's peace again while I live, nor a moment's happiness. No, Nellie——" and Banford began to weep bitterly.

The boy outside could hear the stifled sound of the woman's sobbing, and could hear March's soft, deep, tender voice comforting,. with wonderful gentleness and tenderness, the weeping woman.

His eyes were so round and wide that he seemed to see the whole night, and his ears were almost jumping off his head. He was frozen stiff. He crept back to bed, but felt as if the top of his head were coming off. He could not sleep. He could not keep still. He rose, quietly dressed himself, and crept out on to the landing once more. The women were silent. He went softly downstairs and out to the kitchen.

Then he put on his boots and his overcoat, and took the gun. He did not think to go away from the farm. No, he only took the gun. As softly as possible he unfastened the door and went out into the frosty December night. The air was still, the stars bright, the pine-trees seemed to bristle audibly in the sky. He went stealthily away down a fence-side, looking for something to shoot. At the same time he remembered that he ought not to shoot and frighten the women.

So he prowled round the edge of the gorse cover, and through the grove of tall old hollies, to the woodside. There he skirted the fence, peering through the darkness with dilated eyes that seemed to be able to grow black and full of sight in the dark, like a cat's. An owl was slowly and mournfully whooing round a great oak-tree. He stepped stealthily with his gun, listening, listening, watching.

As he stood under the oaks of the wood-edge he heard the dogs from the neighbouring cottage up the hill yelling suddenly and startlingly, and the wakened dogs from the farms around barking answer. And suddenly, it seemed to him England was little and tight, he felt the landscape was constricted even in the dark, and that there were too many dogs in the night, making a noise like a fence of sound, like the network of English hedges netting the view. He felt the fox didn't have a chance. For it must be the fox that had started all this hullabaloo.

Why not watch for him, anyhow ! He would, no doubt, be coming sniffing round. The lad walked downhill to where the farmstead with its few pine-trees crouched blackly. In the angle of the long shed, in the black dark, he crouched down. He knew the fox would be coming. It seemed to him it would be the last of the foxes in this loudly barking, thick-voiced England, tight with innumerable little houses.

He sat a long time with his eyes fixed unchanging upon the open gateway, where a little light seemed to fall from the stars or from the horizon, who knows. He was sitting on a log in a dark corner with the gun across his knees. The pine-trees snapped. Once a chicken fell off its perch in the barn with a loud crawk and cackle and commotion that startled him, and he stood up, watching with all his eyes, thinking it might be a rat. But he *felt* it was nothing. So he sat down again with the gun on his knees and his hands tucked in to keep them warm, and his eyes fixed unblinking on the pale reach of the open gateway. He felt he could smell the hot, sickly, rich smell of live chickens on the cold air.

And then—a shadow. A sliding shadow in the gateway. He gathered all his vision into a concentrated spark, and saw the shadow of the fox, the fox creeping on his belly through the gate. There he went, on his belly like a snake. The boy smiled to himself and brought the gun to his shoulder. He knew quite well what would happen. He knew the fox would go to where the fowl-door was boarded up, and sniff there. He knew he would lie there for a minute, sniffing the fowls within. And then he would start again prowling under the edge of the old barn, waiting to get in.

The fowl-door was at the top of a slight incline. Soft, soft as a shadow the fox slid up this incline, and crouched with his nose to the boards. And at the same moment there was the awful crash of a gun reverberating between the old buildings, as if all the night had gone smash. But the boy watched keenly. He saw even the white belly of the fox as the beast beat his paws in death. So he went forward.

There was a commotion everywhere. The fowls were scuffling and crawking, the ducks were quark-quarking, the pony had stamped wildly to his feet. But the fox was on his side, struggling in his last tremors. The boy bent over him and smelt his foxy smell.

There was a sound of a window opening upstairs, then March's voice calling :

" Who is it ? "

" It's me," said Henry ; " I've shot the fox."

" Oh, goodness ! You nearly frightened us to death."

" Did I ? I'm awfully sorry."

" Whatever made you get up ? "

" I heard him about."

" And have you shot him ? "

P

"Yes, he's here," and the boy stood in the yard holding up the warm, dead brute. "You can't see, can you? Wait a minute." And he took his flashlight from his pocket, and flashed it on to the dead animal. He was holding it by the brush. March saw, in the middle of the darkness, just the reddish fleece and the white belly and the white underneath of the pointed chin, and the queer, dangling paws. She did not know what to say.

"He's a beauty," he said. "He will make you a lovely fur."

"You don't catch me wearing a fox fur," she replied.

"Oh!" he said. And he switched off the light.

"Well, I should think you'll come in and go to bed again now," she said.

"Probably I shall. What time is it?"

"What time is it, Jill?" called March's voice. It was a quarter to one.

That night March had another dream. She dreamed that Banford was dead, and that she, March, was sobbing her heart out. Then she had to put Banford into her coffin. And the coffin was the rough wood-box in which the bits of chopped wood were kept in the kitchen, by the fire. This was the coffin, and there was no other, and March was in agony and dazed bewilderment, looking for something to line the box with, something to make it soft with, something to cover up the poor, dead darling. Because she couldn't lay her in there just in her white, thin nightdress, in the horrible wood-box. So she hunted and hunted, and picked up thing after thing, and threw it aside in the agony of dream-frustration. And in her dream-despair all she could find that would do was a fox-skin. She knew that it wasn't right, that this was not what she should have. But it was all she could find. And so she folded the brush of the fox, and laid her darling Jill's head on this, and she brought round the skin of the fox and laid it on the top of the body, so that it seemed to make a whole ruddy, fiery coverlet, and she cried and cried, and woke to find the tears streaming down her face.

The first thing that both she and Banford did in the morning was to go out to see the fox. Henry had hung it up by the heels in the shed, with its poor brush falling backwards. It was a lovely dog-fox in its prime, with a handsome, thick, winter coat : a lovely golden-red colour, with grey as it passed to the belly, and belly all white, and a great full brush with a delicate black and grey and pure white tip.

"Poor brute!" said Banford. "If it wasn't such a thieving wretch, you'd feel sorry for it."

March said nothing, but stood with her foot trailing aside, one hip out ; her face was pale and her eyes big and black, watching the dead animal that was suspended upside down. White and soft as snow his belly : white and soft as snow. She passed her hand softly down it. And his wonderful black-glinted brush was full and frictional, wonderful. She passed her hand down this also, and quivered. Time after time, she took the full fur of that thick tail between her fingers, and passed her hand slowly downwards. Wonderful, sharp, thick, splendour of a tail. And he was dead ! She pursed her lips, and her eyes went black and vacant. Then she took the head in her hand.

Henry was sauntering up, so Banford walked rather pointedly away. March stood there bemused, with the head of the fox in her hand. She was wondering, wondering, wondering over his long fine muzzle. For some reason it reminded her of a spoon or a spatula. She felt she could not understand it. The beast was a strange beast to her, incomprehensible, out of her range. Wonderful silver whiskers he had, like ice-threads. And pricked ears with hair inside. But that long, long, slender spoon of a nose !—and the marvellous white teeth beneath ! It was to thrust forward and bite with, deep, deep into the living prey, to bite and bite the blood.

" He's a beauty, isn't he ? " said Henry, standing by.

" Oh yes, he's a fine big fox. I wonder how many chickens he's responsible for," she replied.

" A good many. Do you think he's the same one you saw in the summer ? "

" I should think very likely he is," she replied.

He watched her, but he could make nothing of her. Partly she was so shy and virgin, and partly she was so grim, matter-of-fact, shrewish. What she said seemed to him so different from the look of her big, queer, dark eyes.

" Are you going to skin him ? " she asked.

" Yes, when I've had breakfast, and got a board to peg him on."

" My word, what a strong smell he's got ! Pooo ! It'll take some washing off one's hands. I don't know why I was so silly as to handle him." And she looked at her right hand, that had passed down his belly and along his tail, and had even got a tiny streak of blood from one dark place in his fur.

" Have you seen the chickens when they smell him, how frightened they are ? " he said.

" Yes, aren't they ! "

" You must mind you don't get some of his fleas."

" Oh, fleas ! " she replied, nonchalant.

Later in the day she saw the fox's skin nailed flat on a board, as if crucified. It gave her an uneasy feeling.

The boy was angry. He went about with his mouth shut, as if he had swallowed part of his chin. But in behaviour he was polite and affable. He did not say anything about his intention. And he left March alone.

That evening they sat in the dining-room. Banford wouldn't have him in her sitting-room any more. There was a very big log on the fire. And everybody was busy. Banford had letters to write, March was sewing a dress, and he was mending some little contrivance.

Banford stopped her letter-writing from time to time to look round and rest her eyes. The boy had his head down, his face hidden over his job.

" Let's see," said Banford. " What train do you go by, Henry ? "

He looked up straight at her.

" The morning train. In the morning," he said.

" What, the eight-ten or the eleven-twenty ? "

" The eleven-twenty, I suppose," he said.

" That is the day after to-morrow ? " said Banford.

" Yes, the day after to-morrow."

" Mm ! " murmured Banford, and she returned to her writing. But as she was licking her envelope, she asked :

" And what plans have you made for the future, if I may ask ? "

" Plans ? " he said, his face very bright and angry.

" I mean about you and Nellie, if you are going on with this business. When do you expect the wedding to come off ? " She spoke in a jeering tone.

" Oh, the wedding ! " he replied. " I don't know."

" Don't you know anything ? " said Banford. " Are you going to clear out on Friday and leave things no more settled than they are ? "

" Well, why shouldn't I ? We can always write letters."

" Yes, of course you can. But I wanted to know because of this place. If Nellie is going to get married all of a sudden, I shall have to be looking round for a new partner."

" Couldn't she stay on here if she were married ? " he said. He knew quite well what was coming.

" Oh," said Banford, " this is no place for a married couple. There's not enough work to keep a man going, for one thing. And there's no money to be made. It's quite useless your thinking of staying on here if you marry. Absolutely ! "

" Yes, but I wasn't thinking of staying on here," he said.

" Well, that's what I want to know. And what about Nellie, then ? How long is *she* going to be here with me, in that case."

The two antagonists looked at one another.

" That I can't say," he answered.

" Oh, go along," she cried petulantly. " You must have some idea what you are going to do, if you ask a woman to marry you. Unless it's all a hoax."

" Why should it be a hoax ? I am going back to Canada."

" And taking her with you ? "

" Yes, certainly."

" You hear that, Nellie ? " said Banford.

March, who had had her head bent over her sewing, now looked up with a sharp, pink blush on her face, and a queer, sardonic laugh in her eyes and on her twisted mouth.

" That's the first time I've heard that I was going to Canada," she said.

" Well, you have to hear it for the first time, haven't you ? " said the boy.

" Yes, I suppose I have," she said nonchalantly. And she went back to her sewing.

" You're quite ready, are you, to go to Canada ? Are you, Nellie ? " asked Banford.

March looked up again. She let her shoulders go slack, and let her hand that held the needle lie loose in her lap.

" It depends on *how* I'm going," she said. " I don't think I want to go jammed up in the steerage, as a soldier's wife. I'm afraid I'm not used to that way."

The boy watched her with bright eyes.

" Would you rather stay over here while I go first ? " he asked.

" I would, if that's the only alternative," she replied.

" That's much the wisest. Don't make it any fixed engagement," said Banford. " Leave yourself free to go or not after he's got back and found you a place, Nellie. Anything else is madness, madness."

" Don't you think," said the youth, " we ought to get married before I go—and then go together, or separate, according to how it happens ? "

" I think it's a terrible idea," cried Banford.

But the boy was watching March.

" What do you think ? " he asked her.

She let her eyes stray vaguely into space.

" Well, I don't know," she said. " I shall have to think about it."

" Why ? " he asked, pertinently.

" Why ? " She repeated his question in a mocking way, and looked at him laughing, though her face was pink again. " I should think there's plenty of reasons why."

He watched her in silence. She seemed to have escaped him. She had got into league with Banford against him. There was again the queer sardonic look about her ; she would mock stoically at everything he said or which life offered.

" Of course," he said, " I don't want to press you to do anything you don't wish to do."

" I should think not, indeed," cried Banford indignantly.

At bedtime Banford said plaintively to March :

" You take my hot bottle up for me, Nellie, will you."

" Yes, I'll do it," said March, with the kind of willing unwillingness she so often showed towards her beloved but uncertain Jill.

The two women went upstairs. After a time March called from the top of the stairs : " Good night, Henry. I shan't be coming down. You'll see to the lamp and the fire, won't you ? "

The next day Henry went about with the cloud on his brow and his young cub's face shut up tight. He was cogitating all the time. He had wanted March to marry him and go back to Canada with him. And he had been sure she would do it. Why he wanted her he didn't know. But he did want her. He had set his mind on her. And he was convulsed with a youth's fury at being thwarted. To be thwarted, to be thwarted ! It made him so furious inside that he did not know what to do with himself. But he kept himself in hand. Because even now things might turn out differently. She might come over to him. Of course she might. It was her business to do so.

Things drew to a tension again towards evening. He and Banford had avoided each other all day. In fact, Banford went in to the little town by the 11.20 train. It was market day. She arrived back on the 4.25. Just as the night was falling Henry saw her little figure in a dark-blue coat and a dark blue tam-o'-shanter hat crossing the first meadow from the station. He stood under one of the wild pear-trees, with the old dead leaves round his feet. And he watched the little blue figure advancing persistently over the rough winter-ragged meadow. She had her arms full of parcels, and advanced slowly, frail thing she was, but with that devilish little certainty which he so detested in her. He stood invisible under the pear-tree, watching her every step. And if looks could have affected her, she would have felt a log of iron on each of her ankles as she made her way forward. " You're a nasty little thing, you are," he was saying

softly, across the distance. " You're a nasty little thing. I hope
you'll be paid back for all the harm you've done me for nothing. I
hope you will—you nasty little thing. I hope you'll have to pay for it.
You will, if wishes are anything. You nasty little creature that you are."

She was toiling slowly up the slope. But if she had been slipping
back at every step towards the Bottomless Pit, he would not have
gone to help her with her parcels. Aha, there went March, striding
with her long, land stride in her breeches and her short tunic !
Striding downhill at a great pace, and even running a few steps now
and then, in her great solicitude and desire to come to the rescue of
the little Banford. The boy watched her with rage in his heart. See
her leap a ditch, and run, run as if a house was on fire, just to get to
that creeping, dark little object down there ! So, the Banford just
stood still and waited. And March strode up and took *all* the parcels
except a bunch of yellow chrysanthemums. These the Banford still
carried—yellow chrysanthemums !

" Yes, you look well, don't you," he said softly into the dusk air.
" You look well, pottering up there with a bunch of flowers, you do.
I'd make you eat them for your tea, if you hug them so tight. And
I'd give them you for breakfast again, I would. I'd give you
flowers. Nothing but flowers."

He watched the progress of the two women. He could hear their
voices : March always outspoken and rather scolding in her tenderness, Banford murmuring rather vaguely. They were evidently good
friends. He could not hear what they said till they came to the
fence of the home meadow, which they must climb. Then he saw
March manfully climbing over the bars with all her packages in her
arms, and on the still air he heard Banford's fretful :

" Why don't you let me help you with the parcels ? " She had a
queer, plaintive hitch in her voice. Then came March's robust
and reckless :

" Oh, I can manage. Don't you bother about me. You've all
you can do to get yourself over."

" Yes, that's all very 'well," said Banford fretfully. " You say,
Don't you bother about me, and then all the while you feel injured
because nobody thinks of you."

" When do I feel injured ? " said March.

" Always. You always feel injured. Now you're feeling injured
because I won't have that boy to come and live on the farm."

" I'm not feeling injured at all," said March.

" I know you are. When he's gone you'll sulk over it. I know you
will."

" Shall I ? " said March. " We'll see."

" Yes, we *shall* see, unfortunately. I can't think how you can make yourself so cheap. I can't *imagine* how you can lower yourself like it."

" I haven't lowered myself," said March.

" I don't know what you call it, then. Letting a boy like that come so cheeky and impudent and make a mug of you. I don't know what you think of yourself. How much respect do you think he's going to have for you afterwards ? My word, I wouldn't be in your shoes, if you married him."

" Of course you wouldn't. My boots are a good bit too big for you, and not half dainty enough," said March, with rather a miss-fire sarcasm.

" I thought you had too much pride, really I did. A woman's got to hold herself high, especially with a youth like that. Why, he's impudent. Even the way he forced himself on us at the start."

" We asked him to stay," said March.

" Not till he'd almost forced us to. And then he's so cocky and self-assured. My word, he puts my back up. I simply can't imagine how you can let him treat you so cheaply."

" I don't let him treat me cheaply," said March. " Don't you worry yourself, nobody's going to treat me cheaply. And even you aren't, either." She had a tender defiance, and a certain fire in her voice.

" Yes, it's sure to come back to me," said Banford bitterly. " That's always the end of it. I believe you only do it to spite me."

They went now in silence up the steep, grassy slope and over the brow, through the gorse-bushes. On the other side of the hedge the boy followed in the dusk, at some little distance. Now and then, through the huge ancient hedge of hawthorn, risen into trees, he saw the two dark figures creeping up the hill. As he came to the top of the slope he saw the homestead dark in the twilight, with a huge old pear-tree leaning from the near gable, and a little yellow light twinkling in the small side windows of the kitchen. He heard the clink of the latch and saw the kitchen door open into light as the two women went indoors. So, they were at home.

And so !—this was what they thought of him. It was rather in his nature to be a listener, so he was not at all surprised whatever he heard. The things people said about him always missed him person-ally. He was only rather surprised at the women's way with one another. And he disliked the Banford with an acid dislike. And he felt drawn to the March again. He felt again irresistibly drawn to her. He felt there was a secret bond, a secret thread between him and her, something very exclusive, which shut out everybody else and made him and her possess each other in secret.

He hoped again that she would have him. He hoped with his blood suddenly firing up that she would agree to marry him quite quickly : at Christmas, very likely. Christmas was not far off. He wanted, whatever else happened, to snatch her into a hasty marriage and a consummation with him. Then for the future, they could arrange later. But he hoped it would happen as he wanted it. He hoped that to-night she would stay a little while with him, after Banford had gone upstairs. He hoped he could touch her soft, creamy cheek, her strange, frightened face. He hoped he could look into her dilated, frightened dark eyes, quite near. He hoped he might even put his hand on her bosom and feel her soft breasts under her tunic. His heart beat deep and powerful as he thought of that. He wanted very much to do so. He wanted to make sure of her soft woman's breasts under her tunic. She always kept the brown linen coat buttoned so close up to her throat. It seemed to him like some perilous secret, that her soft woman's breasts must be buttoned up in that uniform. It seemed to him, moreover, that they were so much softer, tenderer, more lovely and lovable, shut up in that tunic, than were the Banford's breasts, under her soft blouses and chiffon dresses. The Banford would have little iron breasts, he said to himself. For all her frailty and fretfulness and delicacy, she would have tiny iron breasts. But March, under her crude, fast, workman's tunic, would have soft, white breasts, white and unseen. So he told himself, and his blood burned.

When he went in to tea, he had a surprise. He appeared at the inner door, his face very ruddy and vivid and his blue eyes shining, dropping his head forward as he came in, in his usual way, and hesitating in the doorway to watch the inside of the room, keenly and cautiously, before he entered. He was wearing a long-sleeved waistcoat. His face seemed extraordinarily like a piece of the out-of-doors come indoors : as holly-berries do. In his second of pause in the doorway he took in the two women sitting at table, at opposite ends, saw them sharply. And to his amazement March was dressed in a dress of dull, green silk crape. His mouth came open in surprise. If she had suddenly grown a moustache he could not have been more surprised.

" Why," he said, " do you wear a dress, then ? "

She looked up, flushing a deep rose colour, and twisting her mouth with a smile, said ·

P *

" Of course I do. What else do you expect me to wear, but a dress ? "

" A land-girl's uniform, of course," said he.

" Oh," she cried, nonchalant, " that's only for this dirty, mucky work about here."

" Isn't it your proper dress, then ? " he said.

" No, not indoors it isn't," she said. But she was blushing all the time as she poured out his tea. He sat down in his chair at table, unable to take his eyes off her. Her dress was a perfectly simple slip of bluey-green crape, with a line of gold stitching round the top and round the sleeves, which came to the elbow. It was cut just plain and round at the top, and showed her white, soft throat. Her arms he knew, strong and firm muscled, for he had often seen her with her sleeves rolled up. But he looked her up and down, up and down.

Banford, at the other end of the table, said not a word, but piggled with the sardine on her plate. He had forgotten her existence. He just simply stared at March, while he ate his bread and margarine in huge mouthfuls, forgetting even his tea.

" Well, I never knew anything make such a difference ! " he murmured, across his mouthfuls.

" Oh goodness ! " cried March, blushing still more. " I might be a pink monkey ! "

And she rose quickly to her feet and took the teapot to the fire, to the kettle. And as she crouched on the hearth with her green slip about her, the boy stared more wide-eyed than ever. Through the crape her woman's form seemed soft and womanly. And when she stood up and walked he saw her legs move soft within her modernly short skirt. She had on black silk stockings, and small patent shoes with little gold buckles.

No, she was another being. She was something quite different. Seeing her always in the hard-cloth breeches, wide on the hips, buttoned on the knee, strong as armour, and in the brown puttees and thick boots, it had never occurred to him that she had a woman's legs and feet. Now it came upon him. She had a woman's soft, skirted legs, and she was accessible. He blushed to the roots of his hair, shoved his nose in his tea-cup and drank his tea with a little noise that made Banford simply squirm : and strangely, suddenly he felt a man, no longer a youth. He felt a man, with all a man's grave weight of responsibility. A curious quietness and gravity came over his soul. He felt a man, quiet, with a little of the heaviness of male destiny upon him.

She was soft and accessible in her dress. The thought went home in him like an everlasting responsibility.

"Oh, for goodness' sake, say something, somebody," cried Banford fretfully. "It might be a funeral." The boy looked at her, and she could not bear his face.

"A funeral!" said March, with a twisted smile. "Why, that breaks my dream."

Suddenly she had thought of Banford in the wood-box for a coffin.

"What, have you been dreaming of a wedding?" said Banford sarcastically.

"Must have been," said March.

"Whose wedding?" asked the boy.

"I can't remember," said March.

She was shy and rather awkward that evening, in spite of the fact that, wearing a dress, her bearing was much more subdued than in her uniform. She felt unpeeled and rather exposed. She felt almost improper.

They talked desultorily about Henry's departure next morning, and made the trivial arrangement. But of the matter on their minds, none of them spoke. They were rather quiet and friendly this evening; Banford had practically nothing to say. But inside herself she seemed still, perhaps kindly.

At nine o'clock March brought in the tray with the everlasting tea and a little cold meat which Banford had managed to procure. It was the last supper, so Banford did not want to be disagreeable. She felt a bit sorry for the boy, and felt she must be as nice as she could.

He wanted her to go to bed. She was usually the first. But she sat on in her chair under the lamp, glancing at her book now and then, and staring into the fire. A deep silence had come into the room. It was broken by March asking, in a rather small tone:

"What time is it, Jill?"

"Five past ten," said Banford, looking at her wrist.

And then not a sound. The boy had looked up from the book he was holding between his knees. His rather wide, cat-shaped face had its obstinate look, his eyes were watchful.

"What about bed?" said March at last.

"I'm ready when you are," said Banford.

"Oh, very well," said March. "I'll fill your bottle."

She was as good as her word. When the hot-water bottle was ready, she lit a candle and went upstairs with it. Banford remained in her chair, listening acutely. March came downstairs again.

"There you are, then," she said. "Are you going up?"

"Yes, in a minute," said Banford. But the minute passed, and she sat on in her chair under the lamp.

Henry, whose eyes were shining like a cat's as he watched from under his brows, and whose face seemed wider, more chubbed and cat-like with unalterable obstinacy, now rose to his feet to try his throw.

"I think I'll go and look if I can see the she-fox," he said. "She may be creeping round. Won't you come as well for a minute, Nellie, and see if we see anything?"

"Me!" cried March, looking up with her startled, wondering face.

"Yes. Come on," he said. It was wonderful how soft and warm and coaxing his voice could be, how near. The very sound of it made Banford's blood boil. "Come on for a minute," he said, looking down into her uplifted, unsure face.

And she rose to her feet as if drawn up by his young, ruddy face that was looking down on her.

"I should think you're never going out at this time of night, Nellie!" cried Banford.

"Yes, just for a minute," said the boy, looking round on her, and speaking with an odd, sharp yelp in his voice.

March looked from one to the other, as if confused, vague. Banford rose to her feet for battle.

"Why, it's ridiculous. It's bitter cold. You'll catch your death in that thin frock. And in those slippers. You're not going to do any such thing."

There was a moment's pause. Banford turtled up like a little fighting cock, facing March and the boy.

"Oh, I don't think you need worry yourself," he replied. "A moment under the stars won't do anybody any damage. I'll get the rug off the sofa in the dining-room. You're coming, Nellie."

His voice had so much anger and contempt and fury in it as he spoke to Banford : and as much tenderness and proud authority as he spoke to March, that the latter answered :

"Yes, I'm coming."

And she turned with him to the door.

Banford, standing there in the middle of the room, suddenly burst into a long wail and a spasm of sobs. She covered her face with her poor, thin hands, and her thin shoulders shook in an agony of weeping. March looked back from the door.

"Jill!" she cried in a frantic tone, like someone just coming awake. And she seemed to start towards her darling.

But the boy had March's arm in his grip, and she could not move. She did not know why she could not move. It was as in a dream when the heart strains and the body cannot stir.

"Never mind," said the boy softly. "Let her cry. Let her cry. She will have to cry sooner or later. And the tears will relieve her feelings. They will do her good."

So he drew March slowly through the doorway. But her last look was back to the poor little figure which stood in the middle of the room with covered face and thin shoulders shaken with bitter weeping.

In the dining-room he picked up the rug and said :

"Wrap yourself up in this."

She obeyed—and they reached the kitchen door, he holding her soft and firm by the arm, though she did not know it. When she saw the night outside she started back.

"I must go back to Jill," she said. "I *must !* Oh yes, I must."

Her tone sounded final. The boy let go of her and she turned indoors. But he seized her again and arrested her.

"Wait a minute," he said. "Wait a minute. Even if you go, you're not going yet."

"Leave go ! Leave go !" she cried. "My place is at Jill's side. Poor little thing, she's sobbing her heart out."

"Yes," said the boy bitterly. "And your heart too, and mine as well."

"Your heart ? " said March. He still gripped her and detained her.

"Isn't it as good as her heart ? " he said. "Or do you think it's not ? "

"Your heart ? " she said again, incredulous.

"Yes, mine ! Mine ! Do you think I haven't *got* a heart ? " And with his hot grasp he took her hand and pressed it under his left breast. "There's my heart," he said, "if you don't believe in it."

It was wonder which made her attend. And then she felt the deep, heavy, powerful stroke of his heart, terrible, like something from beyond. It was like something from beyond, something awful from outside, signalling to her. And the signal paralysed her. It beat upon her very soul, and made her helpless. She forgot Jill. She could not think of Jill any more. She could not think of her. That terrible signalling from outside !

The boy put his arm round her waist.

"Come with me," he said gently. "Come and let us say what we've got to say."

And he drew her outside, closed the door. And she went with him

darkly down the garden path. That he should have a beating heart !
And that he should have his arm round her, outside the blanket !
She was too confused to think who he was or what he was.

He took her to a dark corner of the shed, where there was a tool-
box with a lid, long and low.

" We'll sit here a minute," he said.

And obediently she sat down by his side.

" Give me your hand," he said.

She gave him both her hands, and he held them between his own.
He was young, and it made him tremble.

" You'll marry me. You'll marry me before I go back, won't
you ? " he pleaded.

" Why, aren't we both a pair of fools ? " she said.

He had put her in the corner, so that she should not look out and
see the lighted window of the house, across the dark yard and
garden. He tried to keep her all there inside the shed with him.

" In what way a pair of fools ? " he said. " If you go back to
Canada with me, I've got a job and a good wage waiting for me,
and it's a nice place, near the mountains. Why shouldn't you marry
me ? Why shouldn't we marry ? I should like to have you there
with me. I should like to feel I'd got somebody there, at the back
of me, all my life."

" You'd easily find somebody else who'd suit you better," she said.

" Yes, I might easily find another girl. I know I could. But not
one I really wanted. I've never met one I really wanted, for good.
You see, I'm thinking of all my life. If I marry, I want to feel it's
for all my life. Other girls : well, they're just girls, nice enough to
go a walk with now and then. Nice enough for a bit of play. But
when I think of my life, then I should be very sorry to have to marry
one of them, I should indeed."

" You mean they wouldn't make you a good wife."

" Yes, I mean that. But I don't mean they wouldn't do their duty
by me. I mean—I don't know what I mean. Only when I think
of my life, and of you, then the two things go together."

" And what if they didn't ? " she said, with her odd, sardonic
touch.

" Well, I think they would."

They sat for some time silent. He held her hands in his, but he
did not make love to her. Since he had realized that she was a
woman, and vulnerable, accessible, a certain heaviness had possessed
his soul. He did not want to make love to her. He shrank from any
such performance, almost with fear. She was a woman, and vulner-

able, accessible to him finally, and he held back from that which was ahead, almost with dread. It was a kind of darkness he knew he would enter finally, but of which he did not want as yet even to think. She was the woman, and he was responsible for the strange vulnerability he had suddenly realized in her.

" No," she said at last, " I'm a fool. I know I'm a fool."

" What for ? " he asked.

" To go on with this business."

" Do you mean me ? " he asked.

" No, I mean myself. I'm making a fool of myself, and a big one."

" Why, because you don't want to marry me, really ? "

" Oh, I don't know whether I'm against it, as a matter of fact. That's just it. I don't know."

He looked at her in the darkness, puzzled. He did not in the least know what she meant.

" And don't you know whether you like to sit here with me this minute, or not ? " he asked.

" No, I don't really. I don't know whether I wish I was some-where else, or whether I like being here. I don't know, really."

" Do you wish you were with Miss Banford ? Do you wish you'd gone to bed with her ? " he asked, as a challenge.

She waited a long time before she answered :

" No," she said at last. " I don't wish that."

" And do you think you would spend all your life with her—when your hair goes white, and you are old ? " he said.

" No," she said, without much hesitation. " I don't see Jill and me two old women together."

" And don't you think, when I'm an old man and you're an old woman, we might be together still, as we are now ? " he said.

" Well, not as we are now," she replied. " But I could imagine—no, I can't. I can't imagine you an old man. Besides, it's dreadful ! "

" What, to be an old man ? "

" Yes, of course."

" Not when the time comes," he said. " But it hasn't come. Only it will. And when it does, I should like to think you'd be there as well."

" Sort of old age pensions," she said drily.

Her kind of witless humour always startled him. He never knew what she meant. Probably she didn't quite know herself.

" No," he said, hurt.

" I don't know why you harp on old age," she said. " I'm not ninety."

" Did anybody ever say you were ? " he asked, offended.

They were silent for some time, pulling different ways in the silence.

" I don't want you to make fun of me," he said.

" Don't you ? " she replied, enigmatic.

" No, because just this minute I'm serious. And when I'm serious, I believe in not making fun of it."

" You mean nobody else must make fun of you," she replied.

" Yes, I mean that. And I mean I don't believe in making fun of it myself. When it comes over me so that I'm serious, then— there it is, I don't want it to be laughed at."

She was silent for some time. Then she said, in a vague, almost pained voice :

" No, I'm not laughing at you."

A hot wave rose in his heart.

" You believe me, do you ? " he asked.

" Yes, I believe you," she replied, with a twang of her old tired nonchalance, as if she gave in because she was tired. But he didn't care. His heart was hot and clamorous.

" So you agree to marry me before I go ?—perhaps at Christmas ? "

" Yes, I agree."

" There ! " he exclaimed. " That's settled it."

And he sat silent, unconscious, with all the blood burning in all his veins, like fire in all the branches and twigs of him. He only pressed her two hands to his chest, without knowing. When the curious passion began to die down, he seemed to come awake to the world.

" We'll go in, shall we ? " he said : as if he realized it was cold.

She rose without answering.

" Kiss me before we go, now you've said it," he said.

And he kissed her gently on the mouth, with a young, frightened kiss. It made her feel so young, too, and frightened, and wondering : and tired, tired, as if she were going to sleep.

They went indoors. And in the sitting-room, there, crouched by the fire like a queer little witch, was Banford. She looked round with reddened eyes as they entered, but did not rise. He thought she looked frightening, unnatural, crouching there and looking round at them. Evil he thought her look was, and he crossed his fingers.

Banford saw the ruddy, elate face of the youth : he seemed strangely tall and bright and looming. And March had a delicate look on her face ; she wanted to hide her face, to screen it, to let it not be seen.

"You've come at last," said Banford uglily.

"Yes, we've come," said he.

"You've been long enough for anything," she said.

"Yes, we have. We've settled it. We shall marry as soon as possible," he replied.

"Oh, you've settled it, have you ! Well, I hope you won't live to repent it," said Banford.

"I hope so too," he replied.

"Are you going to bed *now*, Nellie ? " said Banford.

"Yes, I'm going now."

"Then for goodness' sake come along."

March looked at the boy. He was glancing with his very bright eyes at her and at Banford. March looked at him wistfully. She wished she could stay with him. She wished she had married him already, and it was all over. For oh, she felt suddenly so safe with him. She felt so strangely safe and peaceful in his presence. If only she could sleep in his shelter, and not with Jill. She felt afraid of Jill. In her dim, tender state, it was agony to have to go with Jill and sleep with her. She wanted the boy to save her. She looked again at him.

And he, watching with bright eyes, divined something of what she felt. It puzzled and distressed him that she must go with Jill.

"I shan't forget what you've promised," he said, looking clear into her eyes, right into her eyes, so that he seemed to occupy all her self with his queer, bright look.

She smiled to him, faintly, gently. She felt safe again—safe with him.

But in spite of all the boy's precautions, he had a set-back. The morning he was leaving the farm he got March to accompany him to the market-town, about six miles away, where they went to the registrar and had their names stuck up as two people who were going to marry. He was to come at Christmas, and the wedding was to take place then. He hoped in the spring to be able to take March back to Canada with him, now the war was really over. Though he was so young, he had saved some money.

"You never have to be without *some* money at the back of you, if you can help it," he said.

So she saw him off in the train that was going West : his camp was on Salisbury Plain. And with big, dark eyes she watched him go, and it seemed as if everything real in life was retreating as the train retreated with his queer, chubby, ruddy face, that seemed so broad across the cheeks, and which never seemed to change its expression,

save when a cloud of sulky anger hung on the brow, or the bright
eyes fixed themselves in their stare. This was what happened now.
He leaned there out of the carriage window as the train drew off,
saying good-bye and staring back at her, but his face quite
unchanged. There was no emotion on his face. Only his eyes
tightened and became fixed and intent in their watching like a
cat's when suddenly she sees something and stares. So the boy's
eyes stared fixedly as the train drew away, and she was left feeling
intensely forlorn. Failing his physical presence, she seemed to have
nothing of him. And she had nothing of anything. Only his face
was fixed in her mind : the full, ruddy, unchanging cheeks, and the
straight snout of a nose, and the two eyes staring above. All she
could remember was how he suddenly wrinkled his nose when he
laughed, as a puppy does when he is playfully growling. But him,
himself, and what he was—she knew nothing, she had nothing of him
when he left her.

On the ninth day after he had left her he received this letter.

" DEAR HENRY,

I have been over it all again in my mind, this business of me
and you, and it seems to me impossible. When you aren't there I see
what I fool I am. When you are there you seem to blind me to
things as they actually are. You make me see things all unreal, and
I don't know what. Then when I am alone again with Jill I seem to
come to my own senses and realize what a fool I am making of myself,
and how I am treating you unfairly. Because it must be unfair to
you for me to go on with this affair when I can't feel in my heart that
I really love you. I know people talk a lot of stuff and nonsense
about love, and I don't want to do that. I want to keep to plain
facts and act in a sensible way. And that seems to me what I'm not
doing. I don't see on what grounds I am going to marry you.
I know I am not head over heels in love with you, as I have fancied
myself to be with fellows when I was a young fool of a girl. You are
an absolute stranger to me, and it seems to me you will always be
one. So on what grounds am I going to marry you ? When I think
of Jill, she is ten times more real to me. I know her and I'm awfully
fond of her, and I hate myself for a beast if I ever hurt her little
finger. We have a life together. And even if it can't last for ever,
it is a life while it does last. And it might last as long as either of us
lives. Who knows how long we've got to live ? She is a delicate
little thing, perhaps nobody but me knows how delicate. And as for
me, I feel I might fall down the well any day. What I don't seem to

see at all is you. When I think of what I've been and what I've done with you, I'm afraid I am a few screws loose. I should be sorry to think that softening of the brain is setting in so soon, but that is what it seems like. You are such an absolute stranger, and so different from what I'm used to, and we don't seem to have a thing in common. As for love, the very word seems impossible. I know what love means even in Jill's case, and I know that in this affair with you it's an absolute impossibility. And then going to Canada. I'm sure I must have been clean off my chump when I promised such a thing. It makes me feel fairly frightened of myself. I feel I might do something really silly, that I wasn't responsible for—and end my days in a lunatic asylum. You may think that's all I'm fit for after the way I've gone on, but it isn't a very nice thought for me. Thank goodness Jill is here, and her being here makes me feel sane again, else I don't know what I might do ; I might have an accident with the gun one evening. I love Jill, and she makes me feel safe and sane, with her loving anger against me for being such a fool. Well, what I want to say is, won't you let us cry the whole thing off ? I can't marry you, and really, I won't do such a thing if it seems to me wrong. It is all a great mistake. I've made a complete fool of myself, and all I can do is to apologize to you and ask you please to forget it, and please to take no further notice of me. Your fox skin is nearly ready, and seems all right. I will post it to you if you will let me know if this address is still right, and if you will accept my apology for the awful and lunatic way I have behaved with you, and then let the matter rest.

Jill sends her kindest regards. Her mother and father are staying with us over Christmas.

Yours very sincerely,
ELLEN MARCH."

The boy read this letter in camp as he was cleaning his kit. He set his teeth, and for a moment went almost pale, yellow round the eyes with fury. He said nothing and saw nothing and felt nothing but a livid rage that was quite unreasoning. Balked ! Balked again ! Balked ! He wanted the woman, he had fixed like doom upon having her. He felt that was his doom, his destiny, and his reward, to have this woman. She was his heaven and hell on earth, and he would have none elsewhere. Sightless with rage and thwarted madness he got through the morning. Save that in his mind he was lurking and scheming towards an issue, he would have committed some insane act. Deep in himself he felt like roaring and howling and gnashing his teeth and breaking things. But he was too intelligent. He knew society was on top of him, and he must scheme. So with his teeth bitten together, and his nose curiously slightly lifted, like some creature that is vicious, and his eyes fixed and staring, he went through the morning's affairs drunk with anger and suppression. In his mind was one thing—Banford. He took no heed of all March's outpouring : none. One thorn rankled, stuck in his mind. Banford. In his mind, in his soul, in his whole being, one thorn rankling to insanity. And he would have to get it out. He would have to get the thorn of Banford out of his life, if he died for it.

With this one fixed idea in his mind, he went to ask for twenty-four hours' leave of absence. He knew it was not due to him. His consciousness was supernaturally keen. He knew where he must go—he must go to the captain. But how could he get at the captain ? In that great camp of wooden huts and tents he had no idea where his captain was.

But he went to the officers' canteen. There was his captain standing talking with three other officers. Henry stood in the doorway at attention.

" May I speak to Captain Berryman ? " The captain was Cornish like himself.

" What do you want ? " called the captain.

" May I speak to you, Captain ? "

" What do you want ? " replied the captain, not stirring from among his group of fellow-officers.

Henry watched his superior for a minute without speaking.

" You won't refuse me, sir, will you ? " he asked gravely.

" It depends what it is."

" Can I have twenty-four hours' leave ? "

" No, you've no business to ask."

" I know I haven't. But I must ask you."

" You've had your answer."

" Don't send me away, Captain."

There was something strange about the boy as he stood there so everlasting in the doorway. The Cornish captain felt the strangeness at once, and eyed him shrewdly.

" Why, what's afoot ? " he said, curious.

" I'm in trouble about something. I must go to Blewbury," said the boy.

" Blewbury, eh ? After the girls ? "

" Yes, it is a woman, Captain." And the boy, as he stood there with his head reaching forward a little, went suddenly terribly pale, or yellow, and his lips seemed to give off pain. The captain saw and paled a little also. He turned aside.

" Go on, then," he said. " But for God's sake don't cause any trouble of any sort."

" I won't, Captain, thank you."

He was gone. The captain, upset, took a gin and bitters. Henry managed to hire a bicycle. It was twelve o'clock when he left the camp. He had sixty miles of wet and muddy cross-roads to ride. But he was in the saddle and down the road without a thought of food.

At the farm, March was busy with a work she had had some time in hand. A bunch of Scotch fir-trees stood at the end of the open shed, on a little bank where ran the fence between two of the gorse-shaggy meadows. The furthest of these trees was dead—it had died in the summer, and stood with all its needles brown and sere in the air. It was not a very big tree. And it was absolutely dead. So March determined to have it, although they were not allowed to cut any of the timber. But it would make such splendid firing, in these days of scarce fuel.

She had been giving a few stealthy chops at the trunk for a week or more, every now and then hacking away for five minutes, low down, near the ground, so no one should notice. She had not tried the saw, it was such hard work, alone. Now the tree stood with a great yawning gap in his base, perched as it were on one sinew, and ready to fall. But he did not fall.

It was late in the damp December afternoon, with cold mists creeping out of the woods and up the hollows, and darkness waiting to sink in from above. There was a bit of yellowness where the sun was fading away beyond the low woods of the distance. March took her axe and went to the tree. The small thud-thud of her blows resounded rather ineffectual about the wintry homestead. Banford came out wearing her thick coat, but with no hat on her head, so that her thin, bobbed hair blew on the uneasy wind that sounded in the pines and in the wood.

" What I'm afraid of," said Banford, " is that it will fall on the shed and we sh'll have another job repairing that."

" Oh, I don't think so," said March, straightening herself, and wiping her arm over her hot brow. She was flushed red, her eyes were very wide-open and queer, her upper lip lifted away from her two white, front teeth with a curious, almost rabbit-look.

A little stout man in a black overcoat and a bowler hat came pottering across the yard. He had a pink face and a white beard and smallish, pale-blue eyes. He was not very old, but nervy, and he walked with little short steps.

" What do you think, father ? " said Banford. " Don't you think it might hit the shed in falling ? "

" Shed, no ! " said the old man. " Can't hit the shed. Might as well say the fence."

" The fence doesn't matter," said March, in her high voice.

" Wrong as usual, am I ! " said Banford, wiping her straying hair from her eyes.

The tree stood as it were on one spelch of itself, leaning, and creaking in the wind. It grew on the bank of a little dry ditch between the two meadows. On the top of the bank straggled one fence, running to the bushes uphill. Several trees clustered there in the corner of the field near the shed and near the gate which led into the yard. Towards this gate, horizontal across the weary meadows, came the grassy, rutted approach from the high road. There trailed another ricketty fence, long split poles joining the short, thick, wide-apart uprights. The three people stood at the back of the tree, in the corner of the shed meadow, just above the yard gate. The house, with its two gables and its porch, stood tidy in a little grassed garden across the yard. A little, stout, rosy-faced woman in a little red woollen shoulder shawl had come and taken her stand in the porch.

" Isn't it down yet ? " she cried, in a high little voice.

" Just thinking about it," called her husband. His tone towards the two girls was always rather mocking and satirical. March did not want to go on with her hitting while he was there. As for him, he wouldn't lift a stick from the ground if he could help it, complaining, like his daughter, of rheumatics in his shoulder. So the three stood there a moment silent in the cold afternoon, in the bottom corner near the yard.

They heard the far-off taps of a gate, and craned to look. Away across, on the green horizontal approach, a figure was just swinging on to a bicycle again, and lurching up and down over the grass, approaching.

" Why, it's one of our boys—it's Jack," said the old man.

" Can't be," said Banford.

March craned her head to look. She alone recognized the khaki figure. She flushed, but said nothing.

" No, it isn't Jack, I don't think," said the old man, staring with little round blue eyes under his white lashes.

In another moment the bicycle lurched into sight, and the rider dropped off at the gate. It was Henry, his face wet and red and spotted with mud. He was altogether a muddy sight.

"Oh!" cried Banford, as if afraid. "Why, it's Henry!"

"What!" muttered the old man. He had a thick, rapid, muttering way of speaking, and was slightly deaf. "What? What? Who is it? Who is it, do you say? That young fellow? That young fellow of Nellie's? Oh! Oh!" And the satiric smile came on his pink face and white eyelashes.

Henry, pushing the wet hair off his steaming brow, had caught sight of them and heard what the old man said. His hot, young face seemed to flame in the cold light.

"Oh, are you all there!" he said, giving his sudden, puppy's little laugh. He was so hot and dazed with cycling he hardly knew where he was. He leaned the bicycle against the fence and climbed over into the corner on to the bank, without going into the yard.

"Well, I must say, we weren't expecting *you*," said Banford laconically.

"No, I suppose not," said he, looking at March.

She stood aside, slack, with one knee drooped and the axe resting its head loosely on the ground. Her eyes were wide and vacant, and her upper lip lifted from her teeth in that helpless, fascinated rabbit-look. The moment she saw his glowing, red face it was all over with her. She was as helpless as if she had been bound. The moment she saw the way his head seemed to reach forward.

"Well, who is it? Who is it, anyway?" asked the smiling, satiric old man in his muttering voice.

"Why, Mr. Grenfel, whom you've heard us tell about, father," said Banford coldly.

"Heard you tell about, I should think so. Heard of nothing else practically," muttered the elderly man, with his queer little jeering smile on his face. "How do you do," he added, suddenly reaching out his hand to Henry.

The boy shook hands just as startled. Then the two men fell apart.

"Cycled over from Salisbury Plain, have you?" asked the old man.

"Yes."

"Hm! Longish ride. How long d'it take you, eh? Some time, eh? Several hours, I suppose."

"About four."

"Eh? Four! Yes, I should have thought so. When are you going back, then?"

"I've got till to-morrow evening."

" Till to-morrow evening, eh? Yes. Hm! Girls weren't expecting you, were they? "

And the old man turned his pale-blue, round little eyes under their white lashes mockingly towards the girls. Henry also looked round. He had become a little awkward. He looked at March, who was still staring away into the distance as if to see where the cattle were. Her hand was on the pommel of the axe, whose head rested loosely on the ground.

" What were you doing there? " he asked in his soft, courteous voice. " Cutting a tree down? "

March seemed not to hear, as if in a trance.

" Yes," said Banford. " We've been at it for over a week."

" Oh! And have you done it all by yourselves then? "

" Nellie's done it all, I've done nothing," said Banford.

" Really! You must have worked quite hard," he said, addressing himself in a curious gentle tone direct to March. She did not answer, but remained half averted, staring away towards the woods above as if in a trance.

" *Nellie!* " cried Banford sharply. " Can't you answer? "

" What—me? " cried March, starting round, and looking from one to the other. " Did anyone speak to me? "

" Dreaming! " muttered the old man, turning aside to smile. " Must be in love, eh, dreaming in the day-time! "

" Did you say anything to me? " said March, looking at the boy as from a strange distance, her eyes wide and doubtful, her face delicately flushed.

" I said you must have worked hard at the tree," he replied courteously.

" Oh that! Bit by bit. I thought it would have come down by now."

" I'm thankful it hasn't come down in the night, to frighten us to death," said Banford.

" Let me just finish it for you, shall I? " said the boy.

March slanted the axe-shaft in his direction.

" Would you like to? " she said.

" Yes, if you wish it," he said.

" Oh, I'm thankful when the thing's down, that's all," she replied, nonchalant.

" Which way is it going to fall? " said Banford. " Will it hit the shed? "

" No, it won't hit the shed," he said. " I should think it will fall there—quite clear. Though it might gave a twist and catch the fence."

" Catch the fence ! " cried the old man. " What, catch the fence ! When it's leaning at that angle ? Why, it's further off than the shed. It won't catch the fence."

" No," said Henry, " I don't suppose it will. It has plenty of room to fall quite clear, and I suppose it will fall clear."

" Won't tumble backwards on top of *us*, will it ? " asked the old man, sarcastic.

" No, it won't do that," said Henry, taking off his short overcoat and his tunic. " Ducks ! Ducks ! Go back ! "

A line of four brown-speckled ducks led by a brown-and-green drake were stemming away downhill from the upper meadow, coming like boats running on a ruffled sea, cockling their way top speed downwards towards the fence and towards the little group of people, and cackling as excitedly as if they brought news of the Spanish Armada.

" Silly things ! Silly things ! " cried Banford, going forward to turn them off. But they came eagerly towards her, opening their yellow-green beaks and quacking as if they were so excited to say something.

" There's no food. There's nothing here. You must wait a bit," said Banford to them. " Go away. Go away. Go round to the yard."

They didn't go, so she climbed the fence to swerve them round under the gate and into the yard. So off they waggled in an excited string once more, wagging their rumps like the stems of little gondolas, ducking under the bar of the gate. Banford stood on the top of the bank, just over the fence, looking down on the other three.

Henry looked up at her, and met her queer, round-pupilled, weak eyes staring behind her spectacles. He was perfectly still. He looked away, up at the weak, leaning tree. And as he looked into the sky, like a huntsman who is watching a flying bird, he thought to himself : " If the tree falls in just such a way, and spins just so much as it falls, then the branch there will strike her exactly as she stands on top of that bank."

He looked at her again. She was wiping the hair from her brow again, with that perpetual gesture. In his heart he had decided her death. A terrible still force seemed in him, and a power that was just his. If he turned even a hair's breadth in the wrong direction, he would lose the power.

" Mind yourself, Miss Banford," he said. And his heart held perfectly still, in the terrible pure will that she should not move.

" Who, me, mind myself ? " she cried, her father's jeering tone in her voice. " Why, do you think you might hit me with the axe ? "

"No, it's just possible the tree might, though," he answered
soberly. But the tone of his voice seemed to her to imply that he
was only being falsely solicitous, and trying to make her move because
it was his will to move her.

"Absolutely impossible," she said.

He heard her. But he held himself icy still, lest he should lose
his power.

"No, it's just possible. You'd better come down this way."

"Oh, all right. Let us see some crack Canadian tree-felling,"
she retorted.

"Ready, then," he said, taking the axe, looking round to see he
was clear.

There was a moment of pure, motionless suspense, when the world
seemed to stand still. Then suddenly his form seemed to flash up
enormously tall and fearful, he gave two swift, flashing blows, in
immediate succession, the tree was severed, turning slowly, spinning
strangely in the air and coming down like a sudden darkness on the
earth. No one saw what was happening except himself. No one
heard the strange little cry which the Banford gave as the dark end
of the bough swooped down, down on her. No one saw her crouch
a little and receive the blow on the back of the neck. No one saw
her flung outwards and laid, a little twitching heap, at the foot of the
fence. No one except the boy. And he watched with intense bright
eyes, as he would watch a wild goose he had shot. Was it winged,
or dead? Dead!

Immediately he gave a loud cry. Immediately March gave a wild
shriek that went far, far down the afternoon. And the father started
a strange bellowing sound.

The boy leapt the fence and ran to the figure. The back of the
neck and head was a mass of blood, of horror. He turned it over.
The body was quivering with little convulsions. But she was dead
really. He knew it, that it was so. He knew it in his soul and his
blood. The inner necessity of his life was fulfilling itself, it was he
who was to live. The thorn was drawn out of his bowels. So he
put her down gently. She was dead.

He stood up. March was standing there petrified and absolutely
motionless. Her face was dead white, her eyes big black pools. The
old man was scrambling horribly over the fence.

"I'm afraid it's killed her," said the boy.

The old man was making curious, blubbering noises as he huddled
over the fence. "What!" cried March, starting electric.

"Yes, I'm afraid," repeated the boy.

March was coming forward. The boy was over the fence before she reached it.

" What do you say, killed her ? " she asked in a sharp voice.

" I'm afraid so," he answered softly.

She went still whiter, fearful. The two stood facing one another. Her black eyes gazed on him with the last look of resistance. And then in a last agonized failure she began to grizzle, to cry in a shivery little fashion of a child that doesn't want to cry, but which is beaten from within, and gives that little first shudder of sobbing which is not yet weeping, dry and fearful.

He had won. She stood there absolutely helpless, shuddering her dry sobs and her mouth trembling rapidly. And then, as in a child, with a little crash came the tears and the blind agony of sightless weeping. She sank down on the grass, and sat there with her hands on her breast and her face lifted in sightless, convulsed weeping. He stood above her, looking down on her, mute, pale, and everlasting seeming. He never moved, but looked down on her. And among all the torture of the scene, the torture of his own heart and bowels, he was glad, he had won.

After a long time he stooped to her and took her hands.

" Don't cry," he said softly. " Don't cry."

She looked up at him with tears running from her eyes, a senseless look of helplessness and submission. So she gazed on him as if sightless, yet looking up to him. She would never leave him again. He had won her. And he knew it and was glad, because he wanted her for his life. His life must have her. And now he had won her. It was what his life must have.

But if he had won her, he had not yet got her. They were married at Christmas as he had planned, and he got again ten days' leave. They went to Cornwall, to his own village, on the sea. He realized that it was awful for her to be at the farm any more.

But though she belonged to him, though she lived in his shadow, as if she could not be away from him, she was not happy. She did not want to leave him : and yet she did not feel free with him. Everything around her seemed to watch her, seemed to press on her. He had won her, he had her with him, she was his wife. And she—she belonged to him, she knew it. But she was not glad. And he was still foiled. He realized that though he was married to her and possessed her in every possible way, apparently, and though she *wanted* him to possess her, she wanted it, she wanted nothing else, now, still he did not quite succeed.

Something was missing. Instead of her soul swaying with new

life, it seemed to droop, to bleed, as if it were wounded. She would sit for a long time with her hand in his, looking away at the sea. And in her dark, vacant eyes was a sort of wound, and her face looked a little peaked. If he spoke to her, she would turn to him with a faint new smile, the strange, quivering little smile of a woman who has died in the old way of love, and can't quite rise to the new way. She still felt she ought to do something, to strain herself in some direction. And there was nothing to do, and no direction in which to strain herself. And she could not quite accept the submergence which his new love put upon her. If she was in love, she ought to *exert* herself, in some way, loving. She felt the weary need of our day to *exert* herself in love. But she knew that in fact she must no more exert herself in love. He would not have the love which exerted itself towards him. It made his brow go black. No, he wouldn't let her exert her love towards him. No, she had to be passive, to acquiesce, and to be submerged under the surface of love. She had to be like the seaweeds she saw as she peered down from the boat, swaying forever delicately under water, with all their delicate fibrils put tenderly out upon the flood, sensitive, utterly sensitive and receptive within the shadowy sea, and never, never rising and looking forth above water while they lived. Never. Never looking forth from the water until they died, only then washing, corpses, upon the surface. But while they lived, always submerged, always beneath the wave. Beneath the wave they might have powerful roots, stronger than iron ; they might be tenacious and dangerous in their soft waving within the flood. Beneath the water they might be stronger, more indestructible than resistant oak trees are on land. But it was always under-water, always under-water. And she, being a woman, must be like that.

And she had been so used to the very opposite. She had had to take all the thought for love and for life, and all the responsibility. Day after day she had been responsible for the coming day, for the coming year : for her dear Jill's health and happiness and well-being. Verily, in her own small way, she had felt herself responsible for the well-being of the world. And this had been her great stimulant, this grand feeling that, in her own small sphere, she was responsible for the well-being of the world.

And she had failed. She knew that, even in her small way, she had failed. She had failed to satisfy her own feeling of responsibility. It was so difficult. It seemed so grand and easy at first. And the more you tried, the more difficult it became. It had seemed so easy to make one beloved creature happy. And the more you tried, the worse the failure. It was terrible. She had been all her life reaching, reaching, and what she reached for seemed so near, until she had stretched to her utmost limit. And then it was always beyond her.

Always beyond her, vaguely, unrealizably beyond her, and she was left with nothingness at last. The life she reached for, the happiness she reached for, the well-being she reached for all slipped back, became unreal, the further she stretched her hand. She wanted some goal, some finality—and there was none. Always this ghastly reaching, reaching, striving for something that might be just beyond. Even to make Jill happy. She was glad Jill was dead. For she had realized that she could never make her happy. Jill would always be fretting herself thinner and thinner, weaker and weaker. Her pains grew worse instead of less. It would be so for ever. She was glad she was dead.

And if Jill had married a man it would have been just the same. The woman striving, striving to make the man happy, striving within her own limits for the well-being of her world. And always achieving failure. Little, foolish successes in money or in ambition. But at the very point where she most wanted success, in the anguished effort to make some one beloved human being happy and perfect, there the failure was almost catastrophic. You wanted to make your beloved happy, and his happiness seemed always achievable. If only you did just this, that, and the other. And you did this, that, and the other, in all good faith, and every time the failure became a little more ghastly. You could love yourself to ribbons, and strive and strain yourself to the bone, and things would go from bad to worse, bad to worse, as far as happiness went. The awful mistake of happiness.

Poor March, in her goodwill and her responsibility, she had strained herself till it seemed to her that the whole of life and everything was only a horrible abyss of nothingness. The more you reached after the fatal flower of happiness, which trembles so blue and lovely in a crevice just beyond your grasp, the more fearfully you become aware of the ghastly and awful gulf of the precipice below you, into which you will inevitably plunge, as into the bottomless pit, if you reach any further. You pluck flower after flower—it is never *the* flower. The flower itself—its calyx is a horrible gulf, it is the bottomless pit.

That is the whole history of the search for happiness, whether it be your own or somebody else's that you want to win. It ends, and it always ends, in the ghastly sense of the bottomless nothingness into which you will inevitably fall if you strain any further.

And women? What goal can any woman conceive, except happiness? Just happiness, for herself and the whole world. That, and nothing else. And so, she assumes the responsibility, and sets off towards her goal. She can see it there, at the foot of the rainbow. Or she can see it a little way beyond, in the blue distance. Not far, not far.

But the end of the rainbow is a bottomless gulf down which you can fall forever without arriving, and the blue distance is a void pit which can swallow you and all your efforts into its emptiness, and still be no emptier. You and all your efforts. So, the illusion of attainable happiness!

Poor March, she had set off so wonderfully towards the blue goal. And the further and further she had gone, the more fearful had become the realization of emptiness. An agony, an insanity at last.

She was glad it was over. She was glad to sit on the shore and look westwards over the sea, and know the great strain had ended. She would never strain for love and happiness any more. And Jill was safely dead. Poor Jill, poor Jill. It must be sweet to be dead.

For her own part, death was not her destiny. She would have to leave her destiny to the boy. But then, the boy. He wanted more than that. He wanted her to give herself without defences, to sink and become submerged in him. And she—she wanted to sit still, like a woman on the last milestone, and watch. She wanted to see, to know, to understand. She wanted to be alone : with him at her side.

And he! He did not want her to watch any more, to see any more, to understand any more. He wanted to veil her woman's spirit, as Orientals veil the woman's face. He wanted her to commit herself to him, and to put her independent spirit to sleep. He wanted to take away from her all her effort, all that seemed her very *raison d'être*. He wanted to make her submit, yield, blindly pass away out of all her strenuous consciousness. He wanted to take away her consciousness, and make her just his woman. Just his woman.

And she was so tired, so tired, like a child that wants to go to sleep, but which fights against sleep, as if sleep were death. She seemed to stretch her eyes wider in the obstinate effort and tension of keeping awake. She *would* keep awake. She *would* know. She *would* consider and judge and decide. She *would* have the reins of her own life between her own hands. She *would* be an independent woman, to the last. But she was so tired, so tired of everything. And sleep seemed near. And there was such rest in the boy.

Yet there, sitting in a niche of the high, wild cliffs of West Cornwall, looking over the westward sea, she stretched her eyes wider and wider. Away to the West, Canada, America. She *would* know and she *would* see what was ahead. And the boy, sitting beside her, staring down at the gulls, had a cloud between his brows and the strain of discontent in his eyes. He wanted her asleep, at peace in him. He wanted her at peace, asleep in him. And *there* she was, dying with the strain of her own wakefulness. Yet she would not sleep : no, never. Sometimes he thought bitterly that he ought to have left her. He ought never to have killed Banford. He should have left Banford and March to kill one another.

But that was only impatience : and he knew it. He was waiting, waiting to go west. He was aching almost in torment to leave England, to go west, to take March away. To leave this shore ! He believed that as they crossed the seas, as they left this England which he so hated, because in some way it seemed to have stung him with poison, she would go to sleep. She would close her eyes at last, and give in to him.

And then he would have her, and he would have his own life at last. He chafed, feeling he hadn't got his own life. He would never have it till she yielded and slept in him. Then he would have all his own life as a young man and a male, and she would have all her own life as a woman and a female. There would be no more of this awful straining. She would not be a man any more, an independent woman with a man's responsibility. Nay, even the responsibility for her own soul she would have to commit to him. He knew it was so, and obstinately held out against her, waiting for the surrender.

" You'll feel better when once we get over the seas to Canada over there," he said to her as they sat among the rocks on the cliff

She looked away to the sea's horizon, as if it were not real. Then she looked round at him, with the strained, strange look of a child that is struggling against sleep.

" Shall I ? " she said.

" Yes," he answered quietly.

And her eyelids dropped with the slow motion, sleep weighing them unconscious. But she pulled them open again to say :

" Yes, I may. I can't tell. I can't tell what it will be like over there."

" If only we could go soon ! " he said, with pain in his voice.

I

"I'm getting up, Teddilinks," said Mrs. Whiston, and she sprang out of bed briskly.

"What the Hanover's got you?" asked Whiston.

"Nothing. Can't I get up?" she replied animatedly.

It was about seven o'clock, scarcely light yet in the cold bedroom. Whiston lay still and looked at his wife. She was a pretty little thing, with her fleecy, short black hair all tousled. He watched her as she dressed quickly, flicking her small, delightful limbs, throwing her clothes about her. Her slovenliness and untidiness did not trouble him. When she picked up the edge of her petticoat, ripped off a torn string of white lace, and flung it on the dressing-table, her careless abandon made his spirit glow. She stood before the mirror and roughly scrambled together her profuse little mane of hair. He watched the quickness and softness of her young shoulders, calmly, like a husband, and appreciatively.

"Rise up," she cried, turning to him with a quick wave of her arm—" and shine forth."

They had been married two years. But still, when she had gone out of the room, he felt as if all his light and warmth were taken away, he became aware of the raw, cold morning. So he rose himself, wondering casually what had roused her so early. Usually she lay in bed as late as she could.

Whiston fastened a belt round his loins and went downstairs in shirt and trousers. He heard her singing in her snatchy fashion. The stairs creaked under his weight. He passed down the narrow little passage, which she called a hall, of the seven and sixpenny house which was his first home.

He was a shapely young fellow of about twenty-eight, sleepy now and easy with well-being. He heard the water drumming into the kettle, and she began to whistle. He loved the quick way she dodged the supper cups under the tap to wash them for breakfast. She looked an untidy minx, but she was quick and handy enough.

"Teddilinks," she cried.

" What ? "

" Light a fire, quick."

She wore an old, sack-like dressing-jacket of black silk pinned across her breast. But one of the sleeves, coming unfastened, showed some delightful pink upper-arm.

" Why don't you sew your sleeve up ? " he said, suffering from the sight of the exposed soft flesh.

" Where ? " she cried, peering round. " Nuisance," she said, seeing the gap, then with light fingers went on drying the cups.

The kitchen was of fair size, but gloomy. Whiston poked out the dead ashes.

Suddenly a thud was heard at the door down the passage.

" I'll go," cried Mrs. Whiston, and she was gone down the hall.

The postman was a ruddy-faced man who had been a soldier. He smiled broadly, handing her some packages.

" They've not forgot you," he said impudently.

" No—lucky for them," she said, with a toss of the head. But she was interested only in her envelopes this morning. The postman waited inquisitively, smiling in an ingratiating fashion. She slowly, abstractedly, as if she did not know any one was there, closed the door in his face, continuing to look at the addresses on her letters.

She tore open the thin envelope. There was a long, hideous, cartoon valentine. She smiled briefly and dropped it on the floor. Struggling with the string of a packet, she opened a white cardboard box, and there lay a white silk handkerchief packed neatly under the paper lace of the box, and her initial, worked in heliotrope, fully displayed. She smiled pleasantly, and gently put the box aside. The third envelope contained another white packet—apparently a cotton handkerchief neatly folded. She shook it out. It was a long white stocking, but there was a little weight in the toe. Quickly, she thrust down her arm, wriggling her fingers into the toe of the stocking, and brought out a small box. She peeped inside the box, then hastily opened a door on her left hand, and went into the little, cold sitting-room. She had her lower lip caught earnestly between her teeth.

With a little flash of triumph, she lifted a pair of pearl ear-rings from the small box, and she went to the mirror. There, earnestly, she began to hook them through her ears, looking at herself sideways in the glass. Curiously concentrated and intent she seemed as she fingered the lobes of her ears, her head bent on one side.

Then the pearl ear-rings dangled under her rosy, small ears. She shook her head sharply, to see the swing of the drops. They went chill against her neck, in little, sharp touches. Then she stood still to look at herself, bridling her head in the dignified fashion. Then she simpered at herself. Catching her own eye, she could not help winking at herself and laughing.

She turned to look at the box. There was a scrap of paper with this posy :

"Pearls may be fair, but thou art fairer.
Wear these for me, and I'll love the wearer."

She made a grimace and a grin. But she was drawn to the mirror again, to look at her ear-rings.

Whiston had made the fire burn, so he came to look for her. When she heard him, she started round quickly, guiltily. She was watching him with intent blue eyes when he appeared.

He did not see much, in his morning-drowsy warmth. He gave her, as ever, a feeling of warmth and slowness. His eyes were very blue, very kind, his manner simple.

"What ha' you got ? " he asked.

"Valentines," she said briskly, ostentatiously turning to show him the silk handkerchief. She thrust it under his nose. "Smell how good," she said.

"Who's that from ? " he replied, without smelling.

"It's a valentine," she cried. "How do I know who it's from ? "

"I'll bet you know," he said.

"Ted !—I don't ! " she cried, beginning to shake her head, then stopping because of the ear-rings.

He stood still a moment, displeased.

"They've no right to send you valentines, now," he said.

"Ted !—Why not? You're not jealous, are you? I haven't the least idea who it's from. Look—there's my initial "—she pointed with an emphatic finger at the heliotrope embroidery—

"E for Elsie,
Nice little gelsie,"

she sang.

"Get out," he said. "You know who it's from."

"Truth, I don't," she cried.

He looked round, and saw the white stocking lying on a chair.

"Is this another ? " he said.

"No, that's a sample," she said. "There's only a comic." And she fetched in the long cartoon.

He stretched it out and looked at it solemnly.

"Fools ! " he said, and went out of the room.

She flew upstairs and took off the ear-rings. When she returned, he was crouched before the fire blowing the coals. The skin of his face was flushed, and slightly pitted, as if he had had small-pox. But his neck was white and smooth and goodly. She hung her arms round his neck as he crouched there, and clung to him. He balanced on his toes.

" This fire's a slow-coach," he said.

" And who else is a slow-coach ? " she said.

"One of us two, I know," he said, and he rose carefully. She remained clinging round his neck, so that she was lifted off her feet.

" Ha !—swing me," she cried.

He lowered his head, and she hung in the air, swinging from his neck, laughing. Then she slipped off.

" The kettle is singing," she sang, flying for the teapot. He bent down again to blow the fire. The veins in his neck stood out, his shirt collar seemed too tight.

> " Doctor Wyer,
> Blow the fire,
> Puff ! puff ! puff ! "

she sang, laughing.

He smiled at her.

She was so glad because of her pearl ear-rings.

Over the breakfast she grew serious. He did not notice. She became portentous in her gravity. Almost it penetrated through his steady good-humour to irritate him.

" Teddy ! " she said at last.

" What ? " he asked.

" I told you a lie," she said, humbly tragic.

His soul stirred uneasily.

" Oh aye ? " he said casually.

She was not satisfied. He ought to be more moved.

" Yes," she said.

He cut a piece of bread.

" Was it a good one ? " he asked.

She was piqued. Then she considered—*was* it a good one ? Then she laughed.

" No," she said, " it wasn't up to much."

" Ah ! " he said easily, but with a steady strength of fondness for her in his tone. " Get it out then."

It became a little more difficult.

" You know that white stocking," she said earnestly. " I told you a lie. It wasn't a sample. It was a valentine."

A little frown came on his brow.

" Then what did you invent it as a sample for ? " he said. But he knew this weakness of hers. The touch of anger in his voice frightened her.

" I was afraid you'd be cross," she said pathetically.

" I'll bet you were vastly afraid," he said.

" I *was*, Teddy."

There was a pause. He was resolving one or two things in his mind.

" And who sent it ? " he asked.

" I can guess," she said, " though there wasn't a word with it—except——"

She ran to the sitting-room and returned with a slip of paper.

> " Pearls may be fair, but thou art fairer
> Wear these for me, and I'll love the wearer."

He read it twice, then a dull red flush came on his face.

" And *who* do you guess it is ? " he asked, with a ringing of anger in his voice.

" I suspect it's Sam Adams," she said, with a little virtuous indignation.

Whiston was silent for a moment.

" Fool ! " he said. " An' what's it got to do with pearls ?—and how can he say ' wear these for me ' when there's only one ? He hasn't got the brain to invent a proper verse."

He screwed the slip of paper into a ball and flung it into the fire.

" I suppose he thinks it'll make a pair with the one last year," she said.

" Why, did he send one then ? "

" Yes. I thought you'd be wild if you knew."

His jaw set rather sullenly.

Presently he rose, and went to wash himself, rolling back his sleeves and pulling open his shirt at the breast. It was as if his fine, clear-cut temples and steady eyes were degraded by the lower, rather brutal part of his face. But she loved it. As she whisked about, clearing the table, she loved the way in which he stood washing himself. He was such a man. She liked to see his neck glistening with water as he swilled it. It amused her and pleased her and thrilled her. He was so sure, so permanent, he had her so utterly in his power. It gave her a delightful, mischievous sense of liberty. Within his grasp, she could dart about excitingly.

He turned round to her, his face red from the cold water, his eyes fresh and very blue.

" You haven't been seeing anything of him, have you ? " he asked roughly.

" Yes," she answered, after a moment, as if caught guilty. " He got into the tram with me, and he asked me to drink a coffee and a Benedictine in the Royal."

"You've got it off fine and glib," he said sullenly. "And did you?"

" Yes," she replied, with the air of a traitor before the rack.

The blood came up into his neck and face, he stood motionless, dangerous.

" It was cold, and it was such fun to go into the Royal," she said.

" You'd go off with a nigger for a packet of chocolate," he said, in anger and contempt, and some bitterness. Queer how he drew away from her, cut her off from him.

"Ted—how beastly ! " she cried. " You know quite well——" She caught her lip, flushed, and the tears came to her eyes.

He turned away, to put on his necktie. She went about her work, making a queer pathetic little mouth, down which occasionally dripped a tear.

He was ready to go. With his hat jammed down on his head, and his overcoat buttoned up to his chin, he came to kiss her. He would be miserable all the day if he went without. She allowed herself to be kissed. Her cheek was wet under his lips, and his heart burned. She hurt him so deeply. And she felt aggrieved, and did not quite forgive him.

In a moment she went upstairs to her ear-rings. Sweet they looked nestling in the little drawer—sweet ! She examined them with voluptuous pleasure, she threaded them in her ears, she looked at herself, she posed and postured and smiled and looked sad and tragic and winning and appealing, all in turn before the mirror. And she was happy, and very pretty.

She wore her ear-rings all morning, in the house. She was self-conscious, and quite brilliantly winsome, when the baker came, wondering if he would notice. All the tradesmen left her door with a glow in them, feeling elated, and unconsciously favouring the delightful little creature, though there had been nothing to notice in her behaviour.

She was stimulated all the day. She did not think about her husband. He was the permanent basis from which she took these giddy little flights into nowhere. At night, like chickens and curses, she would come home to him, to roost.

Meanwhile Whiston, a traveller and confidential support of a small firm, hastened about his work, his heart all the while anxious for her, yearning for surety, and kept tense by not getting it.

II

She had been a warehouse girl in Adams's lace factory before she was married. Sam Adams was her employer. He was a bachelor of forty, growing stout, a man well dressed and florid, with a large brown moustache and thin hair. From the rest of his well-groomed, showy appearance, it was evident his baldness was a chagrin to him. He had a good presence, and some Irish blood in his veins.

His fondness for the girls, or the fondness of the girls for him, was notorious. And Elsie, quick, pretty, almost witty little thing—she *seemed* witty, although, when her sayings were repeated, they were entirely trivial—she had a great attraction for him. He would come into the warehouse dressed in a rather sporting reefer coat, of fawn colour, and trousers of fine black-and-white check, a cap with a big peak and scarlet carnation in his button-hole, to impress her. She was only half impressed. He was too loud for her good taste. Instinctively perceiving this, he sobered down to navy blue. Then a well-built man, florid, with large brown whiskers, smart navy blue suit, fashionable boots, and manly hat, he was the irreproachable. Elsie was impressed.

But meanwhile Whiston was courting her, and she made splendid little gestures, before her bedroom mirror, of the constant-and-true sort.

" True, true till death——"

That was her song. Whiston was made that way, so there was no need to take thought for him.

Every Christmas Sam Adams gave a party at his house, to which he invited his superior work-people—not factory hands and labourers but those above. He was a generous man in his way, with a real warm feeling for giving pleasure.

Two years ago Elsie had attended this Christmas-party for the last time. Whiston had accompanied her. At that time he worked for Sam Adams.

She had been very proud of herself, in her close-fitting, full-skirted dress of blue silk. Whiston called for her. Then she tripped beside him, holding her large cashmere shawl across her breast. He strode with long strides, his trousers handsomely strapped under his boots, and her silk shoes bulging the pockets of his full-skirted overcoat.

They passed through the park gates, and her spirits rose. Above them the Castle Rock loomed grandly in the night, the naked trees stood still and dark in the frost, along the boulevard.

They were rather late. Agitated with anticipation, in the cloak-room she gave up her shawl, donned her silk shoes, and looked at herself in the mirror. The loose bunches of curls on either side her face danced prettily, her mouth smiled.

She hung a moment in the door of the brilliantly lighted room. Many people were moving within the blaze of lamps, under the crystal chandeliers, the full skirts of the women balancing and floating, the side-whiskers and white cravats of the men bowing above. Then she entered the light.

In an instant Sam Adams was coming forward, lifting both his arms in boisterous welcome. There was a constant red laugh on his face.

" Come late, would you," he shouted, " like royalty."

He seized her hands and led her forward. He opened his mouth wide when he spoke, and the effect of the warm, dark opening behind the brown whiskers was disturbing. But she was floating into the throng on his arm. He was very gallant.

" Now then," he said, taking her card to write down the dances, " I've got *carte blanche*, haven't I ? "

" Mr. Whiston doesn't dance," she said.

" I am a lucky man ! " he said, scribbling his initials. " I was born with an *amourette* in my mouth."

He wrote on, quietly. She blushed and laughed, not knowing what it meant.

" Why, what is that ? " she said.

" It's you, even littler than you are, dressed in little wings," he said.

" I should have to be pretty small to get in your mouth," she said.

" You think you're too big, do you ! " he said easily.

He handed her her card, with a bow.

" Now I'm set up, my darling, for this evening," he said.

Then, quick, always at his ease, he looked over the room. She waited in front of him. He was ready. Catching the eye of the band, he nodded. In a moment, the music began. He seemed to relax, giving himself up.

" Now then, Elsie," he said, with a curious caress in his voice that seemed to lap the outside of her body in a warm glow, delicious. She gave herself to it. She liked it.

He was an excellent dancer. He seemed to draw her close in to him by some male warmth of attraction, so that she became all soft and pliant to him, flowing to his form, whilst he united her with him and they lapsed along in one movement. She was just carried in a kind of strong, warm flood, her feet moved of themselves, and only the music threw her away from him, threw her back to him, to his clasp, in his strong form moving against her, rhythmically, deliciously.

When it was over, he was pleased and his eyes had a curious gleam which thrilled her and yet had nothing to do with her. Yet it held her. He did not speak to her. He only looked straight into her eyes with a curious, gleaming look that disturbed her fearfully and deliciously. But also there was in his look some of the automatic irony of the *roué*. It left her partly cold. She was not carried away.

She went, driven by an opposite, heavier impulse, to Whiston. He stood looking gloomy, trying to admit that she had a perfect right to enjoy herself apart from him. He received her with rather grudging kindliness.

"Aren't you going to play whist ? " she asked.

"Aye," he said. "Directly."

"I do wish you could dance."

"Well, I can't," he said. "So you enjoy yourself."

"But I should enjoy it better if I could dance with you."

"Nay, you're all right," he said. "I'm not made that way."

"Then you ought to be ! " she cried.

"Well, it's my fault, not yours. You enjoy yourself," he bade her. Which she proceeded to do, a little bit irked.

She went with anticipation to the arms of Sam Adams, when the time came to dance with him. It *was* so gratifying, irrespective of the man. And she felt a little grudge against Whiston, soon forgotten when her host was holding her near to him, in a delicious embrace. And she watched his eyes, to meet the gleam in them, which gratified her.

She was getting warmed right through, the glow was penetrating into her, driving away everything else. Only in her heart was a little tightness, like conscience.

When she got a chance, she escaped from the dancing-room to the card-room. There, in a cloud of smoke, she found Whiston playing cribbage. Radiant, roused, animated, she came up to him and greeted him. She was too strong, too vibrant a note in the quiet room. He lifted his head, and a frown knitted his gloomy forehead.

"Are you playing cribbage ? Is it exciting ? How are you getting on ? " she chattered.

He looked at her. None of these questions needed answering, and he did not feel in touch with her. She turned to the cribbage-board

" Are you white or red ? " she asked.

" He's red," replied the partner.

" Then you're losing," she said, still to Whiston. And she lifted the red peg from the board. " One—two—three—four—five—six—seven—eight——Right up there you ought to jump——"

" Now put it back in its right place," said Whiston.

" Where was it ? " she asked gaily, knowing her transgression. He took the little red peg away from her and stuck it in its hole.

The cards were shuffled.

" What a shame you're losing ! " said Elsie.

" You'd better cut for him," said the partner.

She did so, hastily. The cards were dealt. She put her hand on his shoulder, looking at his cards.

" It's good," she cried, " isn't it ? "

He did not answer, but threw down two cards. It moved him more strongly than was comfortable, to have her hand on his shoulder, her curls dangling and touching his ears, whilst she was roused to another man. It made the blood flame over him.

At that moment Sam Adams appeared, florid and boisterous, intoxicated more with himself, with the dancing, than with wine. In his eye the curious, impersonal light gleamed.

" I thought I should find you here, Elsie," he cried boisterously, a disturbing, high note in his voice.

" What made you think so ? " she replied, the mischief rousing in her.

The florid, well-built man narrowed his eyes to a smile.

" I should never look for you among the ladies," he said, with a kind of intimate, animal call to her. He laughed, bowed, and offered her his arm.

" Madam, the music waits."

She went almost helplessly, carried along with him, unwilling, yet delighted.

That dance was an intoxication to her. After the first few steps, she felt herself slipping away from herself. She almost knew she was going, she did not even want to go. Yet she must have chosen to go. She lay in the arm of the steady, close man with whom she was dancing, and she seemed to swim away out of contact with the room, into him. She had passed into another, denser element of him, an essential privacy. The room was all vague around her, like an atmosphere, like under sea, with a flow of ghostly, dumb movements. But she herself was held real against her partner, and it seemed she was connected with him, as if the movements of his body and limbs were her own movements, yet not her own movements—and oh, delicious ! He also was given up, oblivious, concentrated, into the dance. His eye was unseeing. Only his large, voluptuous body gave off a subtle activity. His fingers seemed to search into her flesh. Every moment, and every moment, she felt she would give way utterly, and sink molten : the fusion point was coming when she would fuse down into perfect unconsciousness at his feet and knees. But he bore her round the room in the dance, and he seemed to sustain all her body with his limbs, his body, and his warmth seemed to come closer into her, nearer, till it would fuse right through her, and she would be as liquid to him, as an intoxication only.

It was exquisite. When it was over, she was dazed, and was scarcely breathing. She stood with him in the middle of the room as if she were alone in a remote place. He bent over her. She expected his lips on her bare shoulder, and waited. Yet they were not alone, they were not alone. It was cruel.

" 'Twas good, wasn't it, my darling ? " he said to her, low and delighted. There was a strange impersonality about his low, exultant call that appealed to her irresistibly. Yet why was she aware of some part shut off in her ? She pressed his arm, and he led her towards the door.

She was not aware of what she was doing, only a little grain of resistant trouble was in her. The man, possessed, yet with a superficial presence of mind, made way to the dining-room, as if to give her refreshment, cunningly working to his own escape with her. He was molten hot, filmed over with presence of mind, and bottomed with cold disbelief. In the dining-room was Whiston, carrying coffee to the plain, neglected ladies. Elsie saw him, but felt as if he could not see her. She was beyond his reach and ken. A sort of fusion existed between her and the large man at her side. She ate her custard, but an incomplete fusion all the while sustained and contained within the being of her employer.

But she was growing cooler. Whiston came up. She looked at him, and saw him with different eyes. She saw his slim, young man's figure real and enduring before her. That was he. But she was in the spell with the other man, fused with him, and she could not be taken away.

" Have you finished your cribbage ? " she asked, with hasty evasion of him.

" Yes," he replied. " Aren't you getting tired of dancing ? "

" Not a bit," she said.

" Not she," said Adams heartily. " No girl with any spirit gets

tired of dancing.   Have something else, Elsie.   Come—sherry.   Have
a glass of sherry with us, Whiston."

Whilst they sipped the wine, Adams watched Whiston almost
cunningly, to find his advantage.

"We'd better be getting back—there's the music," he said.   "See the
women get something to eat, Whiston, will you, there's a good chap."

And he began to draw away.   Elsie was drifting helplessly with
him.   But Whiston put himself beside them, and went along with
them.   In silence they passed through to the dancing-room.   There
Adams hesitated, and looked round the room.   It was as if he could
not see.

A man came hurrying forward, claiming Elsie, and Adams went
to his other partner.   Whiston stood watching during the dance.
She was conscious of him standing there observant of her, like a
ghost, or a judgment, or a guardian angel.   She was also conscious,
much more intimately and impersonally, of the body of the other
man moving somewhere in the room.   She still belonged to him,
but a feeling of distraction possessed her, and helplessness.   Adams
danced on, adhering to Elsie, waiting his time, with the persistence
of cynicism.

The dance was over.   Adams was detained.   Elsie found herself
beside Whiston.   There was something shapely about him as he sat,
about his knees and his distinct figure, that she clung to.   It was as
if he had enduring form.   She put her hand on his knee.

" Are you enjoying yourself ? " he asked.

" *Ever* so," she replied, with a fervent, yet detached tone.

" It's going on for one o'clock," he said.

" Is it ? " she answered.   It meant nothing to her.

" Should we be going ? " he said.

She was silent.   For the first time for an hour or more an inkling
of her normal consciousness returned.   She resented it.

" What for ? " she said.

" I thought you might have had enough," he said.

A slight soberness came over her, an irritation at being frustrated
of her illusion.

" Why ? " she said.

" We've been here since nine," he said.

That was no answer, no reason.   It conveyed nothing to her.
She sat detached from him.   Across the room Sam Adams glanced
at her.   She sat there exposed for him.

" You don't want to be too free with Sam Adams," said Whiston
cautiously, suffering.   " You know what he is."

" How, free ? " she asked.

" Why—you don't want to have too much to do with him."

She sat silent. He was forcing her into consciousness of her position. But he could not get hold of her feelings, to change them. She had a curious, perverse desire that he should not.

" I like him," she said.

" What do you find to like in him ? " he said, with a hot heart.

" I don't know—but I like him," she said.

She was immutable. He sat feeling heavy and dulled with rage. He was not clear as to what he felt. He sat there unliving whilst she danced. And she, distracted, lost to herself between the opposing forces of the two men, drifted. Between the dances, Whiston kept near to her. She was scarcely conscious. She glanced repeatedly at her card, to see when she would dance again with Adams, half in desire, half in dread. Sometimes she met his steady, glaucous eye as she passed him in the dance. Sometimes she saw the steadiness of his flank as he danced. And it was always as if she rested on his arm, were borne along, upborne by him, away from herself. And always there was present the other's antagonism. She was divided.

The time came for her to dance with Adams. Oh, the delicious closing of contact with him, of his limbs touching her limbs, his arm supporting her. She seemed to resolve. Whiston had not made himself real to her. He was only a heavy place in her consciousness.

But she breathed heavily, beginning to suffer from the closeness of strain. She was nervous. Adams also was constrained. A tightness, a tension was coming over them all. And he was exasperated, feeling something counteracting physical magnetism, feeling a will stronger with her than his own, intervening in what was becoming a vital necessity to him.

Elsie was almost lost to her own control. As she went forward with him to take her place at the dance, she stooped for her pocket-handkerchief. The music sounded for quadrilles. Everybody was ready. Adams stood with his body near her, exerting his attraction over her. He was tense and fighting. She stooped for her pocket-handkerchief, and shook it as she rose. It shook out and fell from her hand. With agony, she saw she had taken a white stocking instead of a handkerchief. For a second it lay on the floor, a twist of white stocking. Then, in an instant, Adams picked it up, with a little, surprised laugh of triumph.

" That'll do for me," he whispered—seeming to take possession of her. And he stuffed the stocking in his trousers pocket, and quickly offered her his handkerchief.

The dance began. She felt weak and faint, as if her will were turned to water. A heavy sense of loss came over her. She could not help herself any more. But it was peace.

When the dance was over, Adams yielded her up. Whiston came to her.

" What was it as you dropped ? " Whiston asked.

" I thought it was my handkerchief—I'd taken a stocking by mistake," she said, detached and muted.

" And he's got it ? "

" Yes."

" What does he mean by that ? "

She lifted her shoulders.

" Are you going to let him keep it ? " he asked.

" I don't let him."

There was a long pause.

" Am I to go and have it out with him ? " he asked, his face flushed, his blue eyes going hard with opposition.

" No," she said, pale.

" Why ? "

" No—I don't want you to say anything about it."

He sat exasperated and nonplussed.

" You'll let him keep it, then ? " he asked.

She sat silent and made no form of answer.

" What do you mean by it ? " he said, dark with fury. And he started up.

" No ! " she cried. " Ted ! " And she caught hold of him, sharply detaining him.

It made him black with rage.

" Why ? " he said.

The something about her mouth was pitiful to him. He did not understand, but he felt she must have her reasons.

" Then I'm not stopping here," he said. " Are you coming with me ? "

She rose mutely, and they went out of the room. Adams had not noticed.

In a few moments they were in the street.

" What the hell do you mean ? " he said, in a black fury.

She went at his side, in silence, neutral.

" That great hog, an' all," he added.

Then they went a long time in silence through the frozen, deserted

F

darkness of the town. She felt she could not go indoors. They were drawing near her house.

" I don't want to go home," she suddenly cried in distress and anguish. " I don't want to go home."

He looked at her.

" Why don't you ? " he said.

" I don't want to go home," was all she could sob.

He heard somebody coming.

" Well, we can walk a bit farther," he said.

She was silent again. They passed out of the town into the fields. He held her by the arm—they could not speak.

" What's a-matter ? " he asked at length, puzzled.

She began to cry again.

At last he took her in his arms, to soothe her. She sobbed by herself, almost unaware of him.

" Tell me what's a-matter, Elsie," he said. " Tell me what's a-matter—my dear—tell me, then——"

He kissed her wet face, and caressed her. She made no response. He was puzzled and tender and miserable.

At length she became quiet. Then he kissed her, and she put her arms round him, and clung to him very tight, as if for fear and anguish. He held her in his arms, wondering.

" Ted ! " she whispered, frantic. " Ted ! "

" What, my love ? " he answered, becoming also afraid.

" Be good to me," she cried. " Don't be cruel to me."

" No, my pet," he said, amazed and grieved. " Why ? "

" Oh, be good to me," she sobbed.

And he held her very safe, and his heart was white-hot with love for her. His mind was amazed. He could only hold her against his chest that was white-hot with love and belief in her. So she was restored at last.

III

She refused to go to her work at Adams's any more. Her father had to submit and she sent in her notice—she was not well. Sam Adams was ironical. But he had a curious patience. He did not fight.

In a few weeks, she and Whiston were married. She loved him with passion and worship, a fierce little abandon of love that moved him to the depths of his being, and gave him a permanent surety and sense of realness in himself. He did not trouble about himself any more : he felt he was fulfilled and now he had only the many things in the world to busy himself about. Whatever troubled him, at the bottom was surety. He had found himself in this love.

They spoke once or twice of the white stocking.

" Ah ! " Whiston exclaimed. " What does it matter ? "

He was impatient and angry, and could not bear to consider the matter. So it was left unresolved.

She was quite happy at first, carried away by her adoration of her husband. Then gradually she got used to him. He always was the ground of her happiness, but she got used to him, as to the air she breathed. He never got used to her in the same way.

Inside of marriage she found her liberty. She was rid of the responsibility of herself. Her husband must look after that. She was free to get what she could out of her time.

So that, when, after some months, she met Sam Adams, she was not quite as unkind to him as she might have been. With a young wife's new and exciting knowledge of men, she perceived he was in love with her, she knew he had always kept an unsatisfied desire for her. And, sportive, she could not help playing a little with this, though she cared not one jot for the man himself.

When Valentine's day came, which was near the first anniversary of her wedding day, there arrived a white stocking with a little amethyst brooch. Luckily Whiston did not see it, so she said nothing of it to him. She had not the faintest intention of having anything to do with Sam Adams, but once a little brooch was in her possession, it was hers, and she did not trouble her head for a moment how she had come by it. She kept it.

Now she had the pearl ear-rings. They were a more valuable and a more conspicuous present. She would have to ask her mother to give them to her, to explain their presence. She made a little plan in her head. And she was extraordinarily pleased. As for Sam Adams, even if he saw her wearing them, he would not give her away. What fun, if he saw her wearing his ear-rings ! She would pretend she had inherited them from her grandmother, her mother's mother. She laughed to herself as she went downtown in the afternoon, the pretty drops dangling in front of her curls. But she saw no one of importance.

Whiston came home tired and depressed. All day the male in him had been uneasy, and this had fatigued him. She was curiously against him, inclined, as she sometimes was nowadays, to make mock of him and jeer at him and cut him off. He did not understand this, and it angered him deeply. She was uneasy before him.

She knew he was in a state of suppressed irritation. The veins stood out on the backs of his hands, his brow was drawn stiffly. Yet she could not help goading him.

"What did you do wi' that white stocking?" he asked, out of a gloomy silence, his voice strong and brutal.

"I put it in a drawer—why?" she replied flippantly.

"Why didn't you put it on the fire-back?" he said harshly. "What are you hoarding it up for?"

"I'm not hoarding it up," she said. "I've got a pair."

He relapsed into gloomy silence. She, unable to move him, ran away upstairs, leaving him smoking by the fire. Again she tried on the ear-rings. Then another little inspiration came to her. She drew on the white stockings, both of them.

Presently she came down in them. Her husband still sat immovable and glowering by the fire.

"Look!" she said. "They'll do beautifully."

And she picked up her skirts to her knees, and twisted round, looking at her pretty legs in the neat stockings.

He filled with unreasonable rage, and took the pipe from his mouth.

"Don't they look nice?" she said. "One from last year and one from this, they just do. Save you buying a pair."

And she looked over her shoulders at her pretty calves, and at the dangling frills of her knickers.

"Put your skirts down and don't make a fool of yourself," he said.

"Why a fool of myself?" she asked.

And she began to dance slowly round the room, kicking up her feet half reckless, half jeering, in a ballet-dancer's fashion. Almost fearfully, yet in defiance, she kicked up her legs at him, singing as she did so. She resented him.

"You little fool, ha' done with it," he said. "And you'll backfire them stockings, I'm telling you." He was angry. His face flushed dark, he kept his head bent. She ceased to dance.

"I shan't," she said. "They'll come in very useful."

He lifted his head and watched her, with lighted, dangerous eyes.

"You'll put 'em on the fire-back, I tell you," he said.

It was a war now. She bent forward, in a ballet-dancer's fashion, and put her tongue between her teeth.

"I shan't backfire them stockings," she sang, repeating his words, "I shan't, I shan't, I shan't."

And she danced round the room doing a high kick to the tune of her words. There was a real biting indifference in her behaviour.

"We'll see whether you will or not," he said, "trollops! You'd like Sam Adams to know you was wearing 'em, wouldn't you ? That's what would please you."

" Yes, I'd like him to see how nicely they fit me, he might give me some more then."

And she looked down at her pretty legs.

He knew somehow that she *would* like Sam Adams to see how pretty her legs looked in the white stockings. It made his anger go deep, almost to hatred.

" Yer nasty trolley," he cried. " Put yer petticoats down, and stop being so foul-minded."

" I'm not foul-minded," she said. " My legs are my own. And why shouldn't Sam Adams think they're nice ? "

There was a pause. He watched her with eyes glittering to a point.

" Have you been havin' owt to do with him ? " he asked.

" I've just spoken to him when I've seen him," she said. " He's not as bad as you would make out."

" Isn't he ? " he cried, a certain wakefulness in his voice. " Them who has anything to do wi' him is too bad for me, I tell you."

" Why, what are you frightened of him for ? " she mocked.

She was rousing all his uncontrollable anger. He sat glowering. Every one of her sentences stirred him up like a red-hot iron. Soon it would be too much. And she was afraid herself ; but she was neither conquered nor convinced.

A curious little grin of hate came on his face. He had a long score against her.

" What am I frightened of him for ? " he repeated automatically. " What am I frightened of him for ? Why, for you, you stray-running little bitch."

She flushed. The insult went deep into her, right home.

" Well, if you're so dull——" she said, lowering her eyelids, and speaking coldly, haughtily.

" If I'm so dull I'll break your neck the first word you speak to him," he said, tense.

" Pf ! " she sneered. " Do you think I'm frightened of you ? " She spoke coldly, detached.

She was frightened, for all that, white round the mouth.

His heart was getting hotter.

" You *will* be frightened of me, the next time you have anything to do with him," he said.

" Do you think *you'd* ever be told—ha ! "

Her jeering scorn made him go white-hot, molten. He knew he

was incoherent, scarcely responsible for what he might do. Slowly, unseeing, he rose and went out of doors, stifled, moved to kill her.

He stood leaning against the garden fence, unable either to see or hear. Below him, far off, fumed the lights of the town. He stood still, unconscious with a black storm of rage, his face lifted to the night.

Presently, still unconscious of what he was doing, he went indoors again. She stood, a small, stubborn figure with tight-pressed lips and big, sullen, childish eyes, watching him, white with fear. He went heavily across the floor and dropped into his chair.

There was a silence.

" *You're* not going to tell me everything I shall do, and everything I shan't," she broke out at last.

He lifted his head.

" I tell you *this*," he said, low and intense. " Have anything to do with Sam Adams, and I'll break your neck."

She laughed, shrill and false.

" How I hate your word ' break your neck,' " she said, with a grimace of the mouth. " It sounds so common and beastly. Can't you say something else——"

There was a dead silence.

" And besides," she said, with a queer chirrup of mocking laughter, " what do you know about anything ? He sent me an amethyst brooch and a pair of pearl ear-rings."

" He what ? " said Whiston, in a suddenly normal voice. His eyes were fixed on her.

" Sent me a pair of pearl ear-rings, and an amethyst brooch," she repeated, mechanically, pale to the lips.

And her big, black, childish eyes watched him, fascinated, held in her spell.

He seemed to thrust his face and his eyes forward at her, as he rose slowly and came to her. She watched transfixed in terror. Her throat made a small sound, as she tried to scream.

Then, quick as lightning, the back of his hand struck her with a crash across the mouth, and she was flung black blinded against the wall. The shock shook a queer sound out of her. And then she saw him still coming on, his eyes holding her, his fist drawn back, advancing slowly. At any instant the blow might crash into her.

Mad with terror, she raised her hands with a queer clawing movement to cover her eyes and her temples, opening her mouth in a dumb shriek. There was no sound. But the sight of her slowly arrested him. He hung before her, looking at her fixedly, as she stood crouched against the wall with open, bleeding mouth, and wide-staring eyes, and two hands clawing over her temples. And his lust to see her bleed, to break her and destroy her, rose from an old source against her. It carried him. He wanted satisfaction.

But he had seen her standing there, a piteous, horrified thing, and he turned his face aside in shame and nausea. He went and sat heavily in his chair, and a curious ease, almost like sleep, came over his brain.

She walked away from the wall towards the fire, dizzy, white to the lips, mechanically wiping her small, bleeding mouth. He sat motionless. Then, gradually, her breath began to hiss, she shook, and was sobbing silently, in grief for herself. Without looking, he saw. It made his mad desire to destroy her come back.

At length he lifted his head. His eyes were glowing again, fixed on her.

" And what did he give them you for ? " he asked, in a steady, unyielding voice.

Her crying dried up in a second. She also was tense.

" They came as valentines," she replied, still not subjugated, even if beaten.

" When, to-day ? "

" The pearl ear-rings to-day—the amethyst brooch last year."

" You've had it a year ? "

" Yes."

She felt that now nothing would prevent him if he rose to kill her. She could not prevent him any more. She was yielded up to him. They both trembled in the balance, unconscious.

" What have you had to do with him ? " he asked, in a barren voice.

" I've not had anything to do with him," she quavered.

" You just kept 'em because they were jewellery ? " he said.

A weariness came over him. What was the worth of speaking any more of it ? He did not care any more. He was dreary and sick.

She began to cry again, but he took no notice. She kept wiping her mouth on her handkerchief. He could see it, the blood-mark. It made him only more sick and tired of the responsibility of it, the violence, the shame.

When she began to move about again, he raised his head once more from his dead, motionless position.

" Where are the things ? " he said.

" They are upstairs," she quavered. She knew the passion had gone down in him.

"Bring them down," he said.

"I won't," she wept, with rage. "You're not going to bully me and hit me like that on the mouth."

And she sobbed again. He looked at her in contempt and compassion and in rising anger.

"Where are they?" he said.

"They're in the little drawer under the looking-glass," she sobbed.

He went slowly upstairs, struck a match, and found the trinkets. He brought them downstairs in his hand.

"These?" he said, looking at them as they lay in his palm.

She looked at them without answering. She was not interested in them any more.

He looked at the little jewels. They were pretty.

"It's none of their fault," he said to himself.

And he searched round slowly, persistently, for a box. He tied the things up and addressed them to Sam Adams. Then he went out in his slippers to post the little package.

When he came back she was still sitting crying.

"You'd better go to bed," he said.

She paid no attention. He sat by the fire. She still cried.

"I'm sleeping down here," he said. "Go you to bed."

In a few moments she lifted her tear-stained, swollen face and looked at him with eyes all forlorn and pathetic. A great flash of anguish went over his body. He went over, slowly, and very gently took her in his hands. She let herself be taken. Then as she lay against his shoulder, she sobbed aloud:

"I never meant——"

"My love—my little love——" he cried, in anguish of spirit, holding her in his arms.

HE was working on the edge of the common, beyond the small brook that ran in the dip at the bottom of the garden, carrying the garden path in continuation from the plank bridge on to the common. He had cut the rough turf and bracken, leaving the grey, dryish soil bare. But he was worried because he could not get the path straight, there was a pleat between his brows. He had set up his sticks, and taken the sights between the big pine trees, but for some reason everything seemed wrong. He looked again, straining his keen blue eyes, that had a touch of the Viking in them, through the shadowy pine trees as through a doorway, at the green-grassed garden-path rising from the shadow of alders by the log bridge up to the sunlit flowers. Tall white and purple columbines, and the butt-end of the old Hampshire cottage that crouched near the earth amid flowers, blossoming in the bit of shaggy wildness round about.

There was a sound of children's voices calling and talking : high, childish, girlish voices, slightly didactic and tinged with domineering : " If you don't come quick, nurse, I shall run out there to where there are snakes." And nobody had the sang-froid to reply : " Run then, little fool." It was always, " No, darling. Very well, darling. In a moment, darling. Darling, you *must* be patient."

His heart was hard with disillusion : a continual gnawing and resistance. But he worked on. What was there to do but submit !

The sunlight blazed down upon the earth, there was a vividness of flamy vegetation, of fierce seclusion amid the savage peace of the commons. Strange how the savage England lingers in patches : as here, amid these shaggy gorse commons, and marshy, snake-infested places near the foot of the south downs. The spirit of place lingering on primeval, as when the Saxons came, so long ago.

Ah, how he had loved it ! The green garden path, the tufts of flowers, purple and white columbines, and great oriental red poppies with their black chaps and mulleins tall and yellow : this flamy garden which had been a garden for a thousand years, scooped out in the little hollow among the snake-infested commons. He had made it flame with flowers, in a sun cup under its hedges and trees. So old, so old a place ! And yet he had re-created it.

The timbered cottage with its sloping, cloak-like roof was old and forgotten. It belonged to the old England of hamlets and yeomen. Lost all alone on the edge of the common, at the end of a wide, grassy, briar-entangled lane shaded with oak, it had never known the world of to-day. Not till Egbert came with his bride. And he had come to fill it with flowers.

The house was ancient and very uncomfortable. But he did not want to alter it. Ah, marvellous to sit there in the wide, black, time-old chimney, at night when the wind roared overhead, and the wood which he had chopped himself sputtered on the hearth! Himself on one side the angle, and Winifred on the other.

Ah, how he had wanted her : Winifred ! She was young and beautiful and strong with life, like a flame in sunshine. She moved with a slow grace of energy like a blossoming, red-flowered bush in motion. She, too, seemed to come out of the old England, ruddy, strong, with a certain crude, passionate quiescence and a hawthorn robustness. And he, he was tall and slim and agile, like an English archer with his long supple legs and fine movements. Her hair was nut-brown and all in energic curls and tendrils. Her eyes were nut-brown, too, like a robin's for brightness. And he was white-skinned with fine, silky hair that had darkened from fair, and a slightly arched nose of an old country family. They were a beautiful couple.

The house was Winifred's. Her father was a man of energy, too. He had come from the north poor. Now he was moderately rich. He had bought this fair stretch of inexpensive land, down in Hampshire. Not far from the tiny church of the almost extinct hamlet stood his own house, a commodious old farm-house standing back from the road across a bare grassed yard. On one side of this quadrangle was the long, long barn or shed which he had made into a cottage for his youngest daughter Priscilla. One saw little blue-and-white check curtains at the long windows, and inside, overhead, the grand old timbers of the high-pitched shed. This was Prissy's house. Fifty yards away was the pretty little new cottage which he had built for his daughter Magdalen, with the vegetable garden stretching away to the oak copse. And then away beyond the lawns and rose-trees of the house-garden went the track across a shaggy, wild grass space, towards the ridge of tall black pines that grew on a dyke-bank, through the pines and above the sloping little bog, under the wide, desolate oak trees, till there was Winifred's cottage crouching unexpectedly in front, so much alone, and so primitive.

It was Winifred's own house, and the gardens and the bit of common and the boggy slope were hers : her tiny domain. She had married just at the time when her father had bought the estate, about ten years before the war, so she had been able to come to Egbert with this for a marriage portion. And who was more delighted, he or she, it would be hard to say. She was only twenty at the time, and he was only twenty-one. He had about a hundred and fifty pounds a year of his own—and nothing else but his very considerable personal attractions. He had no profession : he earned nothing. But he talked of literature and music, he had a passion for old folk-music, collecting folk-songs and folk-dances, studying the Morris-dance and the old customs. Of course, in time he would make money in these ways.

Meanwhile youth and health and passion and promise. Winifred's father was always generous : but still, he was a man from the north with a hard head and a hard skin too, having received a good many knocks. At home he kept the hard head out of sight, and played at poetry and romance with his literary wife and his sturdy, passionate girls. He was a man of courage, not given to complaining, bearing his burdens by himself. No, he did not let the world intrude far into his home. He had a delicate, sensitive wife whose poetry won some fame in the narrow world of letters. He himself, with his tough old barbarian fighting spirit, had an almost child-like delight in verse, in sweet poetry, and in the delightful game of a cultured home. His blood was strong even to coarseness. But that only made the home more vigorous, more robust and Christmassy. There was always a touch of Christmas about him, now he was well off. If there was poetry after dinner, there were also chocolates, and nuts, and good little out-of-the-way things to be munching.

Well then, into this family came Egbert. He was made of quite a different paste. The girls and the father were strong-limbed, thick-blooded people, true English, as holly-trees and hawthorn are English. Their culture was grafted on to them, as one might perhaps graft a common pink rose on to a thorn-stem. It flowered oddly enough, but it did not alter their blood.

And Egbert was a born rose. The age-long breeding had left him with a delightful spontaneous passion. He was not clever, nor even "literary." No, but the intonation of his voice, and the movement of his supple, handsome body, and the fine texture of his flesh and his hair, the slight arch of his nose, the quickness of his blue eyes would easily take the place of poetry. Winifred loved him, loved him, this southerner, as a higher being. A *higher* being, mind you. Not a deeper. And as for him, he loved her in passion with every fibre of him. She was the very warm stuff of life to him.

Wonderful then, those days at Crockham Cottage, the first days, all alone save for the woman who came to work in the mornings. Marvellous days, when she had all his tall, supple, fine-fleshed youth to herself, for herself, and he had her like a ruddy fire into which he could cast himself for rejuvenation. Ah, that it might never end, this passion, this marriage! The flame of their two bodies burnt again into that old cottage, that was haunted already by so much bygone, physical desire. You could not be in the dark room for an hour without the influences coming over you. The hot blood-desire of bygone yeomen, there in this old den where they had lusted and bred for so many generations. The silent house, dark, with thick, timbered walls and the big black chimney-place, and the sense of secrecy. Dark, with low, little windows, sunk into the earth. Dark, like a lair where strong beasts had lurked and mated, lonely at night and lonely by day, left to themselves and their own intensity for so many generations. It seemed to cast a spell on the two young people. They became different. There was a curious secret glow about them, a certain slumbering flame hard to understand, that enveloped them both. They too felt that they did not belong to the London world any more. Crockham had changed their blood : the sense of the snakes that lived and slept even in their own garden, in the sun, so that he, going forward with the spade, would see a curious coiled brownish pile on the black soil, which suddenly would start up, hiss, and dazzle rapidly away, hissing. One day Winifred heard the strangest scream from the flower-bed under the low window of the living room : ah, the strangest scream, like the very soul of the dark past crying aloud. She ran out, and saw a long brown snake on the flower-bed, and in its flat mouth the one hind leg of a frog was striving to escape, and screaming its strange, tiny, bellowing scream. She looked at the snake, and from its sullen flat head it looked at her, obstinately. She gave a cry, and it released the frog and slid angrily away.

That was Crockham. The spear of modern invention had not passed through it, and it lay there secret, primitive, savage as when the Saxons first came. And Egbert and she were caught there, caught out of the world.

He was not idle, nor was she. There were plenty of things to be done, the house to be put into final repair after the workmen had gone, cushions and curtains to sew, the paths to make, the water to fetch and attend to, and then the slope of the deep-soiled, neglected garden to level, to terrace with little terraces and paths, and to fill with flowers. He worked away, in his shirt-sleeves, worked all day intermittently doing this thing and the other. And she, quiet and rich in herself, seeing him stooping and labouring away by himself, would come to help him, to be near him. He of course was an amateur—a born amateur. He worked so hard, and did so little, and nothing he ever did would hold together for long. If he terraced the garden, he held up the earth with a couple of long narrow planks that soon began to bend with the pressure from behind, and would not need many years to rot through and break and let the soil slither all down again in a heap towards the stream-bed. But there you are. He had not been brought up to come to grips with anything, and he thought it would do. Nay, he did not think there was anything else except little temporary contrivances possible, he who had such a passion for his old enduring cottage, and for the old enduring things of the bygone England. Curious that the sense of permanency in the past had such a hold over him, whilst in the present he was all amateurish and sketchy.

Winifred could not criticize him. Town-bred, everything seemed to her splendid, and the very digging and shovelling itself seemed romantic. But neither Egbert nor she yet realized the difference between work and romance.

Godfrey Marshall, her father, was at first perfectly pleased with the ménage down at Crockham Cottage. He thought Egbert was wonderful, the many things he accomplished, and he was gratified by the glow of physical passion between the two young people. To the man who in London still worked hard to keep steady his modest fortune, the thought of this young couple digging away and loving one another down at Crockham Cottage, buried deep among the commons and marshes, near the pale-showing bulk of the downs, was like a chapter of living romance. And they drew the sustenance for their fire of passion from him, from the old man. It was he who fed their flame. He triumphed secretly in the thought. And it was to her father that Winifred still turned, as the one source of all surety and life and support. She loved Egbert with passion. But behind her was the power of her father. It was the power of her father she referred to, whenever she needed to refer. It never occurred to her to refer to Egbert, if she were in difficulty or doubt. No, in all the *serious* matters she depended on her father.

For Egbert had no intention of coming to grips with life. He had no ambition whatsoever. He came from a decent family, from a pleasant country home, from delightful surroundings. He should, of course, have had a profession. He should have studied law or entered business in some way. But no—that fatal three pounds a week would keep him from starving as long as he lived, and he did not want to give himself into bondage. It was not that he was idle. He was always doing something, in his amateurish way. But he had no desire to give himself to the world, and still less had he any desire to fight his way in the world. No, no, the world wasn't worth it. He wanted to ignore it, to go his own way apart, like a casual pilgrim down the forsaken side-tracks. He loved his wife, his cottage and garden. He would make his life there, as a sort of epicurean hermit. He loved the past, the old music and dances and customs of old England. He would try and live in the spirit of these, not in the spirit of the world of business.

But often Winifred's father called her to London : for he loved to have his children round him. So Egbert and she must have a tiny flat in town, and the young couple must transfer themselves from time to time from the country to the city. In town Egbert had plenty of friends, of the same ineffectual sort as himself, tampering with the arts, literature, painting, sculpture, music. He was not bored.

Three pounds a week, however, would not pay for all this. Winifred's father paid. He liked paying. He made her only a very small allowance, but he often gave her ten pounds—or gave Egbert ten pounds. So they both looked on the old man as the mainstay. Egbert didn't mind being patronized and paid for. Only when he felt the family was a little *too* condescending, on account of money, he began to get huffy.

Then of course children came : a lovely little blonde daughter with a head of thistle-down. Everybody adored the child. It was the first exquisite blonde thing that had come into the family, a little mite with the white, slim, beautiful limbs of its father, and as it grew up the dancing, dainty movement of a wild little daisy-spirit. No wonder the Marshalls all loved the child : they called her Joyce. They themselves had their own grace, but it was slow, rather heavy. They had every one of them strong, heavy limbs and darkish skins, and they were short in stature. And now they had for one of their own this light little cowslip child. She was like a little poem in herself.

But nevertheless, she brought a new difficulty. Winifred must have a nurse for her. Yes, yes, there must be a nurse. It was the family decree. Who was to pay for the nurse ? The grandfather— seeing the father himself earned no money. Yes, the grandfather would pay, as he had paid all the lying-in expenses. There came a slight sense of money-strain. Egbert was living on his father-in-law.

After the child was born, it was never quite the same between him and Winifred. The difference was at first hardly perceptible. But it was there. In the first place Winifred had a new centre of interest. She was not going to adore her child. But she had what the modern mother so often has in the place of spontaneous love : a profound sense of duty towards her child. Winifred appreciated her darling little girl, and felt a deep sense of duty towards her. Strange, that this sense of duty should go deeper than the love for her husband. But so it was. And so it often is. The responsibility of motherhood was the prime responsibility in Winifred's heart : the responsibility of wifehood came a long way second.

Her child seemed to link her up again in a circuit with her own family. Her father and mother, herself, and her child, that was the human trinity for her. Her husband——? Yes, she loved him still. But that was like play. She had an almost barbaric sense of duty and of family. Till she married, her first human duty had been towards her father : he was the pillar, the source of life, the everlasting support. Now another link was added to the chain of duty : her father, herself, and her child.

Egbert was out of it. Without anything happening, he was gradually, unconsciously excluded from the circle. His wife still loved him, physically. But, but—he was *almost* the unnecessary party in the affair. He could not complain of Winifred. She still did her duty towards him. She still had a physical passion for him, that physical passion on which he had put all his life and soul. But—but——

It was for a long while an ever-recurring *but*. And then, after the second child, another blonde, winsome touching little thing, not so proud and flame-like as Joyce—after Annabel came, then Egbert began truly to realize how it was. His wife still loved him. But—and now the but had grown enormous—her physical love for him was of secondary importance to her. It became ever less important. After all, she had had it, this physical passion, for two years now. It was not this that one lived from. No, no—something sterner, realer.

She began to resent her own passion for Egbert—just a little she began to despise it. For after all there he was, he was charming, he was lovable, he was terribly desirable. But—but—oh, the awful looming cloud of that *but* !—he did not stand firm in the landscape of her life like a tower of strength, like a great pillar of significance. No, he was like a cat one has about the house, which will one day disappear and leave no trace. He was like a flower in the garden, trembling in the wind of life, and then gone, leaving nothing to show. As an adjunct, as an accessory, he was perfect. Many a woman would have adored to have him about her all her life, the most beautiful and desirable of all her possessions. But Winifred belonged to another school.

The years went by, and instead of coming more to grips with life, he relaxed more. He was of a subtle, sensitive, passionate nature. But he simply *would* not give himself to what Winifred called life, *Work*. No, he would not go into the world and work for money. No, he just would not. If Winifred liked to live beyond their small income—well, it was her look-out.

And Winifred did not really want him to go out into the world to work for money. Money became, alas, a word like a firebrand between them, setting them both aflame with anger. But that is because we must talk in symbols. Winifred did not really care about money. She did not care whether he earned or did not earn anything. Only she knew she was dependent on her father for three-fourths of the money spent for herself and her children, that she let that be the *casus belli*, the drawn weapon between herself and Egbert.

What did she want—what did she want? Her mother once said to her, with that characteristic touch of irony : " Well, dear, if it is your fate to consider the lilies, that toil not, neither do they spin, that is one destiny among many others, and perhaps not so unpleasant as most. Why do you take it amiss, my child ? "

The mother was subtler than her children, they very rarely knew how to answer her. So Winifred was only more confused. It was not a question of lilies. At least, if it were a question of lilies, then her children were the little blossoms. They at least *grew*. Doesn't Jesus say : " Consider the lilies *how they grow*." Good then, she had her growing babies. But as for that other tall, handsome flower of a father of theirs, he was full grown already, so she did not want to spend her life considering him in the flower of his days.

No, it was not that he didn't earn money. It was not that he was idle. He was *not* idle. He was always doing something, always working away, down at Crockham, doing little jobs. But, oh dear, the little jobs—the garden paths—the gorgeous flowers—the chairs to mend, old chairs to mend !

It was that he stood for nothing. If he had done something unsuccessfully, and *lost* what money they had ! If he had but striven with something. Nay, even if he had been wicked, a waster, she would have been more free. She would have had something to resist, at least. A waster stands for something, really. He says : " No, I will not aid and abet society in this business of increase and hanging together, I will upset the apple-cart as much as I can, in my small way." Or else he says : " No, I will *not* bother about others. If I have lusts, they are my own, and I prefer them to other people's virtues." So, a waster, a scamp, takes a sort of stand. He exposes himself to opposition and final castigation : at any rate in story-books.

But Egbert ! What are you to do with a man like Egbert ? He had no vices. He was really kind, nay generous. And he was not weak. If he had been weak Winifred could have been kind to him. But he did not even give her that consolation. He was not weak, and he did not want her consolation or her kindness. No, thank you. He was of a fine passionate temper, and of a rarer steel than she. He knew it, and she knew it. Hence she was only the more baffled and maddened, poor thing. He, the higher, the finer, in his way the stronger, played with his garden, and his old folk-songs and Morris-dances, just played, and let her support the pillars of the future on her own heart.

And he began to get bitter, and a wicked look began to come on his face. He did not give in to her ; not he. There were seven devils inside his long, slim, white body. He was healthy, full of restrained life. Yes, even he himself had to lock up his own vivid life inside himself, now she would not take it from him. Or rather, now that she only took it occasionally. For she had to yield at times. She loved him so, she desired him so, he was so exquisite to her, the fine creature that he was, finer than herself. Yes, with a groan she had to give in to her own unquenched passion for him. And he came to her then—ah, terrible, ah, wonderful, sometimes she wondered how either of them could live after the terror of the passion that swept between them. It was to her as if pure lightning, flash after flash, went through every fibre of her, till extinction came.

But it is the fate of human beings to live on. And it is the fate of clouds that seem nothing but bits of vapour slowly to pile up, to pile up and fill the heavens and blacken the sun entirely.

So it was. The love came back, the lightning of passion flashed tremendously between them. And there was blue sky and gorgeousness for a little while. And then, as inevitably, as inevitably, slowly the clouds began to edge up again above the horizon, slowly, slowly to lurk about the heavens, throwing an occasional cold and hateful shadow : slowly, slowly to congregate, to fill the empyrean space.

And as the years passed, the lightning cleared the sky more and more rarely, less and less the blue showed. Gradually the grey lid sank down upon them, as if it would be permanent.

Why didn't Egbert do something, then? Why didn't he come to grips with life? Why wasn't he like Winifred's father, a pillar of society, even if a slender, exquisite column? Why didn't he go into harness of some sort? Why didn't he take *some* direction?

Well, you can bring an ass to the water, but you cannot make him drink. The world was the water and Egbert was the ass. And he wasn't having any. He couldn't : he just couldn't. Since necessity did not force him to work for his bread and butter, he would not work for work's sake. You can't make the columbine flowers nod in January, nor make the cuckoo sing in England at Christmas. Why? It isn't his season. He doesn't want to. Nay, he *can't* want to.

And there it was with Egbert. He couldn't link up with the world's work, because the basic desire was absent from him. Nay, at the bottom of him he had an even stronger desire : to hold aloof. To hold aloof. To do nobody any damage. But to hold aloof. It was not his season.

Perhaps he should not have married and had children. But you can't stop the waters flowing.

Which held true for Winifred, too. She was not made to endure aloof. Her family tree was a robust vegetation that had to be stirring and believing. In one direction or another her life *had* to go. In her own home she had known nothing of this diffidence which she found in Egbert, and which she could not understand, and which threw her into such dismay. What was she to do, what was she to do, in face of this terrible diffidence?

It was all so different in her own home. Her father may have had his own misgivings, but he kept them to himself. Perhaps he had no very profound belief in this world of ours, this society which we have elaborated with so much effort, only to find ourselves elaborated to death at last. But Godfrey Marshall was of tough, rough fibre, not without a vein of healthy cunning through it all. It was for him a question of winning through, and leaving the rest to heaven. Without having many illusions to grace him, he still *did* believe in heaven. In a dark and unquestioning way, he had a sort of faith : an acrid faith like the sap of some not-to-be-exterminated tree. Just a blind acrid faith as sap is blind and acrid, and yet pushes on in growth and in faith. Perhaps he was unscrupulous, but only as a striving tree is unscrupulous, pushing its single way in a jungle of others.

In the end, it is only this robust, sap-like faith which keeps man going. He may live on for many generations inside the shelter of the social establishment which he has erected for himself, as pear-trees and currant bushes would go on bearing fruit for many seasons, inside a walled garden, even if the race of man were suddenly exterminated. But bit by bit the wall-fruit-trees would gradually pull down the very walls that sustained them. Bit by bit every establishment collapses, unless it is renewed or restored by living hands, all the while.

Egbert could not bring himself to any more of this restoring or renewing business. He was not aware of the fact : but awareness doesn't help much, anyhow. He just couldn't. He had the stoic and epicurean quality of his old, fine breeding. His father-in-law, however, though he was not one bit more of a fool than Egbert, realized that since we are here we may as well live. And so he applied himself to his own tiny section of the social work, and to doing the best for his family, and to leaving the rest to the ultimate will of heaven. A certain robustness of blood made him able to go on. But sometimes even from him spurted a sudden gall of bitterness against the world and its make-up. And yet—he had his own will-to-succeed, and this carried him through. He refused to ask himseli what the success would amount to. It amounted to the estate down in Hampshire, and his children lacking for nothing, and himself of some importance in the world : and *basta !*—Basta ! Basta !

Nevertheless do not let us imagine that he was a common pusher. He was not. He knew as well as Egbert what disillusion meant. Perhaps in his soul he had the same estimation of success. But he had a certain acrid courage, and a certain will-to-power. In his own small circle he would emanate power, the single power of his own blind self. With all his spoiling of his children, he was still the father of the old English type. He was too wise to make laws and to domineer in the abstract. But he had kept, and all honour to him, a certain primitive dominion over the souls of his children, the old, almost magic prestige of paternity. There it was, still burning in him, the old smoky torch of paternal godhead.

And in the sacred glare of this torch his children had been brought up. He had given the girls every liberty, at last. But he had never really let them go beyond his power. And they, venturing out into the hard white light of our fatherless world, learned to see with the eyes of the world. They learned to criticize their father, even, from some effulgence of worldly white light, to see him as inferior. But this was all very well in the head. The moment they forgot their tricks of criticism, the old red glow of his authority came over them again. He was not to be quenched.

Let the psycho-analyst talk about father complex. It is just a word invented. Here was a man who had kept alive the old red flame of fatherhood, fatherhood that had even the right to sacrifice the child to God, like Isaac. Fatherhood that had life-and-death authority over the children : a great natural power. And till his children could be brought under some other great authority as girls ; or could arrive at manhood and become themselves centres of the same power, continuing the same male mystery as men ; until such time, willy-nilly, Godfrey Marshall would keep his children.

It had seemed as if he might lose Winifred. Winifred had *adored* her husband, and looked up to him as to something wonderful. Perhaps she had expected in him another great authority, a male authority greater, finer than her father's. For having once known the glow of male power, she would not easily turn to the cold white light of feminine independence. She would hunger, hunger all her life for the warmth and shelter of true male strength.

And hunger she might, for Egbert's power lay in the abnegation of power. He was himself the living negative of power. Even of responsibility. For the negation of power at last means the negation of responsibility. As far as these things went, he would confine himself to himself. He would try to confine his own *influence* even to himself. He would try, as far as possible, to abstain from in-fluencing his children by assuming any responsibility for them. " A little child shall lead them——" His child should lead, then. He would try not to make it go in any direction whatever. He would abstain from influencing it. Liberty !—

Poor Winifred was like a fish out of water in this liberty, gasping for the denser element which should contain her. Till her child came. And then she knew that she must be responsible for it, that she must have authority over it.

But here Egbert, silently and negatively, stepped in. Silently, negatively, but fatally he neutralized her authority over her children.

There was a third little girl born. And after this Winifred wanted no more children. Her soul was turning to salt.

So she had charge of the children, they were her responsibility. The money for them had come from her father. She would do her very best for them, and have command over their life and death. But no ! Egbert would not take the responsibility. He would not even provide the money. But he would not let her have her way. Her dark, silent, passionate authority he would not allow. It was a battle between them, the battle between liberty and the old blood-power. And of course he won. The little girls loved him and adored him. " Daddy ! Daddy ! " They could do as they liked with him. Their mother would have ruled them. She would have ruled them passionately, with indulgence, with the old dark magic of parental authority, something looming and unquestioned and, after all, divine: if we believe in divine authority. The Marshalls did, being Catholic.

And Egbert, he turned her old dark, Catholic blood-authority into a sort of tyranny. He would not leave her her children. He stole them from her, and yet without assuming responsibility for them. He stole them from her, in emotion and spirit, and left her only to command their behaviour. A thankless lot for a mother. And her children adored him, adored him, little knowing the empty bitterness they were preparing for themselves when they too grew up to have husbands : husbands such as Egbert, adorable and null.

Joyce, the eldest, was still his favourite. She was now a quicksilver little thing of six years old. Barbara, the youngest, was a toddler of two years. They spent most of their time down at Crockham, because he wanted to be there. And even Winifred loved the place really. But now, in her frustrated and blinded state, it was full of menace for her children. The adders, the poison-berries, the brook, the marsh, the water that might not be pure—one thing and another. From mother and nurse it was a guerilla gunfire of commands, and blithe, quicksilver disobedience from the three blonde, never-still little girls. Behind the girls was the father, against mother and nurse. And so it was.

" If you don't come quick, nurse, I shall run out there to where there are snakes."

" Joyce, you *must* be patient. I'm just changing Annabel."

There you are. There it was : always the same. Working away on the common across the brook he heard it. And he worked on, just the same.

Suddenly he heard a shriek, and he flung the spade from him and started for the bridge, looking up like a startled deer. Ah, there was Winifred—Joyce had hurt herself. He went on up the garden.

" What is it ? "

The child was still screaming—now it was—" Daddy ! Daddy ! Oh—oh, Daddy ! " And the mother was saying :

" Don't be frightened, darling. Let mother look."

But the child only cried :

" Oh, Daddy, Daddy, Daddy ! "

She was terrified by the sight of the blood running from her own knee. Winifred crouched down, with her child of six in her lap, to examine the knee. Egbert bent over also.

" Don't make such a noise, Joyce," he said irritably. " How did she do it ? "

" She fell on that sickle thing which you left lying about after cutting the grass," said Winifred, looking into his face with bitter accusation as he bent near.

He had taken his handkerchief and tied it round the knee. Then he lifted the still sobbing child in his arms, and carried her into the house and upstairs to her bed. In his arms she became quiet. But his heart was burning with pain and with guilt. He had left the sickle there lying on the edge of the grass, and so his first-born child whom he loved so dearly had come to hurt. But then it was an accident—it was an accident. Why should he feel guilty ? It would probably be nothing, better in two or three days. Why take it to heart, why worry ? He put it aside.

The child lay on the bed in her little summer frock, her face very white now after the shock. Nurse had come carrying the youngest child : and little Annabel stood holding her skirt. Winifred, terribly serious and wooden-seeming, was bending over the knee, from which she had taken his blood-soaked handkerchief. Egbert bent forward, too, keeping more sang-froid in his face than in his heart. Winifred went all of a lump of seriousness, so he had to keep some reserve. The child moaned and whimpered.

The knee was still bleeding profusely—it was a deep cut right in the joint.

" You'd better go for the doctor, Egbert," said Winifred bitterly.

" Oh, no ! Oh, no ! " cried Joyce in a panic.

" Joyce, my darling, don't cry ! " said Winifred, suddenly catching the little girl to her breast in a strange tragic anguish, the *Mater Dolorata*. Even the child was frightened into silence. Egbert looked at the tragic figure of his wife with the child at her breast, and turned away. Only Annabel started suddenly to cry : " Joycey, Joycey, don't have your leg bleeding ! "

Egbert rode four miles to the village for the doctor. He could not help feeling that Winifred was laying it on rather. Surely the knee itself wasn't hurt ! Surely not. It was only a surface cut.

The doctor was out. Egbert left the message and came cycling swiftly home, his heart pinched with anxiety. He dropped sweating off his bicycle and went into the house, looking rather small, like a man who is at fault. Winifred was upstairs sitting by Joyce, who was looking pale and important in bed, and was eating some tapioca pudding. The pale, small, scared face of his child went to Egbert's heart.

" Doctor Wing was out. He'll be here about half-past two," said Egbert.

" I don't want him to come," whimpered Joyce.

"Joyce, dear, you must be patient and quiet," said Winifred. " He won't hurt you. But he will tell us what to do to make your knee better quickly. That is why he must come."

Winifred always explained carefully to her little girls : and it always took the words off their lips for the moment.

" Does it bleed yet ? " said Egbert.

Winifred moved the bedclothes carefully aside.

" I think not," she said.

Egbert stooped also to look.

" No, it doesn't," he said. Then he stood up with a relieved look on his face. He turned to the child.

" Eat your pudding, Joyce," he said. " It won't be anything. You've only got to keep still for a few days."

" You haven't had your dinner, have you, Daddy ? "

" Not yet."

" Nurse will give it to you," said Winifred.

" You'll be all right, Joyce," he said, smiling to the child and pushing the blonde hair aside off her brow. She smiled back winsomely into his face.

He went downstairs and ate his meal alone. Nurse served him. She liked waiting on him. All women liked him and liked to do things for him.

The doctor came—a fat country practitioner, pleasant and kind. " What, little girl, been tumbling down, have you ? There's a thing to be doing, for a smart little lady like you ! What ! And cutting your knee ! Tut-tut-tut ! That *wasn't* clever of you, now was it ? Never mind, never mind, soon be better. Let us look at it. Won't hurt you. Not the least in life. Bring a bowl with a little warm water, nurse. Soon have it all right again, soon have it all right."

Joyce smiled at him with a pale smile of faint superiority. This was *not* the way in which she was used to being talked to.

He bent down, carefully looking at the little, thin, wounded knee of the child. Egbert bent over him.

" Oh, dear, oh, dear ! Quite a deep little cut. Nasty little cut. Nasty little cut. But, never mind. Never mind, little lady. We'll soon have it better. Soon have it better, little lady. What's your name ? "

" My name is Joyce," said the child distinctly.

" Oh, really ! " he replied. " Oh, really ! Well, that's a fine name too, in my opinion. Joyce, eh ?—And how old might Miss Joyce be ? Can she tell me that ? "

" I'm six," said the child, slightly amused and very condescending.

" Six ! There now. Add up and count as far as six, can you ? Well, that's a clever little girl, a clever little girl. And if she has to drink a spoonful of medicine, she won't make a murmur, I'll be bound. Not like *some* little girls. What ? Eh ? "

" I take it if mother wishes me to," said Joyce.

" Ah, there now ! That's the style ! That's what I like to hear from a little lady in bed because she's cut her knee. That's the style——"

The comfortable and prolix doctor dressed and bandaged the knee and recommended bed and a light diet for the little lady. He thought a week or a fortnight would put it right. No bones or ligatures damaged—fortunately. Only a flesh cut. He would come again in a day or two.

So Joyce was reassured and stayed in bed and had all her toys up. Her father often played with her. The doctor came the third day. He was fairly pleased with the knee. It was healing. It was healing—yes—yes. Let the child continue in bed. He came again after a day or two. Winifred was a trifle uneasy. The wound seemed to be healing on the top, but it hurt the child too much. It didn't look quite right. She said so to Egbert.

" Egbert, I'm sure Joyce's knee isn't healing properly."

" I think it is," he said. " I think it's all right."

" I'd rather Doctor Wing came again—I don't feel satisfied."

" Aren't you trying to imagine it worse than it really is ? "

" You would say so, of course. But I shall write a post card to Doctor Wing now."

The doctor came next day. He examined the knee. Yes, there was inflammation. Yes, there *might* be a little septic poisoning—there might. There might. Was the child feverish ?

So a fortnight passed by, and the child *was* feverish, and the knee was more inflamed and grew worse and was painful, painful. She cried in the night, and her mother had to sit up with her. Egbert still insisted it was nothing, really—it would pass. But in his heart he was anxious.

Winifred wrote again to her father. On Saturday the elderly man appeared. And no sooner did Winifred see the thick, rather short figure in its grey suit than a great yearning came over her.

" Father, I'm not satisfied with Joyce. I'm not satisfied with Doctor Wing."

"Well, Winnie, dear, if you're not satisfied we must have further advice, that is all."

The sturdy, powerful, elderly man went upstairs, his voice sounding rather grating through the house, as if it cut upon the tense atmosphere.

"How are you, Joyce, darling?" he said to the child. "Does your knee hurt you? Does it hurt you, dear?"

"It does sometimes." The child was shy of him, cold towards him.

"Well, dear, I'm sorry for that. I hope you try to bear it, and not trouble mother too much."

There was no answer. He looked at the knee. It was red and stiff.

"Of course," he said, "I think we must have another doctor's opinion. And if we're going to have it, we had better have it at once. Egbert, do you think you might cycle in to Bingham for Doctor Wayne? I found him *very* satisfactory for Winnie's mother."

"I can go if you think it necessary," said Egbert.

"Certainly I think it necessary. Even if there *is* nothing, we can have peace of mind. Certainly I think it necessary. I should like Doctor Wayne to come this evening if possible."

So Egbert set off on his bicycle through the wind, like a boy sent on an errand, leaving his father-in-law a pillar of assurance, with Winifred.

Doctor Wayne came, and looked grave. Yes, the knee was certainly taking the wrong way. The child might be lame for life.

Up went the fire of fear and anger in every heart. Doctor Wayne came again the next day for a proper examination. And, yes, the knee had really taken bad ways. It should be X-rayed. It was very important.

Godfrey Marshall walked up and down the lane with the doctor, beside the standing motor-car : up and down, up and down in one of those consultations of which he had had so many in his life.

As a result he came indoors to Winifred.

"Well, Winnie, dear, the best thing to do is to take Joyce up to London, to a nursing home where she can have proper treatment. Of course this knee has been allowed to go wrong. And apparently there is a risk that the child may even lose her leg. What do you think, dear? You agree to our taking her up to town and putting her under the best care?"

"Oh, father, you *know* I would do anything on earth for her."

"I know you would, Winnie darling. The pity is that there has been this unfortunate delay already. I can't think what Doctor Wing was doing. Apparently the child is in danger of losing her leg. Well then, if you will have everything ready, we will take her up to town to-morrow. I will order the large car from Denley's to be here at ten. Egbert, will you take a telegram at once to Doctor Jackson? It is a small nursing home for children and for surgical cases, not far from Baker Street. I'm sure Joyce will be all right there."

" Oh, father, can't I nurse her myself? "

" Well, darling, if she is to have proper treatment, she had best be in a home. The X-ray treatment, and the electric treatment, and whatever is necessary."

" It will cost a great deal——" said Winifred.

" We can't think of cost, if the child's leg is in danger—or even her life. No use speaking of cost," said the elder man impatiently.

And so it was. Poor Joyce, stretched out on a bed in the big closed motor-car—the mother sitting by her head, the grandfather in his short grey beard and a bowler hat, sitting by her feet, thick, and implacable in his responsibility—they rolled slowly away from Crockham, and from Egbert who stood there bareheaded and a little ignominious, left behind. He was to shut up the house and bring the rest of the family back to town, by train, the next day.

Followed a dark and bitter time. The poor child. The poor, poor child, how she suffered, an agony and a long crucifixion in that nursing home. It was a bitter six weeks which changed the soul of Winifred for ever. As she sat by the bed of her poor, tortured little child, tortured with the agony of the knee, and the still worse agony of these diabolic, but perhaps necessary modern treatments, she felt her heart killed and going cold in her breast. Her little Joyce, her frail, brave, wonderful, little Joyce, frail and small and pale as a white flower ! Ah, how had she, Winifred, dared to be so wicked, so wicked, so careless, so sensual.

" Let my heart die ! Let my woman's heart of flesh die ! Saviour, let my heart die. And save my child. Let my heart die from the world and from the flesh. Oh, destroy my heart that is so wayward. Let my heart of pride die. Let my heart die."

She prayed beside the bed of her child. And like the Mother with the seven swords in her breast, slowly her heart of pride and passion died in her breast, bleeding away. Slowly it died, bleeding away, and she turned to the Church for comfort, to Jesus, to the Mother of God, but most of all, to that great and enduring institution, the Roman Catholic Church. She withdrew into the shadow of the Church. She was a mother with three children. But in her soul she died, her heart of pride and passion and desire bled to death, her soul belonged to her Church, her body belonged to her duty as a mother.

Her duty as a wife did not enter. As a wife she had no sense of duty : only a certain bitterness towards the man with whom she had known such sensuality and distraction. She was purely the *Mater Dolorata*. To the man she was closed as a tomb.

Egbert came to see his child. But Winifred seemed to be always seated there, like the tomb of his manhood and his fatherhood. Poor Winifred : she was still young, still strong and ruddy and beautiful like a ruddy hard flower of the field. Strange—her ruddy, healthy face, so sombre, and her strong, heavy, full-blooded body, so still. She, a nun ! Never. And yet the gates of her heart and soul had shut in his face with a slow, resonant clang, shutting him out for ever. There was no need for her to go into a convent. Her will had done it.

And between this young mother and this young father lay the crippled child, like a bit of pale silk floss on the pillow, and a little white pain-quenched face. He could not bear it. He just could not bear it. He turned aside. There was nothing to do but to turn aside. He turned aside, and went hither and thither, desultory. He was still attractive and desirable. But there was a little frown between his brow as if he had been cleft there with a hatchet : cleft right in, for ever, and that was the stigma.

The child's leg was saved : but the knee was locked stiff. The fear now was lest the lower leg should wither, or cease to grow. There must be long-continued massage and treatment, daily treatment, even when the child left the nursing home. And the whole of the expense was borne by the grandfather.

Egbert now had no real home. Winifred with the children and nurse was tied to the little flat in London. He could not live there : he could not contain himself. The cottage was shut-up—or lent to friends. He went down sometimes to work in his garden and keep the place in order. Then with the empty house around him at night, all the empty rooms, he felt his heart go wicked. The sense of frustration and futility, like some slow, torpid snake, slowly bit right through his heart. Futility, futility, futility : the horrible marsh-poison went through his veins and killed him.

As he worked in the garden in the silence of day he would listen for a sound. No sound. No sound of Winifred from the dark inside of the cottage : no sound of children's voices from the air, from the common, from the near distance. No sound, nothing but the old dark marsh-venomous atmosphere of the place. So he worked spasmodically through the day, and at night made a fire and cooked some food alone.

He was alone. He himself cleaned the cottage and made his bed. But his mending he did not do. His shirts were slit on the shoulders, when he had been working, and the white flesh showed through. He would feel the air and the spots of rain on his exposed flesh. And he would look again across the common, where the dark, tufted gorse was dying to seed, and the bits of cat-heather were coming pink in tufts, like a sprinkling of sacrificial blood.

His heart went back to the savage old spirit of the place : the desire for old gods, old, lost passions, the passion of the cold-blooded, darting snakes that hissed and shot away from him, the mystery of blood-sacrifices, all the lost, intense sensations of the primeval people of the place, whose passions seethed in the air still, from those long days before the Romans came. The seethe of a lost, dark passion in the air. The presence of unseen snakes.

A queer, baffled, half-wicked look came on his face. He could not stay long at the cottage. Suddenly he must swing on to his bicycle and go—anywhere. Anywhere, away from the place. He would stay a few days with his mother in the old home. His mother adored him and grieved as a mother would. But the little, baffled, half-wicked smile curled on his face, and he swung away from his mother's solicitude as from everything else.

Always moving on—from place to place, friend to friend : and always swinging away from sympathy. As soon as sympathy, like a soft hand, was reached out to touch him, away he swerved, instinctively, as a harmless snake swerves and swerves and swerves away from an outstretched hand. Away he must go. And periodically he went back to Winifred.

He was terrible to her now, like a temptation. She had devoted herself to her children and her Church. Joyce was once more on her feet ; but, alas ! lame, with iron supports to her leg, and a little crutch. It was strange how she had grown into a long, pallid, wild little thing. Strange that the pain had not made her soft and docile, but had brought out a wild, almost mænad temper in the child. She was seven, and long and white and thin, but by no means subdued. Her blonde hair was darkening. She still had long sufferings to face, and, in her own childish consciousness, the stigma of her lameness to bear.

And she bore it. An almost mænad courage seemed to possess

her, as if she were a long, thin, young weapon of life. She acknowledged all her mother's care. She would stand by her mother for ever.
But some of her father's fine-tempered desperation flashed in her.

When Egbert saw his little girl limping horribly—not only limping
but lurching horribly in crippled, childish way, his heart again
hardened with chagrin, like steel that is tempered again. There
was a tacit understanding between him and his little girl : not
what we would call love, but a weapon-like kinship. There was a
tiny touch of irony in his manner towards her, contrasting sharply
with Winifred's heavy, unleavened solicitude and care. The child
flickered back to him with an answering little smile of irony and
recklessness : an odd flippancy which made Winifred only the more
sombre and earnest.

The Marshalls took endless thought and trouble for the child,
searching out every means to save her limb and her active freedom.
They spared no effort and no money, they spared no strength of
will. With all their slow, heavy power of will they willed that Joyce
should save her liberty of movement, should win back her wild, free
grace. Even if it took a long time to recover, it should be recovered.

So the situation stood. And Joyce submitted, week after week,
month after month, to the tyranny and pain of the treatment.
She acknowledged the honourable effort on her behalf. But her
flamy reckless spirit was her father's. It was he who had all the
glamour for her. He and she were like members of some forbidden
secret society who know one another but may not recognize one
another. Knowledge they had in common, the same secret of life,
the father and the child. But the child stayed in the camp of her
mother, honourably, and the father wandered outside like Ishmael,
only coming sometimes to sit in the home for an hour or two, an
evening or two beside the camp fire, like Ishmael, in a curious
silence and tension, with the mocking answer of the desert speaking
out of his silence, and annulling the whole convention of the domestic
home.

His presence was almost an anguish to Winifred. She prayed
against it. That little cleft between his brow, that flickering, wicked
little smile that seemed to haunt his face, and above all, the triumphant loneliness, the Ishmael quality. And then the erectness of his
supple body, like a symbol. The very way he stood, so quiet, so
insidious, like an erect, supple symbol of life, the living body, con-
fronting her downcast soul, was torture to her. He was like a supple
living idol moving before her eyes, and she felt if she watched him
she was damned.

And he came and made himself at home in her little home. When he was there, moving in his own quiet way, she felt as if the whole great law of sacrifice, by which she had elected to live, were annulled. He annulled by his very presence the laws of her life. And what did he substitute ? Ah, against that question she hardened herself in recoil.

It was awful to her to have to have him about—moving about in his shirt-sleeves, speaking in his tenor, throaty voice to the children. Annabel simply adored him, and he teased the little girl. The baby, Barbara, was not sure of him. She had been born a stranger to him. But even the nurse, when she saw his white shoulder of flesh through the slits of his torn shirt, thought it a shame.

Winifred felt it was only another weapon of his against her.

" You have other shirts—why do you wear that old one that is all torn, Egbert ? " she said.

" I may as well wear it out," he said subtly.

He knew she would not offer to mend it for him. She *could* not. And no, she would not. Had she not her own gods to honour ? And could she betray them, submitting to his Baal and Ashtaroth ? And it was terrible to her, his unsheathed presence, that seemed to annul her and her faith, like another revelation. Like a gleaming idol evoked against her, a vivid life-idol that might triumph.

He came and he went—and she persisted. And then the great war broke out. He was a man who could not go to the dogs. He could not dissipate himself. He was pure-bred in his Englishness, and even when he would have liked to be vicious, he could not.

So when the war broke out his whole instinct was against it : against war. He had not the faintest desire to overcome any foreigners or to help in their death. He had no conception of Imperial England, and Rule Britannia was just a joke to him. He was a pure-blooded Englishman, perfect in his race, and when he was truly himself he could no more have been aggressive on the score of his Englishness than a rose can be aggressive on the score of its rosiness.

No, he had no desire to defy Germany and to exalt England. The distinction between German and English was not for him the distinction between good and bad. It was the distinction between blue water-flowers and red or white bush-blossoms : just difference. The difference between the wild boar and the wild bear. And a man was good or bad according to his nature, not according to his nationality.

Egbert was well-bred, and this was part of his natural understanding. It was merely unnatural to him to hate a nation *en bloc*. Certain individuals he disliked, and others he liked, and the mass he knew nothing about. Certain deeds he disliked, certain deeds seemed natural to him, and about most deeds he had no particular feeling.

He had, however, the one deepest pure-bred instinct. He recoiled inevitably from having his feelings dictated to him by the mass feeling. His feelings were his own, his understanding was his own, and he would never go back on either, willingly. Shall a man become inferior to his own true knowledge and self, just because the mob expects it of him?

What Egbert felt subtly and without question, his father-in-law felt also in a rough, more combative way. Different as the two men were, they were two real Englishmen, and their instincts were almost the same.

And Godfrey Marshall had the world to reckon with. There was German military aggression, and the English non-military idea of liberty and the "conquests of peace"—meaning industrialism. Even if the choice between militarism and industrialism were a choice of evils, the elderly man asserted his choice of the latter, perforce. He whose soul was quick with the instinct of power.

Egbert just refused to reckon with the world. He just refused even to decide between German militarism and British industrialism. He chose neither. As for atrocities, he despised the people who committed them, as inferior criminal types. There was nothing national about crime.

And yet, war! War! Just war! Not right or wrong, but just war itself. Should he join? Should he give himself over to war? The question was in his mind for some weeks. Not because he thought England was right and Germany wrong. Probably Germany was wrong, but he refused to make a choice. Not because he felt inspired. No. But just—war.

The deterrent was, the giving himself over into the power of other men, and into the power of the mob-spirit of a democratic army. Should he give himself over? Should he make over his own life and body to the control of something which he *knew* was inferior, in spirit, to his own self? Should he commit himself into the power of an inferior control? Should he? Should he betray himself?

He was going to put himself into the power of his inferiors, and he knew it. He was going to subjugate himself. He was going to be ordered about by petty *canaille* of non-commissioned officers—and even commissioned officers. He who was born and bred free. Should he do it?

H

He went to his wife, to speak to her.

" Shall I join up, Winifred ? "

She was silent. Her instinct also was dead against it. And yet a certain profound resentment made her answer :

" You have three children dependent on you. I don't know whether you have thought of that."

It was still only the third month of the war, and the old pre-war ideas were still alive.

" Of course. But it won't make much difference to them. I shall be earning a shilling a day, at least."

" You'd better speak to father, I think," she replied heavily.

Egbert went to his father-in-law. The elderly man's heart was full of resentment.

" I should say," he said rather sourly, " it is the best thing you could do."

Egbert went and joined up immediately, as a private soldier. He was drafted into the light artillery.

Winifred now had a new duty towards him : the duty of a wife towards a husband who is himself performing his duty towards the world. She loved him still. She would always love him, as far as earthly love went. But it was duty she now lived by. When he came back to her in khaki, a soldier, she submitted to him as a wife. It was her duty. But to his passion she could never again fully submit. Something prevented her, for ever : even her own deepest choice.

He went back again to camp. It did not suit him to be a modern soldier. In the thick, gritty, hideous khaki his subtle physique was extinguished as if he had been killed. In the ugly intimacy of the camp his thorough-bred sensibilities were just degraded. But he had chosen, so he accepted. An ugly little look came on to his face, of a man who has accepted his own degradation.

In the early spring Winifred went down to Crockham to be there when primroses were out, and the tassels hanging on the hazel-bushes. She felt something like a reconciliation towards Egbert, now he was a prisoner in camp most of his days. Joyce was wild with delight at seeing the garden and the common again, after the eight or nine months of London and misery. She was still lame. She still had the irons up her leg. But she lurched about with a wild, crippled agility.

Egbert came for a week-end, in his gritty, thick, sandpaper khaki and puttees and the hideous cap. Nay, he looked terrible. And on his face a slightly impure look, a little sore on his lip, as if he had eaten too much or drunk too much or let his blood become a little unclean. He was almost uglily healthy, with the camp life. It did not suit him.

Winifred waited for him in a little passion of duty and sacrifice, willing to serve the soldier, if not the man. It only made him feel a little more ugly inside. The week-end was torment to him : the memory of the camp, the knowledge of the life he led there ; even the sight of his own legs in that abhorrent khaki. He felt as if the hideous cloth went into his blood and made it gritty and dirty. Then Winifred so ready to serve the *soldier*, when she repudiated the man. And this made the grit worse between his teeth. And the children running around playing and calling in the rather mincing fashion of children who have nurses and governesses and literature in the family. And Joyce so lame ! It had all become unreal to him, after the camp. It only set his soul on edge. He left at dawn on the Monday morning, glad to get back to the realness and vulgarity of the camp.

Winifred would never meet him again at the cottage—only in London, where the world was with them. But sometimes he came alone to Crockham, perhaps when friends were staying there. And then he would work awhile in his garden. This summer still it would flame with blue anchusas and big red poppies, the mulleins would sway their soft, downy erections in the air : he loved mulleins : and the honeysuckle would stream out scent like memory, when the owl was whooing. Then he sat by the fire with the friends and with Winifred's sisters, and they sang the folk-songs. He put on thin civilian clothes and his charm and his beauty and the supple dominancy of his body glowed out again. But Winifred was not there.

At the end of the summer he went to Flanders, into action. He seemed already to have gone out of life, beyond the pale of life. He hardly remembered his life any more, being like a man who is going to take a jump from a height, and is only looking to where he must land.

He was twice slightly wounded, in two months. But not enough to put him off duty for more than a day or two. They were retiring again, holding the enemy back. He was in the rear—three machine-guns. The country was all pleasant, war had not yet trampled it. Only the air seemed shattered, and the land awaiting death. It was a small, unimportant action in which he was engaged.

The guns were stationed on a little bushy hillock just outside a village. But occasionally, it was difficult to say from which direction came the sharp crackle of rifle-fire, and beyond, the far-off thud of cannon. The afternoon was wintry and cold.

A lieutenant stood on a little iron platform at the top of the ladders, taking the sights and giving the aim, calling in a high, tense, mechanical voice. Out of the sky came the sharp cry of the directions, then the warning numbers, then " Fire ! " The shot went, the piston of the gun sprang back, there was a sharp explosion, and a very faint film of smoke in the air. Then the other two guns fired, and there was a lull. The officer was uncertain of the enemy's position. The thick clump of horse-chestnut trees below was without change. Only in the far distance the sound of heavy firing continued, so far off as to give a sense of peace.

The gorse bushes on either hand were dark, but a few sparks of flowers showed yellow. He noticed them almost unconsciously as he waited, in the lull. He was in his shirt-sleeves, and the air came chill on his arms. Again his shirt was slit on the shoulders, and the flesh showed through. He was dirty and unkempt. But his face was quiet. So many things go out of consciousness before we come to the end of consciousness.

Before him, below, was the highroad, running between high banks of grass and gorse. He saw the whitish, muddy tracks and deep scores in the road, where the part of the regiment had retired. Now all was still. Sounds that came, came from the outside. The place where he stood was still silent, chill, serene : the white church among the trees beyond seemed like a thought only.

He moved into a lightning-like mechanical response at the sharp cry from the officer overhead. Mechanism, the pure mechanical action of obedience at the guns. Pure mechanical action at the guns. It left the soul unburdened, brooding in dark nakedness. In the end, the soul is alone, brooding on the face of the uncreated flux, as a bird on a dark sea.

Nothing could be seen but the road, and a crucifix knocked slanting and the dark, autumnal fields and woods. There appeared three horsemen on a little eminence, very small, on the crest of a ploughed field. They were our own men. Of the enemy, nothing.

The lull continued. Then suddenly came sharp orders, and a new direction of the guns, and an intense, exciting activity. Yet at the centre the soul remained dark and aloof, alone.

But even so, it was the soul that heard the new sound : the new, deep " papp ! " of a gun that seemed to touch right upon the soul. He kept up the rapid activity at the machine-gun, sweating. But in his soul was the echo of the new, deep sound, deeper than life.

And in confirmation came the awful faint whistling of a shell, advancing almost suddenly into a piercing, tearing shriek that would tear through the membrane of life. He heard it in his ears, but he heard it also in his soul, in tension. There was relief when the thing had swung by and struck, away beyond. He heard the hoarseness of its explosion, and the voice of the soldier calling to the horses. But he did not turn round to look. He only noticed a twig of holly with red berries fall like a gift on to the road below.

Not this time, not this time. Whither thou goest I will go. Did he say it to the shell, or to whom ? Whither thou goest I will go. Then, the faint whistling of another shell dawned, and his blood became small and still to receive it. It drew nearer, like some horrible blast of wind ; his blood lost consciousness. But in the second of suspension he saw the heavy shell swoop to earth, into the rocky bushes on the right, and earth and stones poured up into the sky. It was as if he heard no sound. The earth and stones and fragments of bush fell to earth again, and there was the same un-changing peace. The Germans had got the aim.

Would they move now ? Would they retire ? Yes. The officer was giving the last lightning-rapid orders to fire before withdrawing. A shell passed unnoticed in the rapidity of action. And then, into the silence, into the suspense where the soul brooded, finally crashed a noise and a darkness and a moment's flaming agony and horror. Ah, he had seen the dark bird flying towards him, flying home this time. In one instant life and eternity went up in a conflagration of agony, then there was a weight of darkness.

When faintly something began to struggle in the darkness, a consciousness of himself, he was aware of a great load and a clanging sound. To have known the moment of death ! And to be forced, before dying, to review it. So, fate, even in death.

There was a resounding of pain. It seemed to sound from the outside of his consciousness : like a loud bell clanging very near. Yet he knew it was himself. He must associate himself with it. After a lapse and a new effort, he identified a pain in his head, a large pain that clanged and resounded. So far he could identify himself with himself. Then there was a lapse.

After a time he seemed to wake up again, and waking, to know that he was at the front, and that he was killed. He did not open his eyes. Light was not yet his. The clanging pain in his head rang out the rest of his consciousness. So he lapsed away from consciousness, in unutterable sick abandon of life.

Bit by bit, like a doom, came the necessity to know. He was hit in the head. It was only a vague surmise at first. But in the swinging of the pendulum of pain, swinging ever nearer and nearer, to touch him into an agony of consciousness and a consciousness of agony, gradually the knowledge emerged—he must be hit in the head—hit on the left brow ; if so, there would be blood—was there blood ?—could he feel blood in his left eye ? Then the clanging seemed to burst the membrane of his brain, like death-madness.

Was there blood on his face ? Was hot blood flowing ? Or was it dry blood congealing down his cheek ? It took him hours even to ask the question : time being no more than an agony in darkness, without measurement.

A long time after he had opened his eyes he realized he was seeing something—something, something, but the effort to recall what was too great. No, no ; no recall !

Were they the stars in the dark sky ? Was it possible it was stars in the dark sky ? Stars ? The world ? Ah, no, he could not know it ! Stars and the world were gone for him, he closed his eyes. No stars, no sky, no world. No, no ! The thick darkness of blood alone. It should be one great lapse into the thick darkness of blood in agony.

Death, oh, death ! The world all blood, and the blood all writhing with death. The soul like the tiniest little light out on a dark sea, the sea of blood. And the light guttering, beating, pulsing in a windless storm, wishing it could go out, yet unable.

There had been life. There had been Winifred and his children. But the frail death-agony effort to catch at straws of memory, straws of life from the past, brought on too great a nausea. No, no ! No Winifred, no children. No world, no people. Better the agony of dissolution ahead than the nausea of the effort backwards. Better the terrible work should go forward, the dissolving into the black sea of death, in the extremity of dissolution, than that there should be any reaching back towards life. To forget ! To forget ! Utterly, utterly to forget, in the great forgetting of death. To break the core and the unit of life, and to lapse out on the great darkness. Only that. To break the clue, and mingle and commingle with the one darkness, without afterwards or forwards. Let the black sea of death itself solve the problem of futurity. Let the will of man break and give up.

What was that ? A light ! A terrible light ! Was it figures ? Was it legs of a horse colossal—colossal above him : huge, huge ?

The Germans heard a slight noise, and started. Then, in the glare of a light-bomb, by the side of the heap of earth thrown up by the shell, they saw the dead face.

I

THEY had marched more than thirty kilometres since dawn, along the white, hot road where occasional thickets of trees threw a moment of shade, then out into the glare again. On either hand, the valley, wide and shallow, glittered with heat ; dark green patches of rye, pale young corn, fallow and meadow and black pine woods spread in a dull, hot diagram under a glistening sky. But right in front the mountains ranged across, pale blue and very still, snow gleaming gently out of the deep atmosphere. And towards the mountains, on and on, the regiment marched between the rye fields and the meadows, between the scraggy fruit trees set regularly on either side the high road. The burnished, dark green rye threw off a suffocating heat, the mountains drew gradually nearer and more distinct. While the feet of the soldiers grew hotter, sweat ran through their hair under their helmets, and their knapsacks could burn no more in contact with their shoulders, but seemed instead to give off a cold, prickly sensation.

He walked on and on in silence, staring at the mountains ahead, that rose sheer out of the land, and stood fold behind fold, half earth, half heaven, the heaven, the barrier with slits of soft snow, in the pale, bluish peaks.

He could now walk almost without pain. At the start, he had determined not to limp. It had made him sick to take the first steps, and during the first mile or so, he had compressed his breath, and the cold drops of sweat had stood on his forehead. But he had walked it off. What were they after all but bruises ! He had looked at them, as he was getting up : deep bruises on the backs of his thighs. And since he had made his first step in the morning, he had been conscious of them, till now he had a tight, hot place in his chest, with suppressing the pain, and holding himself in. There seemed no air when he breathed. But he walked almost lightly.

The Captain's hand had trembled at taking his coffee at dawn : his orderly saw it again. And he saw the fine figure of the Captain

wheeling on horseback at the farm-house ahead, a handsome figure
in pale blue uniform with facings of scarlet, and the metal gleaming
on the black helmet and the sword-scabbard, and dark streaks of
sweat coming on the silky bay horse. The orderly felt he was connected with that figure moving so suddenly on horseback : he
followed it like a shadow, mute and inevitable and damned by it.
And the officer was always aware of the tramp of the company
behind, the march of his orderly among the men.

The Captain was a tall man of about forty, grey at the temples.
He had a handsome, finely knit figure, and was one of the best horsemen in the West. His orderly, having to rub him down, admired the
amazing riding-muscles of his loins.

For the rest, the orderly scarcely noticed the officer any more
than he noticed himself. It was rarely he saw his master's face :
he did not look at it. The Captain had reddish brown, stiff hair, that
he wore short upon his skull. His moustache was also cut short and
bristly over a full, brutal mouth. His face was rather rugged, the
cheeks thin. Perhaps the man was the more handsome for the deep
lines in his face, the irritable tension of his brow, which gave him the
look of a man who fights with life. His fair eyebrows stood bushy
over light blue eyes that were always flashing with cold fire.

He was a Prussian aristocrat, haughty and overbearing. But his
mother had been a Polish Countess. Having made too many
gambling debts when he was young, he had ruined his prospects in the Army, and remained an infantry captain. He had never
married : his position did not allow of it, and no woman had ever
moved him to it. His time he spent riding—occasionally he rode
one of his own horses at the races—and at the officers' club. Now
and then he took himself a mistress. But after such an event, he
returned to duty with his brow still more tense, his eyes still more
hostile and irritable. With the men, however, he was merely impersonal, though a devil when roused ; so that, on the whole,
they feared him, but had no great aversion from him. They
accepted him as the inevitable.

To his orderly he was at first cold and just and indifferent : he
did not fuss over trifles. So that his servant knew practically nothing
about him, except just what orders he would give, and how he
wanted them obeyed. That was quite simple. Then the change
gradually came.

The orderly was a youth of about twenty-two, of medium height,
and well built. He had strong, heavy limbs, was swarthy, with a
soft, black, young moustache. There was something altogether

warm and young about him. He had firmly marked eyebrows over
dark, expressionless eyes, that seemed never to have thought, only
to have received life direct through his senses, and acted straight
from instinct.

Gradually the officer had become aware of his servant's young,
vigorous, unconscious presence about him. He could not get away
from the sense of the youth's person, while he was in attendance.
It was like a warm flame upon the older man's tense, rigid body,
that had become almost unliving, fixed. There was something so
free and self-contained about him, and something in the young
fellow's movement, that made the officer aware of him. And this
irritated the Prussian. He did not choose to be touched into life
by his servant. He might easily have changed his man, but he did
not. He now very rarely looked direct at his orderly, but kept his
face averted, as if to avoid seeing him. And yet as the young soldier
moved unthinking about the apartment, the elder watched him,
and would notice the movement of his strong young shoulders
under the blue cloth, the bend of his neck. And it irritated him.
To see the soldier's young, brown, shapely peasant's hand grasp the
loaf or the wine-bottle sent a flash of hate or of anger through the
elder man's blood. It was not that the youth was clumsy : it
was rather the blind, instinctive sureness of movement of an un-
hampered young animal that irritated the officer to such a degree.

Once, when a bottle of wine had gone over, and the red gushed
out on to the tablecloth, the officer had started up with an oath,
and his eyes, bluey like fire, had held those of the confused youth for
a moment. It was a shock for the young soldier. He felt something
sink deeper, deeper into his soul, where nothing had ever gone
before. It left him rather blank and wondering. Some of his natural
completeness in himself was gone, a little uneasiness took its place.
And from that time an undiscovered feeling had held between the
two men.

Henceforward the orderly was afraid of really meeting his master.
His subconsciousness remembered those steely blue eyes and the
harsh brows, and did not intend to meet them again. So he always
stared past his master, and avoided him. Also, in a little anxiety,
he waited for the three months to have gone, when his time would be
up. He began to feel a constraint in the Captain's presence, and
the soldier even more than the officer wanted to be left alone, in his
neutrality as servant.

He had served the Captain for more than a year, and knew his
duty. This he performed easily, as if it were natural to him. The

officer and his commands he took for granted, as he took the sun and the rain, and he served as a matter of course. It did not implicate him personally.

But now if he were going to be forced into a personal interchange with his master he would be like a wild thing caught, he felt he must get away.

But the influence of the young soldier's being had penetrated through the officer's stiffened discipline, and perturbed the man in him. He, however, was a gentleman, with long, fine hands and cultivated movements, and was not going to allow such a thing as the stirring of his innate self. He was a man of passionate temper, who had always kept himself suppressed. Occasionally there had been a duel, an outburst before the soldiers. He knew himself to be always on the point of breaking out. But he kept himself hard to the idea of the Service. Whereas the young soldier seemed to live out his warm, full nature, to give it off in his very movements, which had a certain zest, such as wild animals have in free movement. And this irritated the officer more and more.

In spite of himself, the Captain could not regain his neutrality of feeling towards his orderly. Nor could he leave the man alone. In spite of himself, he watched him, gave him sharp orders, tried to take up as much of his time as possible. Sometimes he flew into a rage with the young soldier, and bullied him. Then the orderly shut himself off, as it were out of earshot, and waited, with sullen, flushed face, for the end of the noise. The words never pierced to his intelligence, he made himself, protectively, impervious to the feelings of his master.

He had a scar on his left thumb, a deep seam going across the knuckle. The officer had long suffered from it, and wanted to do something to it. Still it was there, ugly and brutal on the young, brown hand. At last the Captain's reserve gave way. One day, as the orderly was smoothing out the tablecloth, the officer pinned down his thumb with a pencil, asking :

" How did you come by that ? "

The young man winced and drew back at attention.

" A wood axe, Herr Hauptmann," he answered.

The officer waited for further explanation. None came. The orderly went about his duties. The elder man was sullenly angry. His servant avoided him. And the next day he had to use all his will-power to avoid seeing the scarred thumb. He wanted to get hold of it and—— A hot flame ran in his blood.

He knew his servant would soon be free, and would be glad. As yet, the soldier had held himself off from the elder man. The Captain grew madly irritable. He could not rest when the soldier was away, and when he was present, he glared at him with tormented eyes. He hated those fine, black brows over the unmeaning, dark eyes, he was infuriated by the free movement of the handsome limbs, which no military discipline could make stiff. And he became harsh and cruelly bullying, using contempt and satire. The young soldier only grew more mute and expressionless.

" What cattle were you bred by, that you can't keep straight eyes ? Look me in the eyes when I speak to you."

And the soldier turned his dark eyes to the other's face, but there was no sight in them : he stared with the slightest possible cast, holding back his sight, perceiving the blue of his master's eyes, but receiving no look from them. And the elder man went pale, and his reddish eyebrows twitched. He gave his order, barrenly.

Once he flung a heavy military glove into the young soldier's face. Then he had the satisfaction of seeing the black eyes flare up into his own, like a blaze when straw is thrown on a fire. And he had laughed with a little tremor and a sneer.

But there were only two months more. The youth instinctively tried to keep himself intact : he tried to serve the officer as if the latter were an abstract authority and not a man. All his instinct was to avoid personal contact, even definite hate. But in spite of himself the hate grew, responsive to the officer's passion. However, he put it in the background. When he had left the Army he could dare acknowledge it. By nature he was active, and had many friends. He thought what amazing good fellows they were. But, without knowing it, he was alone. Now this solitariness was intensified. It would carry him through his term. But the officer seemed to be going irritably insane, and the youth was deeply frightened.

The soldier had a sweetheart, a girl from the mountains, independent and primitive. The two walked together, rather silently. He went with her, not to talk, but to have his arm round her, and for the physical contact. This eased him, made it easier for him to ignore the Captain ; for he could rest with her held fast against his chest. And she, in some unspoken fashion, was there for him. They loved each other.

The Captain perceived it, and was mad with irritation. He kept the young man engaged all the evenings long, and took pleasure in the dark look that came on his face. Occasionally, the eyes of the two men met, those of the younger sullen and dark, doggedly unalterable, those of the elder sneering with restless contempt.

The officer tried hard not to admit the passion that had got hold of him. He would not know that his feeling for his orderly was anything but that of a man incensed by his stupid, perverse servant. So, keeping quite justified and conventional in his consciousness, he let the other thing run on. His nerves, however, were suffering. At last he slung the end of a belt in his servant's face. When he saw the youth start back, the pain-tears in his eyes and the blood on his mouth, he had felt at once a thrill of deep pleasure and of shame.

But this, he acknowledged to himself, was a thing he had never done before. The fellow was too exasperating. His own nerves must be going to pieces. He went away for some days with a woman.

It was a mockery of pleasure. He simply did not want the woman. But he stayed on for his time. At the end of it, he came back in an agony of irritation, torment, and misery. He rode all the evening, then came straight in to supper. His orderly was out. The officer sat with his long, fine hands lying on the table, perfectly still, and all his blood seemed to be corroding.

At last his servant entered. He watched the strong, easy young figure, the fine eyebrows, the thick black hair. In a week's time the youth had got back his old well-being. The hands of the officer twitched and seemed to be full of mad flame. The young man stood at attention, unmoving, shut off.

The meal went in silence. But the orderly seemed eager. He made a clatter with the dishes.

" Are you in a hurry? " asked the officer, watching the intent, warm face of his servant. The other did not reply.

" Will you answer my question ? " said the Captain.

" Yes, sir," replied the orderly, standing with his pile of deep Army plates. The Captain waited, looked at him, then asked again :

" Are you in a hurry ? "

" Yes, sir," came the answer, that sent a flash through the listener.

" For what ? "

" I was going out, sir."

" I want you this evening."

There was a moment's hesitation. The officer had a curious stiffness of countenance.

" Yes, sir," replied the servant, in his throat.

" I want you to-morrow evening also—in fact you may consider your evenings occupied, unless I give you leave."

The mouth with the young moustache set close.

" Yes, sir," answered the orderly, loosening his lips for a moment. He again turned to the door.

" And why have you a piece of pencil in your ear ? "

The orderly hesitated, then continued on his way without answering. He set the plates in a pile outside the door, took the stump of pencil from his ear, and put it in his pocket. He had been copying a verse for his sweetheart's birthday card. He returned to finish clearing the table. The officer's eyes were dancing, he had a little, eager smile.

" Why have you a piece of pencil in your ear ? " he asked.

The orderly took his hands full of dishes. His master was standing near the great green stove, a little smile on his face, his chin thrust forward. When the young soldier saw him his heart suddenly ran hot. He felt blind. Instead of answering, he turned dazedly to the door. As he was crouching to set down the dishes, he was pitched forward by a kick from behind. The pots went in a stream down the stairs, he clung to the pillar of the banisters. And as he was rising he was kicked heavily again and again, so that he clung sickly to the post for some moments. His master had gone swiftly into the room and closed the door. The maid-servant downstairs looked up the staircase and made a mocking face at the crockery disaster.

The officer's heart was plunging. He poured himself a glass of wine, part of which he spilled on the floor, and gulped the remainder, leaning against the cool, green stove. He heard his man collecting the dishes from the stairs. Pale, as if intoxicated, he waited. The servant entered again. The Captain's heart gave a pang, as of pleasure, seeing the young fellow bewildered and uncertain on his feet, with pain.

" Schöner ! " he said.

The soldier was a little slower in coming to attention.

" Yes, sir ! "

The youth stood before him, with pathetic young moustache, and fine eyebrows very distinct on his forehead of dark marble.

" I asked you a question."

" Yes, sir."

The officer's tone bit like acid.

" Why had you a pencil in your ear ? "

Again the servant's heart ran hot, and he could not breathe. With dark, strained eyes, he looked at the officer, as if fascinated. And he stood there sturdily planted, unconscious. The withering smile came into the Captain's eyes, and he lifted his foot.

" I—I forgot it—sir," panted the soldier, his dark eyes fixed on the other man's dancing blue ones.

" What was it doing there ? "

He saw the young man's breast heaving as he made an effort for words.

" I had been writing."

" Writing what ? "

Again the soldier looked him up and down. The officer could hear him panting. The smile came into the blue eyes. The soldier worked his dry throat, but could not speak. Suddenly the smile lit like a flame on the officer's face, and a kick came heavily against the orderly's thigh. The youth moved a pace sideways. His face went dead, with two black, staring eyes.

" Well ? " said the officer.

The orderly's mouth had gone dry, and his tongue rubbed in it as on dry brown-paper. He worked his throat. The officer raised his foot. The servant went stiff.

" Some poetry, sir," came the crackling, unrecognizable sound of his voice.

" Poetry, what poetry ? " asked the Captain, with a sickly smile.

Again there was the working in the throat. The Captain's heart had suddenly gone down heavily, and he stood sick and tired.

" For my girl, sir," he heard the dry, inhuman sound.

" Oh ! " he said, turning away. " Clear the table."

" Click ! " went the soldier's throat ; then again, " click ! " and then the half-articulate :

" Yes, sir."

The young soldier was gone, looking old, and walking heavily.

The officer, left alone, held himself rigid, to prevent himself from thinking. His instinct warned him that he must not think. Deep inside him was the intense gratification of his passion, still working powerfully. Then there was a counter-action, a horrible breaking down of something inside him, a whole agony of reaction. He stood there for an hour motionless, a chaos of sensations, but rigid with a will to keep blank his consciousness, to prevent his mind grasping. And he held himself so until the worst of the stress had passed, when he began to drink, drank himself to an intoxication, till he slept obliterated. When he woke in the morning he was shaken to the base of his nature. But he had fought off the realization of what he had done. He had prevented his mind from taking it in, had suppressed it along with his instincts, and the conscious man had nothing to do with it. He felt only as after a bout of intoxication, weak, but the affair itself all dim and not to be recovered. Of the drunkenness of his passion he successfully refused remembrance. And when his orderly appeared with coffee, the officer assumed the same self he had had the morning before. He refused the event of the past night—denied it had ever been—and was successful in his denial. He had not done any such thing—not he himself. Whatever there might be lay at the door of a stupid, insubordinate servant.

The orderly had gone about in a stupor all the evening. He drank some beer because he was parched, but not much, the alcohol made his feeling come back, and he could not bear it. He was dulled, as if nine-tenths of the ordinary man in him were inert. He crawled about disfigured. Still, when he thought of the kicks, he went sick, and when he thought of the threat of more kicking, in the room afterwards, his heart went hot and faint, and he panted, remembering the one that had come. He had been forced to say, " For my girl." He was much too done even to want to cry. His mouth hung slightly open, like an idiot's. He felt vacant, and wasted. So, he wandered at his work, painfully, and very slowly and clumsily, fumbling blindly with the brushes, and finding it difficult, when he sat down, to summon the energy to move again. His limbs, his jaw, were slack and nerveless. But he was very tired. He got to bed at last, and slept inert, relaxed, in a sleep that was rather stupor than slumber, a dead night of stupefaction shot through with gleams of anguish.

In the morning were the manœuvres. But he woke even before the bugle sounded. The painful ache in his chest, the dryness of his throat, the awful steady feeling of misery made his eyes come awake and dreary at once. He knew, without thinking, what had happened. And he knew that the day had come again, when he must go on with his round. The last bit of darkness was being pushed out of the room. He would have to move his inert body and go on. He was so young, and had known so little trouble, that he was bewildered. He only wished it would stay night, so that he could lie still, covered up by the darkness. And yet nothing would prevent the day from coming, nothing would save him from having to get up and saddle the Captain's horse, and make the Captain's coffee. It was there, inevitable. And then, he thought, it was impossible. Yet they would not leave him free. He must go and take the coffee to the Captain. He was too stunned to understand it. He only knew it was inevitable—inevitable, however long he lay inert.

At last, after heaving at himself, for he seemed to be a mass of inertia, he got up. But he had to force every one of his movements from behind, with his will. He felt lost, and dazed, and helpless. Then he clutched hold of the bed, the pain was so keen. And looking at his thighs he saw the darker bruises on his swarthy flesh, and he knew that if he pressed one of his fingers on one of the bruises, he should faint. But he did not want to faint—he did not want anybody to know. No one should ever know. It was between him and the Captain. There were only the two people in the world now—himself and the Captain.

Slowly, economically, he got dressed and forced himself to walk. Everything was obscure, except just what he had his hands on. But he managed to get through his work. The very pain revived his dull senses. The worst remained yet. He took the tray and went up to the Captain's room. The officer, pale and heavy, sat at the table. The orderly, as he saluted, felt himself put out of existence. He stood still for a moment submitting to his own nullification—then he gathered himself, seemed to regain himself, and then the Captain began to grow vague, unreal, and the younger soldier's heart beat up. He clung to this situation—that the Captain did not exist—so that he himself might live. But when he saw his officer's hand tremble as he took the coffee, he felt everything falling shattered. And he went away, feeling as if he himself were coming to pieces, disintegrated. And when the Captain was there on horseback, giving orders, while he himself stood, with rifle and knapsack, sick with pain, he felt as if he must shut his eyes—as if he must shut his eyes on everything. It was only the long agony of marching with a parched throat that filled him with one single, sleep-heavy intention : to save himself.

II

He was getting used even to his parched throat. That the snowy peaks were radiant among the sky, that the whity-green glacier-river twisted through its pale shoals, in the valley below, seemed almost supernatural. But he was going mad with fever and thirst. He plodded on uncomplaining. He did not want to speak, not to anybody. There were two gulls, like flakes of water and snow, over the river. The scent of green rye soaked in sunshine came like a sickness. And the march continued, monotonously, almost like a bad sleep.

At the next farm-house, which stood low and broad near the high road, tubs of water had been put out. The soldiers clustered round to drink. They took off their helmets, and the steam mounted from their wet hair. The Captain sat on horseback, watching. He needed to see his orderly. His helmet threw a dark shadow over his light, fierce eyes, but his moustache and mouth and chin were distinct in the sunshine. The orderly must move under the presence of the figure of the horseman. It was not that he was afraid, or cowed. It was as if he was disembowelled, made empty, like an empty shell. He felt himself as nothing, a shadow creeping under the sunshine. And, thirsty as he was, he could scarcely drink, feeling the Captain near him. He would not take off his helmet to wipe his wet hair. He wanted to stay in shadow, not to be forced into consciousness. Starting, he saw the light heel of the officer prick the belly of the horse ; the Captain cantered away, and he himself could relapse into vacancy.

Nothing, however, could give him back his living place in the hot, bright morning. He felt like a gap among it all. Whereas the Captain was prouder, overriding. A hot flash went through the young servant's body. The Captain was firmer and prouder with life, he himself was empty as a shadow. Again the flash went through him, dazing him out. But his heart ran a little firmer.

The company turned up the hill, to make a loop for the return. Below, from among the trees, the farm-bell clanged. He saw the labourers, mowing bare-foot at the thick grass, leave off their work and go downhill, their scythes hanging over their shoulders, like long, bright claws curving down behind them. They seemed like dream-people, as if they had no relation to himself. He felt as in a blackish dream : as if all the other things were there and had form, but he himself was only a consciousness, a gap that could think and perceive.

The soldiers were tramping silently up the glaring hill-side. Gradually his head began to revolve, slowly, rhythmically. Sometimes it was dark before his eyes, as if he saw this world through a smoked glass, frail shadows and unreal. It gave him a pain in his head to walk.

The air was too scented, it gave no breath. All the lush green-stuff seemed to be issuing its sap, till the air was deathly, sickly with the smell of greenness. There was the perfume of clover, like pure honey and bees. Then there grew a faint acrid tang—they were near the beeches ; and then a queer clattering noise, and a suffocating, hideous smell ; they were passing a flock of sheep, a shepherd in a black smock, holding his crook. Why should the sheep huddle together under this fierce sun ? He felt that the shepherd would not see him, though he could see the shepherd.

At last there was the halt. They stacked rifles in a conical stack, put down their kit in a scattered circle around it, and dispersed a little, sitting on a small knoll high on the hill-side. The chatter began. The soldiers were steaming with heat, but were lively. He sat still, seeing the blue mountains rising upon the land, twenty kilometres away. There was a blue fold in the ranges, then out of that, at the foot, the broad, pale bed of the river, stretches of whity-green water between pinkish-grey shoals among the dark pine woods. There it was, spread out a long way off. And it seemed to come downhill, the river. There was a raft being steered, a mile away. It was a strange country. Nearer, a red-roofed, broad farm with white base and square dots of windows crouched beside the wall of beech foliage on the wood's edge. There were long strips of rye and clover and pale green corn. And just at his feet, below the knoll, was a darkish bog, where globe flowers stood breathless still on their slim stalks. And some of the pale gold bubbles were burst, and a broken fragment hung in the air. He thought he was going to sleep.

Suddenly something moved into this coloured mirage before his eyes. The Captain, a small, light-blue and scarlet figure, was trotting evenly between the strips of corn, along the level brow of the hill. And the man making flag-signals was coming on. Proud and sure moved the horseman's figure, the quick, bright thing, in which was concentrated all the light of this morning, which for the rest lay a fragile, shining shadow. Submissive, apathetic, the young soldier sat and stared. But as the horse slowed to a walk, coming up the last steep path, the great flash flared over the body and soul of the orderly. He sat waiting. The back of his head felt as if it were weighted with a heavy piece of fire. He did not want to eat. His hands trembled slightly as he moved them. Meanwhile the officer on horseback was approaching slowly and proudly. The tension grew in the orderly's soul. Then again, seeing the Captain ease himself on the saddle, the flash blazed through him.

The Captain looked at the patch of light blue and scarlet, and dark heads, scattered closely on the hill-side. It pleased him. The command pleased him. And he was feeling proud. His orderly was among them in common subjection. The officer rose a little on his stirrups to look. The young soldier sat with averted, dumb face. The Captain relaxed on his seat. His slim-legged, beautiful horse, brown as a beech nut, walked proudly uphill. The Captain passed into the zone of the company's atmosphere : a hot smell of men, of sweat, of leather. He knew it very well. After a word with the lieutenant, he went a few paces higher, and sat there, a dominant figure, his sweat-marked horse swishing its tail, while he looked down on his men, on his orderly, a nonentity among the crowd.

The young soldier's heart was like fire in his chest, and he breathed with difficulty. The officer, looking downhill, saw three of the young soldiers, two pails of water between them, staggering across a sunny green field. A table had been set up under a tree, and there the slim lieutenant stood, importantly busy. Then the Captain summoned himself to an act of courage. He called his orderly.

The flame leapt into the young soldier's throat as he heard the command, and he rose blindly, stifled. He saluted, standing below the officer. He did not look up. But there was the flicker in the Captain's voice.

" Go to the inn and fetch me . . . " the officer gave his commands. " Quick ! " he added.

At the last word, the heart of the servant leapt with a flash, and he felt the strength come over his body. But he turned in mechanical obedience, and set off at a heavy run downhill, looking almost like a bear, his trousers bagging over his military boots. And the officer watched this blind, plunging run all the way.

But it was only the outside of the orderly's body that was obeying so humbly and mechanically. Inside had gradually accumulated a core into which all the energy of that young life was compact and concentrated. He executed his commission, and plodded quickly back uphill. There was a pain in his head as he walked that made him twist his features unknowingly. But hard there in the centre of his chest was himself, himself, firm, and not to be plucked to pieces.

The Captain had gone up into the wood. The orderly plodded through the hot, powerfully smelling zone of the company's atmosphere. He had a curious mass of energy inside him now. The Captain was less real than himself. He approached the green entrance to the wood. There, in the half-shade, he saw the horse standing, the sunshine and the flickering shadow of leaves dancing over his brown body. There was a clearing where timber had lately been felled. Here, in the gold-green shade beside the brilliant cup of sunshine, stood two figures, blue and pink, the bits of pink showing out plainly. The Captain was talking to his lieutenant.

The orderly stood on the edge of the bright clearing, where great trunks of trees, stripped and glistening, lay stretched like naked, brown-skinned bodies. Chips of wood littered the trampled floor, like splashed light, and the bases of the felled trees stood here and there, with their raw, level tops. Beyond was the brilliant, sunlit green of a beech.

"Then I will ride forward," the orderly heard his Captain say. The lieutenant saluted and strode away. He himself went forward. A hot flash passed through his belly, as he tramped towards his officer.

The Captain watched the rather heavy figure of the young soldier stumble forward, and his veins, too, ran hot. This was to be man to man between them. He yielded before the solid, stumbling figure with bent head. The orderly stooped and put the food on a level-sawn tree-base. The Captain watched the glistening, sun-inflamed, naked hands. He wanted to speak to the young soldier, but could not. The servant propped a bottle against his thigh, pressed open the cork, and poured out the beer into the mug. He kept his head bent. The Captain accepted the mug.

"Hot!" he said, as if amiably.

The flame sprang out of the orderly's heart, nearly suffocating him.

"Yes, sir," he replied, between shut teeth.

And he heard the sound of the Captain's drinking, and he clenched his fists, such a strong torment came into his wrists. Then came the faint clang of the closing of the pot-lid. He looked up. The Captain was watching him. He glanced swiftly away. Then he saw the officer stoop and take a piece of bread from the tree-base. Again the flash of flame went through the young soldier, seeing the stiff body stoop beneath him, and his hands jerked. He looked away. He could feel the officer was nervous. The bread fell as it was being broken. The officer ate the other piece. The two men stood tense and still, the master laboriously chewing his bread, the servant staring with averted face, his fist clenched.

Then the young soldier started. The officer had pressed open the lid of the mug again. The orderly watched the lid of the mug, and the white hand that clenched the handle, as if he were fascinated. It was raised. The youth followed it with his eyes. And then he saw the thin, strong throat of the elder man moving up and down as he drank, the strong jaw working. And the instinct which had been jerking at the young man's wrists suddenly jerked free. He jumped, feeling as if it were rent in two by a strong flame.

The spur of the officer caught in a tree-root, he went down backwards with a crash, the middle of his back thudding sickeningly against a sharp-edged tree-base, the pot flying away. And in a second the orderly, with serious, earnest young face, and under-lip between his teeth, had got his knee in the officer's chest and was pressing the chin backward over the farther edge of the tree-stump, pressing, with all his heart behind in a passion of relief, the tension of his wrists exquisite with relief. And with the base of his palms he shoved at the chin, with all his might. And it was pleasant, too, to have that chin, that hard jaw already slightly rough with beard, in his hands. He did not relax one hair's breadth, but, all the force of all his blood exulting in his thrust, he shoved back the head of the other man, till there was a little " cluck " and a crunching sensation. Then he felt as if his head went to vapour. Heavy convulsions shook the body of the officer, frightening and horrifying the young soldier. Yet it pleased him, too, to repress them. It pleased him to keep his hands pressing back the chin, to feel the chest of the other man yield in expiration to the weight of his strong, young knees, to feel the hard twitchings of the prostrate body jerking his own whole frame, which was pressed down on it.

But it went still. He could look into the nostrils of the other man, the eyes he could scarcely see. How curiously the mouth was pushed out, exaggerating the full lips, and the moustache bristling up from them. Then, with a start, he noticed the nostrils gradually filled with blood. The red brimmed, hesitated, ran over, and went in a thin trickle down the face to the eyes.

It shocked and distressed him. Slowly, he got up. The body twitched and sprawled there, inert. He stood and looked at it in silence. It was a pity *it* was broken. It represented more than the thing which had kicked and bullied him. He was afraid to look at the eyes. They were hideous now, only the whites showing, and the blood running to them. The face of the orderly was drawn with horror at the sight. Well, it was so. In his heart he was satisfied. He had hated the face of the Captain. It was extinguished now. There was a heavy relief in the orderly's soul. That was as it should be. But he could not bear to see the long, military body lying broken over the tree-base, the fine fingers crisped. He wanted to hide it away.

Quickly, busily, he gathered it up and pushed it under the felled tree-trunks, which rested their beautiful, smooth length either end on logs. The face was horrible with blood. He covered it with the helmet. Then he pushed the limbs straight and decent, and brushed the dead leaves off the fine cloth of the uniform. So, it lay quite still in the shadow under there. A little strip of sunshine ran along the breast, from a chink between the logs. The orderly sat by it for a few moments. Here his own life also ended.

Then, through his daze, he heard the lieutenant, in a loud voice, explaining to the men outside the wood, that they were to suppose the bridge on the river below was held by the enemy. Now they were to march to the attack in such and such a manner. The lieutenant had no gift of expression. The orderly, listening from habit, got muddled. And when the lieutenant began it all again he ceased to hear.

He knew he must go. He stood up. It surprised him that the leaves were glittering in the sun, and the chips of wood reflecting white from the ground. For him a change had come over the world. But for the rest it had not—all seemed the same. Only he had left it. And he could not go back. It was his duty to return with the beer-pot and the bottle. He could not. He had left all that. The lieutenant was still hoarsely explaining. He must go, or they would overtake him. And he could not bear contact with any one now.

He drew his fingers over his eyes, trying to find out where he was. Then he turned away. He saw the horse standing in the path. He went up to it and mounted. It hurt him to sit in the saddle. The pain of keeping his seat occupied him as they cantered through the wood. He would not have minded anything, but he could not get away from the sense of being divided from the others. The path led out of the trees. On the edge of the wood he pulled up and stood watching. There in the spacious sunshine of the valley soldiers were moving in a little swarm. Every now and then, a man harrowing on a strip of fallow shouted to his oxen, at the turn. The village and the white-towered church was small in the sunshine. And he no longer belonged to it—he sat there, beyond, like a man outside in the dark. He had gone out from everyday life into the unknown and he could not, he even did not want to go back.

Turning from the sun-blazing valley, he rode deep into the wood. Tree-trunks, like people standing grey and still, took no notice as he went. A doe, herself a moving bit of sunshine and shadow, went running through the flecked shade. There were bright green rents in the foliage. Then it was all pine wood, dark and cool. And he was sick with pain, he had an intolerable great pulse in his head, and he was sick. He had never been ill in his life. He felt lost, quite dazed with all this. ·

Trying to get down from the horse, he fell, astonished at the pain and his lack of balance. The horse shifted uneasily. He jerked its bridle and sent it cantering jerkily away. It was his last connection with the rest of things.

But he only wanted to lie down and not be disturbed. Stumbling through the trees, he came on a quiet place where beeches and pine trees grew on a slope. Immediately he had lain down and closed his eyes, his consciousness went racing on without him. A big pulse of sickness beat in him as if it throbbed through the whole earth. He was burning with dry heat. But he was too busy, too tearingly active in the incoherent race of delirium to observe.

III.

He came to with a start. His mouth was dry and hard, his heart beat heavily, but he had not the energy to get up. His heart beat heavily. Where was he?—the barracks—at home? There was something knocking. And, making an effort, he looked round— trees, and litter of greenery, and reddish, bright, still pieces of sunshine on the floor. He did not believe he was himself, he did not believe what he saw. Something was knocking. He made a struggle towards consciousness, but relapsed. Then he struggled again. And gradually his surroundings fell into relationship with himself. He knew, and a great pang of fear went through his heart. Somebody was knocking. He could see the heavy, black rags of a fir tree overhead. Then everything went black. Yet he did not believe he had closed his eyes. He had not. Out of the blackness sight slowly emerged again. And someone was knocking. Quickly, he saw the blood-disfigured face of his Captain, which he hated. And he held himself still with horror. Yet, deep inside him, he knew that it was so, the Captain should be dead. But the physical delirium got hold of him. Someone was knocking. He lay perfectly still, as if dead, with fear. And he went unconscious.

When he opened his eyes again he started, seeing something creeping swiftly up a tree-trunk. It was a little bird. And the bird was whistling overhead. Tap-tap-tap—it was the small, quick bird rapping the tree-trunk with its beak, as if its head were a little round hammer. He watched it curiously. It shifted sharply, in its creeping fashion. Then, like a mouse, it slid down the bare trunk. Its swift creeping sent a flash of revulsion through him. He raised his head. It felt a great weight. Then, the little bird ran out of the shadow across a still patch of sunshine, its little head bobbing swiftly, its white legs twinkling brightly for a moment. How neat it was in its build, so compact, with pieces of white on its wings. There were several of them. They were so pretty—but they crept like swift, erratic mice, running here and there among the beech-mast.

He lay down again exhausted, and his consciousness lapsed. He had a horror of the little creeping birds. All his blood seemed to be darting and creeping in his head. And yet he could not move.

He came to with a further ache of exhaustion. There was the pain in his head, and the horrible sickness, and his inability to move. He had never been ill in his life. He did not know where he was or what he was. Probably he had got sunstroke. Or what else?— he had silenced the Captain for ever—some time ago—oh, a long time ago. There had been blood on his face, and his eyes had turned upwards. It was all right, somehow. It was peace. But now he had got beyond himself. He had never been here before. Was it life, or not life? He was by himself. They were in a big, bright place, those others, and he was outside. The town, all the country, a big bright place of light : and he was outside, here, in the darkened open beyond, where each thing existed alone. But they would all have to come out there sometime, those others. Little, and left behind him, they all were. There had been father and mother and sweetheart. What did they all matter? This was the open land.

He sat up. Something scuffled. It was a little brown squirrel running in lovely undulating bounds over the floor, its red tail completing the undulation of its body—and then, as it sat up, furling and unfurling. He watched it, pleased. It ran on again, friskily, enjoying itself. It flew wildly at another squirrel, and they were chasing each other, and making little scolding, chattering noises. The soldier wanted to speak to them. But only a hoarse sound came out of his throat. The squirrels burst away—they flew up the trees. And then he saw the one peeping round at him, half-way up a tree-trunk. A start of fear went through him, though in so far as he was conscious, he was amused. It still stayed, its little keen face staring at him half way up the tree-trunk, its little ears pricked up, its clawey little hands clinging to the bark, its white breast reared. He started from it in panic.

Struggling to his feet, he lurched away. He went on walking, walking, looking for something—for a drink. His brain felt hot and inflamed for want of water. He stumbled on. Then he did not know anything. He went unconscious as he walked. Yet he stumbled on, his mouth open.

When, to his dumb wonder, he opened his eyes on the world again, he no longer tried to remember what it was. There was thick, golden light behind golden-green glitterings, and tall, grey-purple shafts, and darknesses further off, surrounding him, growing deeper. He was conscious of a sense of arrival. He was amid the reality, on the real, dark bottom. But there was the thirst burning in his brain. He felt lighter, not so heavy. He supposed it was newness. The air was muttering with thunder. He thought he was walking wonderfully swiftly and was coming straight to relief—or was it to water?

Suddenly he stood still with fear. There was a tremendous flare of gold, immense—just a few dark trunks like bars between him and it. All the young level wheat was burnished gold glaring on its silky green. A woman, full-skirted, a black cloth on her head for head-dress, was passing like a block of shadow through the glistening, green corn, into the full glare. There was a farm, too, pale blue in shadow, and the timber black. And there was a church spire, nearly fused away in the gold. The woman moved on, away from him. He had no language with which to speak to her. She was the bright, solid unreality. She would make a noise of words that would confuse him, and her eyes would look at him without seeing him. She was crossing there to the other side. He stood against a tree.

When at last he turned, looking down the long, bare grove whose flat bed was already filling dark, he saw the mountains in a wonder-light, not far away, and radiant. Behind the soft, grey ridge of the nearest range the further mountains stood golden and pale grey, the snow all radiant like pure, soft gold. So still, gleaming in the sky, fashioned pure out of the ore of the sky, they shone in their silence. He stood and looked at them, his face illuminated. And like the golden, lustrous gleaming of the snow he felt his own thirst bright in him. He stood and gazed, leaning against a tree. And then everything slid away into space.

During the night the lightning fluttered perpetually, making the whole sky white. He must have walked again. The world hung livid round him for moments, fields a level sheen of grey-green light, trees in dark bulk, and the range of clouds black across a white sky. Then the darkness fell like a shutter, and the night was whole. A faint flutter of a half-revealed world, that could not quite leap out of the darkness!—Then there again stood a sweep of pallor for the land, dark shapes looming, a range of clouds hanging overhead. The world was a ghostly shadow, thrown for a moment upon the pure darkness, which returned ever whole and complete.

And the mere delirium of sickness and fever went on inside him— his brain opening and shutting like the night—then sometimes convulsions of terror from something with great eyes that stared round a tree—then the long agony of the march, and the sun decomposing his blood—then the pang of hate for the Captain, followed by a pang of tenderness and ease. But everything was distorted, born of an ache and resolving into an ache.

In the morning he came definitely awake. Then his brain flamed with the sole horror of thirstiness ! The sun was on his face, the dew was steaming from his wet clothes. Like one possessed, he got up. There, straight in front of him, blue and cool and tender, the mountains ranged across the pale edge of the morning sky. He wanted them—he wanted them alone—he wanted to leave himself and be identified with them. They did not move, they were still and soft, with white, gentle markings of snow. He stood still, mad with suffering, his hands crisping and clutching. Then he was twisting in a paroxysm on the grass.

He lay still, in a kind of dream of anguish. His thirst seemed to have separated itself from him, and to stand apart, a single demand. Then the pain he felt was another single self. Then there was the clog of his body, another separate thing. He was divided among all kinds of separate beings. There was some strange, agonized connection between them, but they were drawing further apart. Then they would all split. The sun, drilling down on him, was drilling through the bond. Then they would all fall, fall through the everlasting lapse of space. Then again, his consciousness reasserted itself. He roused on to his elbow and stared at the gleaming mountains. There they ranked, all still and wonderful between earth and heaven. He stared till his eyes went black, and the mountains, as they stood in their beauty, so clean and cool, seemed to have it, that which was lost in him.

IV

When the soldiers found him, three hours later, he was lying with his face over his arm, his black hair giving off heat under the sun. But he was still alive. Seeing the open, black mouth the young soldiers dropped him in horror.

He died in the hospital at night, without having seen again.

The doctors saw the bruises on his legs, behind, and were silent.

The bodies of the two men lay together, side by side, in the mortuary, the one white and slender, but laid rigidly at rest, the other looking as if every moment it must rouse into life again, so young and unused, from a slumber.

AT seventy-two, Pauline Attenborough could still sometimes be mistaken, in the half-light, for thirty. She really was a wonderfully preserved woman, of perfect *chic*. Of course, it helps a great deal to have the right frame. She would be an exquisite skeleton, and her skull would be an exquisite skull, like that of some Etruscan woman, with feminine charm still in the swerve of the bone and the pretty naïve teeth.

Mrs. Attenborough's face was of the perfect oval, and slightly flat type that wears best. There is no flesh to sag. Her nose rode serenely, in its finely bridged curve. Only her big grey eyes were a tiny bit prominent on the surface of her face, and they gave her away most. The bluish lids were heavy, as if they ached sometimes with the strain of keeping the eyes beneath them arch and bright ; and at the corners of the eyes were fine little wrinkles which would slacken with haggardness, then be pulled up tense again, to that bright, gay look like a Leonardo woman who really could laugh outright.

Her niece Cecilia was perhaps the only person in the world who was aware of the invisible little wire which connected Pauline's eye-wrinkles with Pauline's will-power. Only Cecilia *consciously* watched the eyes go haggard and old and tired, and remain so, for hours ; until Robert came home. Then ping !—the mysterious little wire that worked between Pauline's will and her face went taut, the weary, haggard, prominent eyes suddenly began to gleam, the eyelids arched, the queer curved eyebrows which floated in such frail arches on Pauline's forehead began to gather a mocking significance, and you had the *real* lovely lady, in all her charm.

She really had the secret of everlasting youth ; that is to say, she could don her youth again like an eagle. But she was sparing of it. She was wise enough not to try being young for too many people. Her son Robert, in the evenings, and Sir Wilfred Knipe sometimes in the afternoon to tea : then occasional visitors on Sunday, when Robert was home : for these she was her lovely and changeless self, that age could not wither, nor custom stale : so bright and kindly and yet subtly mocking, like Mona Lisa who knew a thing or two. But Pauline knew more, so she needn't be smug at all, she could laugh that lovely mocking Bacchante laugh of hers, which was at the same time never malicious, always good-naturedly tolerant, both of virtues and vices. The former, of course, taking much more tolerating. So she suggested, roguishly.

Only with her niece Cecilia she did not trouble to keep up the glamour. Ciss was not very observant, anyhow : and more than that, she was plain : more still, she was in love with Robert : and most of all, she was thirty, and dependent on her Aunt Pauline. Oh, Cecilia ! Why make music for her !

Cecilia, called by her aunt and by her cousin Robert just Ciss, like a cat spitting, was a big dark-complexioned pug-faced young woman who very rarely spoke, and when she did, couldn't get it out. She was the daughter of a poor Congregational minister. who had been, while he lived, brother to Ronald, Aunt Pauline's husband. Ronald and the Congregational minister were both well dead, and Aunt Pauline had had charge of Ciss for the last five years.

They lived all together in a quite exquisite though rather small Queen Anne house some twenty-five miles out of town, secluded in a little dale, and surrounded by small but very quaint and pleasant grounds. It was an ideal place and an ideal life for Aunt Pauline, at the age of seventy-two. When the kingfishers flashed up the little stream in the garden, going under the alders, something still flashed in her heart. She was that kind of woman.

Robert, who was two years older than Ciss, went every day to town, to his chambers in one of the Inns. He was a barrister, and, to his secret but very deep mortification, he earned about a hundred pounds a year. He simply *couldn't* get above that figure, though it was rather easy to get below it. Of course, it didn't matter. Pauline had money. But then what was Pauline's was Pauline's, and though she could give almost lavishly, still, one was always aware of having a *lovely* and *undeserved* present made to one : presents are so much nicer when they are undeserved, Aunt Pauline would say.

Robert too was plain, and almost speechless. He was medium-sized, rather broad and stout, though not fat. Only his creamy, clean-shaven face was rather fat, and sometimes suggestive of an Italian priest, in its silence and its secrecy. But he had grey eyes like his mother, but very shy and uneasy, not bold like hers. Perhaps Ciss was the only person who fathomed his awful shyness and *malaise*, his habitual feeling that he was in the wrong place : almost like a soul that has got into the wrong body. But he never did

anything about it. He went up to his chambers, and read law. It
was, however, all the weird old processes that interested him. He
had, unknown to everybody but his mother, a quite extraordinary
collection of old Mexican legal documents, reports of processes and
trials, pleas, accusations, the weird and awful mixture of ecclesias-
tical law and common law in seventeenth-century Mexico. He had
started a study in this direction through coming across a report of
a trial of two English sailors, for murder, in Mexico in 1620, and
he had gone on, when the next document was an accusation against
a Don Miguel Estrada for seducing one of the nuns of the Sacred
Heart Convent in Oaxaca in 1680.

Pauline and her son Robert had wonderful evenings with these
old papers. The lovely lady knew a little Spanish. She even looked
a trifle Spanish herself, with a high comb and a marvellous dark
brown shawl embroidered in thick silvery silk embroidery. So she
would sit at the perfect old table, soft as velvet in its deep brown
surface, a high comb in her hair, ear-rings with dropping pendants
in her ears, her arms bare and still beautiful, a few strings of pearls
round her throat, a puce velvet dress on and this or another beautiful
shawl, and by candlelight she looked, yes, a Spanish high-bred beauty
of thirty-two or three. She set the candles to give her face just the
chiaroscuro she knew suited her ; her high chair that rose behind
her face was done in old green brocade, against which her face
emerged like a Christmas rose.

They were always three at table ; and they always drank a bottle
of champagne : Pauline two glasses, Ciss two glasses, Robert the rest.
The lovely lady sparkled and was radiant. Ciss, her black hair
bobbed, her broad shoulders in a very nice and becoming dress that
Aunt Pauline had helped her to make, stared from her aunt to her
cousin and back again, with rather confused, mute, hazel eyes, and
played the part of an audience suitably impressed. She *was* impressed, somewhere, all the time. And even rendered speechless by
Pauline's brilliancy, even after five years. But at the bottom of her
consciousness were the data of as weird a document as Robert ever
studied : all the things she knew about her aunt and cousin.

Robert was always a gentleman, with an old-fashioned punctilious
courtesy that covered his shyness quite completely. He was, and
Ciss knew it, more confused than shy. He was worse than she was.
Cecilia's own confusion dated from only five years back—Robert's
must have started before he was born. In the lovely lady's womb
he must have felt *very* confused.

He paid all his attention to his mother, drawn to her as a humble flower to the sun. And yet, priest-like, he was all the time aware, with the tail of his consciousness, that Ciss was there, and that she was a bit shut out of it, and that something wasn't right. He was aware of the third consciousness in the room. Whereas to Pauline, her niece Cecilia was an appropriate part of her own setting, rather than a distinct consciousness.

Robert took coffee with his mother and Ciss in the warm drawing-room, where all the furniture was so lovely, all collectors' pieces— Mrs. Attenborough had made her own money, dealing privately in pictures and furniture and rare things from barbaric countries—and the three talked desultorily till about eight or half-past. It was very pleasant, very cosy, very homely even : Pauline made a real home cosiness out of so much elegant material. The chat was simple, and nearly always bright. Pauline was her *real* self, emanating a friendly mockery and an odd, ironic gaiety. Till there came a little pause.

At which Ciss always rose and said good night and carried out the coffee tray, to prevent Burnett from intruding any more.

And then ! Oh, then, the lovely glowing intimacy of the evening, between mother and son, when they deciphered manuscripts and discussed points, Pauline with that eagerness of a girl, for which she was famous. And it was quite genuine. In some mysterious way she had *saved up* her power for being thrilled, in connection with a man. Robert, solid, rather quiet and subdued, seemed like the elder of the two : almost like a priest with a young girl pupil. And that was rather how he felt.

Ciss had a flat for herself just across the courtyard, over the old coachhouse and stables. There were no horses. Robert kept his car in the coachhouse. Ciss had three very nice rooms up there, stretching along in a row one after another, and she had got used to the ticking of the stable clock.

But sometimes she did not go up to her rooms. In the summer she would sit on the lawn, and from the open window of the drawing-room upstairs she would hear Pauline's wonderful heart-searching laugh. And in the winter the young woman would put on a thick coat and walk slowly to the little balustraded bridge over the stream, and then look back at the three lighted windows of that drawing-room where mother and son were so happy together.

Ciss loved Robert, and she believed that Pauline intended the two of them to marry : when she was dead. But poor Robert, he was so convulsed with shyness already, with man or woman. What would he be when his mother was dead—in a dozen more years ? He would be just a shell, the shell of a man who had never lived.

The strange unspoken sympathy of the young with one another, when they are overshadowed by the old, was one of the bonds between Robert and Ciss. But another bond, which Ciss did not know how to draw tight, was the bond of passion. Poor Robert was by nature a passionate man. His silence and his agonized, though hidden, shyness were both the result of a secret physical passionateness. And how Pauline could play on this ! Ah, Ciss was not blind to the eyes which he fixed on his mother, eyes fascinated yet humiliated, full of shame. He was ashamed that he was not a man. And he did not love his mother. He was fascinated by her. Completely fascinated. And for the rest, paralysed in a life-long confusion.

Ciss stayed in the garden till the lights leapt up in Pauline's bedroom—about ten o'clock. The lovely lady had retired. Robert would now stay another hour or so, alone. Then he too would retire. Ciss, in the dark outside, sometimes wished she could creep up to him and say : " Oh, Robert ! It's all wrong ! " But Aunt Pauline would hear. And anyhow, Ciss couldn't do it. She went off to her own rooms, once more, and so for ever.

In the morning coffee was brought up on a tray to each of the three relatives. Ciss had to be at Sir Wilfred Knipe's at nine o'clock, to give two hours' lessons to his little granddaughter. It was her sole serious occupation, except that she played the piano for the love of it. Robert set off to town about nine. And, as a rule, Aunt Pauline appeared to lunch, though sometimes not until tea-time. When she appeared, she looked fresh and young. But she was inclined to fade rather quickly, like a flower without water, in the day-time. Her hour was the candle hour.

So she always rested in the afternoon. When the sun shone, if possible she took a sun bath. This was one of her secrets. Her lunch was very light, she could take her sun-and-air-bath before noon or after, as it pleased her. Often it was in the afternoon, when the sun shone very warmly into a queer little yew-walled square just behind the stables. Here Ciss stretched out the lying-chair and rugs, and put the light parasol handy in the silent little enclosure of thick dark yew-hedges beyond the red walls of the unused stables. And hither came the lovely lady with her book. Ciss then had to be on guard in one of her own rooms, should her aunt, who was very keen-eared, hear a footstep.

One afternoon it occurred to Cecilia that she herself might while away this rather long afternoon by taking a sun bath. She was growing restive. The thought of the flat roof of the stable buildings, to which she could climb from a loft at the end, started her on a new adventure. She often went on to the roof : she had to, to wind up the stable clock, which was a job she had assumed to herself. Now she took a rug, climbed out under the heavens, looked at the sky and the great elm-tops, looked at the sun, then took off her things and lay down perfectly serenely, in a corner of the roof under the parapet, full in the sun.

It was rather lovely, to bask all one's length like this in warm sun and air. Yes, it was very lovely ! It even seemed to melt some of the hard bitterness of her heart, some of that core of unspoken resentment which never dissolved. Luxuriously, she spread herself, so that the sun should touch her limbs fully, fully. If she had no other lover, she should have the sun ! She rolled voluptuously. And suddenly, her heart stood still in her body, and her hair almost rose on end as a voice said very softly, musingly in her ear :

" No, Henry dear ! It was not my fault you died instead of marrying that Claudia. No, darling. I was quite, quite willing for you to marry her, unsuitable though she was."

Cecilia sank down on her rug powerless and perspiring with dread. That awful voice, so soft, so musing, yet so unatural. Not a human voice at all. Yet there must, there must be someone on the roof ! Oh ! how unspeakably awful !

She lifted her weak head and peeped across the sloping leads. Nobody ! The chimneys were far too narrow to shelter anybody. There was nobody on the roof. Then it must be someone in the trees, in the elms. Either that, or terror unspeakable, a bodiless voice ! She reared her head a little higher.

And as she did so, came the voice again :

" No, darling ! I told you you would tire of her in six months. And you see, it was true, dear. It was true, true, true ! I wanted to spare you that. So it wasn't I who made you feel weak and disabled, wanting that very silly Claudia ; poor thing, she looked so woebegone afterwards ! Wanting her and not wanting her, you got *yourself* into that perplexity, my dear. I only warned you. What else could I do ? And you lost your spirit and died without ever knowing me again. It was bitter, bitter——"

The voice faded away. Cecilia subsided weakly on to her rug, after the anguished tension of listening. Oh, it was awful. The sun shone, the sky was blue, all seemed so lovely and afternoony and summery. And yet, oh, horror !—she was going to be forced to believe in the supernatural ! And she loathed the supernatural, ghosts and voices and rappings and all the rest.

But that awful creepy bodiless voice, with its rusty sort of whisper of an overtone ! It had something so fearfully familiar in it too ! and yet was so utterly uncanny. Poor Cecilia could only lie there unclothed, and so all the more agonizingly helpless, inert, collapsed in sheer dread.

And then she heard the thing sigh ! A deep sigh that seemed weirdly familiar, yet was not human. " Ah, well ; ah, well, the heart must bleed ! Better it should bleed than break. It is grief, grief ! But it wasn't my fault, dear. And Robert could marry our poor dull Ciss to-morrow, if he wanted her. But he doesn't care about it, so why force him into anything ! " The sounds were very uneven, sometimes only a husky sort of whisper. Listen ! Listen !

Cecilia was about to give vent to loud and piercing screams of hysteria, when the last two sentences arrested her. All her caution and her cunning sprang alert. It was Aunt Pauline ! It must be Aunt Pauline, practising ventriloquism or something like that ! What a devil she was !

Where was she ? She must be lying down there, right below where Cecilia herself was lying. And it was either some fiend's trick of ventriloquism, or else thought transference that conveyed itself like sound. The sounds were very uneven. Sometimes quite inaudible, sometimes only a brushing sort of noise. Ciss listened intently. No, it could not be ventriloquism. It was worse, some form of thought transference. Some horror of that sort. Cecilia still lay weak and inert, terrified to move, but she was growing calmer with suspicion. It was some diabolic trick of that unnatural woman.

But *what a devil* of a woman ! She even knew that she, Cecilia, had mentally accused her of killing her son Henry. Poor Henry was Robert's elder brother, twelve years older than Robert. He had died suddenly when he was twenty-two, after an awful struggle with himself, because he was passionately in love with a young and very good-looking actress, and his mother had humorously despised him for the attachment. So he had caught some sudden ordinary disease, but the poison had gone to his brain and killed him, before he ever regained consciousness. Ciss knew the few facts from her own father. And lately, she had been thinking that Pauline was going to kill Robert as she had killed Henry. It was clear murder : a mother murdering her sensitive sons, who were fascinated by her : the Circe !

" I suppose I may as well get up," murmured the dim unbreaking voice. " Too much sun is as bad as too little. Enough sun, enough love thrill, enough proper food, and not too much of any of them, and a woman might live for ever. I verily believe for ever. If she absorbs as much vitality as she expends! Or perhaps a trifle more!"

It was certainly Aunt Pauline! How, how horrible! She, Ciss, was hearing Aunt Pauline's thoughts. Oh, how ghastly! Aunt Pauline was sending out her thoughts in a sort of radio, and she, Ciss, had to *hear* what her aunt was thinking. How ghastly! How insufferable! One of them would surely have to die.

She twisted and she lay inert and crumpled, staring vacantly in front of her. Vacantly! Vacantly! And her eyes were staring almost into a hole. She was staring into it unseeing, a hole going down in the corner from the lead gutter. It meant nothing to her. Only it frightened her a little more.

When suddenly out of the hole came a sigh and a last whisper. " Ah, well! Pauline! Get up, it's enough for to-day!" Good God! Out of the hole of the rain-pipe! The rain-pipe was acting as a speaking-tube! Impossible! No, quite possible. She had read of it even in some book. And Aunt Pauline, like the old and guilty woman she was, talked aloud to herself. That was it!

A sullen exultance sprang into Ciss's breast. *That* was why she would never have anybody, not even Robert, in her bedroom. That was why she never dozed in a chair, never sat absent-minded anywhere, but went to her room, and kept to her room, except when she roused herself to be alert. When she slackened off, she talked to herself! She talked in a soft little crazy voice, to herself. But she was not crazy. It was only her thoughts murmuring themselves aloud.

So she had qualms about poor Henry! Well she might have! Ciss believed that Aunt Pauline had loved her big, handsome, brilliant first-born much more than she loved Robert, and that his death had been a terrible blow and a chagrin to her. Poor Robert had been only ten years old when Henry died. Since then he had been the substitute.

Ah, how awful!

But Aunt Pauline was a strange woman. She had left her husband when Henry was a small child, some years even before Robert was born. There was no quarrel. Sometimes she saw her husband again, quite amicably, but a little mockingly. And she even gave him money.

For Pauline earned all her own. Her father had been a Consul in the East and in Naples : and a devoted collector of beautiful and exotic things. When he died, soon after his grandson Henry was born, he left his collection of treasures to his daughter. And Pauline, who had really a passion and a genius for loveliness, whether in texture or form or colour, had laid the basis of her fortune on her father's collection. She had gone on collecting, buying where she could, and selling to collectors and to museums. She was one of the first to sell old, weird African wooden figures to the museums, and ivory carvings from New Guinea. She bought Renoir as soon as she saw his pictures. But not Rousseau. And all by herself, she made a fortune.

After her husband died, she had not married again. She was not even *known* to have had lovers. If she did have lovers, it was not among the men who admired her most and paid her devout and open attendance. To these she was a " friend."

Cecilia slipped on her clothes and caught up her rug, hastened carefully down the ladder to the loft. As she descended she heard the ringing musical call : " All right, Ciss ! " which meant that the lovely lady was finished, and returning to the house. Even her voice was marvellously young and sonorous, beautifully balanced and self-possessed. So different from the little voice in which she talked to herself. *That* was much more the voice of an old woman.

Ciss hastened round to the yew enclosure, where lay the comfortable chaise-longue with the various delicate rugs. Everything Pauline had was choice, to the fine straw mat on the floor. The great yew walls were beginning to cast long shadows. Only in the corner, where the rugs tumbled their delicate colours, was there hot, still sunshine.

The rugs folded up, the chair lifted away, Cecilia stooped to look at the mouth of the rain-pipe. There it was, in the corner, under a little hood of masonry and just projecting from the thick leaves of the creeper on the wall. If Pauline, lying there, turned her face towards the wall, she would speak into the very mouth of the hole. Cecilia was reassured. She had heard her aunt's thoughts indeed, but by no uncanny agency.

That evening, as if aware of something, Pauline was a little quicker than usual, though she looked her own serene, rather mysterious self. And after coffee she said to Robert and Ciss : " I'm so sleepy. The sun has made me so sleepy. I feel full of sunshine like a bee. I shall go to bed, if you don't mind. You two sit and have a talk."

Cecilia looked quickly at her cousin.

" Perhaps you would rather be alone," she said to him.

" No, no," he replied. " Do keep me company for a while, if it doesn't bore you."

The windows were open, the scent of the honeysuckle wafted in, with the sound of an owl. Robert smoked in silence. There was a sort of despair in the motionless, rather squat body. He looked like a caryatid bearing a weight.

" Do you remember Cousin Henry ? " Cecilia asked him suddenly. He looked up in surprise.

" Yes, very well," he said.

" What did he look like ? " she said, glancing into her cousin's big secret-troubled eyes, in which there was so much frustration.

" Oh, he was handsome : tall and fresh-coloured, with mother's soft brown hair." As a matter of fact, Pauline's hair was grey. " The ladies admired him very much ; he was at all the dances."

" And what kind of character had he ? "

" Oh, very good-natured and jolly. He liked to be amused. He was rather quick and clever, like mother, and very good company."

" And did he love your mother ? "

" Very much. She loved him too—better than she does me, as a matter of fact. He was so much more nearly her idea of a man."

" Why was he more her idea of a man ? "

" Tall—handsome—attractive, and very good company—and would, I believe, have been very successful at law. I'm afraid I am merely negative in all those respects."

Ciss looked at him attentively, with her slow-thinking hazel eyes. Under his impassive mask, she knew he suffered.

" Do you think you are so much more negative than he ? " she said.

He did not lift his face. But after a few moments he replied : " My life, certainly, is a negative affair."

She hesitated before she dared ask him :

" And do you mind ? "

He did not answer her at all. Her heart sank.

" You see, I am afraid my life is as negative as yours is," she said. " And I'm beginning to mind bitterly. I'm thirty."

She saw his creamy, well-bred hand tremble.

" I suppose," he said, without looking at her, "'one will rebel when it is too late."

That was queer, from him.

" Robert," she said, " do you like me at all ? "

She saw his dusky, creamy face, so changeless in its folds, go pale.

" I am very fond of you," he murmured.

" Won't you kiss me ? Nobody ever kisses me," she said pathetically.

He looked at her, his eyes strange with fear and a certain haughtiness. Then he rose and came softly over to her, and kissed her gently on the cheek.

" It's an awful shame, Ciss ! " he said softly.

She caught his hand and pressed it to her breast.

" And sit with me sometime in the garden," she said, murmuring with difficulty. " Won't you ? "

He looked at her anxiously and searchingly.

" What about. mother ? " he said.

Ciss smiled a funny little smile, and looked into his eyes. He suddenly flushed crimson, turning aside his face. It was a painful sight.

" I know," he said, " I am no lover of women."

He spoke with sarcastic stoicism against himself, but even she did not know the shame it was to him.

" You never try to be ! " she said.

Again his eyes changed uncannily.

" Does one have to try ? " he said.

" Why, yes ! One never does anything if one doesn't try."

He went pale again.

" Perhaps you are right," he said.

In a few minutes she left him, and went to her rooms. At least, she had tried to take off the everlasting lid from things.

The weather continued sunny, Pauline continued her sun-baths, and Ciss lay on the roof eavesdropping in the literal sense of the word. But Pauline was not to be heard. No sound came up the pipe. She must be lying with her face away into the open. Ciss listened with all her might. She could just detect the faintest, faintest murmur away below, but no audible syllable.

And at night, under the stars, Cecilia sat and waited in silence, on the seat which kept in view the drawing-room windows and the side-door into the garden. She saw the light go up in her aunt's room. She saw the lights at last go out in the drawing-room. And she waited. But he did not come. She stayed on in the darkness half the night, while the owl hooted. But she stayed alone.

Two days she heard nothing, her aunt's thoughts were not revealed and at evening nothing happened. Then the second night, as she sat with heavy, helpless persistence in the garden, suddenly she started. He had come out. She rose and went softly over the grass to him.

" Don't speak," he murmured.

And in silence, in the dark, they walked down the garden and over the little bridge to the paddock, where the hay, cut very late, was in cock. There they stood disconsolate under the stars.

" You see," he said, " how can I ask for love, if I don't feel any love in myself. You know I have a real regard for you——"

" How can you feel any love, when you never feel anything ? " she said.

" That is true," he replied.

And she waited for what next.

" And how can I marry ? " he said. " I am a failure even at making money. I can't ask my mother for money."

She sighed deeply.

" Then don't bother yet about marrying," she said. " Only love me a little. Won't you ? "

He gave a short laugh.

" It sounds so atrocious, to say it is hard to begin," he said.

She sighed again. He was so stiff to move.

" Shall we sit down a minute," she said. And then as they sat on the hay, she added : " May I touch you ? Do you mind ? "

" Yes, I mind ! But do as you wish," he replied, with that mixture of shyness and queer candour which made him a little ridiculous, as he knew quite well. But in his heart there was almost murder.

She touched his black, always tidy hair with her fingers.

" I suppose I shall rebel one day," he said again, suddenly.

They sat some time, till it grew chilly. And he held her hand fast, but he never put his arms round her. At last she rose and went indoors, saying good night.

The next day, as Cecilia lay stunned and angry on the roof, taking her sun-bath, and becoming hot and fierce with sunshine, suddenly she started. A terror seized her in spite of herself. It was the voice.

" *Caro, caro, tu non l'hai visto !* " it was murmuring away, in a language Cecilia did not understand. She lay and writhed her limbs in the sun, listening intently to words she could not follow. Softly, whisperingly, with infinite caressiveness and yet with that subtle, insidious arrogance under its velvet, came the voice, murmuring in Italian : " *Bravo, si molto bravo, poverino, ma uomo come te non lo sara mai, mai, mai !* " Oh, especially in Italian Cecilia heard the poisonous charm of the voice, so caressive, so soft and flexible, yet so utterly egoistic. She hated it with intensity as it sighed and whispered out of nowhere. Why, why should it be so delicate, so subtle and flexible and beautifully controlled, while she herself was so clumsy ! Oh, poor Cecilia, she writhed in the afternoon sun, knowing her own clownish clumsiness and lack of suavity, in comparison.

" No, Robert dear, you will never be the man your father was, though you have some of his looks. He was a marvellous lover, soft as a flower yet piercing as a humming-bird. No, Robert dear, you will never know how to serve a woman as Monsignor Mauro did. *Cara, cara mia bellissima, ti ho aspettato come l'agonizzante aspetta la morte, morte deliziosa, quasi quasi troppo deliziosa per un' anima humana*—Soft as a flower, yet probing like a humming-bird. He gave himself to a woman as he gave himself to God. Mauro ! Mauro ! How you loved me ! "

The voice ceased in reverie, and Cecilia knew what she had guessed before, that Robert was not the son of her Uncle Ronald, but of some Italian.

" I am disappointed in you, Robert. There is no poignancy in you. Your father was a Jesuit, but he was the most perfect and poignant lover in the world. You are a Jesuit like a fish in a tank. And that Ciss of yours is the cat fishing for you. It is less edifying even than poor Henry."

Cecilia suddenly bent her mouth down to the tube, and said in a deep voice :

" Leave Robert alone ! Don't kill him as well."

There was a dead silence, in the hot July afternoon that was lowering for thunder. Cecilia lay prostrate, her heart beating in great thumps. She was listening as if her whole soul were an ear. At last she caught the whisper :

" Did someone speak ? "

She leaned again to the mouth of the tube.

" Don't kill Robert as you killed me," she said with slow enunciation, and a deep but small voice.

" Ah ! " came the sharp little cry. " Who is that speaking ? "

" Henry ! " said the deep voice.

There was a dead silence. Poor Cecilia lay with all the use gone out of her. And there was dead silence. Till at last came the whisper :

" I didn't kill Henry. No, NO ! Henry, surely you can't blame me ! I loved you, dearest. I only wanted to help you."

" You killed me ! " came the deep, artificial, accusing voice. " Now, let Robert live. Let him go ! Let him marry ! "

There was a pause.

" How very, very awful ! " mused the whispering voice. " Is it possible, Henry, you are a spirit, and you condemn me ? "

" Yes ! I condemn you ! "

Cecilia felt all her pent-up rage going down that rain-pipe. At the same time, she almost laughed. It was awful.

She lay and listened and listened. No sound ! As if time had ceased, she lay inert in the weakening sun. The sky was yellowing. Quickly she dressed herself, went down, and out to the corner of the stables.

" Aunt Pauline ! " she called discreetly. " Did you hear thunder ? "

" Yes ! I am going in. Don't wait," came a feeble voice.

Cecilia retired, and from the loft watched, spying, as the figure of the lovely lady, wrapped in a lovely wrap of old blue silk, went rather totteringly to the house.

The sky gradually darkened, Cecilia hastened in with the rugs. Then the storm broke. Aunt Pauline did not appear to tea. She found the thunder trying. Robert also did not arrive till after tea, in the pouring rain. Cecilia went down the covered passage to her own house, and dressed carefully for dinner, putting some white columbines at her breast.

The drawing-room was lit with a softly-shaded lamp. Robert, dressed, was waiting, listening to the rain. He too seemed strangely crackling and on edge. Cecilia came in, with the white flowers nodding at her breast. Robert was watching her curiously, a new look on his face. Cecilia went to the bookshelves near the door, and was peering for something, listening acutely. She heard a rustle, then the door softly opening. And as it opened, Ciss suddenly switched on the strong electric light by the door.

Her aunt, in a dress of black lace over ivory colour, stood in the doorway. Her face was made up, but haggard with a look of unspeakable irritability, as if years of suppressed exasperation and dislike of her fellow-men had suddenly crumpled her into an old witch.

" Oh, aunt ! " cried Cecilia.

" Why, mother, you're a little old lady ! " came the astounded voice of Robert : like an astonished boy : as if it were a joke.

" Have you only just found it out ? " snapped the old woman venomously.

" Yes ! Why, I thought——" his voice tailed out in misgiving.

The haggard, old Pauline, in a frenzy of exasperation, said :

" Aren't we going down ? "

She had never even noticed the excess of light, a thing she shunned. And she went downstairs almost tottering.

At table she sat with her face like a crumpled mask of unspeakable irritability. She looked old, very old, and like a witch. Robert and Cecilia fetched furtive glances at her. And Ciss, watching Robert, saw that he was so astonished and repelled by his mother's looks, that he was another man.

" What kind of a drive home did you have ? " snapped Pauline, with an almost gibbering irritability.

" It rained, of course," he said.

" How clever of you to have found that out ! " said his mother, with the grisly grin of malice that had succeeded her arch smirk.

" I don't understand," he said with quiet suavity.

" It's apparent," said his mother, rapidly and sloppily eating her food.

She rushed through the meal like a crazy dog, to the utter consternation of the servant. And the moment it was over, she darted in a queer, crab-like way upstairs. Robert and Cecilia followed her, thunderstruck, like two conspirators.

" You pour the coffee. I loathe it ! I'm going ! Good night ! " said the old woman, in a succession of sharp shots. And she scrambled out of the room.

There was a dead silence. At last he said :

" I'm afraid mother isn't well. I must persuade her to see a doctor."

" Yes ! " said Cecilia.

The evening passed in silence. Robert and Ciss stayed on in the drawing-room, having lit a fire. Outside was cold rain. Each pretended to read. They did not want to separate. The evening passed with ominous mysteriousness, yet quickly.

At about ten o'clock, the door suddenly opened, and Pauline appeared, in a blue wrap. She shut the door behind her, and came to the fire. Then she looked at the two young people in hate, real hate.

" You two had better get married quickly," she said in an ugly voice. " It would look more decent ; such a passionate pair of lovers ! "

Robert looked up at her quietly.

" I thought you believed that cousins should not marry, mother," he said.

" I do ! But you're not cousins. Your father was an Italian priest." Pauline held her daintily-slippered foot to the fire, in an old coquettish gesture. Her body tried to repeat all the old graceful gestures. But the nerve had snapped, so it was a rather dreadful caricature.

" Is that really true, mother ? " he asked.

" True ! What do you think ? He was a distinguished man, or he wouldn't have been my lover. He was far too distinguished a man to have had you for a son. But that joy fell to me."

" How unfortunate all round," he said slowly.

" Unfortunate for you ? *You* were lucky. It was *my* misfortune," she said acidly to him.

She was really a dreadful sight, like a piece of lovely Venetian glass that has been dropped, and gathered up again in horrible, sharp-edged fragments.

Suddenly she left the room again.

For a week it went on. She did not recover. It was as if every nerve in her body had suddenly started screaming in an insanity of discordance. The doctor came, and gave her sedatives, for she never slept. Without drugs, she never slept at all, only paced back and forth in her room, looking hideous and evil, reeking with malevolence. She could not bear to see either her son or her niece. Only when either of them came, she asked in pure malice :

" Well ! When's the wedding ! Have you celebrated the nuptials yet ? "

At first Cecilia was stunned by what she had done. She realized vaguely that her aunt, once a definite thrust of condemnation had penetrated her beautiful armour, had just collapsed squirming inside her shell. It was too terrible. Ciss was almost terrified into repentance. Then she thought : This is what she always was. Now let her live the rest of her days in her true colours.

But Pauline would not live long. She was literally shrivelling away. She kept her room, and saw no one. She had her mirrors taken away.

Robert and Cecilia sat a good deal together. The jeering of the mad Pauline had not driven them apart, as she had hoped. But Cecilia dared not confess to him what she had done.

" Do you think your mother ever loved anybody ? " Ciss asked him tentatively, rather wistfully, one evening.

He looked at her fixedly.

" Herself ! " he said at last.

" She didn't even *love* herself," said Ciss. " It was something else—what was it ? " She lifted a troubled, utterly puzzled face to him.

" Power ! " he said curtly.

" But what power ? " she asked. " I don't understand."

" Power to feed on other lives," he said bitterly. " She was beautiful, and she fed on life. She has fed on me as she fed on Henry. She put a sucker into one's soul, and sucked up one's essential life."

" And don't you forgive her ? "

" No."

" Poor Aunt Pauline ! "

But even Ciss did not mean it. She was only aghast.

" I *know* I've got a heart," he said, passionately striking his breast. " But it's almost sucked dry. I *know* people who want power over others."

Ciss was silent ; what was there to say ?

And two days later, Pauline was found dead in her bed, having taken too much veronal, for her heart was weakened. From the grave even she hit back at her son and her niece. She left Robert the noble sum of one thousand pounds ; and Ciss one hundred. All the rest, with the nucleus of her valuable antiques, went to form the " Pauline Attenborough Museum."

" HANNELE ! "

" Ja—a."

" Wo bist du ? "

" Hier."

" Wo dann ? "

Hannele did not lift her head from her work. She sat in a low chair under a reading-lamp, a basket of coloured silk pieces beside her, and in her hands a doll, or mannikin, which she was dressing. She was doing something to the knee of the mannikin, so that the poor little gentleman flourished head downwards with arms wildly tossed out. And it was not at all seemly, because the doll was a Scotch soldier in tight-fitting tartan trews.

There was a tap at the door, and the same voice, a woman's, calling :

" Hannele ? "

" Ja—a ! "

" Are you here ? Are you alone ? " asked the voice, in German.

" Yes—come in."

Hannele did not sound very encouraging. She turned round her doll as the door opened, and straightened his coat. A dark-eyed young woman peeped in through the door, with a roguish coyness. She was dressed fashionably for the street, in a thick cape-wrap, and a little black hat pulled down to her ears.

" Quite, quite alone ! " said the newcomer, in a tone of wonder. " Where is he, then ? "

" That I don't know," said Hannele.

" And you sit here alone, and wait for him ? But no ! That I call courage ! Aren't you afraid ? " Mitchka strolled across to her friend.

" Why shall I be afraid ? " said Hannele curtly.

" But no ! And what are you doing ? Another puppet ? He is a good one, though ! Ha—ha—ha ! *Him !* It is him ! No—no—that is too beautiful ! No—that is too beautiful, Hannele. It is him—exactly him. Only the trousers."

358

"He wears those trousers too," said Hannele, standing her doll on her knee. It was a perfect portrait of an officer of a Scottish regiment, slender, delicately made, with a slight, elegant stoop of the shoulders, and close-fitting tartan trousers. The face was beautifully modelled, and a wonderful portrait, dark-skinned, with a little, close-cut, dark moustache, and wide-open dark eyes, and that air of aloofness and perfect diffidence which marks an officer and a gentleman.

Mitchka bent forward, studying the doll. She was a handsome woman with a warm, dark golden skin and clear black eyebrows over her russet-brown eyes.

"No," she whispered to herself, as if awestruck. "That is him. That is him. Only not the trousers. Beautiful, though, the trousers. Has he really such beautiful fine legs?"

Hannele did not answer.

"Exactly him. Just as finished as he is. Just as complete. He is just like that : finished off. Has he seen it?"

"No," said Hannele.

"What will he say, then?" She started. Her quick ear had caught a sound on the stone stairs. A look of fear came to her face. She flew to the door and out of the room, closing the door to behind her.

"Who is it?" her voice was heard calling anxiously down the stairs.

The answer came in German. Mitchka immediately opened the door again and came back to join Hannele.

"Only Martin," she said.

She stood waiting. A man appeared in the doorway—erect, military.

"Ah! Countess Hannele," he said in his quick, precise way, as he stood on the threshold in the distance. "May one come in?"

"Yes, come in," said Hannele.

The man entered with a quick, military step, bowed, and kissed the hand of the woman who was sewing the doll. Then, much more intimately, he touched Mitchka's hand with his lips.

Mitchka meanwhile was glancing round the room. It was a very large attic, with the ceiling sloping and then bending in two handsome movements towards the walls. The light from the dark-shaded reading-lamp fell softly on the huge white-washed vaulting of the ceiling, on the various objects round the walls, and made a brilliant pool of colour where Hannele sat in her soft, red dress, with her basket of silks.

Q

She was a fair woman with dark-blond hair and a beautiful fine skin. Her face seemed luminous, a certain quick gleam of life about it as she looked up at the man. He was handsome, clean-shaven, with very blue eyes strained a little too wide. One could see the war in his face.

Mitchka was wandering round the room, looking at everything, and saying : " Beautiful ! But beautiful ! .Such good taste ! A man, and such good taste ! No, they don't need a woman. No, look here, Martin, the Captain Hepburn has arranged all this room himself. Here you have the man. Do you see ? So simple, yet so elegant. He needs no woman."

The room was really beautiful, spacious, pale, soft-lighted. It was heated by a large stove of dark-blue tiles, and had very little furniture save large peasant cupboards or presses of painted wood, and a huge writing table, on which were writing materials and some scientific apparatus and a cactus plant with fine scarlet blossoms. But it was a man's room. Tobacco and pipes were on a little tray, on the pegs in the distance hung military overcoats and belts, and two guns on a bracket. Then there were two telescopes, one mounted on a stand near a window. Various astronomical apparatus lay upon the table.

" And he reads the stars. Only think—he is an astronomer and reads the stars. Queer, queer people, the English ! "

" He is Scottish," said Hannele.

" Yes, Scottish," said Mitchka. " But, you know, I am afraid when I am with him. He is at a closed end. I don't know where I can get to with him. Are you afraid of him, too, Hannele ? Ach, like a closed road ! "

" Why should I be ? "

" Ah, you ! Perhaps you don't know when you should be afraid. But if he were to come and find us here ? No, no—let us go. Let us go, Martin. Come, let us go. I don't want the Captain Hepburn to come and find me in his room. Oh no ! " Mitchka was busily pushing Martin to the door, and he was laughing with the queer, mad laugh in his strained eyes. " Oh no ! I don't like. I don't like it," said Mitchka, trying her English now. She spoke a few sentences prettily. " Oh no, Sir Captain, I don't want that you come. I don't like it, to be here when you come. Oh no. Not at all. I go. I go, Hannele. I go, my Hannele. And you will really stay here and wait for him ? But when will he come ? You don't know ? Oh dear, I don't like it, I don't like it. I do not wait in the man's room. No, no—never—*jamais, jamais, voyez vous*. Ach, you poor Hannele !

And he has got wife and children in England? Nevair! No, nevair shall I wait for him."

She had bustlingly pushed Martin through the door, and settled her wrap and taken a mincing, elegant pose, ready for the street, and waved her hand and made wide, scared eyes at Hannele, and was gone. The Countess Hannele picked up the doll again and began to sew its shoe. What living she now had she earned making these puppets.

But she was restless. She pressed her arms into her lap, as if holding them bent had wearied her. Then she looked at the little clock on his writing table. It was long after dinner-time—why hadn't he come? She sighed rather exasperated. She was tired of her doll.

Putting aside her basket of silks, she went to one of the windows. Outside the stars seemed white, and very near. Below was the dark agglomeration of the roofs of houses, a fume of light came up from beneath the darkness of roofs, and a faint breakage of noise from the town far below. The room seemed high, remote, in the sky.

She went to the table and looked at his letter-clip with letters in it, and at his sealing-wax, and his stamp-box, touching things and moving them a little, just for the sake of the contrast, not really noticing what she touched. Then she took a pencil, and in stiff gothic characters began to write her name—Johanna zu Rassentlow—time after time her own name—and then once, bitterly, curiously, with a curious sharpening of her nose : Alexander Hepburn.

But she threw the pencil down, having no more interest in her writing. She wandered to where the large telescope stood near a further window, and stood for some minutes with her fingers on the barrel, where it was a little brighter from his touching it. Then she drifted restlessly back to her chair. She had picked up her puppet when she heard him on the stairs. She lifted her face and watched as he entered.

"Hello, you there!" he said quietly, as he closed the door behind him. She glanced at him swiftly, but did not move nor answer.

He took off his overcoat, with quick, quiet movements, and went to hang it up on the pegs. She heard his step, and looked again. He was like the doll, a tall, slender, well-bred man in uniform. When he turned, his dark eyes seemed very wide open. His black hair was growing grey at the temples—the first touch.

She was sewing her doll. Without saying anything, he wheeled round the chair from the writing table, so that he sat with his knees almost touching her. Then he crossed one leg over the other. He wore fine tartan socks. His ankles seemed slender and elegant, his brown shoes fitted as if they were part of him. For some moments he watched her as she sat sewing. The light fell on her soft, delicate hair, that was full of strands of gold and of tarnished gold and shadow. She did not look up.

In silence he held out his small, naked-looking brown hand for the doll. On his forearm were black hairs.

She glanced up at him. Curious how fresh and luminous her face looked in contrast to his.

" Do you want to see it ? " she asked, in natural English.

" Yes," he said.

She broke off her thread of cotton and handed him the puppet. He sat with one leg thrown over the other, holding the doll in one hand, and smiling inscrutably with his dark eyes. His hair, parted perfectly on one side, was jet black and glossy.

" You've got me," he said at last, in his amused, melodious voice.

" What ? " she said.

" You've got me," he repeated.

" I don't care," she said.

" What—— You don't care ? " His face broke into a smile. He had an odd way of answering, as if he were only half attending, as if he were thinking of something else.

" You are very late, aren't you ? " she ventured.

" Yes. I am rather late."

" Why are you ? "

" Well, as a matter of fact, I was talking with the Colonel."

" About me ? "

" Yes. It was about you."

She went pale as she sat looking up into his face. But it was impossible to tell whether there was distress on his dark brow or not.

" Anything nasty? " she said.

" Well, yes. It was rather nasty. Not about you, I mean. But rather awkward for me."

She watched him. But still he said no more.

" What was it ? " she said.

" Oh, well—only what I expected. They seem to know rather too much about you—about you and me, I mean. Not that anybody cares one bit, you know, unofficially. The trouble is, they are apparently going to have to take official notice."

" Why ? "

" Oh, well—it appears my wife has been writing letters to the

Major-General. He is one of her family acquaintances—known her all his life. And I suppose she's been hearing rumours. In fact, I know she has. She said so in her letter to me."

" And what do you say to her then ? "

" Oh, I tell her I'm all right—not to worry."

" You don't expect *that* to stop her worrying, do you ? " she asked.

" Oh, I don't know. Why should she worry ? " he said.

" I think she might have some reason," said Hannele. " You've not seen her for a year. And if she adores you——"

" Oh, I don't think she adores me. I think she quite likes me."

" Do you think you matter as little as that to her ? "

" I don't see why not. Of course she likes to feel *safe* about me."

" But now she doesn't feel safe ? "

" No—exactly. Exactly. That's the point. That's where it is. The Colonel advises me to go home on leave."

He sat gazing with curious bright, dark, unseeing eyes at the doll which he held by one arm. It was an extraordinary likeness of himself, true even to the smooth parting of his hair and his peculiar way of fixing his dark eyes.

" For how long ? " she asked.

" I don't know. For a month," he replied, first vaguely, then definitely.

" For a month ! " She watched him, and seemed to see him fade from her eyes.

" And will you go ? " she asked.

" I don't know. I don't know." His head remained bent, he seemed to muse rather vaguely. " I don't know," he repeated. " I can't make up my mind what I shall do."

" Would you like to go ? " she asked.

He lifted his brows and looked at her. Her heart always melted in her when he looked straight at her with his black eyes, and that curious, bright unseeing look that was more like second sight than direct human vision. She never knew what he saw when he looked at her.

" No," he said simply. " I don't *want* to go. I don't think I've any desire at all to go to England."

" Why not ? " she asked.

" I can't say." Then again he looked at her, and a curious white light seemed to shine on his eyes, as he smiled slowly with his mouth, and said : " I suppose you ought to know, if anybody does."

A glad, half-frightened look came on her face.

" You mean you don't want to leave me ? " she asked, breathless.

" Yes. I suppose that's what I mean."

" But you aren't sure ? "

" Yes, I am, I'm quite sure," he said, and the curious smile lingered on his face, and the strange light shone in his eyes.

" That you don't want to leave me ? " she stammered, looking aside.

" Yes, I'm quite sure I don't want to leave you," he repeated. He had a curious, very melodious Scottish voice. But it was the incomprehensible smile on his face that convinced and frightened her. It was almost a gargoyle smile, a strange, lurking, changeless-seeming grin.

She was frightened, and turned aside her face. When she looked at him again, his face was like a mask, with strange, deep-graven lines and a glossy dark skin and a fixed look—as if carved half grotesque in some glossy stone. His black hair on his smooth, beautifully-shaped head seemed changeless.

" Are you rather tired ? " she asked him.

" Yes, I think I am." He looked at her with black, unseeing eyes, and a mask-like face. Then he glanced aside as if he heard something. Then he rose with his hand on his belt, saying : " I'll take off my belt, and change my coat, if you don't mind."

He walked across the room, unfastening his broad, brown belt. He was in well-fitting, well-cut khaki. He hung up his belt and came back to her wearing an old, light tunic, which he left unbuttoned. He carried his slippers in one hand. When he sat down to unfasten his shoes, she noticed again how black and hairy his forearm was, how naked his brown hand seemed. His hair was black and smooth and perfect on his head, like some close helmet, as he stooped down.

He put on his slippers, carried his shoes aside, and resumed his chair, stretching luxuriously.

" There," he said. " I feel better now." And he looked at her. " Well," he said, " and how are you ? "

" Me ? " she said. " Do I matter ? " She was rather bitter.

" Do you matter ? " he repeated, without noticing her bitterness. " Why, what a question ! Of course you are of the very highest importance. What ? Aren't you ? " And smiling his curious smile —it made her for a moment think of the fixed sadness of monkeys, of those Chinese carved soapstone apes. He put his hand under her chin, and gently drew his finger along her cheek. She flushed deeply.

" But I'm not as important as you, am I ? " she asked defiantly.

" As important as me ! Why, bless you, I'm not important a bit.

I'm not important a bit ! "—the odd, straying sound of his words mystified her. What did he really mean ?

" And I'm even less important than that," she said bitterly.

" Oh no, you're not. Oh no, you're not. You're very important. You're very important indeed, I assure you."

" And your wife ? "—the question came rebelliously. " Your wife ? Isn't she important ? "

" My wife ? My wife ? " he seemed to let the word stray out of him as if he did not quite know what it meant. " Why, yes, I suppose she is important in her own sphere."

" What sphere ? " blurted Hannele, with a laugh.

" Why, her own sphere, of course. Her own house, her own home, and her two children ; that's her sphere."

" And you ?—where do you come in ? "

" At present I don't come in," he said.

" But isn't that just the trouble," said Hannele. " If you have a wife and a home, it's your business to belong to it, isn't it ? "

" Yes, I suppose it is, if I want to," he replied.

" And you *do* want to ? " she challenged.

" No, I don't," he replied.

" Well, then ? " she said.

" Yes, quite," he answered. " I admit it's a dilemma."

" But what will you *do* ? " she insisted.

" Why, I don't know. I don't know yet. I haven't made up my mind what I'm going to do."

" Then you'd better begin to make it up," she said.

" Yes, I know that. I know that."

He rose, and began to walk uneasily up and down the room. But the same vacant darkness was on his brow. He had his hands in his pockets. Hannele sat feeling helpless. She couldn't help being in love with the man : with his hands, with his strange, fascinating physique, with his incalculable presence. She loved the way he put his feet down, she loved the way he moved his legs as he walked, she loved the mould of his loins, she loved the way he dropped his head a little, and the strange, dark vacancy of his brow, his not-thinking. But now his restlessness only made her unhappy. Nothing would come of it. Yet she had driven him to it.

He took his hands out of his pockets and returned to her like a piece of iron returning to a magnet. He sat down again in front of her and put his hands out to her, looking into her face.

" Give me your hands," he said softly, with that strange, mindless, soft, suggestive tone which left her powerless to disobey. " Give me your hands, and let me feel that we are together. Words mean so little. They mean nothing. And all that one thinks and plans doesn't amount to anything. Let me feel that we are together, and I don't care about all the rest."

He spoke in his slow, melodious way, and closed her hands in his. She struggled still for voice.

"But you'll *have* to care about it. You'll *have* to make up your mind. You'll just *have* to," she insisted.

"Yes, I suppose I shall. I suppose I shall. But now that we are together, I won't bother. Now that we are together, let us forget it."

"But when we *can't* forget it any more?"

"Well—then I don't know. But—to-night—it seems to me—we might just as well forget it."

The soft, melodious, straying sound of his voice made her feel helpless. She felt that he never answered her. Words of reply seemed to stray out of him, in the need to say *something*. But he himself never spoke. There he was, a continual blank silence in front of her.

She had a battle with herself. When he put his hand again on her cheek, softly, with the most extraordinary soft half-touch, as a kitten's paw sometimes touches one, like a fluff of living air, then, if it had not been for the magic of that almost indiscernible caress of his hand, she would have stiffened herself and drawn away and told him she could have nothing to do with him, while he was so half-hearted and unsatisfactory. She wanted to tell him these things. But when she began he answered invariably in the same soft, straying voice, that seemed to spin gossamer threads all over her, so that she could neither think nor act nor even feel distinctly. Her soul groaned rebelliously in her. And yet, when he put his hand softly under her chin, and lifted her face and smiled down on her with that gargoyle smile of his—she let him kiss her.

"What are you thinking about to-night?" he said. "What are you thinking about?"

"What did your Colonel say to you, exactly?" she replied, trying to harden her eyes.

"Oh, that!" he answered. "Never mind that. That is of no significance whatever."

"But what *is* of any significance?" she insisted. She almost hated him.

"What is of any significance? Well, nothing to me, outside of this room, at this minute. Nothing in time or space matters to me."

"Yes, *this minute*!" she repeated bitterly. "But then there's the future. *I've* got to live in the future."

" The future ! The future ! The future is used up every day. The future to me is like a big tangle of black thread. Every morning you begin to untangle one loose end—and that's your day. And every evening you break off and throw away what you've untangled, and the heap is so much less : just one thread less, one day less. That's all the future matters to me."

" Then nothing matters to you. And I don't matter to you. As you say, only an end of waste thread," she resisted him.

" No, there you're wrong. You aren't the future to me."

" What am I then ?—the past ? "

" No, not any of those things. You're nothing. As far as all that goes, you're nothing."

" Thank you," she said sarcastically, " if I'm nothing."

But the very irrelevancy of the man overcame her. He kissed her with half discernible, dim kisses, and touched her throat. And the meaningless of him fascinated her and left her powerless. She could ascribe no meaning to him, none whatever. And yet his mouth, so strange in kissing, and his hairy forearms, and his slender, beautiful breast with black hair—it was all like a mystery to her, as if one of the men from Mars were loving her. And she was heavy and spellbound, and she loved the spell that bound her. But also she didn't love it.

II

Countess zu Rassentlow had a studio in one of the main streets. She was really a refugee. And nowadays you can be a grand-duke and a pauper, if you are a refugee. But Hannele was not a pauper, because she and her friend Mitchka had the studio where they made these dolls, and beautiful cushions of embroidered coloured wools, and such-like objects of feminine art. The dolls were quite famous, so the two women did not starve.

Hannele did not work much in the studio. She preferred to be alone in her own room, which was another fine attic, not quite so large as the captain's, under the same roof. But often she went to the studio in the afternoon, and if purchasers came, then they were offered a cup of tea.

The Alexander doll was never intended for sale. What made Hannele take it to the studio one afternoon, we do not know. But she did so, and stood it on a little bureau. It was a wonderful little portrait of an officer and gentleman, the physique modelled so that it made you hold your breath.

" And *that*—that is genius ! " cried Mitchka. " That is a *chef*

Q *

d'œuvre ! That is my masterpiece, Hannele. That is really marvellous. And beautiful ! A beautiful man, what ! But no, that is *too* real. I don't understand how you *dare*. I always thought you were *good*, Hannele, so much better-natured than I am. But now you frighten me. I am afraid you are wicked, do you know. It frightens me to think that you are wicked. *Aber nein !* But you won't leave him there ? "

" Why not ? " said Hannele, satiric.

Mitchka made big dark eyes of wonder, reproach, and fear.

" But you *must* not," she said.

" Why not ? "

" No, that you *may* not do. You love the man."

" What then ? "

" You can't leave his puppet standing there."

" Why can't I ? "

" But you are really wicked. *Du bist wirklich bös.* Only think ! —and he is an English officer."

" He isn't sacrosanct even then."

" They will expel you from the town. They will deport you."

" Let them, then."

" But no ! What will you do ? That would be horrible if we had to go to Berlin or to Munich and begin again. Here everything has happened so well."

" I don't care," said Hannele.

Mitchka looked at her friend and said no more. But she was angry. After some time she turned and uttered her ultimatum.

" When you are not there," she said, " I shall put the puppet away in a drawer. I shall show it to nobody, nobody. And I must tell you, it makes me afraid to see it there. It makes me afraid. And you have no right to get me into trouble, do you see. It is not I who look at the English officers. I don't like them, they are too cold and finished off for me. I shall never bring trouble on *myself* because of the English officers."

" Don't be afraid," said Hannele. " They won't trouble *you*. They know everything we do, well enough. They have their spies everywhere. Nothing will happen to you."

" But if they make you go away—and I am planted here with the studio——"

It was no good, however ; Hannele was obstinate.

So, one sunny afternoon there was a ring at the door : a little lady in white, with a wrinkled face that still had its prettiness.

" Good afternoon ! "—in rather lardy-dardy middle-class English. " I wonder if I may see your things in your studio."

" Oh yes ! " said Mitchka. " Please to come in."

Entered the little lady in her finery and her crumpled prettiness. She would not be very old ; perhaps younger than fifty. And it was odd that her face had gone so crumpled, because her figure was very trim, her eyes were bright, and she had pretty teeth when she laughed. She was very fine in her clothes : a dress of thick knitted white silk, a large ermine scarf with the tails only at the ends, and a black hat over which dripped a trail of green feathers of the osprey sort. She wore rather a lot of jewellery, and two bangles tinkled over her white kid gloves as she put up her fingers to touch her hair whilst she stood complacently and looked round.

" You've got a *charming* studio—*charming*—perfectly delightful ! I couldn't imagine anything more delightful."

Mitchka gave a slight ironic bow, and said, in her odd, plangent English :

" Oh yes. We like it very much also."

Hannele, who had dodged behind a screen, now came quickly forth.

" Oh, how do you do ! " smiled the elderly lady. " I heard there were two of you. Now which is which, if I may be so bold ? This " —and she gave a winsome smile and pointed a white kid finger at Mitchka—" is the——? "

" Annamaria von Prielau-Carolath," said Mitchka, slightly bowing.

" Oh ! "—and the white kid finger jerked away. " Then this——"

" Johanna zu Rassentlow," said Hannele, smiling.

" Ah, yes ! Countess von Rassentlow ! And this is Baroness von— von—but I shall never remember even if you tell me, for I'm awful at names. Anyhow, I shall call one *Countess* and the other *Baroness*. That will do, won't it, for poor me ! Now I should like awfully to see your things, if I may. I want to buy a little present to take back to England with me. I suppose I shan't have to pay the world in duty on things like these, shall I ? "

" Oh no," said Mitchka. " No duty. Toys, you know, they— there is—— " Her English stammered to an end, so she turned to Hannele.

" They don't charge duty on toys, and the embroideries they don't notice," said Hannele.

" Oh well. Then I'm all right," said the visitor. " I hope I can buy something really nice ! I see a perfectly lovely jumper over there, perfectly delightful. But a little too gay for me, I'm afraid.

I'm not quite so young as I was, alas." She smiled her winsome little smile, showing her pretty teeth, and the old pearls in her ears shook.

" I've heard so much about your dolls. I hear they're perfectly exquisite, quite works of art. May I see some, please."

" Oh yes," came Mitchka's invariable answer, this exclamation being the foundation stone of all her English.

There were never more than three or four dolls in stock. This time there were only two. The famous captain was hidden in his drawer.

" Perfectly beautiful ! Perfectly wonderful ! " murmured the little lady, in an artistic murmur. " I think they're perfectly delightful. It's wonderful of you, Countess, to make them. It is you who make them, is it not ? Or do you both do them together ? "

Hannele explained, and the inspection and the rhapsody went on together. But it was evident that the little lady was a cautious buyer. She went over the things very carefully, and thought more than twice. The dolls attracted her—but she thought them expensive, and hung fire.

" I do wish," she said wistfully, " there had been a larger selection of the dolls. I feel, you know, there might have been one which I *just loved*. Of course these are *darlings*—darlings they are : and worth every *penny*, considering the work there is in them. And the art, of course. But I have a feeling, don't you know how it is, that if there had been just one or two more, I should have found one which I *absolutely* couldn't live without. Don't you know how it is ? One is so foolish, of course. What does Goethe say—' Dort wo du nicht bist . . .' ? My German isn't even a beginning, so you must excuse it. But it means you always feel you would be happy somewhere else, and not just where you are. Isn't that it ? Ah well, it's so very often true—so very often. But not always, thank goodness." She smiled an odd little smile to herself, pursed her lips, and resumed : " Well now, that's how I feel about the dolls. If only there had been one or two more. Isn't there a single one ? "

She looked winsomely at Hannele.

" Yes," said Hannele, " there is one. But it is ordered. It isn't for sale."

" Oh, do you think I might see it ? I'm sure it's lovely. Oh, I'm dying to see it. You know what woman's curiosity is, don't you ? " —she laughed her tinkling little laugh. " Well, I'm afraid I'm all woman, unfortunately. One is so much harder if one has a touch of the man in one, don't you think, and more able to bear things. But I'm afraid I'm all woman." She sighed and became silent.

Hannele went quietly to the drawer and took out the captain. She handed him to the little woman. The latter looked frightened. Her eyes became round and childish, her face went yellowish. Her jewels tinkled nervously as she stammered :

" Now *that*—isn't that——" and she laughed a little, hysterical laugh.

She turned round, as if to escape.

" Do you mind if I sit down," she said. " I think the stand-ing——" and she subsided into a chair. She kept her face averted. But she held the puppet fast, her small, white fingers with their heavy jewelled rings clasped round his waist.

" You know," rushed in Mitchka, who was terrified. " You know, that is a life-picture of one of the Englishmen, of a gentleman, you know. A life-picture, you know."

" A portrait," said Hannele brightly.

" Yes," murmured the visitor vaguely. " I'm sure it is. I'm sure it is a very clever portrait indeed."

She fumbled with a chain, and put up a small gold lorgnette before her eyes, as if to screen herself. And from behind the screen of her lorgnette she peered at the image in her hand.

" But," she said, " none of the English officers, or rather Scottish, wear the close-fitting tartan trews any more—except for fancy dress."

Her voice was vague and distant.

" No, they don't now," said Hannele. " But that is the correct dress. I think they are so handsome, don't you ? "

" Well. I don't know. It depends "—and the little woman laughed shakily.

" Oh yes," said Hannele. " It needs well-shapen legs."

" Such as the original of your doll must have had—quite," said the lady.

" Oh yes," said Hannele. " I think his legs are very handsome."

" Quite ! " said the lady. " Judging from his portrait, as you call it. May I ask the name of the gentleman—if it is not too indiscreet ? "

" Captain Hepburn," said Hannele.

" Yes, of course it is. I knew him at once. I've known him for many years."

" Oh, please," broke in Mitchka. " Oh, please, do not tell him you have seen it ! Oh, please ! Please not to tell any one ! "

The visitor looked up with a grey little smile.

" But why not ? " she said. " Anyhow, I can't tell him at once, because I hear he is away at present. You don't happen to know when he will be back ? "

" I believe to-morrow," said Hannele.

" To-morrow ! "

" And please ! " pleaded Mitchka, who looked lovely in her plead-ing distress, " please not to tell anybody that you have seen it."

" Must I promise ? " smiled the little lady wanly. " Very well, then, I won't tell him I've seen it. And now I think I must be going. Yes, I'll just take the cushion cover, thank you. Tell me again how much it is, please."

That evening Hannele was restless. He had been away on some duty for three days. He was returning that night—should have been back in time for dinner. But he had not arrived, and his room was locked and dark. Hannele had heard the servant light the stove some hours ago. Now the room was locked and blank as it had been for three days.

Hannele was most uneasy because she seemed to have forgotten him in the three days whilst he had been away. He seemed to have quite disappeared out of her. She could hardly even remember him. He had become so insignificant to her she was dazed.

Now she wanted to see him again, to know if it was really so. She felt that he was coming. She felt that he was already putting out some influence towards her. But what ? And was he real ? Why had she made his doll ? Why had his doll been so important, if he was nothing ? Why had she shown it to that funny little woman this afternoon ? Why was she herself such a fool, getting herself into tangles in this place where it was so unpleasant to be entangled ? Why was she entangled, after all ? It was all so unreal. And par-ticularly *he* was unreal : as unreal as a person in a dream, whom one has never heard of in actual life. In actual life, her own German friends were real. Martin was real ; German men were real to her. But this other, he was simply not there. He didn't really exist. He was a nullus, in reality. A nullus—and she had somehow got herself complicated with him.

Was it possible ? Was it possible she had been so closely entangled with an absolute nothing ? Now he was absent she couldn't even *imagine* him. He had gone out of her imagination, and even when she looked at his doll she saw nothing but a barren puppet. And yet for this dead puppet, she had been compromising herself, now, when it was so risky for her to be compromised.

Her own German friends—her own German men—they were men, they were real beings. But this English officer, he was neither fish, flesh, fowl, nor good red herring, as they say. He was just a hypothetical presence. She felt that if he never came back, she would be just as if she had read a rather peculiar but false story, a *tour de force* which works up one's imagination all falsely.

Nevertheless she was uneasy. She had a lurking suspicion that there might be something else. So she kept uneasily wandering out on to the landing, and listening, to hear if he might be coming.

Yes—there was a sound. Yes, there was his slow step on the stairs, and the slow, straying purr of his voice. And instantly she heard his voice she was afraid again. She knew there *was* something there. And instantly she felt the reality of his presence, she felt the unreality of her own German men-friends. The moment she heard the peculiar, slow melody of his foreign voice everything seemed to go changed in her, and Martin and Otto and Albrecht, her German friends, seemed to go pale and dim as if one could almost see through them, like unsubstantial things.

This was what she had to reckon with, this recoil from one to the other. When he was present, he seemed so terribly real. When he was absent he was completely vague, and her own men of her own race seemed so absolutely the only reality.

But he was talking. Who was he talking to? She heard the steps echo up the hollows of the stone staircase, slowly, as if wearily, and voices slowly, confusedly mingle. The slow, soft trail of his voice—and then the peculiar, quick tones—yes, of a woman. And not one of the maids, because they were speaking English. She listened hard. The quick, and yet slightly hushed, slightly sad-sounding voice of a woman who talks a good deal, as if talking to herself. Hannele's quick ears caught the sound of what she was saying : " Yes, I thought the Baroness a perfectly beautiful creature, perfectly lovely. But so extraordinarily like a Spaniard. Do you remember, Alec, at Malaga ? I always thought they fascinated you then, with their mantillas. Perfectly lovely she would look in a mantilla. Only perhaps she is too open-hearted, too impulsive, poor thing. She lacks the Spanish reserve. Poor thing, I feel sorry for her. For them both, indeed. It must be very hard to have to do these things for a living, after you've been accustomed to be made much of for your own sake, and for your aristocratic title. It's very hard for them, poor things. Baroness, Countess, it sounds just a little ridiculous, when you're buying woollen embroideries from them. But I suppose, poor things, they can't help it. Better drop the titles altogether, I think——"

" Well, they do, if people will let them. Only English and American people find it so much easier to say Baroness or Countess than Fräulein von Prielau-Carolath, or whatever it is."

" They could say simply Fräulein, as we do to our governesses—or as we used to, when we *had* German governesses," came the voice of *her*.

" Yes, we *could*," said his voice.

" After all, what is the good, what is the good of titles if you have to sell dolls and woollen embroideries—not so very beautiful, either."

" Oh, quite ! Oh, quite ! I think titles are perhaps a mistake, anyhow. But they've always had them," came his slow, musical voice, with its sing-song note of hopeless indifference. He sounded rather like a man talking out of his sleep.

Hannele caught sight of the tail of blue-green crane feathers veering round a turn in the stairs away below, and she beat a hasty retreat.

III

There was a little platform out on the roof, where he used sometimes to stand his telescope and observe the stars or the moon : the moon when possible. It was not a very safe platform, just a little ledge of the roof, outside the window at the end of the top corridor : or rather, the top landing, for it was only the space between the attics. Hannele had the one attic-room at the back, he had the room we have seen, and a little bedroom which was really only a lumber-room. Before he came, Hannele had been alone under the roof. His rooms were then lumber-room and laundry-room, where the clothes were dried. But he had wanted to be high up, because of his stars, and this was the place that pleased him.

Hannele heard him quite late in the night, wandering about. She heard him also on the ledge outside. She could not sleep. He disturbed her. The moon was risen, large and bright in the sky. She heard the bells from the cathedral slowly strike two : two great drops of sound in the livid night. And again, from outside on the roof, she heard him clear his throat. Then a cat howled.

She rose, wrapped herself in a dark wrap, and went down the landing to the window at the end. The sky outside was full of moonlight. He was squatted like a great cat peering up his telescope, sitting on a stool, his knees wide apart. Quite motionless he sat in that attitude, like some leaden figure on the roof. The moonlight glistened with a gleam of plumbago on the great slope of black tiles. She stood still in the window, watching. And he remained fixed and motionless at the end of the telescope.

She tapped softly on the window-pane. He looked round, like

some tom-cat staring round with wide night-eyes. Then he reached down his hand and pulled the window open.

" Hello," he said quietly. " You not asleep ? "

" Aren't *you* tired ? " she replied, rather resentful.

" No, I was as wide awake as I could be. *Isn't* the moon fine to-night ! What ? Perfectly amazing. Wouldn't you like to come up and have a look at her ? "

" No, thank you," she said hastily, terrified at the thought.

He resumed his posture, peering up the telescope.

" Perfectly amazing," he said, murmuring. She waited for some time, bewitched likewise by the great October moon and the sky full of resplendent white-green light. It seemed like another sort of day-time. And there he straddled on the roof like some cat ! It was exactly like day in some other planet.

At length he turned round to her. His face glistened faintly, and his eyes were dilated like a cat's at night.

" You know I had a visitor ? " he said.

" Yes."

" My wife."

" Your *wife* ! "—she looked up really astonished. She had thought it might be an acquaintance—perhaps his aunt—or even an elder sister. " But she's years older than you," she added.

" Eight years," he said. " I'm forty-one."

There was a silence.

" Yes," he mused. " She arrived suddenly, by surprise, yesterday, and found me away. She's staying in the hotel in the Vier Jahreszeiten."

There was a pause.

" Aren't you going to stay with her ? " asked Hannele.

" Yes, I shall probably join her to-morrow."

There was a still longer pause.

" Why not to-night ? " asked Hannele.

" Oh, well—I put it off for to-night. It meant all the bother of my wife changing her room at the hotel—and it was late—and I was all mucky after travelling."

" But you'll go to-morrow ? "

" Yes, I shall go to-morrow. For a week or so. After that I'm not sure what will happen."

There was quite a long pause. He remained seated on his stool on the roof, looking with dilated, blank, black eyes at nothingness. She stood below in the open window-space, pondering.

" Do you want to go to her at the hotel ? " asked Hannele.

" Well, I don't, particularly. But I don't mind, really. We're very good friends. Why, we've been friends for eighteen years—we've been married seventeen. Oh, she's a nice little woman. I don't want to hurt her feelings. I wish her no harm, you know. On the contrary, I wish her all the good in the world."

He had no idea of the blank amazement in which Hannele listened to these stray remarks.

" But——" she stammered. " But doesn't she expect you to make *love* to her ? "

" Oh, yes, she expects that. You bet she does : woman-like."

" And you ? "—the question had a dangerous ring.

" Why, I don't mind, really, you know, if it's only for a short time. I'm used to her. I've always been fond of her, you know—and so if it gives her any pleasure—why, I like her to get what pleasure out of life she can."

" But *you*—you *yourself* ! Don't *you* feel anything ? " Hannele's amazement was reaching the point of incredulity. She began to feel that he was making it up. It was all so different from her own point of view. To sit there so quiet and to make such statements in all good faith : no, it was impossible.

" I don't consider I count," he said naïvely.

Hannele looked aside. If that wasn't lying, it was imbecility, or worse. She had for the moment nothing to say. She felt he was a sort of psychic phenomenon like a grasshopper or a tadpole or an ammonite. Not to be regarded from a human point of view. No, he just wasn't normal. And she had been fascinated by him ! It was only sheer, amazed curiosity that carried her on to her next question.

" But do you *never* count, then ? " she asked, and there was a touch of derision, of laughter in her tone. He took no offence.

" Well—very rarely," he said. " I count very rarely. That's how life appears to me. One matters so *very* little."

She felt quite dizzy with astonishment. And he called himself a man !

" But if you matter so very little, what do you do anything at all for ? " she asked.

" Oh, one has to. And then, why not ? Why not do things even if oneself hardly matters. Look at the moon. It doesn't matter in the least to the moon whether I exist or whether I don't. So why should it matter to me ? "

After a blank pause of incredulity she said :

" I could die with laughter. It seems to me all so ridiculous—no, I can't believe it."

" Perhaps it is a point of view," he said.

There was a long and pregnant silence : we should not like to say pregnant with what.

" And so I don't mean anything to you at all ? " she said.

" I didn't say that," he replied.

" Nothing means anything to you," she challenged.

" I don't say that."

" Whether it's your wife—or me—or the moon—*toute la même chose.*"

" No—no—that's hardly the way to look at it."

She gazed at him in such utter amazement that she felt something would really explode in her if she heard another word. Was this a man ?—or what was it ! It was too much for her, that was all.

" Well, good-bye," she said. " I hope you will have a nice time at the Vier Jahreszeiten."

So she left him still sitting on the roof.

" I suppose," she said to herself, " that is love *à l'anglaise.* But it's more than I can swallow."

IV

" Won't you come and have tea with me—do ! Come right along now. Don't you find it bitterly cold ? Yes—well now—come in with me and we'll have a cup of nice, hot tea, in our little sitting-room. The weather changes so suddenly, and really, one needs a little reinforcement. But perhaps you don't take tea ? "

" Oh yes. I got so used to it in England," said Hannele.

" Did you now ! Well now, were you long in England ? "

" Oh yes——"

The two women had met in the Domplatz. Mrs. Hepburn was looking extraordinarily like one of Hannele's dolls, in a funny little cape of odd striped skins, and a little dark-green skirt, and a rather fuzzy sort of hat. Hannele looked almost huge beside her.

" But now you will come in and have tea, won't you ? Oh, please do. Never mind whether it's *de rigueur* or not. I *always* please myself *what* I do. I'm afraid my husband gets some shocks some-times—but that we can't help. I won't have anybody laying down the law to me." She laughed her winsome little laugh. " So now come along in, and we'll see if there aren't hot scones as well. I love a hot scone for tea in cold weather. And I hope you do. That is, if there are any. We don't know yet." She tinkled her little laugh. " My husband may or may not be in. But that makes no difference to you and me, does it ? There, it's just striking half-past four. In

England we always have tea at half-past. My husband *adores* his tea. I don't suppose our man is five minutes off the half-past, ringing the gong for tea, not once in twelve months. My husband doesn't mind at all if dinner is a little late. But he gets quite—well, quite ' ratty ' if tea is late." She tinkled a laugh. " Though I shouldn't say that. He is the soul of kindness and patience. I don't think I've ever known him to do an unkind thing—or hardly say an unkind word. But I doubt if he will be in to-day."

He *was* in, however, standing with his feet apart and his hands in his trouser pockets in the little sitting-room upstairs in the hotel. He raised his eyebrows the smallest degree, seeing Hannele enter.

" Ah, Countess Hannele—my wife has brought you along ! Very nice, very nice ! Let me take your wrap. Oh, yes, certainly . . ."

" Have you rung for tea, dear ? " asked Mrs. Hepburn.

" Er—yes. I said as soon as you came in they were to bring it."

" Yes—well. Won't you ring again, dear, and say for *three*."

" Yes—certainly. Certainly."

He rang, and stood about with his hands in his pockets waiting for tea.

" Well now," said Mrs. Hepburn, as she lifted the teapot, and her bangles tinkled, and her huge rings of brilliants twinkled, and her big ear-rings of clustered seed-pearls bobbed against her rather withered cheek, " isn't it charming of Countess zu—Countess zu——"

" Rassentlow," said he. " I believe most people say Countess Hannele. I know we always do among ourselves. We say Countess Hannele's shop."

" Countess Hannele's shop ! Now, isn't that perfectly delightful : such a romance in the very sound of it. You take cream ? "

" Thank you," said Hannele.

The tea passed in a cloud of chatter, while Mrs. Hepburn manipulated the teapot, and lit the spirit-flame, and blew it out, and peeped into the steam of the teapot, and couldn't see whether there was any more tea or not—and—" At home I *know*—I was going to say to a teaspoonful—how much tea there is in the pot. But this teapot—I don't know what it's made of—it isn't silver, I know that—it is so heavy in itself, that it's deceived me several times already. And my husband is a greedy man, a greedy man—he likes at least three cups —and four if he can get them, or five ! Yes, dear, I've plenty of tea to-day. You shall have even five, if you don't mind the last two weak. Do let me fill your cup, Countess Hannele. I think it's a *charming* name."

" There's a play called *Hannele*, isn't there ? " said he.

When he had had his five cups, and his wife had got her cigarette perched in the end of a long, long slim white holder, and was puffing like a little China-woman from the distance, there was a little lull.

" Alec, dear," said Mrs. Hepburn. " You won't forget to leave that message for me at Mrs. Rackham's. I'm so afraid it will be forgotten."

" No, dear, I won't forget. Er—would you like me to go round now ? "

Hannele noticed how often he said " er," when he was beginning to speak to his wife. But they *were* such good friends, the two of them.

" Why if you *would*, dear, I should feel perfectly comfortable. But I don't want you to hurry one bit."

" Oh, I may as well go now."

And he went. Mrs. Hepburn detained her guest.

" He *is* so charming to me," said the little woman. " He's really wonderful. And he always has been the same—invariably. So that if he *did* make a little slip—well, you know, I don't have to take it so seriously."

" No," said Hannele, feeling as if her ears were stretching with astonishment.

" It's the war. It's just the war. It's had a terribly deteriorating effect on the men."

" In what way ? " said Hannele.

" Why, morally. Really, there's hardly one man left the same as he was before the war. Terribly degenerated."

" Is that so ? " said Hannele.

" It is indeed. Why, isn't it the same with the German men and officers ? "

" Yes, I think so," said Hannele.

" And I'm sure so, from what I hear. But of course it is the women who are to blame in the first place. We poor women ! We are a guilty race, I am afraid. But I never throw stones. I know what it is myself to have temptations. I have to flirt a little—and when I was younger—well, the men didn't escape me, I assure you. And I was *so* often scorched. But never *quite* singed. My husband never minded. He knew I was *really* safe. Oh yes, I have always been faithful to him. But still—I have been *very* near the flame." And she laughed her winsome little laugh.

Hannele put her fingers to her ears, to make sure they were not falling off.

" Of course during the war it was terrible. I know that in a certain hospital it was quite impossible for a girl to stay on if she kept straight. The matrons and sisters just turned her out. They wouldn't have her unless she was one of themselves. And you know what that means. Quite like the convent in Balzac's story—you know which I mean, I'm sure." And the laugh tinkled gaily.

"But then, what can you expect, when there aren't enough men to go round ! Why, I had a friend in Ireland. She and her husband had been an ideal couple, an *ideal* couple. Real playmates. And you can't say more than that, can you ? Well, then, he became a major during the war. And she was so looking forward, poor thing, to the perfectly lovely times they would have together when he came home. She is like me, and is lucky enough to have a little income of her own—not a great fortune—but—well—— Well now, what was I going to say. Oh yes, she was looking forward to the perfectly lovely times they would have when he came home : building on her dreams, poor thing, as we unfortunate women always do. I suppose we shall never be cured of it." A little tinkling laugh. "Well now, not a bit of it. Not a bit of it." Mrs. Hepburn lifted her heavily-jewelled little hand in a motion of protest. It was curious, her hands were pretty and white, and her neck and breast, now she wore a little tea-gown, were also smooth and white and pretty, under the medley of twinkling little chains and coloured jewels. Why should her face have played her this nasty trick of going all crumpled ? However, it was so.

"Not one bit of it," reiterated the little lady. "He came home quite changed. She said she could hardly recognize him for the same man. Let me tell you one little incident. Just a trifle, but significant. He was coming home—this was some time after he was free from the army—he was coming home from London, and he told her to meet him at the boat : gave her the time and everything. Well, she went to the boat, poor thing, and he didn't come. She waited, and no word of explanation or anything. So she couldn't make up her mind whether to go next day and meet the boat again. However, she decided she wouldn't. So of course, on that boat he arrived. When he got home, he said to her, ' Why didn't you meet the boat ? ' ' Well,' she said, ' I went yesterday, and you didn't come.' ' Then why didn't you meet it again to-day ? ' Imagine it, the sauce ! And they had been real playmates. Heartbreaking, isn't it ? ' Well,' she said in self-defence, ' why didn't you come yesterday ? ' ' Oh,' he said, ' I met a woman in town whom I liked, and she asked me to spend the night with her, so I did.' Now what do you think of that ? Can you conceive of such a thing ? "

"Oh no," said Hannele. "I call that unnecessary brutality."

"Exactly! So terrible to say such a thing to her! The brutality of it! Well, that's how the world is to-day. I'm thankful my husband isn't that sort. I don't say he's perfect. But whatever else he did, he'd never be unkind, and he *couldn't* be brutal. He just couldn't. He'd never tell me a lie—I know *that*. But callous brutality, no, thank goodness, he hasn't a spark of it in him. I'm the wicked one, if either of us is wicked." The little laugh tinkled. "Oh! but he's been perfect to me, perfect. Hardly a cross word. Why, on our wedding night, he kneeled down in front of me and promised, with God's help, to make my life happy. And I must say, as far as possible, he's kept his word. It has been his one aim in life, to make my life happy."

The little lady looked away with a bright, musing look, towards the window. She was being a heroine in a romance. Hannele could see her being a heroine, playing the chief part in her own life-romance. It is such a feminine occupation, that no woman takes offence when she is made audience.

"I'm afraid I've more of the woman than the mother in my composition," resumed the little heroine. "I adore my two children. The boy is at Winchester, and my little girl is in a convent in Brittany. Oh, they are perfect darlings, both of them. But the man is first in my mind, I'm afraid. I fear I'm rather old-fashioned. But never mind. I can see the attractions in other men—can't I indeed! There was a perfectly exquisite creature—he was a very clever engineer—but much, much more than *that*. But never mind." The little heroine sniffed as if there were perfume in the air, folded her jewelled hands, and resumed: "However—I know what it is myself to flutter round the flame. You know I'm Irish myself, and we Irish can't help it. Oh, I wouldn't be English for anything. Just that little touch of imagination, you know . . ." The little laugh tinkled. "And that's what makes me able to sympathize with my husband even when, perhaps, I shouldn't. Why, when he was at home with me, he never gave a thought, not a thought to another woman. I must say, he used to make *me* feel a little guilty sometimes. But there! I don't think he ever thought of another woman as being flesh and blood, after he knew me. I could tell. Pleasant, courteous, charming—but other women were not flesh and blood to him, they were just people, callers—that kind of thing. It used to amaze me, when some perfectly lovely creature came, whom I should have been head over heels in love with in a minute—and he, he was charming, delightful; he could see her points, but she

was no more to him than, let me say, a pot of carnations, or a beautiful old piece of punto di Milano. Not flesh and blood. Well,
perhaps one can feel too safe. Perhaps one needs a tiny pinch of the
salt of jealousy. I believe one does. And I have not had one jealous
moment for seventeen years. So that, *really*, when I heard a whisper
of something going on here, I felt almost pleased. I felt exonerated
for my own little peccadilloes, for one thing. And I felt he was
perhaps a little more human. Because, after all, it is nothing but
human to fall in love, if you are alone for a long time and in the
company of a beautiful woman—and if you're an attractive man
yourself."

Hannele sat with her eyes propped open and her ears buttoned
back with amazement, expecting the next revelations.

" Why, of course," she said, knowing she was expected to say
something.

" Yes, of course," said Mrs. Hepburn, eyeing her sharply. " So
I thought I'd better come and see how far things had gone. I had
nothing but a hint to go on. I knew no name—nothing.
I had just a hint that she was German, and a refugee aristocrat
—and that he used to call at the studio." The little lady eyed
Hannele sharply, and gave a breathless little laugh, clasping her
hands nervously. Hannele sat absolutely blank : really dazed.

" Of course," resumed Mrs. Hepburn, " that was enough. That
was quite a sufficient clue. I'm afraid my intentions when I called
at the studio were not as pure as they might have been. I'm afraid
I wanted to see something more than the dolls. But when you showed
me *his* doll, then I knew. Of course there wasn't a shadow of doubt
after that. And I saw at once that she loved him, poor thing. She
was *so* agitated. And no idea who I was. And you were so unkind
to show me the doll. Of course you had no idea who you were
showing it to. But for her, poor thing, it was such a trial. I could
see how she suffered. And I must say she's very lovely—she's very,
very lovely, with her golden skin and her reddish amber eyes and her
beautiful, beautiful carriage. And such a naïve, impulsive nature.
Gives everything away in a minute. And then her deep voice—
' *Oh yes—Oh please !* '—such a child. And such an aristocrat, that
lovely turn of her head, and her simple, elegant dress. Oh, she's very
charming. And she's just the type I always knew would attract him,
if he hadn't got me. I've thought about it many a time—many a
time. When a woman is older than a man, she does think these
things—especially if he has his attractive points too. And when I've
dreamed of the woman he would love if he hadn't got me, it has

always been a Spanish type. And the Baroness is extraordinarily Spanish in her appearance. She must have had some noble Spanish ancestor. Don't you think so ? "

" Oh yes," said Hannele. " There were such a lot of Spaniards in Austria, too, with the various emperors."

" With Charles V, exactly. Exactly. That's how it must have been. And so she has all the Spanish beauty, and all the German feeling. Of course, for myself, I miss the *reserve*, the haughtiness. But she's very, very lovely, and I'm sure I could never *hate* her. I couldn't even if I tried. And I'm not going to try. But I think she's much too dangerous for my husband to see much of her. Don't you agree, now ? "

" Oh, but really," stammered Hannele. " There's nothing in it, really."

" Well," said the little lady, cocking her head shrewdly aside, " I shouldn't like there to be any *more* in it."

And there was a moment's dead pause. Each woman was reflecting. Hannele wondered if the little lady was just fooling her.

" Anyhow," continued Mrs. Hepburn, " the spark is there, and I don't intend the fire to spread. I am going to be very, very careful, myself, not to fan the flames. The last thing I should think of would be to make my husband scenes. I believe it would be fatal."

" Yes," said Hannele, during the pause.

" I'm going very carefully. You think there isn't much in it— between him and the Baroness ? "

" No—no—I'm sure there isn't," cried Hannele, with a full voice of conviction. She was almost indignant at being slighted so completely herself, in the little lady's suspicions.

" Hm !—mm ! " hummed the little woman, sapiently nodding her head slowly up and down. " I'm not so sure ! I'm not so sure that it hasn't gone pretty far."

" Oh *no* ! " cried Hannele, in real irritation of protest.

" Well," said the other. " In any case, I don't intend it to go any further."

There was dead silence for some time.

" There's more in it than you say. There's more in it than you say," ruminated the little woman. " I know *him*, for one thing. I know he's got a cloud on his brow. And I know it hasn't left his brow for a single minute. And when I told him I had been to the studio, and showed him the cushion-cover, I knew he felt guilty. I am not so easily deceived. We Irish all have a touch of second sight, I believe. Of course I haven't challenged him. I haven't even mentioned the doll. By the way, *who* ordered the doll ? Do you mind telling me ? "

" No, it wasn't ordered," confessed Hannele.

" Ah—I thought not—I thought not ! " said Mrs. Hepburn, lifting her finger. " At least, I knew no outsider had ordered it. Of course I knew." And she smiled to herself.

" So," she continued, " I had too much sense to say anything about it. I don't believe in stripping wounds bare. I believe in gently covering them and letting them heal. But I *did* say I thought her a lovely creature." The little lady looked brightly at Hannele.

" Yes," said Hannele.

" And he was very vague in his manner. ' Yes, not bad,' he said. I thought to myself, Aha, my boy, you don't deceive me with your *not bad*. She's very much more than not bad. I said so, too. I wanted, of course, to let him know I had a suspicion."

" And do you think he knew ? "

" Of course he did. Of course he did. ' She's much too dangerous,' I said, ' to be in a town where there are so many strange men : married and unmarried.' And then he turned round to me and gave himself away, oh, so plainly. ' Why ? ' he said. But such a haughty distant tone. I said to myself, ' It's time, my dear boy, you were removed out of the danger-zone.' But I answered him : ' Surely somebody is bound to fall in love with her.' ' Not at all,' he said, ' she keeps to her own countrymen.' ' You don't tell *me*,' I answered him, ' with her pretty broken English ! It is a wonder the two of them are allowed to stay in the town.' And then again he rounded on me. ' Good gracious ! ' he said. ' Would you have them turned out just because they're beautiful to look at, when they have nowhere else to go, and they make their bit of a livelihood here ? ' I assure you, he hasn't rounded on me in that overbearing way, not once before, in all our married life. So I just said quietly : ' I should like to protect *our own men*.' And he didn't say anything more. But he looked at me under his brows, and went out of the room."

There was a silence. Hannele waited with her hands in her lap, and Mrs. Hepburn mused, with her hands in *her* lap. Her face looked yellow, and *very* wrinkled.

" Well now," she said, breaking again suddenly into life. " What are we to do ? I mean what is to be done ? You are the Baroness' nearest friend. And I wish her *no* harm, none whatever."

" What can we do ? " said Hannele, in the pause.

" I have been urging my husband for some time to get his dis-charge from the army," said the little woman. " I know he could have it in three months' time. But like so many more men, he has no income of his own, and he doesn't want to feel dependent. Perfect nonsense ! . So he says he wants to stay on in the army. I have never known him before go against my real wishes."

" But it *is* better for a man to be independent," said Hannele.

" I know it is. But it is also better for him to be *at home*. And I could get him a post in one of the observatories. He could do some-thing in meteorological work."

Hannele refused to answer any more.

" Of course," said Mrs. Hepburn, " if he *does* stay on here, it would be much better if the Baroness left the town."

" I'm sure she will never leave of her own choice," said Hannele.

" I'm sure she won't either. But she might be made to see that it would be very much *wiser* of her to move of her own free will."

" Why ? " said Hannele.

" Why, because she might any time be removed by the British authorities."

" Why should she ? " said Hannele.

" I think the women who are a menace to our men should be removed."

" But she is *not* a menace to your men."

" Well, I have my own opinion on that point."

Which was a decided deadlock.

" I'm sure I've kept you an awful long time with my chatter," said Mrs. Hepburn. " But I did want to make everything as simple as possible. As I said before, I can't feel any ill-will against her. Yet I can't let things just go on. Heaven alone knows when they may end. Of course if I can persuade my husband to resign his commission and come back to England—anyhow, we will see. I'm sure I am the last person in the world to bear malice."

The tone in which she said it conveyed a dire threat.

Hannele rose from her chair.

" Oh, and one other thing," said her hostess, taking out a tiny lace handkerchief and touching her nose delicately with it. " Do you think "—dab—dab—" that I might have that *doll*—you know—— ? "

" That—— ? "

" Yes, of my husband "—the little lady rubbed her nose with her kerchief.

" The price is three guineas," said Hannele.

"Oh, indeed!"—the tone was very cold. "I thought it was not for sale."

Hannele put on her wrap.

"You'll send it round—will you?—if you will be so kind."

"I must ask my friend, first."

"Yes, of course. But I'm sure she will be so kind as to send it me. It is a little—er—indelicate, don't you think!"

"No," said Hannele. "No more than a painted portrait."

"Don't you?" said her hostess coldly. "Well, even a painted portrait I think I should like in my own possession. This *doll*——"

Hannele waited, but there was no conclusion.

"Anyhow," she said, "the price is three guineas: or the equivalent in marks."

"Very well," said the little lady, "you shall have your three guineas when I get the doll."

V

Hannele went her way pondering. A man never is quite such an abject specimen as his wife makes him look, talking about "my husband." Therefore, if any woman wishes to rescue her husband from the clutches of another female, let her only invite this female to tea and talk quite sincerely about "my husband, you know." Every man has made a ghastly fool of himself with a woman, at some time or other. No woman ever forgets. And most women will give the show away, with real pathos, to another woman. For instance, the picture of Alec at his wife's feet on his wedding night, vowing to devote himself to her lifelong happiness—this picture strayed across Hannele's mind time after time, whenever she thought of her dear captain. With disastrous consequences to the captain. Of course if he had been at her own feet, then Hannele would have thought it almost natural: almost a necessary part of the show of love. But at the feet of that other little woman! And what was that other little woman wearing? Her wedding night! Hannele hoped before heaven it wasn't some awful little nighty of frail flowered silk. Imagine it, that little lady! Perhaps in a chic little boudoir cap of punto di Milano, and this slip of frail flowered silk: and the man, perhaps, in his braces! Oh, merciful heaven, save us from other people's indiscretions. No, let us be sure it was in proper evening dress—twenty years ago—very low cut, with a full skirt gathered behind and trailing a little, and a little feather-erection in her high-dressed hair, and all those jewels: pearls of course: and he in a dinner-jacket and a white waistcoat: probably in an hotel bedroom in Lugano, or Biarritz. And she? Was she standing with one small hand on his shoulder? Or was she seated on the couch in the bedroom? Oh, dreadful thought! And yet, it was almost inevitable, that scene. Hannele had never been married, but she had come quite near enough to the realization of the event to know that such a scene *was* practically inevitable. An indispensable part of any honeymoon. Him on his knees, with his heels up!

And how black and tidy his hair must have been then! And no grey at the temples at all. Such a good-looking bridegroom. Perhaps with a white rose in his button-hole still. And she could see him kneeling there, in his new black trousers, and a wing collar. And she could see his head bowed. And she could hear his plangent, musical voice saying: "With God's help, I will make your life happy. I will live for that and for nothing else." And then the little lady must have had tears in her eyes, and she must have said, rather superbly: "Thank you, dear. I'm perfectly sure of it."

Ach! Ach! Husbands should be left to their own wives: and wives should be left to their own husbands. And *no* stranger should ever be made a party to these terrible bits of connubial staging. Nay, thought Hannele, that scene was really true. It actually took place. And with the man of that scene I have been in love! With the devoted husband of that little lady. Oh God, oh God, how was it possible! Him on his knees, on his knees, with his heels up!

Am I a perfect fool? she thought to herself. Am I really just an idiot, gaping with love for him? How *could* I? How could I? The very way he says "Yes, dear!" to her! The way he does what she tells him! The way he fidgets about the room with his hands in his pockets! The way he goes off when she sends him away because she wants to talk to me. And he knows she wants to talk to me. And he knows what she *might* have to say to me. Yet he goes off on his errand without a question, like a servant. "I will do whatever you wish, darling." He must have said those words time after time, to the little lady. And fulfilled them, also. Performed all his pledges and his promises.

Ach! Ach! Hannele wrung her hands to think of *herself* being mixed up with him. And he had seemed to her so manly. He seemed to have so much silent male passion in him. And yet—the little lady! "My husband has *always* been *perfectly sweet* to me." Think of it! On his knees too. And his "Yes, dear! Certainly. Certainly." Not that he was afraid of the little lady. He was just committed to her, as he might have been committed to gaol, or committed to paradise.

Had she been dreaming, to be in love with him ? Oh, she wished so much she had never been. She *wished* she had never given herself away. To him !—given herself away to him !—and so abjectly. Hung upon his words and his emotions, and looked up to him as if he were Cæsar. So he had seemed to her : like a mute Cæsar. Like Germanicus. Like—she did not know what.

How had it all happened ? What had taken her in ? Was it just his good looks ? No, not really. Because they were the kind of staring good looks she didn't really care for. He must have had charm. He must have charm. Yes, he *had* charm. When it worked.

His charm had not worked on her now for some time—never since that evening after his wife's arrival. Since then he had seemed to her—rather awful. Rather awful—stupid—an ass—a limited, rather vulgar person. That was what he seemed to her when his charm wouldn't work. A limited, rather inferior person. And in a world of *Schiebers* and profiteers and vulgar, pretentious persons, this was the worst thing possible. A limited, inferior, slightly pretentious individual ! The husband of the little lady ! And oh heaven, she was so deeply implicated with him ! He had not, however, spoken with her in private since his wife's arrival. Probably he would never speak with her in private again. She hoped to heaven, never again. The awful thing was the past, that which had been between him and her. She shuddered when she thought of it. The husband of the little lady !

But surely there was something to account for it ! Charm, just charm. He had a charm. And then, oh heaven, when the charm left off working ! It had left off so completely at this moment, in Hannele's case, that her very mouth tasted salt. What *did* it all amount to ?

What was his charm, after all ? How could it have affected her ? She began to think of him again, at his best : his presence, when they were alone high up in that big, lonely attic near the stars. His room ! The big white-washed walls, the first scent of tobacco, the silence, the sense of the stars being near, the telescopes, the cactus with fine scarlet flowers : and above all, the strange, remote, insidious silence of his presence, that was so congenial to her also. The curious way he had of turning his head to listen—to listen to what ?—as if he heard something in the stars. The strange look, like destiny, in his wide-open, almost staring dark eyes. The beautiful lines of his brow, that seemed always to have a certain cloud on it. The slow elegance of his straight, beautiful legs as he walked, and the exquisiteness of his dark, slender chest ! Ah, she could feel the charm mounting over her again. She could feel the snake biting her heart. She could feel the arrows of desire rankling.

But then—and she turned from her thoughts back to this last little tea-party in the Vier Jahreszeiten. She thought of his voice : "Yes, dear. Certainly. Certainly I will." And she thought of the stupid, inferior look on his face. And the something of a servant-like way in which he went out to do his wife's bidding.

And then the charm was gone again, as the glow of sunset goes off a burning city and leaves it a sordid industrial hole. So much for charm !

So much for charm. She had better have stuck to her own sort of men, Martin, for instance, who was a gentleman and a daring soldier, and a queer soul and pleasant to talk to. Only he hadn't any *magic*. Magic? The very word made her writhe. Magic? Swindle. Swindle, that was all it amounted to. Magic !

And yet—let us not be too hasty. If the magic had *really* been there, on those evenings in that great lofty attic. Had it? Yes. Yes, she was bound to admit it. There had been magic. If there had been magic in his presence and in his contact, the husband of the little lady—— But the distaste was in her mouth again.

So she started afresh, trying to keep a tight hold on the tail of that all-too-evanescent magic of his. Dear, it slipped so quickly into disillusion. Nevertheless. If it had existed, it did exist. And if it did exist, it was worth having. You could call it an illusion if you liked. But an illusion which is a real experience is worth having. Perhaps this disillusion was a greater illusion than the illusion itself. Perhaps all this disillusion of the little lady and the husband of the little lady was falser than the illusion and magic of those few evenings. Perhaps the long disillusion of life was falser than the brief moments of real illusion. After all—the delicate darkness of his breast, the mystery that seemed to come with him as he trod slowly across the floor of his room, after changing his tunic—— Nay, nay, if she could keep the illusion of his charm, she would give all disillusion to the devils. Nay, only let her be under the spell of his charm. Only let the spell be upon her. It was all she yearned for. And the thing she had to fight was the vulgarity of disillusion. The vulgarity of the little lady, the vulgarity of the husband of the little lady, the vulgarity of his insincerity, his "Yes, dear. Certainly ! Certainly !" —this was what she had to fight. He *was* vulgar and horrible, then. But also, the queer figure that sat alone on the roof watching the stars ! The wonderful red flower of the cactus. The mystery that advanced with him as he came across the room after changing his

tunic. The glamour and sadness of him, his silence, as he stooped
unfastening his boots. And the strange gargoyle smile, fixed, when
he caressed her with his hand under the chin ! Life is all a choice.
And if she chose the glamour, the magic, the charm, the illusion, the
spell ! Better death than that other, the husband of the little lady.
When all was said and done, was he as much the husband of the
little lady as he was that queer, delicate-breasted Cæsar of her own
knowledge ? Which was he ?

No, she was *not* going to send her the doll. The little lady should
never have the doll.

What a doll she would make herself ! Heavens, what a wizened
jewel !

VI

Captain Hepburn still called occasionally at the house for his post.
The maid always put his letters in a certain place in the hall, so that
he should not have to climb the stairs.

Among his letters—that is to say, along with another letter, for his
correspondence was very meagre—he one day found an envelope
with a crest. Inside this envelope two letters.

" Dear Captain Hepburn,

I had the enclosed letter from Mrs. Hepburn. I don't intend
her to have the doll which is your portrait, so I shall not answer this
note. Also I don't see why she should try to turn us out of the town.
She talked to me after tea that day, and it seems she believes that
Mitchka is your lover. I didn't say anything at all—except that it
wasn't true. But she needn't be afraid of me. I don't want you to
trouble yourself. But you may as well *know* how things are.

Johanna z. R."

The other letter was on his wife's well-known heavy paper, and in
her well-known large, " aristocratic " hand.

" My dear Countess.

I wonder if there has been some mistake, or some misunder-
standing. Four days ago you said you would send round that *doll*
we spoke of, but I have seen no sign of it yet. I thought of calling
at the studio, but did not wish to disturb the Baroness. I should be
very much obliged if you could send the doll at once, as I do not feel
easy while it is out of my possession. You may rely on having a
cheque by return.

Our old family friend, Major-General Barlow, called on me

yesterday, and we had a most interesting conversation on our *Tommies*, and the protection of their morals here. It seems we have full power to send away any person or persons deemed undesirable, with twenty-four hours' notice to leave. But of course all this is done as quietly and with the intention of causing as little scandal as possible.

Please let me have the doll by to-morrow, and perhaps some hint as to your future intentions.

With very best wishes from one who only seeks to be your friend,

Yours very sincerely,

EVANGELINE HEPBURN."

VII

And then a dreadful thing happened : really a very dreadful thing. Hannele read of it in the evening newspaper of the town— the *Abendblatt*. Mitchka came rushing up with the paper at ten o'clock at night, just when Hannele was going to bed.

Mrs. Hepburn had fallen out of her bedroom window, from the third floor of the hotel, down on to the pavement below, and was killed. She was dressing for dinner. And apparently she had in the morning washed a certain little camisole, and put it on the window-sill to dry. She must have stood on a chair reaching for it, when she fell out of the window. Her husband, who was in the dressing-room, heard a queer little noise, a sort of choking cry and came into her room to see what it was. And she wasn't there. The window was open, and the chair by the window. He looked round, and thought she had left the room for a moment, so returned to his shaving. He was half shaved when one of the maids rushed in. When he looked out of the window down into the street he fainted, and would have fallen too if the maid had not pulled him in in time.

The very next day the captain came back to his attic. Hannele did not know, until quite late at night when he tapped on her door. She knew his soft tap immediately.

" Won't you come over for a chat ? " he said.

She paused for some moments before she answered. And then perhaps surprise made her agree : surprise and curiosity.

" Yes, in a minute," she said, closing her door in his face.

She found him sitting quite still, not even smoking, in his quiet attic. He did not rise, but just glanced round with a faint smile. And she thought his face seemed different, more flexible. But in the half-light she could not tell. She sat at some little distance from him.

" I suppose you've heard," he said.

R

" Yes."

After a long pause, he resumed :

" Yes. It seems an impossible thing to have happened. Yet it *has* happened."

Hannele's ears were sharp. But strain them as she might she could not catch the meaning of his voice.

" A terrible thing. A *very* terrible thing," she said.

" Yes."

" Do you think she fell quite accidentally ? " she said.

" Must have done. The maid was in just a minute before, and she seemed as happy as possible. I suppose reaching over that broad window-ledge, her brain must suddenly have turned. I can't imagine why she didn't call me. She could never bear even to look out of a high window. Turned her ill instantly if she saw a space below her. She used to say she couldn't really look at the moon, it made her feel as if she would fall down a dreadful height. She never dared do more than glance at it. She always had the feeling, I suppose, of the awful space beneath her, if she were on the moon."

Hannele was not listening to his words, but to his voice. There was something a little automatic in what he said. But then that is always so when people have had a shock.

" It must have been terrible for you too," she said.

" Ah, yes. At the time it was awful. Awful. I felt the smash right inside me, you know."

" Awful ! " she repeated.

" But now," he said, " I feel very strangely happy about it. I feel happy about it. I feel happy for her sake, if you can understand that. I feel she has got out of some great tension. I feel she's free now for the first time in her life. She was a gentle soul, and an original soul, but she was like a fairy who is condemned to live in houses and sit on furniture and all that, don't you know. It was never her nature."

" No ? " said Hannele, herself sitting in blank amazement.

" I always felt she was born in the wrong period—or on the wrong planet. Like some sort of delicate creature you take out of a tropical forest the moment it is born, and from the first moment teach it to perform tricks. You know what I mean. All her life she performed the tricks of life, clever little monkey she was at it too. Beat me into fits. But her own poor little soul, a sort of fairy soul, those queer Irish creatures, was cooped up inside her all her life, tombed in. There it was, tombed in, while she went through all the tricks of life that you have to go through if you are born to-day."

" But," stammered Hannele, " what would she have done if she *had* been free ? "

" Why, don't you see, there *is* nothing for her to do in the world to-day. Take her language, for instance. She never ought to have been speaking English. I don't know what language she ought to have spoken. Because if you take the Irish language, they only learn it back from English. They think in English, and just put Irish words on top. But English was never her language. It bubbled off her lips, so to speak. And she had no other language. Like a starling that you've made talk from the very beginning, and so it can only shout these talking noises, don't you know. It can't whistle it's own whistling to save its life. Couldn't do it. It's lost it. All its own natural mode of expressing itself has collapsed, and it can only be artificial."

There was a long pause.

" Would she have been wonderful, then, if she had been able to talk in some unknown language ? " said Hannele jealously.

" I don't say she would have been wonderful. As a matter of fact we think a talking starling is much more wonderful than an ordinary starling. I don't myself, but most people do. And she would have been a sort of starling. And she would have had her own language and her own ways. As it was, poor thing, she was always arranging herself and fluttering and chattering inside a cage. And she never knew she was in the cage, any more than we know we are inside our own skins."

" But," said Hannele, with a touch of mockery, " how do you know you haven't made it all up—just to console yourself ? "

" Oh, I've thought it long ago," he said.

" Still," she blurted, " you may have invented it all—as a sort of consolation for—for—for your life."

" Yes, I may," he said. " But I don't think so. It was her eyes. Did you ever notice her eyes ? I often used to catch her eyes. And she'd be talking away, all the language bubbling off her lips. And her eyes were so clear and bright and different. Like a child's that is listening to something, and is going to be frightened. She was always listening—and waiting—for something else. I tell you what, she was exactly like that fairy in the Scotch song, who is in love with a mortal, and sits by the high road in terror waiting for him to come, and hearing the plovers and the curlews. Only nowadays motor lorries go along the moor roads, and the poor thing is struck unconscious, and carried into our world in a state of unconsciousness, and when she comes round, she tries to talk our language, and behave as we behave, and she can't remember anything else, so she goes on and on, till she falls with a crash, back to her own world."

Hannele was silent, and so was he.

" You loved her then ? " she said at length.

" Yes. But in this way. When I was a boy I caught a bird, a black-cap, and I put it in a cage. And I loved that bird. I don't know why, but I loved it. I simply loved that bird. All the gorse, and the heather, and the rock, and the hot smell of yellow gorse-blossom, and the sky that seemed to have no end to it, when I was a boy, everything that I almost was *mad* with, as boys are, seemed to me to be in that little, fluttering black-cap. And it would peck its seed as if it didn't quite know what else to do ; and look round about, and begin to sing. But in quite a few days it turned its head aside and died. Yes, it died. I never had the feeling again that I got from that black-cap when I was a boy—not until I saw her. And then I felt it all again. I felt it all again. And it was the same feeling. I knew, quite soon I knew, that she would die. She would peck her seed and look round in the cage just the same. But she would die in the end. Only it would last much longer. But she would die in the cage, like the black-cap."

" But she loved the cage. She loved her clothes and her jewels. She must have loved her house and her furniture and all that with a perfect frenzy."

" She did. She did. But like a child with playthings. Only they were big, marvellous playthings to her. Oh, yes, she was never away from them. She never forgot her things—her trinkets and her furs and her furniture. She never got away from them for a minute. And everything in her mind was mixed up with them."

" Dreadful ! " said Hannele.

" Yes, it was dreadful," he answered.

" Dreadful," repeated Hannele.

" Yes, quite. Quite ! And it got worse. And her way of talking got worse. As if it bubbled off her lips. But her eyes never lost their brightness, they never lost that faery look. Only I used to see fear in them. Fear of everything—even all the things she surrounded herself with. Just like my black-cap used to look out of his cage—so bright and sharp, and yet as if he didn't know that it was just the cage that was between him and the outside. He thought it was inside himself, the barrier. He thought it was part of his own nature to be shut in. And she thought it was part of her own nature. And so they both died."

" What I can't see," said Hannele, " is what she would have done outside her cage. What other life could she have, except her *bibelots* and her furniture and her talk ? "

" Why, none. There *is* no life outside for human beings."

" Then there's nothing," said Hannele.

" That's true. In a great measure, there's nothing."

" Thank you," said Hannele.

There was a long pause.

" And perhaps I was to blame. Perhaps I ought to have made some sort of a move. But I didn't know what to do. For my life, I didn't know what to do, except try to make her happy. She had enough money—and I didn't think it mattered if she shared it with me. I always had a garden—and the astronomy. It's been an immense relief to me watching the moon. It's been wonderful. Instead of looking inside the cage, as I did at my bird, or at her—I look right out—into freedom—into freedom."

" The moon, you mean ? " said Hannele.

" Yes, the moon."

" And that's your freedom ? "

" That's where I've found the greatest sense of freedom," he said.

" Well, I'm not going to be jealous of the moon," said Hannele at length.

" Why should you. It's not a thing to be jealous of."

In a little while, she bade him good-night, and left him.

VIII

The chief thing that the captain knew, at this juncture, was that a hatchet had gone through the ligatures and veins that connected him with the people of his affection, and that he was left with the bleeding ends of all his vital human relationships. Why it should be so he did not know. But then one never can know the whys and the wherefores of one's passional changes.

He only knew that it was so. The emotional flow between him and all the people he knew and cared for was broken, and for the time being he was conscious only of the cleavage. The cleavage that had occurred between him and his fellow-men, the cleft that was now between him and them. It was not the fault of anybody or anything. He could neither reproach himself nor them. What had happened had been preparing for a long time. Now suddenly the cleavage. There had been a long, slow weaning away : and now this sudden silent rupture.

What it amounted to principally was that he did not want even to see Hannele. He did not want to think of her even. But neither did he want to see anybody else, or to think of anybody else. He shrank with a feeling almost of disgust from his friends and acquaintances, and their expressions of sympathy. It affected him with instantaneous disgust, when anybody wanted to share emotions with him. He did not want to share emotions or feelings of any sort. He wanted to be by himself, essentially, even if he was moving about among other people.

So he went to England to settle his own affairs, and out of duty to see his children. He wished his children all the well in the world— everything except any emotional connection with himself. He decided to take his girl away from the convent at once, and to put her into a jolly English school. His boy was all right where he was.

The captain had now an income sufficient to give him his independence, but not sufficient to keep up his wife's house. So he prepared to sell the house and most of the things in it. He decided also to leave the army as soon as he could be free. And he thought he would wander about for a time, till he came upon something he wanted.

So the winter passed, without his going back to Germany. He was free of the army. He drifted along, settling his affairs. They were of no very great importance. And all the time he never wrote once to Hannele. He could not get over his disgust that people insisted on his sharing their emotions. He could not bear their emotions, neither their activities. Other people might have all the emotions and feelings and earnestnesses and busy activities they liked. Quite nice even that they had such a multifarious commotion for themselves. But the moment they approached him to spread their feelings over him or to entangle him in their activities a helpless disgust came up in him, and until he could get away he felt sick, even physically.

This was no state of mind for a lover. He could not even think of Hannele. Anybody else he felt he need not think about. He was deeply, profoundly thankful that his wife was dead. It was an end of pity now ; because, poor thing, she had escaped and gone her own way into the void, like a flown bird.

IX

Nevertheless, a man hasn't finished his life at forty. He may, however, have finished one great phase of his life.

And Alexander Hepburn was not the man to live alone. All our troubles, says somebody wise, come upon us because we cannot be alone. And that is all very well. We must all be *able* to be alone, otherwise we are just victims. But when we *are* able to be alone, then we realize that the only thing to do is to start a new relationship with another—or even the same—human being. That people should all be stuck up apart, like so many telegraph poles, is nonsense.

So with our dear captain. He had his convulsion into a sort of telegraph-pole isolation : which was absolutely necessary for him. But then he began to bud with a new yearning for—for what ? For love ?

It was a question he kept nicely putting to himself. And really, the nice young girls of eighteen or twenty attracted him very much : so fresh, so impulsive, and looking up to him as if he were something wonderful. If only he could have married two or three of them, instead of just one !

Love ! When a man has no particular ambition, his mind turns back perpetually, as a needle towards the pole. That tiresome word Love. It means so many things. It meant the feeling he had had for his wife. He had loved her. But he shuddered at the thought of having to go through such love again. It meant also the feeling he had for the awfully nice young things he met here and there : fresh, impulsive girls ready to give all their hearts away. Oh yes, he could fall in love with half a dozen of them. But he knew he'd better not.

At last he wrote to Hannele : and got no answer. So he wrote to Mitchka and still got no answer. So he wrote for information—and there was none forthcoming, except that the two women had gone to Munich.

For the time being he left it at that. To him, Hannele did not exactly represent rosy love. Rather a hard destiny. He did not adore her. He did not feel one bit of adoration for her. As a matter of fact, not all the beauties and virtues of woman put together with all the gold in the Indies would have tempted him into the business of adoration any more. He had gone on his knees once, vowing with faltering tones to try and make the adored one happy. And now—never again. Never.

The temptation this time was to be adored. One of those fresh young things would have adored him as if he were a god. And there was something *very* alluring about the thought. Very—very alluring. To be god-almighty in your own house, with a lovely young thing adoring you, and you giving off beams of bright effulgence like a

Gloria ! Who wouldn't be tempted : at the age of forty ? And this
was why he dallied.

But in the end he suddenly took the train to Munich. And when
he got there he found the town beastly uncomfortable, the Bavarians
rude and disagreeable, and no sign of the missing females, not even
in the Café Stephanie. He wandered round and round.

And then one day, oh heaven, he saw his doll in a shop window :
a little art shop. He stood and stared quite spellbound.

" Well, if that isn't the devil," he said. " Seeing yourself in a
shop-window ! "

He was so disgusted that he would not go into the shop.

Then, every day for a week did he walk down that little street
and look at himself in the shop window. Yes, there he stood, with
one hand in his pocket. And the figure had one hand in its pocket.
There he stood, with his cap pulled rather low over his brow. And
the figure had its cap pulled low over its brow. But thank goodness,
his own cap now was a civilian tweed. But there he stood, his head
rather forward, gazing with fixed dark eyes. And himself in little,
that wretched figure, stood there with its head rather forward,
staring with fixed dark eyes. It was such a real little *man* that it
fairly staggered him. The oftener he saw it, the more it staggered
him. And the more he hated it. Yet it fascinated him, and he came
again to look.

And it was always there. A lonely little individual lounging there
with one hand in its pocket, and nothing to do, among the bric-à-
brac and the *bibelots*. Poor devil, stuck so incongruously in the
world. And yet losing none of his masculinity.

A male little devil, for all his forlornness. But such an air of
isolation, of not-belonging. Yet taut and male, in his tartan trews.
And what a situation to be in—lounging with his back against a
little Japanese lacquer cabinet, with a few old pots on his right hand
and a tiresome brass ink-tray on his left, while pieces of not-very-nice
filet lace hung their length up and down the background. Poor
little devil : it was like a deliberate satire.

And then one day it was gone. There was the cabinet and the
filet lace and the tiresome ink-stand tray : and the little gentleman
wasn't there. The captain at once walked into the shop.

" Have you sold that doll—that unknown soldier ? " he added,
without knowing quite what he was saying.

The doll was sold.

" Do you know who bought it ? "

The girl looked at him very coldly, and did not know.

"I once knew the lady who made it. In fact, the doll was *me*," he said.

The girl now looked at him with sudden interest.

"Don't you think it was like me?" he said.

"Perhaps"—she began to smile.

"It was me. And the lady who made it was a friend of mine. Do you know her name?"

"Yes."

"Gräfin zu Rassentlow," he cried, his eyes shining.

"Oh yes. But her dolls are famous."

"Do you know where she is?   Is she in Munich?"

"That I don't now."

"Could you find out?"

"I don't know. I can ask."

"Or the Baroness von Prielau-Carolath."

"The Baroness is dead."

"Dead!"

"She was shot in a riot in Salzburg. They say a lover——"

"How do you know?"

"From the newspapers."

"Dead! Is it possible. Poor Hannele."

There was a pause.

"Well," he said, "if you would enquire about the address—I'll call again."

Then he turned back from the door.

"By the way, do you mind telling me how much you sold the doll for?"

The girl hesitated. She was by no means anxious to give away any of her trade details. But at length she answered reluctantly:

"Five hundred marks."

"So cheap," he said. "Good-day. Then I will call again."

X

Then again he got a trace. It was in the chit-chat column of the *Muenchener Neue Zeitung*: under Studio Comments. "Theodor Worpswede's latest picture is a still-life, containing an entertaining group of a doll, two sun-flowers in a glass jar, and a poached egg on toast. The contrast between the three substances is highly diverting and instructive, and this is perhaps one of the most interesting of Worpswede's works. The doll, by the way, is one of the creations of our fertile Countess Hannele. It is the figure

R *

of an English, or rather Scottish officer, in the famous tartan trousers which, clinging closely to the legs of the lively Gaul, so shocked the eminent Julius Cæsar and his cohorts. We, of course, are no longer shocked, but full of admiration for the creative genius of our dear Countess. The doll itself is a masterpiece, and has begotten another masterpiece in Theodor Worpswede's Still-life. We have heard, by the way, a rumour of Countess zu Rassentlow's engagement. Apparently the Herr Regierungsrat von Poldi, of that most beautiful of summer-resorts, Kaprun, in the Tyrol, is the fortunate man——"

XI

The captain bought the Still-life. This new version of himself along with the poached egg and the sun-flowers was rather frightening. So he packed up for Austria, for Kaprun, with his picture, and had a fight to get the beastly thing out of Germany, and another fight to get it into Austria. Fatigued and furious he arrived in Salzburg, seeing no beauty in anything. Next day he was in Kaprun.

It was an elegant and fashionable watering-place before the war : a lovely little lake in the midst of the Alps, an old Tyrolese town on the water-side, green slopes sheering up opposite, and away beyond, a glacier. It was still crowded and still elegant. But alas, with a broken, bankrupt, desperate elegance, and almost empty shops.

The captain felt rather dazed. He found himself in an hotel full of Jews of the wrong, rich sort, and wondered what next. The place was beautiful, but the life wasn't.

XII

The Herr Regierungsrat was not at first sight prepossessing. He was approaching fifty, and had gone stout and rather loose, as so many men of his class and race do. Then he wore one of those dreadful full-bottom coats, a kind of poor relation to our full-skirted frock-coat : it would best be described as a family coat. It flapped about him as he walked, and he looked at first glance lower middle-class.

But he wasn't. Of course, being in office in the collapsed Austria he was a republican. But by nature he was a monarchist, nay, an imperialist, as every true Austrian is. And he was a true Austrian. And as such he was much finer and subtler than he looked. As one got used to him, his rather fat face, with its fine nose and slightly bitter, pursed mouth, came to have a resemblance to the busts of some of the late Roman emperors. And as one was with him, one

came gradually to realize that out of all his baggy bourgeois appearance came something of a *grande geste*. He could not help it. There
was something sweeping and careless about his soul : big, rather
assertive, and ill-bred-seeming ; but in fact, not ill-bred at all, only
a little bitter and a good deal indifferent to his surroundings. He
looked at first sight so common and *parvenu*. And then one had to
realize that he was a member of a big, old empire, fallen into a sort
of epicureanism, and a little bitter. There was no littleness, no
meanness, and no real coarseness. But he was a great talker, and
relentless towards his audience.

Hannele was attracted to him by his talk. He began as soon as
dinner appeared : and he went on, carrying the decanter and the
wine-glass with him out on to the balcony of the villa, over the lake,
on and on until midnight. The summer night was still and warm :
the lake lay deep and full, and the old town twinkled away across.
There was the faintest tang of snow in the air, from the great glacier-
peaks that were hidden in the night opposite. Sometimes a boat
with a lantern twanged a guitar. The clematis flowers were quite
black, like leaves, dangling from the terrace.

It was so beautiful, there in the very heart of the Tyrol. The
hotels glittered with lights : electric light was still cheap. There
seemed a fulness and a loveliness in the night. And yet for some
reason it was all terrible and devastating : the life-spirit seemed to
be squirming, bleeding all the time.

And on and on talked the Herr Regierungsrat, with all the witty
volubility of the more versatile Austrian. He was really very witty,
very human, and with a touch of salty cynicism that reminded one
of a real old Roman of the Empire. That subtle stoicism, that
unsentimental epicureanism, that kind of reckless hopelessness, of
course, fascinated the women. And particularly Hannele. He
talked on and on—about his work before the war, when he held an
important post and was one of the governing class—then about the
war—then about the hopelessness of the present : and in it all there
seemed a bigness, a carelessness based on indifference, and hopelessness that laughed at its very self. The real old Austria had always
fascinated Hannele. As represented in the witty, bitter-indifferent
Herr Regierungsrat it carried her away.

And he, of course, turned instinctively to her, talking in his rapid,
ceaseless fashion, with a laugh and a pause to drink and a new start
taken. She liked the sound of his Austrian speech : its racy carelessness, its salty indifference to standards of correctness. Oh yes,
here was the *grande geste* still lingering.

He turned his large breast towards her, and made a quick gesture with his fat, well-shapen hand, blurted out another subtle, rough-seeming romance, pursed his mouth, and emptied his glass once more. Then he looked at his half-forgotten cigar and started again.

There was something almost boyish and impulsive about him : the way he turned to her, and the odd way he seemed to open his big breast to her. And again, he seemed almost eternal, sitting there in his chair with knees planted apart. It was as if he would never rise again, but would remain sitting for ever, and talking. He seemed as if he had no legs, save to sit with. As if to stand on his feet and walk would not be natural to him.

Yet he rose at last, and kissed her hand with the grand gesture that France or Germany have never acquired : carelessness, profound indifference to other people's standards, and then such a sudden stillness, as he bent and kissed her hand. Of course she felt a queen in exile.

And perhaps it is more dangerous to feel yourself a queen in exile than a queen *in situ*. She fell in love with him, with this large, stout, loose widower of fifty, with two children. He had no money except some Austrian money that was worth nothing outside Austria. He could not even go to Germany. There he was, fixed in this hollow in the middle of the Tyrol.

But he had an ambition still, old Roman of the decadence that he was. He had year by year and without making any fuss collected the material for a very minute and thorough history of his own district : the Chiemgau and the Pinzgau. Hannele found that his fund of information on this subject was inexhaustible, and his intelligence was so delicate, so human, and his scope seemed so wide, that she felt a touch of reverence for him. He wanted to write this history. And she wanted to help him.

For, of course, as things were he would never write it. He was Regierungsrat : that is, he was the petty local governor of his town and immediate district. The Amthaus was a great old building, and there young ladies in high heels flirted among masses of papers with bare-kneed young gentlemen in Tyrolese costume, and occasionally they parted, to take a pleasant, interesting attitude and write a word or two, after which they fluttered together for a little more interesting diversion. It was extraordinary how many finely built, handsome young people of an age fitted for nothing but love-affairs, ran the governmental business of this department. And the Herr Regierungsrat sailed in and out of the big, old room, his wide coat flying like wings and making the papers flutter, his rathe_r

wine-reddened, old-Roman face smiling with its bitter look. And of course it was a witticism he uttered first, even if Hungary was invading the frontier or cholera was in Vienna.

When he was on his legs, he walked nimbly, briskly, and his coat-bottoms always flew. So he waved through the town, greeting somebody at every few strides, and grinning, and yet with a certain haughty reserve. Oh yes, there was a certain salty *hauteur* about him which made the people trust him. And he spoke the vernacular so racily.

Hannele felt she would like to marry him. She would like to be near him. She would like him to write his history. She would like him to make her feel a queen in exile. No one had ever *quite* kissed her hand as he kissed it : with that sudden stillness and strange, chivalric abandon of himself. How he would abandon himself to her !—terribly—wonderfully—perhaps a little horribly. His wife, whom he had married late, had died after seven years of marriage. Hannele could understand that too. One or the other must die.

She became engaged. But something made her hesitate before marriage. Being in Austria was like being on a wrecked ship that *must* sink after a certain short length of time. And marrying the Herr Regierungsrat was like marrying the doomed captain of the doomed ship. The sense of fatality was part of the attraction.

And yet she hesitated. The summer weeks passed. The strangers flooded in and crowded the town, and ate up the food like locusts. People no longer counted the paper money, they weighed it by the kilogram. Peasants stored it in a corner of the meal-bin, and mice came and chewed holes in it. Nobody knew where the next lot of food was going to come from : yet it always came. And the lake teemed with bathers. When the captain arrived he looked with amazement on the crowds of strapping, powerful fellows who bathed all day long, magnificent blond flesh of men and women. No wonder the old Romans stood in astonishment before the huge blond limbs of the savage Germans.

Well, the life was like a madness. The hotels charged fifteen-hundred kronen a day : the women, old and young, paraded in the peasant-costume, in flowery cotton dresses with gaudy, expensive silk aprons : the men wore the Tyrolese costume, bare knees and little short jackets. And for the men, the correct thing was to have the leathern hose and the blue linen jacket as old as possible. If you had a hole in your leathern seat, so much the better.

Everything so physical. Such magnificent naked limbs and naked bodies, and in the streets, in the hotels, everywhere, bare, white arms of women and bare, brown, powerful knees and thighs of men. The sense of flesh everywhere, and the endless ache of flesh. Even in the peasants who rowed across the lake, standing and rowing with a slow, heavy, gondolier motion at the once curved oar, there was the same endless ache of physical yearning.

XIII

It was August when Alexander met Hannele. She was walking under a chintz parasol, wearing a dress of blue cotton with little red roses, and a red silk apron. She had no hat, her arms were bare and soft, and she had white stockings under her short dress. The Herr Regierungsrat was at her side, large, nimble, and laughing with a new witticism.

Alexander, in a light summer suit and Panama hat, was just coming out of the bank, shoving twenty thousand kronen into his pocket. He saw her coming across from the Amtsgericht, with the Herr Regierungsrat at her side, across the space of sunshine. She was laughing, and did not notice him.

She did not notice till he had taken off his hat and was saluting her. Then what she saw was the black, smooth, shining head, and she went pale. His black, smooth, close head—and all the blue Austrian day seemed to shrivel before her eyes.

" How do you do, Countess ! I hoped I should meet you."

She heard his slow, sad-clanging, straying voice again, and she pressed her hand with the umbrella stick against her breast. She had forgotten it—forgotten his peculiar, slow voice. And now it seemed like a noise that sounds in the silence of night. Ah, how difficult it was, that suddenly the world could split under her eyes, and show this darkness inside. She wished he had not come.

She presented him to the Herr Regierungsrat, who was stiff and cold. She asked where the captain was staying. And then, not knowing what else to say, she said :

" Won't you come to tea ? "

She was staying in a villa across the lake. Yes, he would come to tea.

He went. He hired a boat and a man to row him across. It was not far. There stood the villa, with its brown balconies one above the other, the bright red geraniums and white geraniums twinkling all round, the trees of purple clematis tumbling at one corner. All the green window-doors were open : but nobody about. In the little garden by the water's edge the rose-trees were tall and lank, drawn up by the dark green trees of the background. A white table with chairs and garden seats stood under the shadow of a big willow tree, and a hammock with cushions swung just behind. But no one in sight. There was a little landing bridge on to the garden : and a fairly large boat-house at the garden end.

The captain was not sure that the boat-house belonged to the villa. Voices were shouting and laughing from the water's surface, bathers swimming. A tall, naked youth with a little red cap on his head and a tiny red loin-cloth round his slender young hips was standing on the steps of the boat-house calling to the three women who were swimming near. The dark-haired woman with the white cap swam up to the steps and caught the boy by the ankle. He cried and laughed and remonstrated, and poked her in the breast with his foot.

"Nein, nein, Hardu!" she cried as he tickled her with his toe. "Hardu! Hardu! Hör' auf! Leave off!"—and she fell with a crash back into the water. The youth laughed a loud, deep laugh of a lad whose voice is newly broken.

"Was macht er dann?" cried a voice from the waters. "What is he doing?" It was a dark-skinned girl swimming swiftly, her big dark eyes watching amused from the water-surface.

"Jetzt Hardu hör' auf. Nein. Jetzt ruhig! Now leave off! Now be quiet." And the dark-haired woman was climbing out in the sunshine on to the pale, raw-wood steps of the boat-house, the water glistening on her dark-blue, stockinette, soft-moulded back and loins : while the boy, with his foot stretched out, was trying to push her back into the water. She clambered out, however, and sat on the steps in the sun, panting slightly. She was dark and attractive-looking, with a mature beautiful figure, and handsome, strong woman's legs.

In the garden appeared a black-and-white maid-servant with a tray.

"Kaffee, gnädige Frau!"

The voice came so distinct over the water.

"Hannele! Hannele! Kaffee!" called the woman on the steps of the bathing-house.

"Tante Hannele! Kaffee!" called the dark-eyed girl, turning round in the water, then swimming for home.

"Kaffee! Kaffee!" roared the youth, in anticipation.

"Ja—a! Ich kom—mm," sang Hannele's voice from the water.

The dark-eyed girl, her hair tied up in a silk bandana, had reached the steps and was climbing out, a slim young fish in her close dark suit. The three stood clustered on the steps, the elder woman with one arm over the naked shoulders of the youth, the other arm over the shoulders of the girl. And all in chorus sang :

" Hannele ! Hannele ! Hannele ! Wir warten auf dich."

The boatman had left off rowing, and the boat was drifting slowly in. The family became quiet, because of the intrusion. The attractive-looking woman turned and picked up her blue bath-robe, of a mid-blue colour that became her. She swung it round her as if it were an opera cloak. The youth stared at the boat.

The captain was watching Hannele. With a white kerchief tied round her silky, brownish hair, she was swimming home. He saw her white shoulders, and her white, wavering legs below in the clear water. Round the boat fishes were suddenly jumping.

The three on the steps beyond stood silent, watching the intruding boat with resentment. The boatman twisted his head round and watched them. The captain, who was facing them, watched Hannele. She swam slowly and easily up, caught the rail of the steps and stooping forward, climbed slowly out of the water. Her legs were large and flashing white and looked rich, the rich, white thighs with the blue veins behind, and the full, rich softness of her sloping loins.

" Ach ! Schön ! 'S war schön ! Das Wasser ist gut," her voice was heard, half singing as she took her breath. " It was lovely."

" Heiss," said the woman above. " Zu warm. Too warm."

The youth made way for Hannele, who drew herself erect at the top of the steps, looking round, panting a little, and putting up her hands to the knot of her kerchief on her head. Her legs were magnificent and white.

" Kuck die Leut die da bleiben," said the woman in the blue wrap, in a low voice. " Look at the people stopping there."

" Ja ! " said Hannele negligently. Then she looked. She started as if in fear, looked round, as if to run away, looked back again, and met the eyes of the captain, who took off his hat.

She cried, in a loud frightened voice :

" Oh, but—I thought it was *to-morrow* ! "

" No—to-day," came the quiet voice of the captain over the water.

" *To-day* ! Are you *sure* ? " she cried, calling to the boat.

" Quite sure. But we'll make it to-morrow if you like," he said.

" To-day ! To-day ! " she repeated in bewilderment. " No ! Wait a minute," And she ran into the boat-house.

" Was ist es ? " asked the dark woman, following her. " What is it ? "

" A friend—a visitor—Captain Hepburn," came Hannele's voice.

The boatman now rowed slowly to the landing stage. The dark woman, huddled in her blue wrap as in an opera cloak, walked proudly and unconcernedly across the background of the garden, and up the steps to the first balcony. Hannele, her feet slip-slopping in loose slippers, clutching an old yellow wrap round her, came to the landing stage and shook hands.

"I am so sorry. It is so stupid of me. I was sure it was to-morrow," she said.

"No, it was to-day. But I wish for your sake it had been to-morrow," he replied.

"No. No. It doesn't matter. You won't mind waiting a minute, will you? You mustn't be angry with me for being so stupid."

So she went away, the heel-less slippers flipping up to her naked heels. Then the big-eyed, dusky girl stole into the house : and then the naked youth, who went with sang-froid. He would make a fine, handsome man : and he knew it.

XIV

Hepburn and Hannele were to make a small excursion to the glacier which stood there always in sight, coldly grinning in the sky. The weather had been very hot, but this morning there were loose clouds in the sky. The captain rowed over the lake soon after dawn. Hannele stepped into the little craft, and they pulled back to the town. There was a wind ruffling the water, so that the boat leaped and chuckled. The glacier, in a recess among the folded mountains, looked cold and angry. But morning was very sweet in the sky, and blowing very sweet with a faint scent of the second hay, from the low lands at the head of the lake. Beyond stood naked grey rock like a wall of mountains, pure rock, with faint thin slashes of snow. Yesterday it had rained on the lake. The sun was going to appear from behind the Breitsteinhorn, the sky with its clouds floating in blue light and yellow radiance was lovely and cheering again. But dark clouds seemed to spout up from the Pinzgau valley. And once across the lake, all was shadow, when the water no longer gave back the sky-morning.

The day was a feast day, a holiday. Already so early three young men from the mountains were bathing near the steps of the Badean-stalt. Handsome, physical fellows, with good limbs rolling and swaying in the early morning water. They seemed to enjoy it too. But to Hepburn it was always as if a dark wing were stretched in the sky, over these mountains, like a doom. And these three young, lusty naked men swimming and rolling in the shadow.

Hepburn's was the first boat stirring. He made fast in the hotel boat-house, and he and Hannele went into the little town. It was deep in shadow, though the light of the sky, curdled with cloud, was bright overhead. But dark and chill and heavy lay the shadow in the black-and-white town, like a sediment.

The shops were all shut, but peasants from the hills were already strolling about, in their holiday dress : the men in their short leather trousers, like football drawers, and bare brown knees, and great boots : their little grey jackets faced with green, and their green hats with the proud chamois-brush behind. They seemed to stray about like lost souls, and the proud chamois-brush behind their hats, this proud, cocky, perking-up tail, like a mountain-buck with his tail up, was belied by the lost-soul look of the men, as they loitered about with their hands shoved in the front pockets of their trousers. Some women also were creeping about : peasant women, in the funny little black hats that had thick gold under the brim and long black streamers of ribbon, broad, black, water-wave ribbon starting from a bow under the brim behind, and streaming right to the bottom of the skirt. These women, in their thick, dark dresses with tight bodices, and massive, heavy, full skirts, and bright or dark aprons, strode about with the heavy stride of the mountain women, the heavy, quick, forward-leaning motion. They were waiting for the town-day to begin.

Hepburn had a knapsack on his back, with food for the day. But bread was wanting. They found the door of the bakery open, and got a loaf : a long, hot loaf of pure white bread, beautiful sweet bread. It cost seventy kronen. To Hepburn it was always a mystery where this exquisite bread came from, in a lost land.

In the little square where the clock stood were bunches of people, and a big motor-omnibus, and a motor-car that would hold about eight people. Hepburn had paid his seven hundred kronen for the two tickets. Hannele tied up her head in a thin scarf, and put on her thick coat. She and Hepburn sat in front by the peaked driver. And at seven o'clock away went the car, swooping out of the town, past the handsome old Tyrolese Schloss, or manor, black-and-white, with its little black spires pricking up, past the station, and under the trees by the lake-side. The road was not good, but they ran at a great speed, out past the end of the lake, where the reeds grew, out into the open valley-mouth, where the mountains opened in two clefts. It was cold in the car. Hepburn buttoned himself up to the throat and pulled his hat down on his ears. Hannele's scarf fluttered. She sat without saying anything, erect, her face fine and keen, watching ahead. From the deep Pinzgau valley came the river roaring and raging, a glacier river of pale, seething ice-water. Over went the car, over the log bridge, darting towards the great slopes opposite. And then a sudden immense turn, a swerve under the height of the mountain-side, and again a darting lurch forward, under the pear-trees of the high-road, past the big old ruined castle that so magnificently watched the valley mouth, and the foaming river ; on, rushing under the huge roofs of the balconied peasant houses of a village, then swinging again to take another valley mouth, there where a little village clustered all black and white on a knoll, with a white church that had a black steeple, and a white castle with black spines, and clustering, ample black-and-white houses of the Tyrol. There is a grandeur even in the peasant houses, with their great wide passage halls where the swallows build, and where one could build a whole English cottage.

So the motor-car darted up this new, narrow, wilder, more sinister valley. A herd of almost wild young horses, handsome reddish things, burst around the car, and one great mare with full flanks went crashing up the road ahead, her heels flashing to the car, while her foal whinneyed and screamed from behind. But no, she could not turn from the road. On and on she crashed, forging ahead, the car behind her. And then at last she did swerve aside, among the thin alder trees by the wild river-bed.

" If it isn't a cow, it's a horse," said the driver, who was thin and weaselish and silent, with his ear-flaps over his ears.

But the great mare had shaken herself in a wild swerve, and screaming and whinneying was plunging back to her foal. Hannele had been frightened.

The car rushed on, through water-meadows, along a naked, white bit of mountain road. Ahead was a darkness of mountain front and pine trees. To the right was the stony, furious, lion-like river, tawny-coloured here, and the slope up beyond. But the road for the moment was swinging fairly level through the stunned water-meadows of the savage valley. There were gates to open, and Hepburn jumped down to open them, as if he were the foot-boy. The heavy Jews of the wrong sort, seated behind, of course did not stir.

At a house on a knoll the driver sounded his horn, and out rushed children crying " Papa ! Papa ! "—then a woman with a basket. A few brief words from the weaselish man, who smiled with warm, manly blue eyes at his children, then the car leaped forward. The whole bearing of the man was so different when he was looking at his own family. He could not even say thank-you when Hepburn opened the gates. He hated and even despised his human cargo of middle-class people. Deep, deep is class-hatred, and it begins to swallow all human feeling in its abyss. So, stiff, silent, thin, capable, and neuter towards his fares, sat the little driver with the flaps over his ears, and his thin nose cold.

The car swept round, suddenly, into the trees : and into the ravine. The river shouted at the bottom of a gulf. Bristling pine-trees stood around. The air was black and cold and forever sunless. The motor-car rushed on, in this blackness, under the rock-walls and the fir-trees.

Then it suddenly stopped. There was a huge motor-omnibus ahead, drab and enormous-looking. Tourists and trippers of last night coming back from the glacier. It stood like a great rock. And the smaller motor-car edged past, tilting into the rock-gutter under the face of stone.

So, after a while of this valley of the shadow of death, lurching in steep loops upwards, the motor-car scrambling wonderfully, struggling past trees and rock upwards, at last they came to the end. It was a huge inn or tourist-hotel of brown wood : and here the road ended in a little wide bay surrounded and overhung by trees. Beyond was a garage and a bridge over a roaring river : and always the overhung darkness of trees and the intolerable steep slopes immediately above.

Hannele left her big coat. The sky looked blue above the gloom. They set out across the hollow-sounding bridge, over the everlasting mad rush of ice-water, to the immediate upslope of the path, under dark trees. But a little old man in a sort of sentry-box wanted fifty or sixty kronen : apparently for the upkeep of the road, a sort of toll.

The other tourists were coming—some stopping to have a drink first. The second omnibus had not yet arrived. Hannele and Hepburn were the first two, treading slowly up that dark path, under the trees. The grasses hanging on the rock face were still dewy. There were a few wild raspberries, and a tiny tuft of bil-berries with black berries here and there, and a few tufts of unripe cranberries. The many hundreds of tourists who passed up and down did not leave much to pick. Some mountain hare-bells, like bells of blue water, hung coldly glistening in their darkness. Some-times the hairy mountain-bell, pale-blue and bristling, stood alone, curving his head right down, stiff and taut. There was an occasional big, moist, lolling daisy.

So the two climbed slowly up the steep ledge of a road. This valley was just a mountain cleft, cleft sheer in the hard, living rock, with black trees like hair flourishing in this secret, naked place of the earth. At the bottom of the open wedge forever roared the rampant, insatiable water. The sky from above was like a sharp wedge forcing its way into the earth's cleavage, and that eternal ferocious water was like the steel edge of the wedge, the terrible tip biting in into the rocks' intensity. Who could have thought that the soft sky of light, and the soft foam of water could thrust and penetrate into the dark, strong earth ? But so it was. Hannele and Hepburn, toiling up the steep little ledge of a road that hung half-way down the gulf, looked back, time after time, back down upon the brown timbers and shingle roofs of the hotel, that now, away below, looked damp and wedged in like boulders. Then back at the next tourists struggling up. Then down at the water, that rushed like a beast of prey. And then, as they rose higher, they looked up also, at the livid great sides of rock, livid bare rock that sloped from the sky-ridge in a hideous sheer swerve downwards.

In his heart of hearts Hepburn hated it. He hated it, he loathed it, it seemed almost obscene, this livid, naked slide of rock, unthinkably huge and massive, sliding down to this gulf where bushes grew like hair in the darkness, and water roared. Above, there were thin slashes of snow.

So the two climbed slowly on, up the eternal side of that valley, sweating with the exertion. Sometimes the sun, now risen high, shone full on their side of the gulley. Tourists were trickling down-hill too : two maidens with bare arms and bare heads and huge boots : men tourists with great knapsacks and edelweiss in their hats : giving Bergheil for a greeting. But the captain said Good-day. He refused this Bergheil business. People swarming touristy on these horrible mountains made him feel almost sick.

He and Hannele also were not in good company together. There was a sort of silent hostility between them. She hated the effort of climbing ; but the high air, the cold in the air, the savage cat-howling sound of the water, those awful flanks of livid rock, all this thrilled and excited her to another sort of savageness. And he, dark, rather slender and feline, with something of the physical suavity of a delicate-footed race, he hated beating his way up the rock, he hated the sound of the water, it frightened him, and the high air bit him in his chest, like a viper.

"Wonderful ! Wonderful ! " she cried, taking great breaths in her splendid chest.

"Yes. And horrible. Detestable," he said.

She turned with a flash, and the high strident sound of the mountain in her voice.

" If you don't like it," she said, rather jeering, " why ever did you come ? "

" I had to try," he said.

" And if you don't like it," she said, " why should you try to spoil it for me ? "

" I hate it," he answered.

They were climbing more into the height, more into the light, into the open, in the full sun. The valley-cleft was sinking below them. Opposite was only the sheer livid slide of the naked rock, tipping from the pure sky. At a certain angle they could see away beyond, the lake lying far off and small, the wall of those other rocks like a curtain of stone, dim and diminished to the horizon. And the sky with curdling clouds and blue sunshine intermittent.

" Wonderful, wonderful, to be high up," she said, breathing great breaths.

" Yes," he said. " It *is* wonderful. But very detestable. I want to live near the sea-level. I am no mountain-topper."

" Evidently not," she said.

" Bergheil ! " cried a youth with bare arms and bare chest, bare head, terrific fanged boots, a knapsack and an alpenstock, and all the bronzed wind and sun of the mountain snow in his skin and his faintly bleached hair. With his great heavy knapsack, his rumpled thick stockings, his ghastly fanged boots, Hepburn found him repulsive.

" Guten Tag," he answered coldly.

" Grüss Gott," said Hannele.

And the young Tannhäuser, the young Siegfried, this young Balder beautiful strode climbing down the rocks, marching and swinging with his alpenstock. And immediately after the youth came a maiden, with hair on the wind and her shirt-breast open, striding in corduroy breeches, rumpled worsted stockings, thick boots, a knapsack, and an alpenstock. She passed without greeting. And our pair stopped in angry silence and watched her dropping down the mountain-side.

XV

Ah, well, everything comes to an end, even the longest up-climb. So, after much sweat and effort and crossness, Hepburn and Hannele emerged on to the rounded bluff where the road wound out of that hideous great valley-cleft, into upper regions. So they emerged more on the level, out of the trees as out of something horrible, on to a naked, great bank of rock and grass.

" Thank the Lord ! " said Hannele.

So they trudged on round the bluff, and then in front of them saw what is always, always wonderful, one of those shallow upper valleys, naked, where the first waters are rocked. A flat, shallow, utterly desolate valley, wide as a wide bowl under the sky, with rock slopes and grey stone-slides and precipices all around, and the zig-zag of snow-stripes and ice-roots descending, and then rivers, streams and rivers rushing from many points downwards, down out of the ice-roots and the snow-dagger-points, waters rushing in newly-liberated frenzy downwards, down in waterfalls and cascades and threads, down into the wide, shallow bed of the valley, strewn with rocks and stones innumerable, and not a tree, not a visible bush.

Only, of course, two hotels or restaurant places. But these no more than low, sprawling, peasant-looking places lost among the stones, with stones on their roofs so that they seemed just a part of the valley bed. There was the valley, dotted with rock and rolled-down stone, and these two house-places, and woven with innumerable new waters, and one hoarse stone-tracked river in the desert, and the thin road-track winding along the desolate flat, past first one house, then the other, over one stream, then another, on to the far rock-face above which the glacier seemed to loll like some awful great tongue put out.

" Ah, it is wonderful ! " he said, as if to himself.

And she looked quickly at his face, saw the queer, blank, sphinx-look with which he gazed out beyond himself. His eyes were black and set, and he seemed so motionless, as if he were eternal, facing these upper facts.

She thrilled with triumph. She felt he was overcome.

" It *is* wonderful," she said.

" Wonderful. And for ever wonderful," he said.

" Ah, in *winter*——" she cried.

His face changed, and he looked at her.

" In winter you couldn't get up here," he said.

They went on. Up the slopes cattle were feeding : came that isolated tong-tong-tong of cowbells, dropping like the slow clink of ice on the arrested air. The sound always woke in him a primeval, almost hopeless melancholy. Always made him feel *navré*. He looked round. There was no tree, no bush, only great grey rocks and pale boulders scattered in place of trees and bushes. But yes, clinging on one side like a dark close beard were the alpenrose shrubs.

" In May," he said, " that side there must be all pink with alpen-roses."

" I *must* come. I *must* come ! " she cried.

There were tourists dotted along the road : and two tiny low carts drawn by silky, long-eared mules. These carts went right down to meet the motor-cars, and to bring up provisions for the Glacier Hotel : for there was still another big hotel ahead. Hepburn was happy in that upper valley, that first rocking cradle of early water. He liked to see the great fangs and slashes of ice and snow thrust down into the rock, as if the ice had bitten into the flesh of the earth. And from the fang-tips the hoarse water crying its birth-cry, rushing down.

By the turfy road and under the rocks were many flowers : wonderful hare-bells, big and cold and dark, almost black, and seeming like purple-dark ice : then little tufts of tiny pale-blue bells, as if some fairy frog had been blowing spume-bubbles out of the ice : then the bishop's-crozier of the stiff, bigger, hairy mountain-bell : then many stars of pale-lavender gentian, touched with earth-colour : and then monkshood, yellow, primrose yellow monkshood and sudden places full of dark monkshood. That dark-blue, black-blue, terrible colour of the strange rich monkshood made Hepburn look and look and look again. How did the ice come by that lustrous blue-purple intense darkness ? And by that royal poison—that laughing-snake gorgeousness of much monkshood ?

XVI

By one of the loud streams, under a rock in the sun, with scented minty or thyme flowers near, they sat down to eat some lunch. It was about eleven o'clock. A thin bee went in and out the scented flowers and the eyebright. The water poured with all the lust and greed of unloosed water over the stones. He took a cupful for our Hannele, bright and icy, and she mixed it with the red Hungarian wine.

Down the road strayed the tourists like pilgrims, and at the closed end of the valley they could be seen, quite tiny, climbing the cut-out road that went up like a stair-way. Just by their movement you perceived them. But on the valley-bed they went like rolling stones, little as stones. A very elegant mule came stepping by, following a middle-aged woman in tweeds and a tall, high-browed man in knickerbockers. The mule was drawing a very amusing little cart, a chair, rather like a round office-chair upholstered in red velvet, and mounted on two wheels. The red velvet had gone gold and orange and like fruit-juice, being old : really a lovely colour. And the muleteer, a little shabby creature, waddled beside excitedly.

" Ach," cried Hannele, " that looks almost like before the war : almost as peaceful."

" Except that the chair is too shabby, and that they all feel exceptional," he remarked.

There in that upper valley, there was no sense of peace. The rush of the waters seemed like weapons, and the tourists all seemed in a sort of frenzy, in a frenzy to be happy, or to be thrilled. It was a feeling that desolated the heart.

The two sat in the changing sunshine under their rock, with the mountain flowers scenting the snow-bitter air, and they ate their eggs and sausage and cheese, and drank the bright-red Hungarian wine. It seemed lovely : almost like before the war : almost the same feeling of eternal holiday, as if the world was made for man's everlasting holiday. But not quite. Never again quite the same. The world is not made for man's everlasting holiday.

As Alexander was putting the bread back into his shoulder-sack, he exclaimed :

" Oh, look here ! "

She looked, and saw him drawing out a flat package wrapped in paper : evidently a picture.

" A picture ! " she cried.

He unwrapped the thing, and handed it to her. It was Theodor Worpswede's Still-leben : not very large, painted on a board.

Hannele looked at it, and went pale.

" It's *good*," she cried, in an equivocal tone.

" Quite good," he said.

" Especially the poached egg," she said.

" Yes, the poached egg is almost living."

" But where did you find it ? "

" Oh, I found it in the artist's studio." And he told her how he had traced her.

" How extraordinary ! " she cried. " But why did you buy it ? "

" I don't quite know."

" Did you *like* it ? "

" No, not quite that."

" You could *never* hang it up."

" No, never," he said.

" But do you think it is good as a work of art ? "

" I think it is quite clever as a painting. I don't like the spirit of it, of course. I'm too catholic for that."

" No. No," she faltered. " It's rather horrid really. That's why I wonder why you bought it."

" Perhaps to prevent any one else's buying it," he said.

" Do you mind very much then ? " she asked.

" No, I don't mind very much. I didn't quite like it that you sold the doll," he said.

" I needed the money," she said quietly.

" Oh, quite."

There was a pause for some moments.

" I felt you'd sold *me*," she said, quiet and savage.

" When ? "

" When your wife appeared. And when you *disappeared*."

Again there was a pause : his pause this time.

" I did write to you," he said.

" When ? "

" Oh—March, I believe."

" Oh, yes. I had that letter." Her tone was just as quiet, and even savager.

So there was a pause that belonged to both of them. Then she rose.

" I want to be going," she said. " We shall never get to the glacier at this rate."

He packed up the picture, slung on his knapsack, and they set off. She stooped now and then to pick the starry, earth-lavender gentians from the road-side. As they passed the second of the valley hotels, they saw the man and wife sitting at a little table outside eating bread and cheese, while the mule-chair with its red velvet waited aside on the grass. They passed a whole grove of black-purple nightshade on the left, and some long, low cattle-huts which, with the stones on their roofs, looked as if they had grown up as stones grow in such places through the grass. In the wild, desert place some black pigs were snouting.

So they wound into the head of the valley, and saw the steep face ahead, and high up, like vapour or foam dripping from the fangs of a beast, waterfalls vapouring down from the deep fangs of ice. And there was one end of the glacier, like a great bluey-white fur just slipping over the slope of the rock.

As the valley closed in again the flowers were very lovely, especially the big, dark, icy bells, like hare-bells, that would sway so easily, but which hung dark and with that terrible motionlessness of upper mountain flowers. And the road turned to get on to the long slant in the cliff-face, where it climbed like a stair. Slowly, slowly the two climbed up. Now again they saw the valley below, behind. The mule-chair was coming, hastening, the lady seated tight facing backwards, as the chair faced, and wrapped in rugs. The tall, fair, middle-aged husband in knickerbockers strode just behind, bare-headed.

Alexander and Hannele climbed slowly, slowly up the slant, under the dripping rock-face where the white and veined flowers of the grass of Parnassus still rose straight and chilly in the shadow, like water which had taken on itself white flower-flesh. Above they saw the slipping edge of the glacier, like a terrible great paw, bluey. And from the skyline dark grey clouds were fuming up, fuming up as if breathed black and icily out from some ice-cauldron.

" It is going to rain," said Alexander.

" Not much," said Hannele shortly.

" I hope not," said he.

And still she would not hurry up that steep slant, but insisted on standing to look. So the dark, ice-black clouds fumed solid, and the rain began to fly on a cold wind. The mule-chair hastened past, the lady sitting comfortably with her back to the mule, a little pheasant-trimming in her tweed hat, while her Tannhäuser husband reached for his dark, cape-frilled mantle.

Alexander had his dust-coat, but Hannele had nothing but a light knitted jersey-coat, such as women wear indoors. Over the hollow crest above came the cold, steel rain. They pushed on up the slope. From behind came another mule, and a little old man hurrying, and a little cart like a hand-barrow, on which were hampers with cabbage and carrots and peas and joints of meat, for the hotel above.

" Wird es viel sein ? " asked Alexander of the little gnome. " Will it be much ? "

" Was meint der Herr ? " replied the other. " What does the gentleman say ? "

" Der Regen, wird es lang dauern ? Will the rain last long ? "

" Nein. Nein. Dies ist kein langer Regen."

So, with his mule which had to stand exactly at that spot to make droppings, the little man resumed his way, and Hannele and Alexander were the last on the slope. The air smelt steel-cold of rain, and of hot mule-droppings. Alexander watched the rain beat on the shoulders and on the blue skirt of Hannele.

" It is a pity you left your big coat down below," he said.

" What good is it saying so now ! " she replied, pale at the nose with anger.

" Quite," he said, as his eyes glowed and his brow blackened. " What good suggesting anything at any time, apparently ! "

She turned round on him in the rain, as they stood perched nearly at the summit of that slanting cliff-climb, with a glacier-paw hung almost invisible above, and waters gloating aloud in the gulf below.

She faced him, and he faced her.

" What have you ever suggested to me ? " she said, her face naked as the rain itself with an ice-bitter fury. " What have you ever suggested to me ? "

" When have you ever been open to suggestion ? " he said, his face dark and his eyes curiously glowing.

" I ? I ? Ha ! Haven't I waited for you to suggest something ? And all you can do is to come here with a picture to reproach me for having sold your doll. Ha ! I'm glad I sold it. A foolish barren effigy it was too, a foolish staring thing. What should I do but sell it. Why should I keep it, do you imagine ? "

" Why do you come here with me to-day, then ? "

" Why do I come here with you to-day ? " she replied. " I come to see the mountains, which are wonderful, and give me strength. And I come to see the glacier. Do you think I come here to see *you* ? Why should I ? You are always in some hotel or other away below."

" You came to see the glacier and the mountains *with* me," he replied.

" Did I ? Then I made a mistake. You can do nothing but find fault even with God's mountains."

A dark flame suddenly went over his face.

" Yes," he said, " I hate them, I hate them. I hate their snow and their affectations."

" *Affectation !* " she laughed. " Oh ! Even the mountains are affected for you, are they ? "

" Yes," he said. " Their loftiness and their uplift. I hate their uplift. I hate people prancing on mountain-tops and feeling exalted. I'd like to make them all stop up there, on their mountain-tops, and chew ice to fill their stomachs. I wouldn't let them down again, I wouldn't. I hate it all, I tell you ; I hate it."

She looked in wonder on his dark, glowing, ineffectual face. It seemed to her like a dark flame burning in the daylight and in the ice-rains : very ineffectual and unnecessary.

" You must be a little mad," she said superbly, " to talk like that about the mountains. They are so much bigger than you."

" No," he said. " No ! They are not."

" What ! " she laughed aloud. " The mountains are not bigger than you ? But you are extraordinary."

" They are not bigger than me," he cried. " Any more than you are bigger than me if you stand on a ladder. They are not bigger than me. They are less than me."

" Oh ! Oh ! " she cried in wonder and ridicule. " The mountains are less than you."

" Yes," he cried, " they are less."

He seemed suddenly to go silent and remote as she watched him. The speech had gone out of his face again, he seemed to be standing a long way off from her, beyond some border-line. And in the midst of her indignant amazement she watched him with wonder and a touch of fascination. To what country did he belong then—to what dark, different atmosphere ?

" You must suffer from megalomania," she said. And she said what she felt.

But he only looked at her out of dark, dangerous, haughty eyes.

They went on their way in the rain in silence. He was filled with a passionate silence and imperiousness, a curious, dark, masterful force that supplanted thought in him. And she, who always pondered, went pondering : " Is he mad ? What does he mean ? Is he a madman ? He wants to bully me. He wants to bully me into something. What does he want to bully me into ? Does he want me to love him ? "

At this final question she rested. She decided that what he wanted was that she should love him. And this thought flattered her vanity and her pride and appeased her wrath against him. She felt quite mollified towards him.

But what a way he went about it ! He wanted her to love him. Of this she was sure. He had always wanted her to love him, even from the first. Only he had not made up his *mind* about it. He had not made up his mind. After his wife had died he had gone away to make up his mind. Now he had made it up. He wanted her to love him. And he was offended, mortally offended because she had sold his doll.

So, this was the conclusion to which Hannele came. And it pleased her, and it flattered her. And it made her feel quite warm towards him, as they walked in the rain. The rain, by the way, was abating. The spume over the hollow crest to which they were approaching was thinning considerably. They could again see the glacier-paw hanging out, a little beyond. The rain was going to pass. And they were not far now from the hotel, and the third level of Lammerboden.

He wanted her to love him. She felt again quite glowing and

triumphant inside herself, and did not care a bit about the rain on her shoulders. He wanted her to love him. Yes, that was how she had to put it. He didn't want to *love* her. No. He wanted *her* to love *him*.

But then, of course, woman-like, she took his love for granted. So many men had been so very ready to love her. And this one—to her amazement, to her indignation, and rather to her secret satisfaction—just blackly insisted that *she* must love *him*. Very well—she would give him a run for his money. That was it : he blackly insisted that *she* must love *him*. What he felt was not to be considered. *She* must love *him*. And be bullied into it. That was what it amounted to. In his silent, black, overbearing soul, he wanted to compel her, he wanted to have power over her. He wanted to make her love him so that he had power over her. He wanted to bully her, physically, sexually, and from the inside.

And she ! Well, she was just as confident that she was not going to be bullied. She would love him : probably she would : most probably she did already. But she was not going to be bullied by him in any way whatsoever. No, he must go down on his knees to her if he wanted her love. And then she would love him. Because she *did* love him. But a dark-eyed little master and bully she would never have.

And this was her triumphant conclusion. Meanwhile the rain had almost ceased, they had almost reached the rim of the upper level, towards which they were climbing, and he was walking in that silent diffidence which made her watch him because she was not sure what he was feeling, what he was thinking, or even what he was. He was a puzzle to her : eternally incomprehensible in his feelings and even his sayings. There seemed to her no logic and no reason in what he felt and said. She could never tell what his next mood would come out of. And this made her uneasy, made her watch him. And at the same time it piqued her attention. He had some of the fascination of the incomprehensible. And his curious inscrutable face—it wasn't really only a meaningless mask, because she had seen it half an hour ago melt with a quite incomprehensible and rather, to her mind, foolish passion. Strange, black, inconsequential passion. Asserting with that curious dark ferocity that he was bigger than the mountains. Madness ! Madness ! Megalomania.

But because he gave himself away, she forgave him and even liked him. And the strange passion of his, that gave out incomprehensible flashes, *was* rather fascinating to her. She felt just a tiny bit sorry for him. But she wasn't going to be bullied by him. She wasn't going to give in to him and his black passion. No, never. It must be love on equal terms, or nothing. For love on equal terms she was quite ready. She only waited for him to offer it.

XVII

In the hotel was a buzz of tourists. Alexander and Hannele sat in the restaurant drinking hot coffee and milk, and watching the maidens in cotton frocks and aprons and bare arms, and the fair youths with maidenly necks and huge voracious boots, and the many Jews of the wrong sort and the wrong shape. These Jews were all being very Austrian, in Tyrol costume that didn't sit on them, assuming the whole gesture and intonation of aristocratic Austria, so that you might think they *were* Austrian aristocrats, if you weren't properly listening, or if you didn't look twice. Certainly they were lords of the Alps, or at least lords of the Alpine hotels this summer, let prejudice be what it might. Jews of the wrong sort. And yet even they imparted a wholesome breath of sanity, disillusion, unsentimentality to the excited " Bergheil " atmosphere. Their dark-eyed, sardonic presence seemed to say to the maidenly-necked mountain youths : " Don't sprout wings of the spirit too much, my dears."

The rain had ceased. There was a wisp of sunshine from a grey sky. Alexander left the knapsack, and the two went out into the air. Before them lay the last level of the up-climb, the Lammerboden. It was a rather gruesome hollow between the peaks, a last shallow valley about a mile long. At the end the enormous static stream of the glacier poured in from the blunt mountain-top of ice. The ice was dull, sullen-coloured, melted on the surface by the very hot summer : and so it seemed a huge, arrested, sodden flood, ending in a wave-wall of stone-speckled ice upon the valley bed of rocky débris. A gruesome descent of stone and blocks of rock, the little valley bed, with a river raving through. On the left rose the grey rock, but the glacier was there, sending down great paws of ice. It was like some great, deep-furred ice-bear lying spread upon the top heights, and reaching down terrible paws of ice into the valley : like some immense sky-bear fishing in the earth's solid hollows from above. Hepburn it just filled with terror. Hannele too it scared, but it gave her a sense of ecstasy. Some of the immense, furrowed, paws of ice held down between the rock were vivid blue in colour, but of a frightening, poisonous blue, like crystal copper-sulphate. Most of the ice was a sullen, semi-translucent greeny grey.

The two set off to walk through the massy, desolate stone-bed, under rocks and over waters, to the main glacier. The flowers were even more beautiful on this last reach. Particularly the dark hare-bells were large and almost black and ice-metallic : one could imagine they gave a dull ice-chink. And the grass of Parnassus stood erect, white-veined big cups held terribly naked and open to their ice-air.

From behind the great blunt summit of ice that blocked the distance at the end of the valley, a pale-grey, woolly mist or cloud was fusing up, exhaling huge, like some grey-dead aura into the sky, and covering the top of the glacier. All the way along the valley people were threading, strangely insignificant, among the grey dishevel of stone and rock, like insects. Hannele and Alexander went ahead quickly, along the tiring track.

" Are you glad now that you came ? " she said, looking at him triumphant.

" Very glad I came," he said. His eyes were dilated with excite-ment that was ordeal or mystic battle rather than the Bergheil ecstasy. The curious vibration of his excitement made the scene strange, rather horrible to her. She too shuddered. But it still seemed to her to hold the key to all glamour and ecstasy, the great silent, living glacier. It seemed to her like a grand beast.

As they came near they saw the wall of ice : the glacier end, thick crusted and speckled with stone and dirt débris. From underneath, secret in stones, water rushed out. When they came quite near, they saw the great monster was sweating all over, trickles and rivulets of sweat running down his sides of pure, slush-translucent ice. There it was, the glacier, ending abruptly in the wall of ice under which they stood. Near to, the ice was pure, but waterlogged, all the surface rather rotten from the hot summer. It was sullenly translucent, and of a watery, darkish bluey-green colour. But near the earth it became again bright coloured, gleams of green like jade, gleams of blue like thin, pale sapphire, in little caverns above the wet stones where the walls trickled forever.

Alexander wanted to climb on to the glacier. It was his one desire—to stand upon it. So under the pellucid wet wall they toiled among rocks upwards, to where the guide-track mounted the ice. Several other people were before them—mere day-tourists—and all uncertain about venturing any further. For the ice-slope rose steep and slithery, pure, sun-locked, sweating ice. Still, it was like a curved back. One could scramble on to it, and on up to the first level, like the flat on top of some huge paw.

There stood the little cluster of people, facing the uphill of sullen, pure, sodden-looking ice. They were all afraid : naturally. But being human, they all wanted to go beyond their fear. It was strange that the ice looked so pure, like flesh. Not bright, because the surface was soft like a soft, deep epidermis. But pure ice away down to immense depths.

Alexander, after some hesitation, began gingerly to try the ice. He was frightened of it. And he had no stick, and only smooth-soled boots. But he had a great desire to stand on the glacier. So, gingerly and shakily, he began to struggle a few steps up the pure slope. The ice was soft on the surface, he could kick his heel in it and get a little sideways grip. So, staggering and going sideways he got up a few yards, and was on the naked ice-slope.

Immediately the youths and the fat man below began to tackle it too : also two maidens. For some time, however, Alexander gingerly and scramblingly led the way. The slope of ice was steeper, and rounded, so that it was difficult to stand up in any way. Sometimes he slipped, and was clinging with burnt finger-ends to the soft ice-mass. Then he tried throwing his coat down, and getting a foot-hold on that. Then he went quite quickly by bending down and get-ting a little grip with his fingers, and going ridiculously as on four legs.

Hannele watched from below, and saw the ridiculous exhibition, and was frightened and amused, but more frightened. And she kept calling, to the great joy of the Austrians down below :
" Come back. Do come back."

But when he got on to his feet again he only waved his hand at her, half crossly, as she stood away down there in her blue frock. The other fellows with sticks and nail-boots had now taken heart and were scrambling like crabs past our hero, doing better than he.

He had come to a rift in the ice. He sat near the edge and looked down. Clean, pure ice, fused with pale colour, and fused into intense copper-sulphate blue away down in the crack. It was not like crystal, but fused as one fuses a borax bead under a blow-flame. And keenly, wickedly blue in the depths of the crack.

He looked upwards. He had not half mounted the slope. So on he went, upon the huge body of the soft-fleshed ice, slanting his way sometimes on all fours, sometimes using his coat, usually hitting-in with the side of his heel. Hannele down below was crying him to come back. But two other youths were now almost level with him.

So he struggled on till he was more or less over the brim. There he stood and looked at the ice. It came down from above in a great hollow world of ice. A world, a terrible place of hills and valleys

s

and slopes, all motionless, all of ice. Away above the grey mist-cloud was looming bigger. And near at hand were long huge cracks, side by side, like gills in the ice. It would seem as if the ice breathed through these great ridged gills. One could look down into the series of gulfs, fearful depths, and the colour burning that acid, intense blue, intenser as the crack went deeper. And the crests of the open gills ridged and grouped pale blue above the crevices. It seemed as if the ice breathed there.

The wonder, the terror, and the bitterness of it. Never a warm leaf to unfold, never a gesture of life to give off. A world sufficient unto itself in lifelessness, all this ice.

He turned to go down, though the youths were passing beyond him. And seeing the naked translucent ice heaving downwards in a vicious curve, always the same dark translucency underfoot, he was afraid. If he slipped, he would certainly slither the whole way down, and break some of his bones. Even when he sat down, he had to cling with his finger-nails in the ice, because if he had started to slide he would have slid the whole way down on his trouser-seat, precipitously, and have landed heaven knows how.

Hannele was watching from below. And he was frightened, perched seated on the shoulder of ice and not knowing how to get off. Above he saw the great blue gills of ice ridging the air. Down below were two blue cracks—then the last wet level claws of ice upon the stones. And there stood Hannele and the three or four people who had got so far.

However, he found that by striking in his heels sideways with sufficient sharpness he could keep his footing, no matter how steep the slope. So he started to jerk his way zig-zag downwards.

As he descended, arrived a guide with a black beard and all the paraphernalia of ropes and pole and bristling boots. He and his gentleman began to strike their way up the ice. With those bristling nails like teeth in one's boots, it was quite easy : and a pole to press on to.

Hannele, who had got sick of waiting, and who was also frightened, had gone scuttling on the return journey. He hurried after her, thankful to be off the ice, but excited and gratified. Looking round, he saw the guide and the man on the ice watching the ice-world and the weather. Then they too turned to come down. The day wasn't safe.

XVIII

Pondering, rather thrilled, they threaded their way through the desert of rock and rushing water back to the hotel. The sun was shining warmly for a moment, and he felt happy, though his finger-ends were bleeding a little from the ice.

" But one day," said Hannele, " I should love to go with a guide right up, high, right into the glacier."

" No," said he. " I've been far enough. I prefer the world where cabbages will grow on the soil. Nothing grows on glaciers."

" They say there are glacier-fleas, which only live on glaciers," she said.

" Well, to me the ice didn't look good to eat, even for a flea."

" You never know," she laughed. " But you're glad you've been, aren't you ? "

" Very glad. Now I need never go again."

" But you *did* think it wonderful ? "

" Marvellous. And awful, to my mind."

XIX

They ate venison and spinach in the hotel, then set off down again. Both felt happier. She gathered some flowers, and put them in her handkerchief so they should not die. And again they sat by the stream, to drink a little wine.

But the fume of cloud was blowing up again, thick from behind the glacier. Hannele was uneasy. She wanted to get down. So they went fairly quickly. Many other tourists were hurrying downwards also. The rain began—a sharp handful of drops flung from beyond the glacier. So Hannele and he did not stay to rest, but dropped easily down the steep, dark valley towards the motor-car terminus.

There they had tea, rather tired but comfortably so. The big hotel restaurant was hideous, and seemed sordid. So in the gloom of a grey, early twilight they went out again and sat on a seat, watching the tourists and the trippers and the motor-car men. There were three Jews from Vienna : and the girl had a huge white woolly dog, as big as a calf, and white and woolly and silky and amiable as a toy. The men, of course, came patting it and admiring it, just as men always do, in life and in novels. And the girl, holding the leash, posed and leaned backwards in the attitude of heroines on novel-covers. She said the white cool monster was a Siberian steppe-dog. Alexander wondered what the steppes made of such a wuffer. And the three Jews pretended they were elegant Austrians out of popular romances.

" Do you think," said Alexander, " you will marry the Herr Regierungsrat ? "

She looked round, making wide eyes.

" It looks like it, doesn't it ! " she said.

" Quite," he said.

Hannele watched the woolly white dog. So of course it came wagging its ever-amiable hindquarters towards her. She looked at it still, but did not touch it.

" What makes you ask such a question," she said.

" I can't say. But even so you haven't really answered. Do you really fully intend to marry the Herr Regierungsrat ? Is that your final intention at this moment ? "

She looked at him again.

" But before I answer," she said, " oughtn't I to know why you ask ? "

" Probably you know already," he said.

" I assure you I don't."

He was silent for some moments. The huge, woolly dog stood in front of him and breathed enticingly, with its tongue out. He only looked at it blankly.

" Well," he said, " if you were not going to marry the Herr Regierungsrat, I should suggest that you marry me."

She stared away at the auto-garage, a very faint look of amusement, or pleasure, or ridicule on her face : or all three. And a certain shyness.

" But why ? " she said.

" Why what ? " he returned.

" Why should you suggest that I should marry you ? "

" *Why ?* " he replied, in his lingering tones. " *Why ?* Well, for what purpose does a man usually ask a woman to marry him ? "

" For what *purpose* ! " she repeated, rather haughtily.

" For what reason, then ! " he corrected.

She was silent for some moments. Her face was closed and a little numb-looking, her hands lay very still in her lap. She looked away from him, across the road.

" There is usually only one reason," she replied, in a rather small voice.

" Yes ? " he replied curiously. " What would you say that was ? "

She hesitated. Then she said, rather stiffly :

" Because he really loved her, I suppose. That seems to me the only excuse for a man asking a woman to marry him."

Followed a dead silence, which she did not intend to break. He knew he would have to answer, and for some reason he didn't want to say what was obviously the thing to say.

"Leaving aside the question of whether you love me or I love you——" he began.

"I certainly *won't* leave it aside," she said.

"And I certainly won't consider it," he said, just as obstinately.

She turned now and looked full at him, with amazement, ridicule, and anger in her face.

"I really think you must be mad," she said.

"I doubt if you do think that," he replied. "It is only a method of retaliation, that is. I think you understand my point very clearly."

"Your point!" she cried. "Your point! Oh, so you have a point in all this palavering?"

"Quite!" said he.

She was silent with indignation for some time. Then she said angrily :

"I assure you I do *not* see your point. I don't see any point at all. I see only impertinence."

"Very good," he replied. "The point is whether we marry on a basis of love."

"Indeed! Marry! We, marry! I don't think that is by any means the point."

He took his knapsack from under the seat, between his feet. And from the knapsack he took the famous picture.

"When," he said, "we were supposed to be in love with one another, you made that doll of me, didn't you?" And he sat looking at the odious picture.

"I never for one moment deluded myself that you *really* loved me," she said bitterly.

"Take the other point, whether *you* loved *me*, or not," said he.

"How could I love you, when I couldn't believe in your love for me?" she cried.

He put the picture down between his knees again.

"All this about love," he said, "is very confusing, and very complicated."

"Very! In *your* case. Love to me is simple enough," she said.

"Is it? Is it? And was it simple love which made you make that doll of me?"

"Why shouldn't I make a doll of you? Does it do you any harm? And *weren't* you a doll, good heavens! You *were* nothing but a doll. So what hurt does it do you?"

"Yes, it does. It does me the greatest possible damage," he replied.

She turned on him with wide-open eyes of amazement and rage.

"Why? Pray why? Can you tell me why?"

"Not quite, I can't," he replied, taking up the picture and holding it in front of him. She turned her face from it as a cat turns its nose away from a lighted cigarette. "But when I look at it—when I look at this—then I *know* that there's no love between you and me."

"Then why are you talking at me in this shameful way," she flashed at him, tears of anger and mortification rising to her eyes. "You want your little revenge on me, I suppose, because I made that doll of you."

"That may be so, in a small measure," he said.

"That is *all*. That is all and everything," she cried. "And that is all you came back to me for—for this petty revenge. Well, you've had it now. But please don't speak to me any more. I shall see if I can go home in the big omnibus."

She rose and walked away. He saw her hunting for the motor-bus conductor. He saw her penetrate into the yard of the garage. And he saw her emerge again, after a time, and take the path to the river. He sat on in front of the hotel. There was nothing else to do.

The tourists who had arrived in the big 'bus now began to collect. And soon the huge drab vehicle itself rolled up, and stood big as a house before the hotel door. The passengers began to scramble into their seats. The two men of the white dog were going: but the woman of the white dog, and the dog, were staying behind. Hepburn wondered if Hannele had managed to get herself transferred. He doubted it, because he knew the omnibus was crowded.

Moreover, he had her ticket.

The passengers were packed in. The conductor was collecting the tickets. And at last the great 'bus rolled away. The bay of the road-end seemed very empty. Even the woman with the white dog had gone. Soon the other car, the Luxus, so-called, must appear. Hepburn sat and waited. The evening was falling chilly, the trees looked gruesome.

At last Hannele sauntered up again, unwillingly.

"I think," she said, "you have my ticket."

"Yes, I have," he replied.

"Will you give it me, please?"

He gave it to her. She lingered a moment. Then she walked away. There was the sound of a motor-car. With a triumphant purr the Luxus came steering out of the garage yard, and drew up at the hotel door. Hannele came hastening also. She went straight to one of the hinder doors—she and Hepburn had their seats in front, beside the driver. She had her foot on the step of the back seat. And then

she was afraid. The little sharp-faced driver—there was no conductor—came round looking at the car. He looked at her with his
sharp, metallic eye of a mechanic.

" Are all the people going back who came ? " she asked, shrinking.

" Jawohl."

" It is full—this car ? "

" Jawohl."

" There's no other place ? "

" Nein."

Hannele shrank away. The driver was absolutely laconic.

Six of the passengers were here : four were already seated.
Hepburn sat still by the hotel door, Hannele lingered in the road by
the car, and the little driver, with a huge woollen muffler round his
throat, was running round and in and out looking for the two missing
passengers. Of course there were two missing passengers. No, he
could not find them. And off he trotted again, silently, like a weasel
after two rabbits. And at last, when everybody was getting cross,
he unearthed them and brought them scuttling to the car.

Now Hannele took her seat, and Hepburn beside her. The driver
snapped up the tickets and climbed in past them. With a vindictive
screech the car glided away down the ravine. Another beastly
trip was over, another infernal joyful holiday done with.

" I think," said Hepburn, " I may as well finish what I had to say."

" What ? " cried Hannele, fluttering in the wind of the rushing car.

" I may as well finish what I had to say," shouted he, his breath
blown away.

" Finish then," she screamed, the ends of her scarf flickering
behind her.

" When my wife died," he said loudly, " I knew I couldn't love
any more."

" Oh—h ! " she screamed ironically.

" In fact," he shouted, " I realised that, as far as I was concerned,
love was a mistake."

" *What* was a mistake ? " she screamed.

" Love," he bawled.

" Love ! " she screamed. " A mistake ? " Her tone was derisive.

" For me personally," he said, shouting.

" Oh, only for you personally," she cried, with a pouf of laughter.

The car gave a great swerve, and she fell on the driver. Then she
righted herself. It gave another swerve, and she fell on Alexander.
She righted herself angrily. And now they ran straight on : and it
seemed a little quieter.

"I realized," he said, "that I had always made a mistake, undertaking to love."

"It must have been an undertaking, for _you_," she cried.

"Yes, I'm afraid it was. I never really wanted it. But I thought I did. And that's where I made my mistake."

"Whom have you ever loved—even as an undertaking?" she asked.

"To begin with, my mother : and that was a mistake. Then my sister : and that was a mistake. Then a girl I had known all my life : and that was a mistake. Then my wife : and that was my most terrible mistake. And then I began the mistake of loving you."

"Undertaking to love me, you mean," she said. "But then you never did properly undertake it. You never really _undertook_ to love me."

"Not quite, did I?" said he.

And she sat feeling angry that he had never made the undertaking.

"No," he continued. "Not quite. That is why I came back to you. I don't want to love you. I don't want marriage on a basis of love."

"On a basis of what, then?"

"I think you know without my putting it into words," he said.

"Indeed, I assure you I don't. You are much too mysterious," she replied.

Talking in a swiftly-running motor-car is a nerve-wracking business. They both had a pause, to rest, and to wait for a quieter stretch of road.

"It isn't very easy to put it into words," he said. "But I tried marriage once on a basis of love, and I must say it was a ghastly affair in the long run. And I believe it would be so, for me, _whatever_ woman I had."

"There must be something wrong with you, then," said she.

"As far as love goes. And yet I want marriage. I want marriage. I want a woman to honour and obey me."

"If you are quite reasonable and _very_ sparing with your commands," said Hannele. "And very careful how you give your orders."

"In fact, I want a sort of patient Griselda. I want to be honoured and obeyed. I don't want love."

"How Griselda managed to honour that fool of a husband of hers, even if she obeyed him, is more than I can say," said Hannele. "I'd like to know what she _really_ thought of him. Just what any woman thinks of a bullying fool of a husband."

" Well," said he, " that's no good to me."

They were silent now until the car stopped at the station. There they descended and walked on under the trees by the lake.

" Sit on a seat," he said, " and let us finish."

Hannele, who was really anxious to hear what he should say, and who, woman-like, was fascinated by a man when he began to give away his own inmost thoughts—no matter how much she might jeer afterwards—sat down by his side. It was a grey evening, just falling dark. Lights twinkled across the lake, the hotel over there threaded its strings of light. Some little boats came rowing quietly to shore. It was a grey, heavy evening, with that special sense of dreariness with which a public holiday usually winds up.

" Honour, and obedience : and the proper physical feelings," he said. " To me that is marriage. Nothing else."

" But what are the proper physical feelings but love ? " asked Hannele.

" No," he said. " A woman wants you to adore her, and be in love with her—and I shan't. I will not do it again, if I live a monk for the rest of my days. I will neither adore you nor be in love with you."

" You won't get a chance, thank you. And what do you call the proper physical feelings, if you are not in love ? I think you want something vile."

" If a woman honours me—absolutely from the bottom of her nature honours me—and obeys me because of that, I take it, my desire for her goes very much deeper than if I was in love with her, or if I adored her."

" It's the same thing. If you love, then everything is there—all the lot : your honour and obedience and everything. And if love isn't there, nothing is there," she said.

" That isn't true," he replied. " A woman may love you, she may adore you, but she'll neither honour you nor obey you. The most loving and adoring woman to-day could any minute start and make a doll of her husband—as you made of me."

" Oh, that eternal doll ! What makes it stick so in your mind ? "

" I don't know. But there it is. It wasn't malicious. It was flattering, if you like. But it just sticks in me like a thorn : like a thorn. And there it is, in the world, in Germany somewhere. And you can say what you like, but *any* woman, to-day, no matter *how* much she loves her man—she could start any minute and make a doll of him. And the doll would be her hero : and her hero would be no more than her doll. My wife might have done it. She did do it,

s *

in her mind. She had her doll of me right enough. Why, I heard her talk about me to other women. And her doll was a great deal sillier than the one you made. But it's all the same. If a woman loves you, she'll make a doll out of you. She'll never be satisfied till she's made your doll. And when she's got your doll, that's all she wants. And that's what love means. And so, I won't be loved. And I won't love. I won't have anybody loving me. It is an insult. I feel I've been insulted for forty years : by love, and the women who've loved me. I won't be loved. And I won't love. I'll be honoured and I'll be obeyed : or nothing."

" Then it'll most probably be nothing," said Hannele sarcastically. " For I assure you, I've nothing but love to offer."

" Then keep your love," said he.

She laughed shortly.

" And you ? " she cried. " You ! Even suppose you *were* honoured and obeyed. I suppose all you've got to do is to sit there like a sultan and sup it up."

" Oh no, I have many things to do. And woman or no woman, I'm going to start to do them."

" What, pray ? "

" Why, nothing very exciting. I'm going to East Africa to join a man who's breaking his neck to get his three thousand acres of land under control. And when I've done a few more experiments and observations, and got all the necessary facts, I'm going to do a book on the moon. Woman or no woman, I'm going to do that."

" And the woman—supposing you got the poor thing ? "

"Why, she'll come along with me, and we'll set ourselves up out there."

" And she'll do all the honouring and obeying and housekeeping incidentally, while you ride about in the day and stare at the moon in the night."

He did not answer. He was staring away across the lake.

" What will you do for the woman, poor thing, while she's racking herself to pieces honouring you and obeying you and doing frightful housekeeping in Africa : because I know it can be *awful* : awful."

" Well," he said slowly, " she'll be my wife, and I shall treat her as such. If the marriage service says love and cherish—well, in that sense I shall do so."

" Oh ! " cried Hannele. " What, *love* her ? Actually love the poor thing ? "

" Not in that sense of the word, no. I shan't adore her or be in love with her. But she'll be my wife, and I shall love and cherish her as such."

"Just because she's your wife. Not because she's herself. Ghastly fate for any miserable woman," said Hannele.

"I don't think so. I think it's her highest fate."

"To be your wife?"

"To be a wife—and to be loved and shielded as a wife—not as a flirting woman."

"To be loved and cherished just because you're his wife! No, thank you. All I can admire is the conceit and impudence of it."

"Very well, then—there it is," he said, rising.

She rose too, and then went on towards where the boat was tied.

As they were rowing in silence over the lake, he said:

"I shall leave to-morrow."

She made no answer. She sat and watched the lights of the villa draw near. And then she said:

"I'll come to Africa with you. But I won't promise to honour and obey you."

"I don't want you otherwise," he said, very quietly.

The boat was drifting to the little landing stage. Hannele's friends were hallooing to her from the balcony.

"Hallo!" she cried. "Ja. Da bin ich. Ja, 's war wunderschön."

Then to him she said:

"You'll come in?"

"No," he said, "I'll row straight back."

From the villa they were running down the steps to meet Hannele.

"But won't you have me even if I love you?" she asked him.

"You must promise the other," he said. "It comes in the marriage service."

"Hat's geregnet? Wie war das Wetter? Warst du auf dem Gletscher?" cried the voices from the garden.

"Nein—kein Regen. Wunderschön! Ja, er war ganz auf dem Gletscher," cried Hannele in reply. And to him, *sotto voce:*

"Don't be a solemn ass. Do come in."

"No," he said, "I don't want to come in."

"Do you want to go away to-morrow? Go if you *do*. But anyway, I won't say it *before* the marriage service. I needn't, need I?"

She stepped from the boat on to the plank.

"Oh," she said, turning round, "give me that picture, please, will you? I want to burn it."

He handed it to her.

"And come to-morrow, will you?" she said.

"Yes, in the morning."

He pulled back quickly into the darkness.

" He is very fine and strong somewhere, but he does need a level-headed woman to look after him."

That was the *friendly* feminine verdict upon him. It flattered him, it pleased him, it galled him.

Having divorced a very charming and clever wife, who had held this opinion for ten years, and at last had got tired of the level-headed protective game, his gall was uppermost.

" I want to throw Jimmy out on the world, but I know the poor little man will go and fall on some woman's bosom. That's the worst of him. If he could only stand alone for ten minutes. But he can't. At the same time, there *is* something fine about him, something rare."

This had been Clarissa's summing-up as she floated away in the arms of the rich young American. The rich young American got rather angry when Jimmy's name was mentioned. Clarissa was now *his* wife. But she did sometimes talk as if she were still married to Jimmy.

Not in Jimmy's estimation, however. That worm had turned. Gall was uppermost. Gall and wormwood. He knew exactly what Clarissa thought—and said—about him. And the " something fine, something rare, something strong " which he was supposed to have " about him " was utterly outbalanced, in his feelings at least, by the " poor little man " nestled upon " some woman's bosom," which he was supposed to *be*.

" I am *not*," he said to himself, " a poor little man nestled upon some woman's bosom. If I could only find the right sort of woman, she should nestle on mine."

Jimmy was now thirty-five, and this point, to nestle or to be nestled, was the emotional crux and turning-point.

He imagined to himself some really *womanly* woman, to whom he should be *only* " fine and strong," and not for one moment " the poor little man." Why not some simple uneducated girl, some Tess of the D'Urbervilles, some wistful Gretchen, some humble Ruth gleaning an aftermath ? Why not ? Surely the world was full of such !

The trouble was he never met them. He only met sophisticated women. He really never had a chance of meeting " real " people. So few of us ever do. Only the people we *don't* meet are the " real " people, the simple, genuine, direct, spontaneous, unspoilt souls. Ah, the simple, genuine, unspoilt people we *don't* meet ! What a tragedy it is !

Because, of course, they must be there ! Somewhere ! Only we never come across them.

Jimmy was terribly handicapped by his position. It brought him into contact with so many people. Only never the right sort. Never the " real " people : the simple, genuine, unspoilt, etc. etc.

He was editor of a high-class, rather high-brow, rather successful magazine, and his rather personal, very candid editorials brought him shoals, swarms, hosts of admiring acquaintances. Realize that he was handsome, and could be extraordinarily " nice," when he liked, and was really very clever, in his own critical way, and you see how many chances he had of being adored and protected.

In the first place his good looks : the fine, clean lines of his face, like the face of the laughing faun in one of the faun's unlaughing, moody moments. The long, clean lines of the cheeks, the strong chin and the slightly arched, full nose, the beautiful dark-grey eyes with long lashes, and the thick black brows. In his mocking moments, when he seemed most himself, it was a pure Pan face, with thick black eyebrows cocked up, and grey eyes with a sardonic goaty gleam, and nose and mouth curling with satire. A good-looking, smooth-skinned satyr. That was Jimmy at his best. In the opinion of his men friends.

In his own opinion, he was a sort of Martyred Saint Sebastian, at whom the wicked world shot arrow after arrow—Mater Dolorosa nothing to him—and he counted the drops of blood as they fell : when he could keep count. Sometimes—as for instance when Clarissa said she was really departing with the rich young American, and should she divorce Jimmy, or was Jimmy going to divorce her ?—then the arrows assailed him like a flight of starlings, flying straight at him, jabbing at him, and the drops of martyred blood simple spattered down, he couldn't keep count.

So, naturally, he divorced Clarissa.

In the opinion of his men friends, he was, or should be, a consistently grinning faun, satyr, or Pan-person. In his own opinion, he was a Martyred Saint Sebastian with the mind of a Plato. In the opinion of his woman friends, he was a fascinating little man with a profound understanding of life and the capacity really to understand a woman and to make a woman feel a queen ; which of course was to make a woman feel her *real* self. . . .

He might, naturally, have made rich and resounding marriages, especially after the divorce. He didn't. The reason was, secretly, his resolve never to make any woman feel a queen any more. It was the turn of the women to make him feel a king.

Some unspoilt, unsophisticated, wild-blooded woman, to whom he would be a sort of Solomon of wisdom, beauty, and wealth. She would need to be in reduced circumstances to appreciate his wealth, which amounted to the noble sum of three thousand pounds and a little week-ending cottage in Hampshire. And to be unsophisticated she would have to be a woman of the people. Absolutely.

At the same time, not just the " obscure vulgar simplican."

He received many letters, many, many, many, enclosing poems, stories, articles, or more personal unbosomings. He read them all : like a solemn rook pecking and scratching among the litter.

And one—not one letter, but one correspondent—might be *the* one —Mrs. Emilia Pinnegar, who wrote from a mining village in Yorkshire. She was, of course, unhappily married.

Now Jimmy had always had a mysterious feeling about these dark and rather dreadful mining villages in the north. He himself had scarcely set foot north of Oxford. He felt that these miners up there must be the real stuff. And Pinnegar was a name, surely ! And Emilia !

She wrote a poem, with a brief little note, that, if the editor of the *Commentator* thought the verses of no value, would he simply destroy them. Jimmy, as editor of the *Commentator*, thought the verses quite good and admired the brevity of the note. But he wasn't sure about printing the poem. He wrote back, Had Mrs. Pinnegar nothing else to submit ?

Then followed a correspondence. And at length, upon request, this from Mrs. Pinnegar :

" You ask me about myself, but what shall I say ? I am a woman of thirty-one, with one child, a girl of eight, and I am married to a man who lives in the same house with me, but goes to another woman. I try to write poetry, if it is poetry, because I have no other way of expressing myself at all, and even if it doesn't matter to anybody besides myself, I feel I must and will express myself, if only to save myself from developing cancer or some disease that women have. I was a school-teacher before I was married, and I got my certificates at Rotherham College. If I could, I would teach again, and live alone. But married women teachers can't get jobs any more, they aren't allowed——"

THE COAL-MINER

By His Wife

The donkey-engine's beating noise
And the rattle, rattle of the sorting screens
Come down on me like the beat of his heart,
And mean the same as his breathing means.

The burning big pit-hill with fumes
Fills the air like the presence of that fair-haired man.
And the burning fire burning deeper and deeper
Is his will insisting since time began.

As he breathes the chair goes up and down
In the pit-shaft ; he lusts as the wheel-fans spin
The sucking air : he lives in the coal
Underground : and his soul is a strange engine.

That is the manner of man he is.
I married him and I should know.
The mother earth from bowels of coal
Brought him forth for the overhead woe.

This was the poem that the editor of the *Commentator* hesitated about. He reflected, also, that Mrs. Pinnegar didn't sound like one of the nestling, unsophisticated rustic type. It was something else that still attracted him : something desperate in a woman, something tragic.

THE NEXT EVENT

If at evening, when the twilight comes,
  You ask me what the day has been,
I shall not know. The distant drums
  Of some new-comer intervene

Between me and the day that's been.
  Some strange man leading long columns
Of unseen soldiers through the green
  Sad twilight of these smoky slums.

And as the darkness slowly numbs
  My senses, everything I've seen
Or heard the daylight through, becomes
  Rubbish behind an opaque screen.

> Instead, the sound of muffled drums
>   Inside myself : I have to lean
> And listen as my strength succumbs,
>   To hear what these oncomings mean.
>
> Perhaps the Death-God striking his thumbs
>   On the drums in a deadly rat-ta-ta-plan.
> Or a strange man marching slow as he strums
>   The tune of a new weird hope in Man.
>
> What does it matter ! The day that began
>   In coal-dust is ending the same, in crumbs
> Of darkness like coal. I live if I can ;
>   If I can't, then I welcome whatever comes.

This poem sounded so splendidly desperate, the editor of the *Commentator* decided to print it, and, moreover, to see the authoress. He wrote, Would she care to see him, if he happened to be in her neighbourhood ? He was going to lecture in Sheffield. She replied, Certainly.

He gave his afternoon lecture, on *Men in Books and Men in Life*. Naturally, men in books came first. Then he caught a train to reach the mining village where the Pinnegars lived.

It was February, with gruesome patches of snow. It was dark when he arrived at Mill Valley, a sort of thick, turgid darkness full of menace, where men speaking in a weird accent went past like ghosts, dragging their heavy feet and emitting the weird scent of the coal-mine underworld. Weird and a bit gruesome it was.

He knew he had to walk uphill to the little market-place. As he went, he looked back and saw the black valleys with bunches of light, like camps of demons it seemed to him. And the demonish smell of sulphur and coal in the air, in the heavy, pregnant, clammy darkness.

They directed him to New London Lane, and down he went down another hill. His skin crept a little. The place felt uncanny and hostile, hard, as if iron and minerals breathed into the black air. Thank goodness he couldn't see much, or be seen. When he had to ask his way the people treated him in a " heave-half-a-brick-at-him " fashion.

After much weary walking and asking, he entered a lane between trees, in the cold slushy mud of the unfrozen February. The mines, apparently, were on the outskirts of the town, in some mud-sunk country. He could see the red, sore fires of the burning pit-hill through the trees, and he smelt the sulphur. He felt like some modern Ulysses wandering in the realms of Hecate. How much more dismal and horrible, a modern Odyssey among mines and factories, than any Sirens, Scyllas or Charybdises.

So he mused to himself as he waded through icy black mud, in a black lane, under black trees that moaned an accompaniment to the sound of the coal-mine's occasional hissing and chuffing, under a black sky that quenched even the electric sparkle of the colliery. And the place seemed unhabitated like a cold black jungle.

At last he came in sight of a glimmer. Apparently, there were dwellings. Yes, a new little street, with one street-lamp, and the houses all apparently dark. He paused. Absolute desertion. Then three children.

They told him the house, and he stumbled up a dark passage. There was light on the little back-yard. He knocked, in some trepidation. A rather tall woman, looking down at him with a " Who are you ? " look, from the step above.

" Mrs. Pinnegar ? "

" Oh, is it you, Mr. Frith ? Come in."

He stumbled up the step into the glaring light of the kitchen. There stood Mrs. Pinnegar, a tall woman with a face like a mask of passive anger, looking at him coldly. Immediately he felt his own shabbiness and smallness. In utter confusion, he stuck out his hand.

" I had an awful time getting here," he said. " I'm afraid I shall make a frightful mess of your house." He looked down at his boots.

" That's all right," she said. " Have you had your tea ? "

" No—but don't you bother about me."

There was a little girl with fair hair in a fringe over her forehead, troubled blue eyes under the fringe, and two dolls. He felt easier.

" Is this your little girl ? " he asked. " She's awfully nice. What is her name ? "

" Jane."

" How are you, Jane ? " he said. But the child only stared at him with the baffled, bewildered, pained eyes of a child who lives with hostile parents.

Mrs. Pinnegar set his tea, bread, and butter, jam, and buns. Then she sat opposite him. She was handsome, dark straight brows and grey eyes with yellow grains in them, and a way of looking straight at you as if she were used to holding her own. Her eyes were the nicest part of her. They had a certain kindliness, mingled, like the yellow grains among the grey, with a relentless, unyielding feminine will. Her nose and mouth were straight, like a Greek mask, and the expression was fixed. She gave him at once the impression of a woman who has made a mistake, who knows it, but who will not change : who cannot now change.

He felt very uneasy. Being a rather small, shambling man, she made him aware of his physical inconspicuousness. And she said not a word, only looked down on him, as he drank his tea, with that changeless look of a woman who is holding her own against Man and Fate. While, from the corner across the kitchen, the little girl with her fair hair and her dolls, watched him also in absolute silence, from her hot blue eyes.

" This seems a pretty awful place," he said to her.

" It is. It's absolutely awful," the woman said.

" You ought to get away from it," he said.

But she received this in dead silence.

It was exceedingly difficult to make any headway. He asked about Mr. Pinnegar. She glanced at the clock.

" He comes up at nine," she said.

" Is he down the mine ? "

" Yes. He's on the afternoon shift."

There was never a sound from the little girl.

" Doesn't Jane ever talk ? " he asked.

" Not much," said the mother, glancing round.

He talked a little about his lectures, about Sheffield, about London. But she was not really interested. She sat there rather distant, very laconic, looking at him with those curious unyielding eyes. She looked to him like a woman who has had her revenge, and is left stranded on the reefs where she wrecked her opponent. Still unrelenting, unregretting, unyielding, she seemed rather undecided as to what her revenge had been, and what it had all been about.

" You ought to get away from here," he said to her.

" Where to ? " she asked.

" Oh "—he made a vague gesture—" anywhere, so long as it is *quite* away."

She seemed to ponder this, under her portentous brow.

" I don't see what difference it would make," she said. Then glancing round at her child : " I don't see what difference anything would make, except getting out of the world altogether. But there's *her* to consider." And she jerked her head in the direction of the child.

Jimmy felt definitely frightened. He wasn't used to this sort of grimness. At the same time he was excited. This handsome, laconic woman, with her soft brown hair and her unflinching eyes with their gold flecks, seemed to be challenging him to something. There was a touch of challenge in her remaining gold-flecked kindness. Somewhere, she had a heart. But what had happened to it? And why?

What had gone wrong with her? In some way, she must have gone against herself.

" Why don't you come and live with me ? " he said, like the little gambler he was.

The queer, conflicting smile was on his face. He had taken up her challenge, like a gambler. The very sense of a gamble, in which he could not lose desperately, excited him. At the same time, he was scared of her, and determined to get beyond his scare.

She sat and watched him, with the faintest touch of a grim smile on her handsome mouth.

" How do you mean, live with you ? " she said.

" Oh—I mean what it usually means," he said, with a little puff of self-conscious laughter.

" You're evidently not happy here. You're evidently in the wrong circumstances altogether. You're obviously *not* just an ordinary woman. Well, then, break away. When I say, Come and live with me, I mean just what I say. Come to London and live with me as my wife, if you like, and then if we want to marry, when you get a divorce, why, we can do it."

Jimmy made this speech more to himself than to the woman. That was how he was. He worked out all his things inside himself, as if it were all merely an interior problem of his own. And while he did so, he had an odd way of squinting his left eye and wagging his head loosely, like a man talking absolutely to himself, and turning his eyes inwards.

The woman watched him in a sort of wonder. This was something she was *not* used to. His extraordinary manner, and his extraordinary bald proposition, roused her from her own tense apathy.

" Well ! " she said. " That's got to be thought about. What about *her* ? "—and again she jerked her head towards the round-eyed child in the corner. Jane sat with a completely expressionless face, her little red mouth fallen a little open. She seemed in a sort of trance : as if she understood like a grown-up person, but, as a child, sat in a trance, unconscious.

The mother wheeled round in her chair and stared at her child. The little girl stared back at her mother, with hot, troubled, almost guilty blue eyes. And neither said a word. Yet they seemed to exchange worlds of meaning.

" Why, of course," said Jimmy, twisting his head again ; " she'd come, too."

The woman gave a last look at her child, then turned to him, and started watching *him* with that slow, straight stare.

" It's not "—he began, stuttering—" it's not anything *sudden* and unconsidered on my part. I've been considering it for quite a long time—ever since I had the first poem, and your letter."

He spoke still with his eyes turned inwards, talking to himself. And the woman watched him unflinchingly.

" Before you ever saw me ? " she asked, with a queer irony.

" Oh, of course. Of course before I ever saw you. Or else I never *should* have seen you. From the very first, I had a definite feeling——"

He made odd, sharp gestures, like a drunken man, and he spoke like a drunken man, his eyes turned inward, talking to himself. The woman was no more than a ghost moving inside his own consciousness, and he was addressing her there.

The actual woman sat outside looking on in a sort of wonder. This was really something new to her.

" And now you see me, do you want me, really, to come to London ? "

She spoke in a dull tone of incredulity. The thing was just a little preposterous to her. But why not ? It would have to be something a little preposterous, to get her out of the tomb she was in.

" Of course I do ! " he cried, with another scoop of his head and scoop of his hand. " *Now* I do *actually* want you, now I actually see you." He never looked at her. His eyes were still turned in. He was still talking to himself, in a sort of drunkenness with himself.

To her, it was something extraordinary. But it roused her from apathy.

He became aware of the hot blue eyes of the hot-cheeked little girl fixed upon him from the distant corner. And he gave a queer little giggle.

" Why, it's more than I could ever have hoped for," he said, " to have you and Jane to live with me ! Why, it will mean *life* to me." He spoke in an odd, strained voice, slightly delirious. And for the first time he looked up at the woman and, apparently, *straight* at her. But, even as he seemed to look straight at her, the curious cast was in his eye, and he was only looking at himself, inside himself, at the shadows inside his own consciousness.

" And when would you like me to come ? " she asked, rather coldly.

" Why, as soon as possible. Come back with me to-morrow, if

you will. I've got a little house in St. John's Wood, *waiting* for you. Come with me to-morrow. That's the simplest."

She watched him for some time, as he sat with ducked head. He looked like a man who is drunk—drunk with himself. He was going bald at the crown, his rather curly black hair was thin.

"I couldn't come to-morrow, I should need a few days," she said.

She wanted to see his face again. It was as if she could not remember what his face was like, this strange man who had appeared out of nowhere, with such a strange proposition.

He lifted his face, his eyes still cast in that inturned, blind look. He looked now like a Mephistopheles who has gone blind. With his black brows cocked up, Mephistopheles, Mephistopheles blind and begging in the street.

"Why, of course it's wonderful that it's happened like this for me," he said, with odd pouting emphasis, pushing out his lips. "I was finished, absolutely finished. I was finished while Clarissa was with me. But after she'd gone, I was *absolutely* finished. And I thought there was no chance for me in the world again. It seems to me perfectly marvellous that this has happened—that I've come across you——" he lifted his face sightlessly—" and Jane—Jane—why she's *really* too good to be true." He gave a slight hysterical laugh. "She really is."

The woman, and Jane, watched him with some embarrassment.

"I shall have to settle up here, with Mr. Pinnegar," she said, rather coldly musing. "Do you want to see him?"

"Oh, I——" he said, with a deprecating gesture, "I don't *care*. But if you think I'd better—why, certainly——"

"I do think you'd better," she said.

"Very well, then, I *will*. I'll see him whenever you like."

"He comes in soon after nine," she said.

"All right, I'll see him then. Much better. But I suppose I'd better see about finding a place to sleep first. Better not leave it too late."

"I'll come with you and ask for you."

"Oh, you'd better not, really. If you tell me where to go——"

He had taken on a protective tone : he was protecting her against herself and against scandal. It was his manner, his rather Oxfordy manner, more than anything else, that went beyond her. She wasn't used to it.

Jimmy plunged out into the gulfing blackness of the Northern night, feeling how horrible it was, but pressing his hat on his brow in a sense of strong adventure. He was going through with it.

At the baker's shop, where she had suggested he should ask for a bed, they would have none of him. Absolutely they didn't like the looks of him. At the Pub, too, they shook their heads : didn't want to have anything to do with him. But, in a voice more expostulatingly Oxford than ever, he said :

" But look here—you can't ask a man to sleep under one of these hedges. Can't I see the landlady ? "

He persuaded the landlady to promise to let him sleep on the big, soft settee in the parlour, where the fire was burning brightly. Then, saying he would be back about ten, he returned through mud and drizzle up New London Lane.

The child was in bed, a saucepan was boiling by the fire. Already the lines had softened a little in the woman's face.

She spread a cloth on the table. Jimmy sat in silence, feeling that she was hardly aware of his presence. She was absorbed, no doubt, in the coming of her husband. The stranger merely sat on the sofa, and waited. He felt himself wound up tight. And once he was really wound up, he could go through with anything.

They heard the nine o'clock whistle at the mine. The woman then took the saucepan from the fire and went into the scullery. Jimmy could smell the smell of potatoes being strained. He sat quite still. There was nothing for him to do or to say. He was wearing his big black-rimmed spectacles, and his face, blank and expressionless in the suspense of waiting, looked like the death-mask of some sceptical philosopher, who could wait through the ages, and who could hardly distinguish life from death at any time.

Came the heavy-shod tread up the house entry, and the man entered, rather like a blast of wind. The fair moustache stuck out from the blackish, mottled face, and the fierce blue eyes rolled their whites in the coal-blackened sockets.

" This gentleman is Mr. Frith," said Emily Pinnegar.

Jimmy got up, with a bit of an Oxford wriggle, and held out his hand, saying : " How do you do ? "

His grey eyes, behind the spectacles, had an uncanny whitish gleam.

" My hand's not fit to shake hands," said the miner. " Take a seat."

" Oh, nobody minds coal-dust," said Jimmy, subsiding on to the sofa. " It's clean dirt."

" They say so," said Pinnegar.

He was a man of medium height, thin, but energetic in build.

Mrs. Pinnegar was running hot water into a pail from the bright brass tap of the stove, which had a boiler to balance the oven. Pinnegar dropped heavily into a wooden arm-chair, and stooped to pull off his ponderous grey pit-boots. He smelled of the strange, stale underground. In silence he pulled on his slippers, then rose, taking his boots into the scullery. His wife followed with the pail of hot water. She returned and spread a coarse roller-towel on the steel fender. The man could be heard washing in the scullery, in the semi-dark. Nobody said anything. Mrs. Pinnegar attended to her husband's dinner.

After a while, Pinnegar came running in, naked to the waist, and squatted plumb in front of the big red fire, on his heels. His head and face and the front part of his body were all wet. His back was grey and unwashed. He seized the towel from the fender and began to rub his face and head with a sort of brutal vigour, while his wife brought a bowl, and with a soapy flannel silently washed his back, right down to the loins, where the trousers were rolled back. The man was entirely oblivious of the stranger—this washing was part of the collier's ritual, and nobody existed for the moment. The woman, washing her husband's back, stooping there as he kneeled with knees wide apart, squatting on his heels on the rag hearthrug, had a peculiar look on her strong, handsome face, a look sinister and derisive. She was deriding something or somebody ; but Jimmy could not make out whom or what.

It was a new experience for him to sit completely and brutally excluded, from a personal ritual. The collier vigorously rubbed his own fair short hair, till it all stood on end, then he stared into the red-hot fire, oblivious, while the red colour burned in his cheeks. Then again he rubbed his breast and his body with the rough towel, brutally, as if his body were some machine he was cleaning, while his wife, with a peculiar slow movement, dried his back with another towel.

She took away the towel and bowl. The man was dry. He still squatted with his hands on his knees, gazing abstractedly, blankly into the fire. That, too, seemed part of his daily ritual. The colour flushed in his cheeks, his fair moustache was rubbed on end. But his hot blue eyes stared hot and vague into the red coals, while the red glare of the coal fell on his breast and naked body.

He was a man of about thirty-five, in his prime, with a pure smooth skin and no fat on his body. His muscles were not large, but quick, alive with energy. And as he squatted bathing abstractedly in the glow of the fire, he seemed like some pure-moulded engine that sleeps between its motions, with incomprehensible eyes of dark iron-blue.

He looked round, always averting his face from the stranger on the sofa, shutting him out of consciousness. The wife took out a bundle from the dresser-cupboard, and handed it to the outstretched, work-scarred hand of the man on the hearth. Curious, that big, horny, work-battered clean hand, at the end of the suave, thin, naked arm.

Pinnegar unrolled his shirt and undervest in front of the fire, warmed them for a moment in the glow, vaguely, sleepily, then, pulled them over his head. And then at last he rose, with his shirt hanging over his trousers, and in the same abstract, sleepy way, shutting the world out of his consciousness, he went out again to the scullery, pausing at the same dresser-cupboard to take out his rolled-up day trousers.

Mrs. Pinnegar took away the towels and set the dinner on the table —rich, oniony stew out of a hissing brown stew-jar, boiled potatoes, and a cup of tea. The man returned from the scullery, in his clean flannelette shirt and black trousers, his fair hair neatly brushed. He planked his wooden arm-chair beside the table, and sat heavily down, to eat.

Then he looked at Jimmy, as one wary, probably hostile man looks at another.

" You're a stranger in these parts, I gather ? " he said. There was something slightly formal, even a bit pompous, in his speech.

" An absolute stranger," replied Jimmy, with a slight aside grin.

The man dabbed some mustard on his plate, and glanced at his food to see if he would like it.

" Come from a distance, do you ? " he asked, as he began to eat. As he ate, he seemed to become oblivious again of Jimmy, bent his head over his plate, and ate. But probably he was ruminating something all the time, with barbaric wariness.

" From London," said Jimmy, warily.

" London ! " said Pinnegar, without looking from his plate.

Mrs. Pinnegar came and sat, in ritualistic silence, in her tall-backed rocking-chair under the light.

" What brings you this way, then ? " asked Pinnegar, stirring his tea.

" Oh ! " Jimmy writhed a little on the sofa. " I came to see Mrs. Pinnegar."

The miner took a hasty gulp of tea.

" You're acquainted then, are you ? " he said, still without looking round. He sat with his side-face to Jimmy.

" Yes, we are *now*," explained Jimmy. " I didn't know Mrs. Pinnegar till this evening. As a matter of fact, she sent me some poems for the *Commentator*—I'm the editor—and I thought they were good, so I wrote and told her so. Then I felt I wanted to come and see her, and she was willing, so I came."

The man reached out, cut himself a piece of bread, and swallowed a large mouthful.

" You thought her poetry was good ? " he said, turning at last to Jimmy and looking straight at him, with a stare something like the child's, but aggressive. " Are you going to put it in your magazine ? "

" Yes, I think I am," said Jimmy.

" I never read but one of her poems—something about a collier she knew all about, because she'd married him," he said, in his peculiar harsh voice, that had a certain jeering clang in it, and a certain indomitableness.

Jimmy was silent. The other man's harsh fighting-voice made him shrink.

" I could never get on with the *Commentator* myself," said Pinnegar, looking round for his pudding, pushing his meat-plate aside. " Seems to me to go a long way round to get nowhere."

" Well, probably it *does*," said Jimmy, squirming a little. " But so long as the *way* is interesting ! I don't see that anything gets anywhere at present—certainly no periodical."

" I don't know," said Pinnegar. " There's some facts in the *Liberator*—and there's some ideas in the *Janus*. I can't see the use myself, of all these feelings folk say they have. They get you nowhere."

" But," said Jimmy, with a slight pouf of laughter, " where do you *want* to get ? It's all very well talking about getting somewhere, but where, where in the world to-day do you *want* to get ? In general, I mean. If you want a better job in the mine—all right, go ahead and get it. But when you begin to talk about getting somewhere, in *life*—why, you've got to know what you're talking about."

" I'm a man, aren't I ? " said the miner, going very still and hard.

" But what do you *mean*, when you say you're a man ? " snarled Jimmy, really exasperated. " What do you mean ? Yes, you *are* a man. But what about it ? "

" Haven't I the right to say I won't be made use of ? " said the collier, slow, harsh, and heavy.

" You've got a right to *say* it," retorted Jimmy, with a pouf of laughter. " But it doesn't *mean* anything. We're all made use of, from King George downwards. We have to be. When you eat your pudding you're making use of hundreds of people—including your wife."

" I know it. I know it. It makes no difference, though. I'm not going to be made use of."

Jimmy shrugged his shoulders.

" Oh, all right ! " he said. " That's just a phrase, like any other."

The miner sat very still in his chair, his face going hard and remote. He was evidently thinking over something that was stuck like a barb in his consciousness, something he was trying to harden over, as the skin sometimes hardens over a steel splinter in the flesh.

" I'm nothing but made use of," he said, now talking hard and final, to himself, and staring out into space. " Down the pit, I'm made use of, and they give me a wage, such as it is. At the house, I'm made use of, and my wife sets the dinner on the table as if I was a customer in a shop."

" But what do you *expect ?* " cried Jimmy, writhing in his chair.

" Me ? What do I expect ? I expect nothing. But I tell you what——" he turned, and looked straight and hard into Jimmy's eyes—" I'm not going to put up with anything, either."

Jimmy saw the hard finality in the other man's eyes, and squirmed away from it.

" If you *know* what you're not going to put up with——" he said.

" I don't want my wife writing poetry ! And sending it to a parcel of men she's never seen. *I* don't want my wife sitting like Queen Boadicea, when I come home, and a face like a stone wall with holes in it. I don't know what's wrong with her. She doesn't know herself. But she does as she likes. Only, mark you, I do the same."

" Of course ! " cried Jimmy, though there was no of course about it.

" She's told you I've got another woman ? "

" Yes."

" And I'll tell you for why. If I give in to the coal face, and go down the mine every day to eight hours' slavery, more or less, somebody's got to give in to me."

" Then," said Jimmy, after a pause, " if you mean you want your wife to submit to you—well, that's the problem. You have to marry the woman who *will* submit."

It was amazing, this from Jimmy. He sat there and lectured the collier like a Puritan Father, completely forgetting the disintegrating flutter of Clarissa, in his own background.

" I want a wife who'll please me, who'll want to please me," said the collier.

" Why should *you* be pleased, any more than anybody else ? " asked the wife coldly.

" My child, my little girl wants to please me—if her mother would let her. But the women hang together. I tell you "—and here he turned to Jimmy, with a blaze in his dark blue eyes—" I want a woman to please me, a woman who's anxious to please me. And if I can't find her in my own home, I'll find her out of it."

" I hope she pleases you," said the wife, rocking slightly.

" Well," said the man, " she does."

" Then why don't you go and live with her altogether ? " she said. He turned and looked at her.

" Why don't I ? " he said. " Because I've got my home. I've got my house, I've got my wife, let her be what she may, as a woman to live with. And I've got my child. Why should I break it all up ? "

" And what about me ? " she asked, coldly and fiercely.

" You ? You've got a home. You've got a child. You've got a man who works for you. You've got what you want. You do as you like——"

" Do I ? " she asked, with intolerable sarcasm.

" Yes. Apart from the bit of work in the house, you do as you like. If you want to go, you can go. But while you live in my house, you must respect it. You bring no men here, you see."

" Do *you* respect your home ? " she said.

" Yes ! I do ! If I get another woman—who pleases me—I deprive you of nothing. All I ask of you is to do your duty as a housewife."

" Down to washing your back ! " she said, heavily sarcastic ; and, Jimmy thought, a trifle vulgar.

" Down to washing my back, since it's got to be washed," he said.

" What about the other woman ? Let her do it."

" This is my home."

The wife gave a strange movement, like a mad woman.

Jimmy sat rather pale and frightened. Behind the collier's quietness he felt the concentration of almost cold anger and an unchanging will. In the man's lean face he could see the bones, the fixity of the male bones, and it was as if the human soul, or spirit, had gone into the living skull and skeleton, almost invulnerable.

Jimmy, for some strange reason, felt a wild anger against this bony and logical man. It was the hard-driven coldness, fixity, that he could not bear.

" Look here ! " he cried, in a resonant Oxford voice, his eyes glaring and casting inwards behind his spectacles. " You say Mrs. Pinnegar is *free*—free to do as she pleases. In that case, you have no objection if she comes with me right away from here."

The collier looked at the pale, strange face of the editor in wonder.

Jimmy kept his face slightly averted, and sightless, seeing nobody. There was a Mephistophelian tilt about the eyebrows, and a Martyred Sebastian straightness about the mouth.

" Does she *want* to ? " asked Pinnegar, with devastating incredulity. The wife smiled faintly, grimly. She could see the vanity of her husband in his utter inability to believe that she could prefer the other man to him.

" That," said Jimmy, " you must ask her yourself. But it's what I came here for : to ask her to come and live with me, and bring the child."

" You came without having seen her, to ask her that ? " said the husband, in growing wonder.

" Yes," said Jimmy, vehemently, nodding his head with drunken emphasis. " Yes ! Without ever having seen her ! "

" You've caught a funny fish this time, with your poetry," he said turning with curious husband-familiarity to his wife. She hated this off-hand husband-familiarity.

" What sort of fish have *you* caught ? " she retorted. " And what did you catch *her* with ? "

" Bird-lime ! " he said, with a faint, quick grin.

Jimmy was sitting in suspense. They all three sat in suspense, for some time.

" And what are you saying to him ? " said the collier at length.

Jimmy looked up, and the malevolent half-smile on his face made him look rather handsome again, a mixture of faun and Mephisto. He glanced curiously, invitingly, at the woman who was watching him from afar.

" I say yes ! " she replied, in a cool voice.

The husband became very still, sitting erect in his wooden arm-chair and staring into space. It was as if he were fixedly watching something fly away from him, out of his own soul. But he was not going to yield at all, to any emotion.

He could not now believe that this woman should *want* to leave him. Yet she did.

" I'm sure it's all for the best," said Jimmy, in his Puritan Father voice. " You don't mind, really "—he drawled uneasily—" if she brings the child. I give you my word I'll do my very best for it."

The collier looked at him as if he were very far away. Jimmy quailed under the look. He could see that the other man was relentlessly killing the emotion in himself, stripping himself, as it were, of his own flesh, stripping himself to the hard unemotional bone of the human male.

"I give her a blank cheque," said Pinnegar, with numb lips. "She does as she pleases."

"So much for fatherly love, compared with selfishness," she said.

He turned and looked at her with that curious power of remote anger. And immediately she became still, quenched.

"I give you a blank cheque, as far as I'm concerned," he repeated abstractedly.

"It *is* blank indeed!" she said, with her first touch of bitterness.

Jimmy looked at the clock. It was growing late : he might be shut out of the public-house. He rose to go, saying he would return in the morning. He was leaving the next day, at noon, for London.

He plunged into the darkness and mud of that black, night-ridden country. There was a curious elation in his spirits, mingled with fear. But then he always needed an element of fear, really, to elate him. He thought with terror of those two human beings left in that house together. The frightening state of tension! He himself could never bear an extreme tension. He always had to compromise, to become apologetic and pathetic. He would be able to manage Mrs. Pinnegar that way. Emily! He must get used to saying it. Emily! The Emilia was absurd. He had never known an Emily.

He felt really scared, and really elated. He was doing something big. It was not that he was in *love* with the woman. But, my God, he wanted to take her away from that man. And he wanted the adventure of her. Absolutely the adventure of her. He felt really elated, really himself, really manly.

But in the morning he returned rather sheepishly to the collier's house. It was another dark, drizzling day, with black trees, black road, black hedges, blackish brick houses, and the smell and the sound of collieries under a skyless day. Like living in some weird underground.

Unwillingly he went up that passage-entry again, and knocked at the back door, glancing at the miserable little back garden with its cabbage-stalks and its ugly sanitary arrangements.

The child opened the door to him : with her fair hair, flushed cheeks, and hot, dark-blue eyes.

"Hello, Jane!" he said.

The mother stood tall and square, by the table, watching him with portentous eyes, as he entered. She was handsome, but her skin was not very good : as if the battle had been too much for her health. Jimmy glanced up at her smiling his slow, ingratiating smile, that always brought a glow of success into a woman's spirit. And as he saw her gold-flecked eyes searching in his eyes, without a bit of kindliness, he thought to himself : " My God, however am I going to sleep with that woman ! " His will was ready, however, and he would manage it somehow.

And when he glanced at the motionless, bony head and lean figure of the collier seated in the wooden arm-chair by the fire, he was the more ready. He must triumph over that man.

" What train are you going by ? " asked Mrs. Pinnegar.

" By the 12-30." He looked up at her as he spoke, with the wide, shining, childlike, almost coy eyes that were his peculiar asset. She looked down at him in a sort of interested wonder. She seemed almost fascinated by his childlike, shining, inviting dark-grey eyes, with their long lashes : such an absolute change from that resentful unyielding that looked out always from the back of her husband's blue eyes. Her husband always seemed like a menace to her, in his thinness, his concentration, his eternal unyielding. And this man looked at one with the wide, shining, fascinating eyes of a young Persian kitten, something at once bold and shy and coy and strangely inviting. She fell at once under their spell.

" You'll have dinner before you go," she said.

" No ! " he cried in panic, unwilling indeed to eat before that other man. " No, I ate a fabulous breakfast. I will get a sandwich when I change in Sheffield : *really !* "

She had to go out shopping. She said she would go out to the station with him when she got back. It was just after eleven.

" But look here," he said, addressing also the thin abstracted man who sat unnoticing, with a newspaper, " we've got to get this thing settled. I *want* Mrs. Pinnegar to come and live with me, her and the child. And she's coming ! So don't you think, now, it would be better if she came right along with me to-day ! Just put a few things in a bag and come along. Why drag the thing out ? "

" I tell you," replied the husband, " she has a blank cheque from me to do as she likes."

" All right, then ! Won't you do that ? Won't you come along with me now ? " said Jimmy, looking up at her exposedly, but casting his eyes a bit inwards. Throwing himself with deliberate impulsiveness on her mercy.

" I can't ! " she said decisively. " I can't come to-day."

" But why not—really ? Why not, while I'm here ? You have that blank cheque, you can do as you please——"

" The blank cheque won't get me far," she said rudely : " I can't come to-day, anyhow."

"When can you come, then?" he said, with that queer, petulant pleading. "The sooner the better, surely."

"I can come on Monday," she said abruptly.

"Monday!" He gazed up at her in a kind of panic, through his spectacles. Then he set his teeth again, and nodded his head up and down. "All right, then! To-day is Saturday. Then Monday!"

"If you'll excuse me," she said, "I've got to go out for a few things. I'll walk to the station with you when I get back."

She bundled Jane into a little sky-blue coat and bonnet, put on a heavy black coat and black hat herself, and went out.

Jimmy sat very uneasily opposite the collier, who also wore spectacles to read. Pinnegar put down the newspaper and pulled the spectacles off his nose, saying something about a Labour Government.

"Yes," said Jimmy. "After all, best be logical. If you *are* democratic, the only logical thing is a Labour Government. Though, personally, one Government is as good as another, to me."

"Maybe so!" said the collier. "But *something's* got to come to an end, sooner or later."

"Oh, a great deal!" said Jimmy, and they lapsed into silence.

"Have you been married before?" asked Pinnegar, at length.

"Yes. My wife and I are divorced."

"I suppose you want me to divorce *my* wife?" said the collier.

"Why—yes!—that would be best——"

"It's the same to me," said Pinnegar; "divorce or no divorce. I'll *live* with another woman, but I'll never *marry* another. Enough is as good as a feast. But if she wants a divorce, she can have it."

"It would certainly be best," said Jimmy.

There was a long pause. Jimmy wished the woman would come back.

"I look on you as an instrument," said the miner. "Something had to break. You are the instrument that breaks it."

It was strange to sit in the room with this thin, remote, wilful man. Jimmy was a bit fascinated by him. But, at the same time, he hated him because he could not be in the same room with him without being under his spell. He felt himself dominated. And he hated it.

"My wife," said Pinnegar, looking up at Jimmy with a peculiar, almost humourous, teasing grin, "expects to see me go to the dogs when she leaves me. It is her last hope."

Jimmy ducked his head and was silent, not knowing what to say. The other man sat still in his chair, like a sort of infinitely patient prisoner, looking away out of the window and waiting.

" She thinks," he said again, " that she has some wonderful future awaiting her somewhere, and you're going to open the door."

And again the same amused grin was in his eyes.

And again Jimmy was fascinated by the man. And again he hated the spell of this fascination. For Jimmy wanted to be, in his own mind, the strongest man among men, but particularly among women. And this thin, peculiar man could dominate him. He knew it. The very silent unconsciousness of Pinnegar dominated the room, wherever he was.

Jimmy hated this.

At last Mrs. Pinnegar came back, and Jimmy set off with her. He shook hands with the collier.

" Good-bye ! " he said.

" Good-bye ! " said Pinnegar, looking down at him with those amused blue eyes, which Jimmy knew he would never be able to get beyond.

And the walk to the station was almost a walk of conspiracy against the man left behind, between the man in spectacles and the tall woman. They arranged the details for Monday. Emily was to come by the nine o'clock train : Jimmy would meet her at Marylebone, and install her in his house in St. John's Wood. Then, with the child, they would begin a new life. Pinnegar would divorce his wife, or she would divorce him : and then, another marriage.

Jimmy got a tremendous kick out of it all on the journey home. He felt he had really done something desperate and adventurous. But he was in too wild a flutter to analyse any results. Only, as he drew near London, a sinking feeling came over him. He was desperately tired after it all, almost too tired to keep up.

Nevertheless, he went after dinner and sprang it all on Severn.

" You damn fool ! " said Severn, in consternation. " What did you do it for ? "

" Well," said Jimmy, writhing. " Because I *wanted* to."

" Good God ! The woman sounds like the head of Medusa. You're a hero of some stomach, I must say ! Remember Clarissa ? "

" Oh," writhed Jimmy. " But this is different."

" Ay, her name's Emma, or something of that sort, isn't it ? "

" Emily ! " said Jimmy briefly.

" Well, you're a fool, anyway, so you may as well keep on acting in character. I've no doubt, by playing weeping-willow, you'll outlive all the female storms you ever prepare for yourself. I never yet did see a weeping-willow uprooted by a gale, so keep on hanging your harp on it, and you'll be all right. Here's luck ! But for a man who was looking for a little Gretchen to adore him, you're a corker ! "

Which was all that Severn had to say. But Jimmy went home with his knees shaking. On Sunday morning he wrote an anxious letter. He didn't know how to begin it : *Dear Mrs. Pinnegar* and *Dear Emily* seemed either too late in the day or too early. So he just plunged in, without dear anything.

" I want you to have this before you come. Perhaps we have been precipitate. I only beg you to decide *finally*, for yourself, before you come. Don't come, please, unless you are absolutely sure of yourself. If you are *in the least* unsure, wait a while, wait till you are quite certain, one way or the other.

" For myself, if you don't come I shall understand. But please send me a telegram. If you do come, I shall welcome both you and the child. Yours ever—J. F."

He paid a man his return fare, and three pounds extra, to go on the Sunday and deliver this letter.

The man came back in the evening. He had delivered the letter. There was no answer.

Awful Sunday night : tense Monday morning !

A telegram : " *Arrive Marylebone* 12.50 *with Jane. Yours ever. Emily.*"

Jimmy set his teeth and went to the station. But when he felt her looking at him, and so met her eyes : and after that saw her coming slowly down the platform, holding the child by the hand, her slow cat's eyes smouldering under her straight brows, smouldering at him : he almost swooned. A sickly grin came over him as he held out his hand. Nevertheless he said :

" I'm *awfully* glad you came."

And as he sat in the taxi, a perverse but intense desire for her came over him, making him almost helpless. He could feel, so strongly, the presence of that other man about her, and this went to his head like neat spirits. That other man ! In some subtle, inexplicable way, he was actually bodily present, the husband. The woman moved in his aura. She was hopelessly married to him.

And this went to Jimmy's head like neat whisky. Which of the two would fall before him with a greater fall—the woman, or the man, her husband ?

I

SHE had thought that this marriage, of all marriages, would be an adventure. Not that the man himself was exactly magical to her. A little, wiry, twisted fellow, twenty years older than herself, with brown eyes and greying hair, who had come to America a scrap of a wastrel, from Holland, years ago, as a tiny boy, and from the gold-mines of the west had been kicked south into Mexico, and now was more or less rich, owning silver-mines in the wilds of the Sierra Madre : it was obvious that the adventure lay in his circumstances, rather than his person. But he was still a little dynamo of energy, in spite of accidents survived, and what he had accomplished he had accomplished alone. One of those human oddments there is no accounting for.

When she actually *saw* what he had accomplished, her heart quailed. Great green-covered, unbroken mountain-hills, and in the midst of the lifeless isolation, the sharp pinkish mounds of the dried mud from the silver-works. Under the nakedness of the works, the walled-in, one-storey adobe house, with its garden inside, and its deep inner verandah with tropical climbers on the sides. And when you looked up from this shut-in flowered patio, you saw the huge pink cone of the silver-mud refuse, and the machinery of the extracting plant against heaven above. No more.

To be sure, the great wooden doors were often open. And then she could stand outside, in the vast open world. And see great, void, tree-clad hills piling behind one another, from nowhere into no-where. They were green in autumn time. For the rest, pinkish, stark dry and abstract.

And in his battered Ford car her husband would take her into the dead, thrice-dead little Spanish town forgotten among the mountains. The great, sun-dried dead church, the dead portales, the hopeless covered market-place, where, the first time she went, she saw a dead dog lying between the meat stalls and the vegetable array, stretched out as if for ever, nobody troubling to throw it away. Deadness within deadness.

456

Everybody feebly talking silver, and showing bits of ore. But silver was at a standstill. The great war came and went. Silver was a dead market. Her husband's mines were closed down. But she and he lived on in the adobe house under the works, among the flowers that were never very flowery to her.

She had two children, a boy and a girl. And her eldest, the boy, was nearly ten years old before she aroused from her stupor of subjected amazement. She was now thirty-three, a large, blue-eyed, dazed woman, beginning to grow stout. Her little, wiry, tough, twisted, brown-eyed husband was fifty-three, a man as tough as wire, tenacious as wire, still full of energy, but dimmed by the lapse of silver from the market, and by some curious inaccessibility on his wife's part.

He was a man of principles, and a good husband. In a way, he doted on her. He never quite got over his dazzled admiration of her. But essentially, he was still a bachelor. He had been thrown out on the world, a little bachelor, at the age of ten. When he married he was over forty, and had enough money to marry on. But his capital was all a bachelor's. He was boss of his own works, and marriage was the last and most intimate bit of his own works.

He admired his wife to extinction, he admired her body, all her points. And she was to him always the rather dazzling Californian girl from Berkeley, whom he had first known. Like any sheikh, he kept her guarded among those mountains of Chihuahua. He was jealous of her as he was of his silver-mine : and that is saying a lot.

At thirty-three she really was still the girl from Berkeley, in all but physique. Her conscious development had stopped mysteriously with her marriage, completely arrested. Her husband had never become real to her, neither mentally nor physically. In spite of his late sort of passion for her, he never meant anything to her, physically. Only morally he swayed her, downed her, kept her in an invincible slavery.

So the years went by, in the adobe house strung round the sunny patio, with the silver-works overhead. Her husband was never still. When the silver went dead, he ran a ranch lower down, some twenty miles away, and raised pure-bred hogs, splendid creatures. At the same time, he hated pigs. He was a squeamish waif of an idealist, and really hated the physical side of life. He loved work, work, work, and making things. His marriage, his children, were something he was making, part of his business, but with a sentimental income this time.

Gradually her nerves began to go wrong : she must get out. She must get out. So he took her to El Paso for three months. And at least it was the United States.

But he kept his spell over her. The three months ended : back she was, just the same, in her adobe house among those eternal green or pinky-brown hills, void as only the undiscovered is void. She taught her children, she supervised the Mexican boys who were her servants. And sometimes her husband brought visitors, Spaniards or Mexicans or occasionally white men.

He really loved to have white men staying on the place. Yet he had not a moment's peace when they were there. It was as if his wife were some peculiar secret vein of ore in his mines, which no one must be aware of except himself. And she was fascinated by the young gentlemen, mining engineers, who were his guests at times. He, too, was fascinated by a real gentleman. But he was an old-timer miner with a wife, and if a gentleman looked at his wife, he felt as if his mine were being looted, the secrets of it pryed out.

It was one of these young gentlemen who put the idea into her mind. They were all standing outside the great wooden doors of the patio, looking at the outer world. The eternal, motionless hills were all green, it was September, after the rains. There was no sign of anything, save the deserted mine, the deserted works, and a bunch of half-deserted miner's dwellings.

" I wonder," said the young man, " what there is behind those great blank hills."

" More hills," said Lederman. " If you go that way, Sonora and the coast. This way is the desert—you came from there—and the other way, hills and mountains."

" Yes, but what *lives* in the hills and the mountains ? *Surely* there is something wonderful ? It looks *so* like nowhere on earth : like being on the moon."

" There's plenty of game, if you want to shoot. And Indians, if you call *them* wonderful."

" Wild ones ? "

" Wild enough."

" But friendly ? "

" It depends. Some of them are quite wild, and they don't let anybody near. They kill a missionary at sight. And where a missionary can't get, nobody can."

" But what does the government say ? "

" They're so far from everywhere, the government leaves 'em alone. And they're wily ; if they think there'll be trouble, they send a delegation to Chihuahua and make a formal submission. The government is glad to leave it at that."

" And do they live quite wild, with their own savage customs and religion ? "

" Oh, yes. They use nothing but bows and arrows. I've seen them in town, in the Plaza, with funny sort of hats with flowers round them, and a bow in one hand, quite naked except for a sort of shirt, even in cold weather—striding round with their savage's bare legs."

" But don't you suppose it's wonderful, up there in their secret villages ? "

" No. What would there be wonderful about it ? Savages are savages, and all savages behave more or less alike : rather low-down and dirty, unsanitary, with a few cunning tricks, and struggling to get enough to eat."

" But surely they have old, old religions and mysteries—it *must* be wonderful, surely it must."

" I don't know about mysteries—howling and heathen practices, more or less indecent. No, I see nothing wonderful in that kind of stuff. And I wonder that you should, when you have lived in London or Paris or New York——"

" Ah, *everybody* lives in London or Paris or New York "—said the young man, as if this were an argument.

And this peculiar vague enthusiasm for unknown Indians found a full echo in the woman's heart. She was overcome by a foolish romanticism more unreal than a girl's. She felt it was her destiny to wander into the secret haunts of these timeless, mysterious, marvellous Indians of the mountains.

She kept her secret. The young man was departing, her husband was going with him down to Torreon, on business : would be away for some days. But before the departure, she made her husband talk about the Indians : about the wandering tribes, resembling the Navajo, who were still wandering free ; and the Yaquis of Sonora : and the different groups in the different valleys of Chihuahua State.

There was supposed to be one tribe, the Chilchuis, living in a high valley to the south, who were the sacred tribe of all the Indians. The descendants of Montezuma and the old Aztec or Totonac kings still lived among them, and the old priests still kept up the ancient religion, and offered human sacrifices—so it was said. Some scientists had been to the Chilchui country, and had come back gaunt and exhausted with hunger and bitter privation, bringing various curious, barbaric objects of worship, but having seen nothing extraordinary in the hungry, stark village of savages.

Though Lederman talked in this off-hand way, it was obvious he felt some of the vulgar excitement at the idea of ancient and mysterious savages.

" How far away are they ? " she asked.

" Oh—three days on horseback—past Cuchitee and a little lake there is up there."

Her husband and the young man departed. The woman made her crazy plans. Of late, to break the monotony of her life, she had harassed her husband into letting her go riding with him, occasionally, on horseback. She was never allowed to go out alone. The country truly was not safe, lawless and crude.

But she had her own horse, and she dreamed of being free as she had been as a girl, among the hills of California.

Her daughter, nine years old, was now in a tiny convent in the little half-deserted Spanish mining-town five miles away.

" Manuel," said the woman to her house-servant, " I'm going to ride to the convent to see Margarita, and take her a few things. Perhaps I shall stay the night in the convent. You look after Freddy and see everything is all right till I come back."

" Shall I ride with you on the master's horse, or shall Juan ? " asked the servant.

" Neither of you. I shall go alone."

The young man looked her in the eyes, in protest. Absolutely impossible that the woman should ride alone !

" I shall go alone," repeated the large, placid-seeming, fair-complexioned woman, with peculiar overbearing emphasis. And the man silently, unhappily yielded.

" Why are you going alone, mother ? " asked her son, as she made up parcels of food.

" Am I *never* to be let alone ? Not one moment of my life ? " she cried, with sudden explosion of energy. And the child, like the servant, shrank into silence.

She set off without a qualm, riding astride on her strong roan horse, and wearing a riding suit of coarse linen, a riding skirt over her linen breeches, a scarlet neck-tie over her white blouse, and a black felt hat on her head. She had food in her saddle-bags, an army canteen with water, and a large, native blanket tied on behind the saddle. Peering into the distance, she set off from her home. Manuel and the little boy stood in the gateway to watch her go. She did not even turn to wave them farewell.

But when she had ridden about a mile, she left the wild road and took a small trail to the right, that led into another valley, over steep places and past great trees, and through another deserted mining-settlement. It was September, the water was running freely in the little stream that had fed the now-abandoned mine. She got down to drink, and let the horse drink too.

She saw natives coming through the trees, away up the slope. They had seen her, and were watching her closely. She watched in turn. The three people, two women and a youth, were making a wide detour, so as not to come too close to her. She did not care. Mounting, she trotted ahead up the silent valley, beyond the silver-works, beyond any trace of mining. There was still a rough trail that led over rocks and loose stones into the valley beyond. This trail she had already ridden, with her husband. Beyond that she knew she must go south.

Curiously she was not afraid, although it was a frightening country, the silent, fatal-seeming mountain-slopes, the occasional distant, suspicious, elusive natives among the trees, the great carrion birds occasionally hovering, like great flies, in the distance, over some carrion or some ranch house or some group of huts.

As she climbed, the trees shrank and the trail ran through a thorny scrub, that was trailed over with blue convolvulus and an occasional pink creeper. Then these flowers lapsed. She was nearing the pine-trees.

She was over the crest, and before her another silent, void, green-clad valley. It was past midday. Her horse turned to a little runlet of water, so she got down to eat her midday meal. She sat in silence looking at the motionless unliving valley, and at the sharp-peaked hills, rising higher to rock and pine-trees, southwards. She rested two hours in the heat of the day, while the horse cropped around her.

Curious that she was neither afraid nor lonely. Indeed, the loneliness was like a drink of cold water to one who is very thirsty. And a strange elation sustained her from within.

She travelled on, and camped at night in a valley beside a stream, deep among the bushes. She had seen cattle and had crossed several trails. There must be a ranch not far off. She heard the strange wailing shriek of a mountain-lion, and the answer of dogs. But she sat by her small camp fire in a secret hollow place and was not really afraid. She was buoyed up always by the curious, bubbling elation within her.

It was very cold before dawn. She lay wrapped in her blanket looking at the stars, listening to her horse shivering, and feeling like a woman who has died and passed beyond. She was not sure that she had not heard, during the night, a great crash at the centre of herself, which was the crash of her own death. Or else it was a crash at the centre of the earth, and meant something big and mysterious.

With the first peep of light she got up, numb with cold, and made a fire. She ate hastily, gave her horse some pieces of oil-seed cake, and set off again. She avoided any meeting—and since she met nobody, it was evident that she in turn was avoided. She came at last in sight of the village of Cuchitee, with its black houses with their reddish roofs, a sombre, dreary little .cluster below another silent, long-abandoned mine. And beyond, a long, great mountain-side, rising up green and light to the darker, shaggier green of pine-trees. And beyond the pine-trees stretches of naked rock against the sky, rock slashed already and brindled with white stripes of snow. High up, the new snow had already begun to fall.

And now, as she neared, more or less, her destination, she began to go vague and disheartened. She had passed the little lake among yellowing aspen trees whose white trunks were round and suave like the white round arms of some woman. What a lovely place! In California she would have raved about it. But here she looked and saw that it was lovely, but she didn't care. She was weary and spent with her two nights in the open, and afraid of the coming night. She didn't know where she was going, or what she was going for. Her horse plodded dejectedly on, towards that immense and forbidding mountain-slope, following a stony little trail. And if she had had any will of her own left, she would have turned back, to the village, to be protected and sent home to her husband.

But she had no will of her own. Her horse splashed through a brook, and turned up a valley, under immense yellowing cotton-wood trees. She must have been near nine thousand feet above sea-level, and her head was light with the altitude and with weariness. Beyond the cotton-wood trees she could see, on each side, the steep sides of mountain-slopes hemming her in, sharp-plumaged with overlapping aspen, and, higher up, with sprouting, pointed spruce and pine-tree. Her horse went on automatically. In this tight valley, on this slight trail, there was nowhere to go but ahead, climbing.

Suddenly her horse jumped, and three men in dark blankets were on the trail before her.

" Adios ! " came the greeting, in the full, restrained Indian voice.

" Adios ! " she replied, in her assured, American woman's voice.

" Where are you going ? " came the quiet question, in Spanish.

The men in the dark sarapes had come closer, and were looking up at her.

" On ahead," she replied coolly, in her hard, Saxon Spanish.

These were just natives to her : dark-faced, strongly-built men in dark sarapes and straw hats. They would have been the same as the men who worked for her husband, except, strangely, for the long black hair that fell 'over their shoulders. She noted this long black hair with a certain distaste. These must be the wild Indians she had come to see.

" Where do you come from ? " the same man asked. It was always the one man who spoke. He was young, with quick, large, bright black eyes that glanced sideways at her. He had a soft black moustache on his dark face, and a sparse tuft of beard, loose hairs on his chin. His long black hair, full of life, hung unrestrained on his shoulders. Dark as he was, he did not look as if he had washed lately.

His two companions were the same, but older men, powerful and silent. One had a thin black line of moustache, but was beardless. The other had the smooth cheeks and the sparse dark hairs marking the lines of his chin with the beard characteristic of the Indians.

" I come from far away," she replied, with half-jocular evasion.

This was received in silence.

" But where do you live ? " asked the young man, with that same quiet insistence.

" In the north," she replied airily.

Again there was a moment's silence. The young man conversed quietly, in Indian, with his two companions.

" Where do you want to go, up this way ? " he asked suddenly, with challenge and authority, pointing briefly up the trail.

" To the Chilchui Indians," answered the woman laconically.

The young man looked at her. His eyes were quick and black, and inhuman. He saw, in the full evening light, the faint sub-smile of assurance on her rather large, calm, fresh-complexioned face ; the weary, bluish lines under her large blue eyes ; and in her eyes, as she looked down at him, a half-childish, half-arrogant confidence in her own female power. But in her eyes also, a curious look of trance.

" Usted es Señora ? You are a lady ? " the Indian asked her.

" Yes, I am a lady," she replied complacently.

" With a family ? "

" With a husband and two children, boy and girl," she said.

The Indian turned to his companions and translated, in the low, gurgling speech, like hidden water running. They were evidently at a loss.

"Where is your husband?" asked the young man.

"Who knows?" she replied airily. "He has gone away on business for a week."

The black eyes watched her shrewdly. She, for all her weariness, smiled faintly in the pride of her own adventure and the assurance of her own womanhood, and the spell of the madness that was on her.

"And what do *you* want to do?" the Indian asked her.

"I want to visit the Chilchui Indians—to see their houses and to know their gods," she replied.

The young man turned and translated quickly, and there was a silence almost of consternation. The grave elder men were glancing at her sideways, with strange looks, from under their decorated hats. And they said something to the young man, in deep chest voices.

The latter still hesitated. Then he turned to the woman.

"Good!" he said. "Let us go. But we cannot arrive until to-morrow. We shall have to make a camp to-night."

"Good!" she said. "I can make a camp."

Without more ado, they set off at a good speed up the stony trail. The young Indian ran alongside her horse's head, the other two ran behind. One of them had taken a thick stick, and occasionally he struck her horse a resounding blow on the haunch, to urge him forward. This made the horse jump, and threw her back in the saddle, which, tired as she was, made her angry.

"Don't do that!" she cried, looking round angrily at the fellow. She met his black, large, bright eyes, and for the first time her spirit really quailed. The man's eyes were not human to her, and they did not see her as a beautiful white woman. He looked at her with a black, bright inhuman look, and saw no woman in her at all. As if she were some strange, unaccountable *thing*, incomprehensible to him, but inimical. She sat in her saddle in wonder, feeling once more as if she had died. And again he struck her horse, and jerked her badly in the saddle.

All the passionate anger of the spoilt white woman rose in her. She pulled her horse to a standstill, and turned with blazing eyes to the man at her bridle.

"Tell that fellow not to touch my horse again," she cried.

She met the eyes of the young man, and in their bright black inscrutability she saw a fine spark, as in a snake's eye, of derision. He spoke to his companion in the rear, in the low tones of the Indian. The man with the stick listened without looking. Then, giving a strange low cry to the horse, he struck it again on the rear, so that it leaped forward spasmodically up the stony trail, scattering the stones, pitching the weary woman in her seat.

The anger flew like a madness into her eyes, she went white at the gills. Fiercely she reined in her horse. But before she could turn, the young Indian had caught the reins under the horse's throat, jerked them forward, and was trotting ahead rapidly, leading the horse.

The woman was powerless. And along with her supreme anger there came a slight thrill of exultation. She knew she was dead.

The sun was setting, a great yellow light flooded the last of the aspens, flared on the trunks of the pine-trees, the pine-needles bristled and stood out with dark lustre, the rocks glowed with unearthly glamour. And through this effulgence the Indian at her horse's head trotted unweariedly on, his dark blanket swinging, his bare legs glowing with a strange transfigured ruddiness in the powerful light, and his straw hat with its half-absurd decorations of flowers and feathers shining showily above his river of long black hair. At times he would utter a low call to the horse, and then the other Indian, behind, would fetch the beast a whack with the stick.

The wonder-light faded off the mountains, the world began to grow dark, a cold air breathed down. In the sky, half a moon was struggling against the glow in the west. Huge shadows came down from steep rocky slopes. Water was rushing. The woman was conscious only of her fatigue, her unspeakable fatigue, and the cold wind from the heights. She was not aware how moonlight replaced daylight. It happened while she travelled unconscious with weariness.

For some hours they travelled by moonlight. Then suddenly they came to a standstill. The men conversed in low tones for a moment.

" We camp here," said the young man.

She waited for him to help her down. He merely stood holding the horse's bridle. She almost fell from the saddle, so fatigued.

They had chosen a place at the foot of rocks that still gave off a little warmth of the sun. One man cut pine-boughs, another erected little screens of pine-boughs against the rock for shelter, and put boughs of balsam pine for beds. The third made a small fire, to heat tortillas. They worked in silence.

The woman drank water. She did not want to eat—only to lie down.

" Where do I sleep ? " she asked.

The young man pointed to one of the shelters. She crept in and lay inert. She did not care what happened to her, she was so weary, and so beyond everything. Through the twigs of spruce she could see the three men squatting round the fire on their hams, chewing the tortillas they picked from the ashes with their dark fingers, and drinking water from a gourd. They talked in low, muttering tones, with long intervals of silence. Her saddle and saddle-bags lay not far from the fire, unopened, untouched. The men were not interested in her nor her belongings. There they squatted with their hats on their heads, eating, eating mechanically, like animals, the dark sarape with its fringe falling to the ground before and behind, the powerful dark legs naked and squatting like an animal's, showing the dirty white shirt and the sort of loin-cloth which was the only other garment, underneath. And they showed no more sign of interest in her than if she had been a piece of venison they were bringing home from the hunt, and had hung inside a shelter.

After a while they carefully extinguished the fire, and went inside their own shelter. Watching through the screen of boughs, she had a moment's thrill of fear and anxiety, seeing the dark forms cross and pass silently in the moonlight. Would they attack her now ?

But no ! They were as if oblivious of her. Her horse was hobbled ; she could hear it hopping wearily. All was silent, mountain-silent, cold, deathly. She slept and woke and slept in a semi-conscious numbness of cold and fatigue. A long, long night, icy and eterna', and she aware that she had died.

II

Yet when there was a stirring, and a clink of flint and steel, and the form of a man crouching like a dog over a bone, at a red splutter of fire, and she knew it was morning coming, it seemed to her the night had passed too soon.

When the fire was going, she came out of her shelter with one real desire left : for coffee. The men were warming more tortillas.

" Can we make coffee ? " she asked.

The young man looked at her, and she imagined the same faint spark of derision in his eyes. He shook his head.

" We don't take it," he said. " There is no time."

And the elder men, squatting on their haunches, looked up at her in the terrible paling dawn, and there was not even derision in their eyes. Only that intense, yet remote, inhuman glitter which was terrible to her. They were inaccessible. They could not see her as a woman at all. As if she *were* not a woman. As if, perhaps, her whiteness took away all her womanhood, and left her as some giant, female white ant. That was all they could see in her.

Before the sun was up, she was in the saddle again, and they were climbing steeply, in the icy air. The sun came, and soon she was very hot, exposed to the glare in the bare places. It seemed to her they were climbing to the roof of the world. Beyond against heaven were slashes of snow.

During the course of the morning, they came to a place where the horse could not go farther. They rested for a time with a great slant of living rock in front of them, like the glossy breast of some earth-beast. Across this rock, along a wavering crack, they had to go. It seemed to her that for hours she went in torment, on her hands and knees, from crack to crevice, along the slanting face of this pure rock-mountain. An Indian in front and an Indian behind walked slowly erect, shod with sandals of braided leather. But she in her riding-boots dared not stand erect.

Yet what she wondered, all the time, was why she persisted in clinging and crawling along these mile-long sheets of rock. Why she did not hurl herself down, and have done ! The world was below her.

When they emerged at last on a stony slope, she looked back, and saw the third Indian coming carrying her saddle and saddle-bags on his back, the whole hung from a band across his forehead. And he had his hat in his hand, as he stepped slowly, with the slow, soft, heavy tread of the Indian, unwavering in the chinks of rock, as if along a scratch in the mountain's iron shield.

The stony slope led downwards. The Indians seemed to grow excited. One ran ahead at a slow trot, disappearing round the curve of stones. And the track curved round and down, till at last in the full blaze of the mid-morning sun, they could see a valley below them, between walls of rock, as in a great wide chasm let in the mountains. A green valley, with a river, and trees, and clusters of low flat sparkling houses. It was all tiny and perfect, three thousand feet below. Even the flat bridge over the stream, and the square with the houses around it, the bigger buildings piled up at opposite ends of the square, the tall cotton-wood trees, the pastures and stretches of yellow-sere maize, the patches of brown sheep or goats in the distance, on the slopes, the railed enclosures by the stream-side. There it was, all small and perfect, looking magical, as any place will look magical, seen from the mountains above. The unusual thing was that the low houses glittered white, whitewashed, looking like crystals of salt, or silver. This frightened her.

They began the long, winding descent at the head of the barranca, following the stream that rushed and fell. At first it was all rocks ; then the pine-trees began, and soon, the silver-limbed aspens. The flowers of autumn, big pink daisy-like flowers, and white ones, and many yellow flowers, were in profusion. But she had to sit down and rest, she was so weary. And she saw the bright flowers shadowily, as pale shadows hovering, as one who is dead must see them.

At length came grass and pasture-slopes between mingled aspen and pine-trees. A shepherd, naked in the sun save for his hat and his cotton loin-cloth, was driving his brown sheep away. In a grove of trees they sat and waited, she and the young Indian. The one with the saddle had also gone forward.

They heard a sound of someone coming. It was three men, in fine sarapes of red and orange and yellow and black, and with brilliant feather head-dresses. The oldest had his grey hair braided with fur, and his red and orange-yellow sarape was covered with curious black markings, like a leopard-skin. The other two were not grey-haired, but they were elders too. Their blankets were in stripes, and their head-dresses not so elaborate.

The young Indian addressed the elders in a few quiet words. They listened without answering or looking at him or at the woman, keeping their faces averted and their eyes turned to the ground, only listening. And at length they turned and looked at the woman.

The old chief, or medicine-man, whatever he was, had a deeply wrinkled and lined face of dark bronze, with a few sparse grey hairs round the mouth. Two long braids of grey hair, braided with fur and coloured feathers, hung on his shoulders. And yet, it was only his eyes that mattered. They were black and of extraordinary piercing strength, without a qualm of misgiving in their demonish, dauntless power. He looked into the eyes of the white woman with a long, piercing look, seeking she knew not what. She summoned all her strength to meet his eyes and keep up her guard. But it was no good. He was not looking at her as one human being looks at another. He never even perceived her resistance or her challenge, but looked past them both, into she knew not what.

She could see it was hopeless to expect any human communication with this old being.

He turned and said a few words to the young Indian.

" He asks what do you seek here ? " said the young man in Spanish.

" I ? Nothing ! I only came to see what it was like."

This was again translated, and the old man turned his eyes on her once more. Then he spoke again, in his low muttering tone, to the young Indian.

"He says, why does she leave her house with the white men? Does she want to bring the white man's God to the Chilchui?"

"No," she replied, foolhardy. "I came away from the white man's God myself. I came to look for the God of the Chilchui."

Profound silence followed, when this was translated. Then the old man spoke again, in a small voice almost of weariness.

"Does the white woman seek the gods of the Chilchui because she is weary of her own God?" came the question.

"Yes, she does. She is tired of the white man's God," she replied, thinking that was what they wanted her to say. She would like to serve the gods of the Chilchui.

She was aware of an extraordinary thrill of triumph and exultance passing through the Indians, in the tense silence that followed when this was translated. Then they all looked at her with piercing black eyes, in which a steely covetous intent glittered incomprehensible. She was the more puzzled, as there was nothing sensual or sexual in the look. It had a terrible glittering purity that was beyond her. She was afraid, she would have been paralysed with fear, had not something died within her, leaving her with a cold, watchful wonder only.

The elders talked a little while, then the two went away, leaving her with the young man and the oldest chief. The old man now looked at her with a certain solicitude.

"He says are you tired?" asked the young man.

"Very tired," she said.

"The men will bring you a carriage," said the young Indian.

The carriage, when it came, proved to be a litter consisting of a sort of hammock of dark woollen frieze, slung on to a pole which was borne on the shoulders of two long-haired Indians. The woollen hammock was spread on the ground, she sat down on it, and the two men raised the pole to their shoulders. Swinging rather as if she were in a sack, she was carried out of the grove of trees, following the old chief, whose leopard-spotted blanket moved curiously in the sunlight.

They had emerged in the valley-head. Just in front were the maize fields, with ripe ears of maize. The corn was not very tall, in this high altitude. The well-worn path went between it, and all she could see was the erect form of the old chief, in the flame and black sarape, stepping soft and heavy and swift, his head forward, looking

2 B

neither to right nor left. Her bearers followed, stepping rhythmically, the long blue-black hair glistening like a river down the
naked shoulders of the man in front.

They passed the maize, and came to a big wall or earthwork made
of earth and adobe bricks. The wooden doors were open. Passing
on, they were in a network of small gardens, full of flowers and herbs
and fruit trees, each garden watered by a tiny ditch of running water.
Among each cluster of trees and flowers was a small, glittering white
house, windowless, and with closed door. The place was a network
of little paths, small streams, and little bridges among square,
flowering gardens.

Following the broadest path—a soft narrow track between leaves
and grass, a path worn smooth by centuries of human feet, no hoof
of horse nor any wheel to disfigure it—they came to the little river of
swift bright water, and crossed on a log bridge. Everything was
silent—there was not a human being anywhere. The road went on
under magnificent cotton-wood trees. It emerged suddenly outside
the central plaza or square of the village.

This was a long oblong of low white houses with flat roofs, and two
bigger buildings, having as it were little square huts piled on top of
bigger long huts, stood at either end of the oblong, facing each other
rather askew. Every little house was a dazzling white, save for the
great round beam-ends which projected under the flat eaves, and for
the flat roofs. Round each of the bigger buildings, on the outside of
the square, was a stockyard fence, inside which was garden with
trees and flowers, and various small houses.

Not a soul was in sight. They passed silently between the houses
into the central square. This was quite bare and arid, the earth
trodden smooth by endless generations of passing feet, passing
across from door to door. All the doors of the windowless houses
gave on to this blank square, but all the doors were closed. The
firewood lay near the threshold, a clay oven was still smoking, but
there was no sign of moving life.

The old man walked straight across the square to the big house at
the end, where the two upper storeys, as in a house of toy bricks,
stood each one smaller than the lower one. A stone staircase, outside, led up to the roof of the first storey.

At the foot of this staircase the litter-bearers stood still, and
lowered the woman to the ground.

"You will come up," said the young Indian who spoke Spanish.

She mounted the stone stairs to the earthen roof of the first house,
which formed a platform round the wall of the second storey. She

followed around this platform to the back of the big house. There they descended again, into the garden at the rear.

So far they had seen no one. But now two men appeared, bareheaded, with long braided hair, and wearing a sort of white shirt gathered into a loin-cloth. These went along with the three newcomers, across the garden where red flowers and yellow flowers were blooming, to a long, low white house. There they entered without knocking.

It was dark inside. There was a low murmur of men's voices. Several men were present, their white shirts showing in the gloom, their dark faces invisible. They were sitting on a great log of smooth old wood, that lay along the far wall. And save for this log, the room seemed empty. But no, in the dark at one end was a couch, a sort of bed, and someone lying there, covered with furs.

The old Indian in the spotted sarape, who had accompanied the woman, now took off his hat and his blanket and his sandals. Laying them aside, he approached the couch, and spoke in a low voice. For some moments there was no answer. Then an old man with the snow-white hair hanging round his darkly-visible face, roused himself like a vision, and leaned on one elbow, looking vaguely at the company, in tense silence.

The grey-haired Indian spoke again, and then the young Indian, taking the woman's hand, led her forward. In her linen riding habit, and black boots and hat, and her pathetic bit of a red tie, she stood there beside the fur-covered bed of the old, old man, who sat reared up, leaning on one elbow, remote as a ghost, his white hair streaming in disorder, his face almost black, yet with a far-off intentness, not of this world, leaning forward to look at her.

His face was so old, it was like dark glass, and the few curling hairs that sprang white from his lips and chin were quite incredible. The long white locks fell unbraided and disorderly on either side of the glassy dark face. And under a faint powder of white eyebrows, the black eyes of the old chief looked at her as if from the far, far dead, seeing something that was never to be seen.

At last he spoke a few deep, hollow words, as if to the dark air.

" He says, do you bring your heart to the god of the Chilchui ? " translated the young Indian.

" Tell him yes," she said, automatically.

There was a pause. The old Indian spoke again, as if to the air. One of the men present went out. There was a silence as if of eternity in the dim room that was lighted only through the open door.

The woman looked round. Four old men with grey hair sat on the log by the wall facing the door. Two other men, powerful and impassive, stood near the door. They all had long hair, and wore white shirts gathered into a loin-cloth. Their powerful legs were naked and dark. There was a silence like eternity.

At length the man returned, with white and dark clothing on his arm. The young Indian took them, and holding them in front of the woman, said :

" You must take off your clothes, and put these on."

" If all you men will go out," she said.

" No one will hurt you," he said quietly.

" Not while you men are here," she said.

He looked at the two men by the door. They came quickly forward, and suddenly gripped her arms as she stood, without hurting her, but with great power. Then two of the old men came, and with curious skill slit her boots down with keen knives, and drew them off, and slit her clothing so that it came away from her. In a few moments she stood there white and uncovered. The old man on the bed spoke, and they turned her round for him to see. He spoke again, and the young Indian deftly took the pins and comb from her fair hair, so that it fell over her shoulders in a bunchy tangle.

Then the old man spoke again. The Indian led her to the bed-side. The white-haired, glassy-dark old man moistened his finger-tips at his mouth, and most delicately touched her on the breasts and on the body, then on the back. And she winced strangely each time, as the finger-tips drew along her skin, as if Death itself were touching her.

And she wondered, almost sadly, why she did not feel shamed in her nakedness. She only felt sad and lost. Because nobody felt ashamed. The elder men were all dark and tense with some other deep, gloomy, incomprehensible emotion, which suspended all her agitation, while the young Indian had a strange look of ecstasy on his face. And she, she was only utterly strange and beyond herself, as if her body were not her own.

They gave her the new clothing : a long white cotton shift, that came to her knees : then a tunic of thick blue woollen stuff, embroid-ered with scarlet and green flowers. It was fastened over one shoulder only, and belted with a braid sash of scarlet and black wool.

When she was thus dressed, they took her away, barefoot, to a little house in the stockaded garden. The young Indian told her she might have what she wanted. She asked for water to wash herself. He brought it in a jar, together with a long wooden bowl. Then he fastened the gate-door of her house, and left her a prisoner. She could see through the bars of the gate-door of her house, the red flowers of the garden, and a humming bird. Then from the roof of the big house she heard the long, heavy sound of a drum, unearthly to her in its summons, and an uplifted voice calling from the house-top in a strange language, with a far-away emotionless intonation, delivering some speech or message. And she listened as if from the dead.

But she was very tired. She lay down on a couch of skins, pulling over her the blanket of dark wool, and she slept, giving up everything.

When she woke it was late afternoon, and the young Indian was entering with a basket-tray containing food, tortillas, and corn-mush with bits of meat, probably mutton, and a drink made of honey, and some fresh plums. He brought her also a long garland of red and yellow flowers with knots of blue buds at the end. He sprinkled the garland with water from a jar, then offered it to her, with a smile. He seemed very gentle and thoughtful, and on his face and in his dark eyes was a curious look of triumph and ecstasy, that frightened her a little. The glitter had gone from the black eyes, with their curving dark lashes, and he would look at her with this strange soft glow of ecstasy that was not quite human, and terribly impersonal, and which made her uneasy.

"Is there anything you want?" he said, in his low, slow, melodious voice, that always seemed withheld, as if he were speaking aside to somebody else, or as if he did not want to let the sound come out to her.

"Am I going to be kept a prisoner here?" she asked.

"No, you can walk in the garden to-morrow," he said softly. Always this curious solicitude.

"Do you like that drink?" he said, offering her a little earthen-ware cup. "It is very refreshing."

She sipped the liquor curiously. It was made with herbs and sweetened with honey, and had a strange, lingering flavour. The young man watched her with gratification.

"It has a peculiar taste," she said.

"It is very refreshing," he replied, his black eyes resting on her always with that look of gratified ecstasy. Then he went away. And presently she began to be sick, and to vomit violently, as if she had no control over herself.

Afterwards she felt a great soothing languor steal over her, her limbs felt strong and loose and full of languor, and she lay on her couch listening to the sounds of the village, watching the yellowing sky, smelling the scent of burning cedar-wood, or pine-wood. So distinctly she heard the yapping of tiny dogs, the shuffle of far-off feet, the murmur of voices, so keenly she detected the smell of smoke, and flowers, and evening falling, so vividly she saw the one bright star infinitely remote, stirring above the sunset, that she felt as if all her senses were diffused on the air, that she could distinguish the sound of evening flowers unfolding, and the actual crystal sound of the heavens, as the vast belts of the world-atmosphere slid past one another, and as if the moisture ascending and the moisture descending in the air resounded like some harp in the cosmos.

She was a prisoner in her house, and in the stockaded garden, but she scarcely minded. And it was days before she realized that she never saw another woman. Only the men, the elderly men of the big house, that she imagined must be some sort of temple, and the men priests of some sort. For they always had the same colours, red, orange, yellow, and black, and the same grave, abstracted demeanour.

Sometimes an old man would come and sit in her room with her, in absolute silence. None spoke any language but Indian, save the one younger man. The older men would smile at her, and sit with her for an hour at a time, sometimes smiling at her when she spoke in Spanish, but never answering save with this slow, benevolent-seeming smile. And they gave off a feeling of almost fatherly solicitude. Yet their dark eyes, brooding over her, had something away in their depths that was awesomely ferocious and relentless. They would cover it with a smile, at once, if they felt her looking. But she had seen it.

Always they treated her with this curious impersonal solicitude, this utterly impersonal gentleness, as an old man treats a child. But underneath it she felt there was something else, something terrible. When her old visitor had gone away, in his silent, insidious, fatherly fashion, a shock of fear would come over her ; though of what she knew not.

The young Indian would sit and talk with her freely, as if with great candour. But with him, too, she felt that everything real was unsaid. Perhaps it was unspeakable. His big dark eyes would rest on her almost cherishingly, touched with ecstasy, and his beautiful, slow, languorous voice would trail out its simple, ungrammatical Spanish. He told her he was the grandson of the old, old man, son of the man in the spotted sarape : and they were caciques, kings from the old, old days, before even the Spaniards came. But he himself had been in Mexico City, and also in the United States.

He had worked as a labourer, building the roads in Los Angeles. He had travelled as far as Chicago.

" Don't you speak English, then ? " she asked.

His eyes rested on her with a curious look of duplicity and conflict, and he mutely shook his head.

" What did you do with your long hair, when you were in the United States ? " she asked. " Did you cut it off ? "

Again, with the look of torment in his eyes, he shook his head.

" No," he said, in a low, subdued voice, " I wore a hat, and a handkerchief tied round my head."

And he relapsed into silence, as if of tormented memories.

" Are you the only man of your people who has been to the United States ? " she asked him.

" Yes. I am the only one who has been away from here for a long time. The others come back soon, in one week. They don't stay away. The old men don't let them."

" And why did you go ? "

" The old men want me to go—because I shall be the cacique——"

He talked always with the same *naïveté*, an almost childish candour. But she felt that this was perhaps just the effect of his Spanish. Or perhaps speech altogether was unreal to him. Anyhow, she felt that all the real things were kept back.

He came and sat with her a good deal—sometimes more than she wished—as if he wanted to be near her. She asked him if he was married. He said he was—with two children.

" I should like to see your children," she said.

But he answered only with that smile, a sweet, almost ecstatic smile, above which the dark eyes hardly changed from their enigmatic abstraction.

It was curious, he would sit with her by the hour, without ever making her self-conscious, or sex-conscious. He seemed to have no sex, as he sat there so still and gentle and apparently submissive, with his head bent a little forward, and the river of glistening black hair streaming maidenly over his shoulders.

Yet when she looked again, she saw his shoulders broad and powerful, his eyebrows black and level, the short, curved, obstinate black lashes over his lowered eyes, the small, fur-like line of moustache above his blackish, heavy lips, and the strong chin, and she knew that in some other mysterious way he was darkly and powerfully male. And he, feeling her watching him, would glance up at her swiftly with a dark, lurking look in his eyes, which immediately he veiled with that half-sad smile.

The days and the weeks went by, in a vague kind of contentment. She was uneasy sometimes, feeling she had lost the power over herself. She was not in her own power, she was under the spell of some other control. And at times she had moments of terror and horror. But then these Indians would come and sit with her, casting their insidious spell over her by their very silent presence, their silent, sexless, powerful physical presence. As they sat they seemed to take her will away, leaving her will-less and victim to her own indifference. And the young man would bring her sweetened drink, often the same emetic drink, but sometimes other kinds. And after drinking, the languor filled her heavy limbs, her senses seemed to float in the air, listening, hearing. They had brought her a little female dog, which she called Flora. And once, in the trance of her senses, she felt she *heard* the little dog conceive, in her tiny womb, and begin to be complex, with young. And another day she could hear the vast sound of the earth going round, like some immense arrow-string booming.

But as the days grew shorter and colder, when she was cold, she would get a sudden revival of her will, and a desire to go out, to go away. And she insisted to the young man, she wanted to go out.

So one day, they let her climb to the topmost roof of the big house where she was, and look down the square. It was the day of the big dance, but not everybody was dancing. Women with babies in their arms stood in their doorways, watching. Opposite, at the other end of the square, there was a throng before the other big house, and a small, brilliant group on the terrace-roof of the first storey, in front of wide open doors of the upper storey. Through these wide open doors she could see fire glinting in darkness and priests in headdresses of black and yellow and scarlet feathers, wearing robe-like blankets of black and red and yellow, with long green fringes, were moving about. A big drum was beating slowly and regularly, in the dense, Indian silence. The crowd below waited.

Then a drum started on a high beat, and there came the deep, powerful burst of men singing a heavy, savage music, like a wind roaring in some timeless forest, many mature men singing in one breath, like the wind ; and long lines of dancers walked out from under the big house. Men with naked, golden-bronze bodies and streaming black hair, tufts of red and yellow feathers on their arms, and kilts of white frieze with a bar of heavy red and black and green embroidery round their waists, bending slightly forward and stamping the earth in their absorbed, monotonous stamp of the dance, a fox-fur, hung by the nose from their belt behind, swaying with the sumptuous swaying of a beautiful fox-fur, the tip of the tail writhing above the dancer's heels. And after each man, a woman with a strange elaborate headdress of feathers and sea-shells, and wearing a short black tunic, moving erect, holding up tufts of feathers in each hand, swaying her wrists rhythmically and subtly beating the earth with her bare feet.

So, the long line of the dance unfurling from the big house oppo-site. And from the big house beneath her, strange scent of incense, strange tense silence, then the answering burst of inhuman male singing, and the long line of the dance unfurling.

It went on all day, the insistence of the drum, the cavernous, roaring, storm-like sound of male singing, the incessant swinging of the fox-skins behind the powerful, gold-bronze, stamping legs of the men, the autumn sun from a perfect blue heaven pouring on the rivers of black hair, men's and women's, the valley all still, the walls of rock beyond, the awful huge bulking of the mountain against the pure sky, its snow seething with sheer whiteness.

For hours and hours she watched, spell-bound, and as if drugged. And in all the terrible persistence of the drumming and the primeval, rushing deep singing, and the endless stamping of the dance of fox-tailed men, the tread of heavy, bird-erect women in their black tunics, she seemed at last to feel her own death ; her own oblitera-tion. As if she were to be obliterated from the field of life again. In the strange towering symbols on the heads of the changeless, absorbed women she seemed to read once more the *Mene Mene Tekel Upharsin*. Her kind of womanhood, intensely personal and individual, was to be obliterated again, and the great primeval symbols were to tower once more over the fallen individual independ-ence of woman. The sharpness and the quivering nervous conscious-ness of the highly-bred white woman was to be destroyed again, womanhood was to be cast once more into the great stream of impersonal sex and impersonal passion. Strangely, as if clairvoyant, she saw the immense sacrifice prepared. And she went back to her little house in a trance of agony.

After this, there was always a certain agony when she heard the drums at evening, and the strange uplifted savage sound of men singing round the drum, like wild creatures howling to the invisible gods of the moon and the vanished sun. Something of the chuckling, sobbing cry of the coyote, something of the exultant bark of the fox, the far-off wild melancholy exultance of the howling wolf, the torment of the puma's scream, and the insistence of the ancient

2 B *

fierce human male, with his lapses of tenderness and his abiding ferocity.

Sometimes she would climb the high roof after nightfall, and listen to the dim cluster of young men round the drum on the bridge just beyond the square, singing by the hour. Sometimes there would be a fire, and in the fire-glow, men in their white shirts or naked save for a loin-cloth, would be dancing and stamping like spectres, hour after hour in the dark cold air, within the fire-glow, forever dancing and stamping like turkeys, or dropping squatting by the fire to rest, throwing their blankets round them.

" Why do you all have the same colours ? " she asked the young Indian. " Why do you all have red and yellow and black, over your white shirts ? And the women have black tunics ? "

He looked into her eyes, curiously, and the faint, evasive smile came on to his face. Behind the smile lay a soft, strange malignancy.

" Because our men are the fire and the daytime, and our women are the spaces between the stars at night," he said.

" Aren't the women even stars ? " she said.

" No. We say they are the spaces between the stars, that keep the stars apart."

He looked at her oddly, and again the touch of derision came into his eyes.

" White people," he said, " they know nothing. They are like children, always with toys. We know the sun, and we know the moon. And we say, when a white woman sacrifice herself to our gods, then our gods will begin to make the world again, and the white man's gods will fall to pieces."

" How sacrifice herself ? " she asked quickly.

And he, as quickly covered, covered himself with a subtle smile.

" She sacrifice her own gods and come to our gods, I mean that," he said, soothingly.

But she was not reassured. An icy pang of fear and certainty was at her heart.

" The sun he is alive at one end of the sky," he continued, " and the moon lives at the other end. And the man all the time have to keep the sun happy in his side of the sky, and the woman have to keep the moon quiet at her side of the sky. All the time she have to work at this. And the sun can't ever go into the house of the moon, and the moon can't ever go into the house of the sun, in the sky. So the woman, she asks the moon to come into her cave, inside her. And the man, he draws the sun down till he has the power of the sun. All the time he do this. Then when the man gets a woman, the sun goes into the cave of the moon, and that is how everything in the world starts."

She listened, watching him closely, as one enemy watches another who is speaking with double meaning.

" Then," she said, " why aren't you Indians masters of the white men ? "

" Because," he said, " the Indian got weak, and lost his power with the sun, so the white men stole the sun. But they can't keep him—they don't know how. They got him, but they don't know what to do with him, like a boy who catch a big grizzly bear, and can't kill him, and can't run away from him. The grizzly bear eats the boy that catch him, when he want to run away from him. White men don't know what they are doing with the sun, and white women don't know what they do with the moon. The moon she got angry with white women, like a puma when someone kills her little ones. The moon, she bites white women—here inside," and he pressed his side. " The moon, she is angry in a white woman's cave. The Indian can see it. And soon," he added, " the Indian women get the moon back and keep her quiet in their house. And the Indian men get the sun, and the power over all the world. White men don't know what the sun is. They never know."

He subsided into a curious exultant silence.

" But," she faltered, " why do you hate us so ? Why do you hate me ? "

He looked up suddenly with a light on his face, and a startling flame of a smile.

" No, we don't hate," he said softly, looking with a curious glitter into her face.

" You do," she said, forlorn and hopeless.

And after a moment's silence, he rose and went away.

III

Winter had now come, in the high valley, with snow that melted in the day's sun, and nights that were bitter cold. She lived on, in a kind of daze, feeling her power ebbing more and more away from her, as if her will were leaving her. She felt always in the same relaxed, confused, victimised state, unless the sweetened herb drink would numb her mind altogether, and release her senses into a sort of heightened, mystic acuteness and a feeling as if she were diffusing out deliciously into the harmony of things. This at length became the only state of consciousness she really recognized : this exquisite sense of bleeding out into the higher beauty and harmony of things. Then she could actually hear the great stars in heaven, which she saw through her door, speaking from their motion and brightness, saying things perfectly to the cosmos, as they trod in perfect ripples, like bells on the floor of heaven, passing one another and grouping in the timeless dance, with the spaces of dark between. And she could hear the snow on a cold, cloudy day twittering and faintly whistling in the sky, like birds that flock and fly away in autumn, suddenly calling farewell to the invisible moon, and slipping out of the plains of the air, releasing peaceful warmth. She herself would call to the arrested snow to fall from the upper air. She would call to the unseen moon to cease to be angry, to make peace again with the unseen sun like a woman who ceases to be angry in her house. And she would smell the sweetness of the moon relaxing to the sun in the wintry heaven, when the snow fell in a faint, cold-perfumed relaxation, as the peace of the sun mingled again in a sort of unison with the peace of the moon.

She was aware too of the sort of shadow that was on the Indians of the valley, a deep stoical disconsolation, almost religious in its depth.

" We have lost our power over the sun, and we are trying to get him back. But he is wild with us, and shy like a horse that has got away. We have to go through a lot." So the young Indian said to her, looking into her eyes with a strained meaning. And she, as if bewitched, replied :

" I hope you will get him back."

The smile of triumph flew over his face.

" Do you hope it ? " he said.

" I do," she answered fatally.

" Then all right," he said. " We shall get him."

And he went away in exultance.

She felt she was drifting on some consummation, which she had no will to avoid, yet which seemed heavy and finally terrible to her.

It must have been almost December, for the days were short when she was taken again before the aged man, and stripped of her clothing, and touched with the old finger-tips.

The aged cacique looked her in the eyes, with his eyes of lonely, far-off, black intentness, and murmured something to her.

" He wants you to make the sign of peace," the young man translated, showing her the gesture. " Peace and farewell to him."

She was fascinated by the black, glass-like, intent eyes of the old cacique, that watched her without blinking, like a basilisk's, overpowering her. In their depths also she saw a certain fatherly compassion, and pleading. She put her hand before her face, in the required manner, making the sign of peace and farewell. He made the sign of peace back again to her, then sank among his furs. She thought he was going to die, and that he knew it.

There followed a day of ceremonial, when she was brought out before all the people, in a blue blanket with white fringe, and holding blue feathers in her hands. Before an altar of one house she was perfumed with incense and sprinkled with ash. Before the altar of the opposite house she was fumigated again with incense by the gorgeous, terrifying priests in yellow and scarlet and black, their faces painted with scarlet paint. And then they threw water on her. Meanwhile she was faintly aware of the fire on the altar, the heavy, heavy sound of a drum, the heavy sound of men beginning power-fully, deeply, savagely to sing, the swaying of the crowd of faces in the plaza below, and the formation for a sacred dance.

But at this time her commonplace consciousness was numb, she was aware of her immediate surroundings as shadows, almost im-material. With refined and heightened senses she could hear the sound of the earth winging on its journey, like a shot arrow, the ripple-rustling of the air, and the boom of the great arrow-string. And it seemed to her there were two great influences in the upper air, one golden towards the sun, and one invisible silver; the first travelling like rain ascending to the gold presence sunwards, the second like rain silverily descending the ladders of space towards the hovering, lurking clouds over the snowy mountain-top. Then between them, another presence, waiting to shake himself free of moisture, of heavy white snow that had mysteriously collected about him. And in summer, like a scorched eagle, he would wait to shake himself clear of the weight of heavy sunbeams. And he was coloured like fire. And he was always shaking himself clear, of snow or of heavy heat, like an eagle rustling.

Then there was a still stranger presence, standing watching from the blue distance, always watching. Sometimes running in upon the wind, or shimmering in the heat-waves. The blue wind itself, rushing as it were out of the holes into the sky, rushing out of the sky down upon the earth. The blue wind, the go-between, the invisible ghost that belonged to two worlds, that played upon the ascending and the descending chords of the rains.

More and more her ordinary personal consciousness had left her, she had gone into that other state of passional cosmic consciousness, like one who is drugged. The Indians, with their heavily religious natures, had made her succumb to their vision.

Only one personal question she asked the young Indian :

" Why am I the only one that wears blue ? "

" It is the colour of the wind. It is the colour of what goes away
and is never coming back, but which is always here, waiting like
death among us. It is the colour of the dead. And it is the colour
that stands away off, looking at us from the distance, that cannot
come near to us. When we go near, it goes farther. It can't be
near. We are all brown and yellow and black hair, and white teeth
and red blood. We are the ones that are here. You with blue eyes,
you are the messengers from the far-away, you cannot stay, and now
it is time for you to go back."

" Where to ? " she asked.

" To the way-off things like the sun and the blue mother of rain,
and tell them that we are the people on the world again, and we can
bring the sun to the moon again, like a red horse to a blue mare ;
we are the people. The white women have driven back the moon
in the sky, won't let her come to the sun. So the sun is angry. And
the Indian must give the moon to the sun."

" How ? " she said.

" The white woman got to die and go like a wind to the sun, tell
him the Indians will open the gate to him. And the Indian women
will open the gate to the moon. The white women don't let the
moon come down out of the blue coral. The moon used to come
down among the Indian women, like a white goat among the flowers.
And the sun want to come down to the Indian men, like an eagle to
the pine-trees. The sun, he is shut out behind the white man, and
the moon she is shut out behind the white woman, and they can't
get away. They are angry, everything in the world gets angrier.
The Indian says, he will give the white woman to the sun, so the
sun will leap over the white man and come to the Indian again.
And the moon will be surprised, she will see the gate open, and she
not know which way to go. But the Indian woman will call to the
moon, *Come ! Come ! Come back into my grasslands. The wicked white
woman can't harm you any more.* Then the sun will look over the heads
of the white men, and see the moon in the pastures of our women,
with the Red Men standing around like pine-trees. Then he will
leap over the heads of the white men, and come running past to the
Indians through the spruce trees. And we, who are red and black
and yellow, we who stay, we shall have the sun on our right hand and
the moon on our left. So we can bring the rain down out of the blue
meadows, and up out of the black ; and we can call the wind that
tells the corn to grow, when we ask him, and we shall make the

clouds to break, and the sheep to have twin lambs. And we shall be
full of power, like a spring day. But the white people will be a hard
winter, without snow——"

"But," said the white woman, "I don't shut out the moon—how
can I?"

"Yes," he said, "you shut the gate, and then laugh, think you
have it all your own way."

She could never quite understand the way he looked at her. He
was always so curiously gentle, and his smile was so soft. Yet there
was such a glitter in his eyes, and an unrelenting sort of hate came
out of his words, a strange, profound, impersonal hate. Personally
he liked her, she was sure. He was gentle with her, attracted by her
in some strange, soft, passionless way. But impersonally he hated
her with a mystic hatred. He would smile at her, winningly. Yet if,
the next moment, she glanced round at him unawares, she would
catch that gleam of pure after-hate in his eyes.

". Have I got to die and be given to the sun?" she asked.

"Sometime," he said, laughing evasively. "Sometime we all die."

They were gentle with her, and very considerate with her.
Strange men, the old priests and the young çacique alike, they
watched over her and cared for her like women. In their soft,
insidious understanding, there was something womanly. Yet their
eyes, with that strange glitter, and their dark, shut mouths that
would open to the broad jaw, the small, strong, white teeth, had
something very primitively male and cruel.

One wintry day, when snow was falling, they took her to a great
dark chamber in the big house. The fire was burning in a corner
on a high raised dais under a sort of hood or canopy of adobe-work.
She saw in the fire-glow the glowing bodies of the almost naked
priests, and strange symbols on the roof and walls of the chamber.
There was no door or window in the chamber, they had descended
by a ladder from the roof. And the fire of pinewood danced continually, showing walls painted with strange devices, which she
could not understand, and a ceiling of poles making a curious
pattern of black and red and yellow, and alcoves or niches in which
were curious objects she could not discern.

The older priests were going through some ceremony near the
fire, in silence, intense Indian silence. She was seated on a low
projection of the wall, opposite the fire, two men seated beside her.
Presently they gave her a drink from a cup, which she took gladly,
because of the semi-trance it would induce.

In the darkness and in the silence she was accurately aware of everything that happened to her : how they took off her clothes, and, standing her before a great, weird device on the wall, coloured blue and white and black, washed her all over with water and the amole infusion ; washed even her hair, softly, carefully, and dried it on white cloths, till it was soft and glistening. Then they laid her on a couch under another great indecipherable image of red and black and yellow, and now rubbed all her body with sweet-scented oil, and massaged all her limbs, and her back, and her sides, with a long, strange, hypnotic massage. Their dark hands were incredibly powerful, yet soft with a watery softness she could not understand. And the dark faces, leaning near her white body, she saw were darkened with red pigment, with lines of yellow round the cheeks. And the dark eyes glittered absorbed, as the hands worked upon the soft white body of the woman.

They were so impersonal, absorbed in something that was beyond her. They never saw her as a personal woman : she could tell that. She was some mystic object to them, some vehicle of passions too remote for her to grasp. Herself in a state of trance, she watched their faces bending over her, dark, strangely glistening with the transparent red paint, and lined with bars of yellow. And in this weird, luminous-dark mask of living face, the eyes were fixed with an unchanging steadfast gleam, and the purplish-pigmented lips were closed in a full, sinister, sad grimness. The immense fundamental sadness, the grimness of ultimate decision, the fixity of revenge, and the nascent exultance of those that are going to triumph —these things she could read in their faces, as she lay and was rubbed into a misty glow by their uncanny dark hands. Her limbs, her flesh, her very bones at last seemed to be diffusing into a roseate sort of mist, in which her consciousness hovered like some sungleam in a flushed cloud.

She knew the gleam would fade, the cloud would go grey. But at present she did not believe it. She knew she was a victim ; that all this elaborate work upon her was the work of victimising her. But she did not mind. She wanted it.

Later, they put a short blue tunic on her and took her to the upper terrace, and presented her to the people. She saw the plaza below her full of dark faces and of glittering eyes. There was no pity : only the curious hard exultance. The people gave a subdued cry when they saw her, and she shuddered. But she hardly cared.

Next day was the last. She slept in a chamber of the big house. At dawn they put on her a big blue blanket with a fringe, and led her out into the plaza, among the throng of silent, dark-blanketed people. There was pure white snow on the ground, and the dark people in their dark-brown blankets looked like inhabitants of another world.

A large drum was slowly pounding, and an old priest was declaring from a housetop. But it was not till noon that a litter came forth, and the people gave that low, animal cry which was so moving. In the sack-like litter sat the old, old cacique, his white hair braided with black braid and large turquoise stones. His face was like a piece of obsidian. He lifted his hand in token, and the litter stopped in front of her. Fixing her with his old eyes, he spoke to her for a few moments, in his hollow voice. No one translated.

Another litter came, and she was placed in it. Four priests moved ahead, in their scarlet and yellow and black, with plumed head-dresses. Then came the litter of the old cacique. Then the light drums began, and two groups of singers burst simultaneously into song, male and wild. And the golden-red, almost naked men, adorned with ceremonial feathers and kilts, the rivers of black hair down their backs, formed into two files and began to tread the dance. So they threaded out of the snowy plaza, in two long, sumptuous lines of dark red-gold and black and fur, swaying with a faint tinkle of bits of shell and flint, winding over the snow between the two bee-clusters of men who sang around the drum.

Slowly they moved out, and her litter, with its attendance of feathered, lurid, dancing priests, moved after. Everybody danced the tread of the dance-step, even, subtly, the litter-bearers. And out of the plaza they went, past smoking ovens, on the trail to the great cotton-wood trees, that stood like grey-silver lace against the blue sky, bare and exquisite above the snow. The river, diminished, rushed among fangs of ice. The chequer-squares of gardens within fences were all snowy, and the white houses now looked yellowish.

The whole valley glittered intolerably with pure snow, away to the walls of the standing rock. And across the flat cradle of snow bed wound the long thread of the dance, shaking slowly and sumptuously in its orange and black motion. The high drums thudded quickly, and on the crystalline frozen air the swell and roar of the chant of savages was like an obsession.

She sat looking out of her litter with big, transfixed blue eyes, under which were the wan markings of her drugged weariness. She knew she was going to die, among the glisten of this snow, at the hands of this savage, sumptuous people. And as she stared at the blaze of the blue sky above the slashed and ponderous mountain, she thought : " I am dead already. What difference does it make, the

transition from the dead I am to the dead I shall be, very soon ! "
Yet her soul sickened and felt wan.

The strange procession trailed on, in perpetual dance, slowly
across the plain of snow, and then entered the slopes between the
pine-trees. She saw the copper-dark men dancing the dance-tread,
onwards, between the copper-pale tree trunks. And at last she, too,
in her swaying litter, entered the pine-trees.

They were travelling on and on, upwards, across the snow under
the trees, past the superb shafts of pale, flaked copper, the rustle and
shake and tread of the threading dance, penetrating into the
forest, into the mountain. They were following a stream-bed : but
the stream was dry, like summer, dried up by the frozenness of the
head-waters. There were dark, red-bronze willow bushes with
wattles like wild hair, and pallid aspen-trees looking cold flesh
against the snow. Then jutting dark rocks.

At last she could tell that the dancers were moving forward no
more. Nearer and nearer she came upon the drums, as to a lair of
mysterious animals. Then through the bushes she emerged into a
strange amphitheatre. Facing was a great wall of hollow rock,
down the front of which hung a great, dripping, fang-like spoke of
ice. The ice came pouring over the rock from the precipice above,
and then stood arrested, dripping out of high heaven, almost down
to the hollow stones where the stream-pool should be below. But
the pool was dry.

On either side the dry pool the lines of dancers had formed, and
the dance was continuing without intermission, against a background of bushes.

But what she felt was that fanged inverted pinnacle of ice, hanging
from the lip of the dark precipice above. And behind the great rope
of ice she saw the leopard-like figures of priests climbing the hollow
cliff face, to the cave that like a dark socket bored a cavity, an orifice,
half-way up the crag.

Before she could realize, her litter-bearers were staggering in the
footholds, climbing the rock. She, too, was behind the ice. There it
hung, like a curtain that is not spread, but hangs like a great fang.
And near above her was the orifice of the cave sinking dark into the
rock. She watched it as she swayed upwards.

On the platform of the cave stood the priests, waiting in all their
gorgeousness of feathers and fringed robes, watching her ascent.
Two of them stooped to help her litter-bearer. And at length she
was on the platform of the cave, far in behind the shaft of ice, above
the hollow amphitheatre among the bushes below, where men were

dancing, and the whole populace of the village was clustered in silence.

The sun was sloping down the afternoon sky, on the left. She knew that this was the shortest day of the year, and the last day of her life. They stood her facing the iridescent column of ice, which fell down marvellously arrested, away in front of her.

Some signal was given, and the dance below stopped. There was now absolute silence. She was given a little to drink, then two priests took off her mantle and her tunic, and in her strange pallor she stood there, between the lurid robes of the priests, beyond the pillar of ice, beyond and above the dark-faced people. The throng below gave the low, wild cry. Then the priest turned her round, so she stood with her back to the open world, her long blond hair to the people below. And they cried again.

She was facing the cave, inwards. A fire was burning and flickering in the depths. Four priests had taken off their robes, and were almost as naked as she was. They were powerful men in the prime of life, and they kept their dark, painted faces lowered.

From the fire came the old, old priest, with an incense-pan. He was naked and in a state of barbaric ecstasy. He fumigated his victim, reciting at the same time in a hollow voice. Behind him came another robeless priest, with two flint knives.

When she was fumigated, they laid her on a large flat stone, the four powerful men holding her by the outstretched arms and legs. Behind stood the aged man, like a skeleton covered with dark glass, holding a knife and transfixedly watching the sun ; and behind him again was another naked priest, with a knife.

She felt little sensation, though she knew all that was happening. Turning to the sky, she looked at the yellow sun. It was sinking. The shaft of ice was like a shadow between her and it. And she realized that the yellow rays were filling half the cave, though they had not reached the altar where the fire was, at the far end of the funnel-shaped cavity.

Yes, the rays were creeping round slowly. As they grew ruddier, they penetrated farther. When the red sun was about to sink, he would shine full through the shaft of ice deep into the hollow of the cave, to the innermost.

She understood now that this was what the men were waiting for. Even those that held her down were bent and twisted round, their black eyes watching the sun with a glittering eagerness, and awe, and craving. The black eyes of the aged cacique were fixed like black mirrors on the sun, as if sightless, yet containing some terrible answer to the reddening winter planet. And all the eyes of the priests were fixed and glittering on the sinking orb, in the reddening, icy silence of the winter afternoon.

They were anxious, terribly anxious, and fierce. Their ferocity wanted something, and they were waiting the moment. And their ferocity was ready to leap out into a mystic exultance, of triumph. But still they were anxious.

Only the eyes of that oldest man were not anxious. Black, and fixed, and as if sightless, they watched the sun, seeing beyond the sun. And in their black, empty concentration there was power, power intensely abstract and remote, but deep, deep to the heart of the earth, and the heart of the sun. In absolute motionlessness he watched till the red sun should send his ray through the column of ice. Then the old man would strike, and strike home, accomplish the sacrifice and achieve the power.

The mastery that man must hold, and that passes from race to race.